oclc+noaalinc
4-12-2009

# studies on the structure and development of vertebrates

BY

# EDWIN S. GOODRICH

## VOLUME I

Dover Publications,
New York

Constable and Company Ltd.
London

Manufactured in the United States of America.

This Edition is Dedicated to
the Memory of


EDWIN STEPHEN GOODRICH

1868-1946

# PREFACE

THIS book has been written in the hope that it may help advanced students and others engaged in teaching and research. It is not a complete treatise, but deals with certain subjects and problems of special interest and importance, some of which receive but scant notice in current text-books. My original intention was to cover the whole range of vertebrate morphology ; but the preparation of this volume has taken so many years, that I thought it better to publish what is ready than to wait for the remainder which might possibly never be completed. The literature dealing with the Morphology of the Vertebrata is so vast, the accumulation of known facts so large, that students are apt to feel discouraged from the start, and to turn perhaps to some newer branch of zoological science. On the one hand, they may think that little remains to be done in so ancient a study ; or, on the other hand, that its conclusions, for instance in Phylogeny, are so insecure that they afford little trustworthy evidence concerning the process of Evolution. It has, therefore, been my endeavour not only to give an account within reasonable compass of the facts already known and to discuss their significance, but also to point out where our knowledge is deficient, and where further research is desirable. During the last fifty years or so much has been accomplished, many old theories have been overthrown, some new conclusions have been firmly established ; yet a great deal remains to be done, and new fields for research are continually being opened up.

The triumph of the doctrine of Evolution has owed much in the past to the study of the structure and development of the Vertebrates, and the correct interpretation of their morphology still plays an important part in the elucidation of the evolutionary process. No other group of animals presents us with so complete a record of the divergent phylogenetic lines along which they have evolved. Although this book is written mainly from the morphological point of view, function has not been lost sight of. For it must not be forgotten that structure and function go hand in hand and evolve *pari passu*.

The bibliography at the end of this volume contains, of course, only a selection of the more important and more recent works ; a complete

v

list would take at least a volume to itself.   Further references the reader
may find in well-known text-books.   For Fishes in particular he may be
referred to Dr. Bashford Dean's excellent " Bibliography ", New York,
1916–23.   The numbers printed in heavy type after authors' names in
the text refer to the bibliography, in which ' Bibl.' has been added to those
works containing good lists of references on special subjects.   Space has not
allowed me to discuss the views of individual authors, except in special
cases, and the citation of a name in brackets does not necessarily imply
that the author holds the view set forth in this volume.   So far as possible
I have tried to verify statements of fact by personal observation, and
sometimes have denoted this by adding the initials E.S.G.

The names of the genera figured will be found in the index ; and the
systematic position of the genera mentioned in the text can be seen in
the scheme of classification at the beginning of the volume.   Much care
has been devoted to the illustrations.   The new figures, over 300 in
number, have been drawn by myself or from my sketches, and many
have been skilfully touched up for reproduction by Mr. A. K. Marshall.

To many authors and the following publishers I am indebted for leave
to reproduce figures :   Messrs. G. Allen & Unwin, Ltd., Messrs. G. Bell &
Sons, Ltd., Messrs. A. & C. Black, Ltd., Messrs. Blakiston's, Sons, & Co.,
Messrs. Constable & Co., Ltd., Messrs. Henry Holt & Co., Messrs. Long-
mans, Green & Co., Ltd., Messrs. Macmillan & Co., Ltd., The Macmillan
Company, The W. B. Saunders Company, Messrs. H. F. & G. Witherby,
The Wistar Institute, The Univ. of Chicago Press, The Cambridge Uni-
versity Press, The Clarendon Press, Oxford, The Akademische Verlagsgesell-
schaft, Messrs. Alb. Bonnier, Stockholm, Messrs. W. Engelmann, Leipzig,
Messrs. G. Fischer, Jena, Messrs. W. de Gruyter & Co., Berlin, Messrs.
Hirzel, Leipzig, Messrs. J. Springer, Berlin ; also the Zoological Society,
the Geological Society, and Linnean Society of London.

It is with pleasure that I gratefully acknowledge the help received
from various friends and colleagues.   More particularly must I thank
Prof. F. H. Edgeworth for the loan of sections, Prof. D. M. S. Watson for
much useful information, Mr. G. R. de Beer for co-operation in the
preparation of several figures in Chapters VI. and VII., and the use of his
accurate wax reconstructions, and particularly to Prof. J. P. Hill for
constant help and the loan of many series of sections from his magnificent
collections at University College, London.

E. S. GOODRICH,

*Department of Zoology and Comparative Anatomy,*
*University Museum, Oxford.*

*February* 6, 1930.

# CONTENTS

## CHAPTER I

## CHAPTER II

vii

## CHAPTER III

## CHAPTER IV

## CHAPTER V

## CHAPTER VI

## CHAPTER VII

CHAPTER VIII

CHAPTER IX

CHAPTER X

## CHAPTER XI

## CHAPTER XII

## CHAPTER XIII

## CHAPTER XIV

# STUDIES ON THE STRUCTURE AND DEVELOPMENT OF VERTEBRATES

## ERRATA ET CORRIGENDA

P. xvi : line 31 from top, for ' Climatias ' read ' Climatius '.

P. xvii : line 9 from top, for ' Tarassius ' read ' Tarrasius '.

P. xxv : from the Order **Ciconiiformes** remove to the Order **Pelecaniformes** the genera Fregata, Odontopteryx*, Pelecanus, Phaethon, Phalacrocorax ; add Anhinga and Sula to the latter Order.

P. xxv : line 25, for ' Scops ' read ' Scopus ' ; line 31, for 'Serpentaria ' read ' Serpentarius ' ; line 34, for ' Laphophorus ' read ' Lophophorus '.

P. xxvi : line 19 from bottom, for ' Cinolus ' read ' Cinclus ' ; in Order **Amphitheria*** insert ' Amphitherium* '.

P. 4 : 5 lines from top, delete ' other '.

P. 68 : 5 lines from top, for ' axial ' read ' atlas '.

P. 221 : in 2nd line of legend and in figure above, ' vr ' should be ' cr '.

P. 233 : in Fig. 245 A, for ' ac ' read ' acv ' ; in legend, insert ' acv, anterior cardinal vein '.

P. 285 : line 3 of legend of Fig. 290, for ' Er ' read ' Fr '.

P. 295 : line 9 from bottom, for ' prefrontal ' read ' postfrontal '.

P. 377 : line 2 from top, for ' prefrontal ' read ' postfrontal '.

P. 407 : line 2 from bottom, for ' *Notidonus* ' read ' *Notidanus* '.

P. 413 : line 4, for ' Figs. 241-2 ' read ' Figs. 493, 494, 495 '.

P. 440 : legend of Fig. 469, *f*, for ' foramen caroticum posterius ' read ' internal jugular foramen ' ; *o*, for ' foramen caroticum anterius ' read ' foramen ovale V3 ' ; *of*, for ' foramen ovale ' read ' sphenoidal fissure + optic foramen = foramen lacerum anterius '.

P. 450 : line 5, for ' ovalis ' read ' rotunda '.

P. 464 : legend of Fig. 490, insert ' *ty*, tympanic '.

P. 481 : line 10 from bottom, for ' Fig. 570 A ' read ' Fig. 507 A '.

# CLASSIFICATION

*(The extinct Orders or lesser divisions down to Genera are marked by an asterisk.)*

### PHYLUM VERTEBRATA (Chordata).

**SUBPHYLUM ACRANIA** (Cephalochorda): Amphioxus (Branchiostoma), Asymmetron.

### SUBPHYLUM CRANIATA.

Branch **MONORHINA.**[1]

Class **Cyclostomata** (Marsipobranchii).

Subclass **Myxinoidea** : Bdellostoma, Myxine, Paramyxine.
Subclass **Petromyzontia** : Petromyzon.
Incertae sedis : Palaeospondylus*.

Branch and Class **Ostracodermi.**
Order **Anaspida***, Birkenia, Lasanius, Pterolepis, Rhyncholepis.
Order **Cephalaspidomorphi*** (Osteostraci): Ateleaspis, Auchenaspis (Thyestes), Cephalaspis, Kiaeraspis, Tremataspis.
Order **Pteraspidomorphi*** (Heterostraci) : Coelolepis, Cyathaspis, Drepanaspis, Pteraspis, Thelodus.
Order **Pterychthyomorphi*** (Antiarchi) : Asterolepis, Bothriolepis, Pterychthys.

---

[1] Much evidence has recently been brought forward by Stensiö (**135**) and Kiaer (**126**) for the view that some of the Ostracodermi are closely related to the Cyclostomata, and possessed like the latter a single median opening for the hypophysis and nasal organs. If confirmed, the Myxinoidea, Petromyzontia, Cephalaspidomorphi, and Anaspida may be united in one Branch Monorhina.

Branch **GNATHOSTOMATA** (Amphirhina).

Grade **Ichthyopterygii.**

Class **Pisces.**

Subgrade **Chondrichthyes.**

Subclass **Elasmobranchii.**

Order **Selachii.**

Group 1. **Notidani** : Chlamydoselachus, Heptanchus, Hexanchus, Notidanus.

Group 2. Division A. Suborder **Heterodonti** : Acrodus*, Cochliodus*, Edestus*, Helodus*, Heterodontus (Cestracion), Hybodus*.

Division B. Subdivision *a*. Suborder **Scyllioidei** : Carcharias, Carcharodon, Cetorhinus (Selache), Lamna, Mitsukurina, Odontaspis, Pristiurus, Rhinodon, Scyllium (Scylliorhinus), Stegostoma, Zygaena.

Subdivision *b*. Suborder **Squaliformes** : Echinorhinus, Laemargus, Pliotrema, Pristiophorus, Squalus (Acanthias).

Suborder **Rajiformes** (Hypotremata).

Section Squatinoidei : Rhina, Squatina.

Section Rhinoraji : Pristis, Raja, Rhinobatus, Rhynchobatus.

Section Centrobatoidei : Myliobatis, Psammodus*, Pteroplatea, Ptychodus*, Rhinoptera, Trygon.

Section Torpedinoidei : Narcine, Torpedo.

Order **Holocephali** : Callorhynchus, Chimaera, Ganodus*, Harriottia, Myriacanthus*, Pyctodus*, Rhinochimaera, Squaloraja*.

Order **Pleuracanthodei*** (Ichthyotomi) : Chondrenchelys, Cratoselache (?), Pleuracanthus, Xenacanthus.

Subclass **Cladoselachii** (Pleuropterygii)* [1] : Cladodus, Cladoselachus, Symmorium.

Subclass **Acanthodii*** : Acanthodes, Cheiracanthus, Climatias, Diplacanthus, Gyracanthus (?).

Subclass **Coccosteomorphi.** [2]

Order **Anarthrodira*** : Macropetalichthys.

Order **Arthrodira*** : Coccosteus, Dinichthys, Homosteus, Mylostoma, Titanichthys.

Incertae sedis : Jagorina*, Rhamphodus*.

---

[1] If Jaekel's description of claspers on the pelvic fins were confirmed, the Cladoselachii could be placed as an Order of the Elasmobranchii.

[2] A group of uncertain affinities, at one time considered to be allied to the Dipnoi. Although superficially resembling the Pterychthyomorphi they are probably true Gnathostomes and derived from an early group of Elasmobranchii provided with bony armour.

Class **Pisces**—*Continued*

Subgrade **Osteichthyes.**

Subclass **Dipnoi** : Ceratodus (Neoceratodus), Ctenodus*, Dipterus*, Lepidosiren, Phaneropleuron*, Protopterus, Sagenodus*, Scaumenacia*, Uronemus*.

Subclass **Teleostomi.**

Division **Crossopterygii.**[1]

Order **Osteolepidoti*.**

Suborder **Haplistia** : Tarassius.

Suborder **Rhipidistia** : Dictyonosteus, Diplopterus, Eusthenopteron, Glyptopomus, Gyroptychius, Holoptychius, Megalichthys, Onychodus, Osteolepis, Rhizodopsis, Sauripterus, Tristichopterus.

Order **Coelacanthini*** : Axelia, Coelacanthus, Macropoma, Undina, Wimania

Division **Actinopterygii.**

Subdivision A.

Order **Chondrostei.**

Suborder **Palaeoniscoidei*** : Acrorhabdus, Birgeria, Boreosomus, Catopterus, Cheirodus, Cheirolepis, Coccolepis, Dictyopyge, Elonichthys, Eurynotus, Gonatodus, Gyrolepis, Oxygnathus, Palaeoniscus, Perleidus, Phanerosteon, Platysomus, Pygopterus, Trissolepis.

Suborder **Acipenseroidei** : Acipenser, Chondrosteus*, Gyrosteus*, Pholidurus*, Polyodon (Spatularia), Psephurus, Scaphirhynchus.

Suborder **Saurichthyoidei*** : Belonorhynchus, Saurichthys.

Order **Polypterini** : Calamoichthys, Polypterus.

Subdivision B. **Holostei.**

Group *a*.[2]

Order **Amioidei** (Protospondyli) : Acentrophorus*, Amia, Archaeonemus*, Callopterus*, Caturus*, Dapedius*, Eurycormus*, Euthynotus*, Gyrodus*, Hypsocormus*, Lepidotus*, Macrosemius*, Megalurus*, Mesodon*, Oligopleurus*, Osteorhachis*, Pachycormus*, Pholidophorus*, Pycnodus*, Semionotus*, Spathiurus*.

Order **Lepidosteoidei** (Aetheospondyli) : Aspidorhynchus (?)*, Lepidosteus.

Group *b*.

Order **Teleostei.**

Division A.

Suborder **Leptolepiformes*** : Leptolepis, Thrissops.

---

[1] Used in a restricted sense, excluding the Polypterini.

[2] Group *a* is distinguished from Group *b* by the 'lepidosteoid' histological structure of the scales and bony skeleton (Goodrich, 36).

Class **Pisces,** Order **Teleostei**—*Continued*

Division B.

Group *a* : **Ostariophysi.**

Suborder **Cypriniformes.**

Tribe Characinoidei (Cyprinoidei) : Abramis, Barbus, Catostomus, Citharinus, Cobitis, Cyprinus, Erythrinus, Gymnotus, Ichthyoborus, Lebiasina, Leucissus, Rhodeus, Tinca.

Tribe Siluroidei : Aspredo, Auchenoglanis, Callichthys, Clarias, Loricaria, Macrones, Malapterurus, Pimelodus, Silurus, Synodontis.

Group *b.*

Subgroup 1.

Suborder **Clupeiformes** (Isospondyli, Malacopterygii) : Albula, Alepocephalus, Arapaima, Argyropelecus, Chanos, Chauliodus, Chirocentrus, Clupea, Coregonus, Cromeria, Crossognathus, Ctenothrissa, Elops, Gonorhynchus, Hyodon. Idiacanthus, Mormyrus, Notopterus, Osmerus, Osteoglossum, Pantodon, Phractolaemus, Salmo, Saurodon, Stomias.

Subgroup 2.

Series 1.

Suborder **Esociformes** (Haplomi) : Dallia, Enchodus, Esox, Galaxias, Umbra.

Suborder **Scopeliformes** (Iniomi) : Alepidosaurus, Ateleopus, Aulopus, Ipnops, Sardinoides, Scopelus, Sudis, Synodus.

Suborder **Lyomeri** : Eurypharynx, Saccopharynx, Series 2.

Suborder **Anguilliformes** (Apodes) : Anguilla, Anguillarus, Conger, Derichthys, Muraena, Nemichthys, Urenchelys.

Suborder **Amblyopsiformes** (Microcyprini): Amblyopsis, Anableps, Cyprinodon, Fundulus, Gambusia, Girardinus, Poecilia, Typhlichthys.

Suborder **Scombresociformes** (Synentognathi) : Belone, Exocoetus, Hemirhamphus, Scombresox.

Suborder **Notacanthiformes** (Heteromi) : Dercetes, Halosaurus, Notacanthus.

Suborder **Symbranchiformes** : Amphipnous, Symbranchus.

Suborder **Gasterosteiformes** (Catosteomi).

Tribe 1. **Gasterosteoidei** : Aulorhynchus, Gasterosteus, Spinachia.

Tribe 2. **Hemibranchii** : Amphisile, Aulostoma, Centriscus, Fistularia, Protosyngnathus.

Class **Pisces,** Order **Teleostei**—*Continued*

Tribe 3. **Lophobranchii** : Hippocampus, Phyllopteryx, Solenostomus, Syngnathus.

Tribe 4. **Hypostomides** : Pegasus.

Suborder **Mugiliformes** (Percesoces) : Anabas, Atherina, Chiasmodon, Mugil, Ophiocephalus, Osphronemus, Sphyraena, Tetragonurus.

Division **Lampridiformes** (Allotriognathi).

Subdivision **Lamproidei** (Selenichthyes) : Lampris.

Subdivision **Veliferoidei** (Histichthyes) : Velifer.

Subdivision **Taeniosomi** : Lophotis, Stylephorus, Trachypterus.

Suborder **Percopsiformes** (Salmopercae) : Aphredoderus, Percopsis.

Suborder **Acanthopterygii.**

Section **Berycoidei.**

Division **Beryciformes** : Beryx, Holocentrum, Hoplopteryx, Monocentris.

Division **Zeiformes** : Antigonia, Capros, Zeus.

Division **Rhombiformes.**

Subdivision **Amphistioidea*** : Amphistium.

Subdivision **Heterosomata** : Arnoglossus, Bothus, Cynoglossus, Limanda, Pleuronectes, Psettodes, Solea.

Section **Percoidei.**

Division **Perciformes** : Brama, Caranx, Cepola, Centrarchus, Cichla, Haplognathus, Mullus, Pagellus, Perca, Psettus, Rhacicentrum, Sciaenus, Serranus, Sparus, Toxotes.

Division **Chaetodontiformes.**

Subdivision **Squammipennes** : Chaetodon, Drepane, Platax, Pomacanthus.

Subdivision **Plectognathi.**

Section *a*. Acanthurus, Siganus, Teuthis.

Section *b*. Subsection 1. **Sclerodermi** : Balistes, Monacanthus, Ostracion, Triacanthus.

Subsection 2. Triodon.

Subsection 3. Diodon, Orthagoriscus, Tetrodon.

Division **Cirrhitiformes** : Chilodactylus, Haplodactylus, Latris.

Division **Pomacentriformes** : Pomacentrus.

Class **Pisces,** Order **Teleostei**—*Continued*

Division **Labriformes** : Labrichthys, Labrus. Scarus.

Division **Embiotociformes** : Embiotoca.

Division **Gadopsiformes** : Gadopsis.

Division **Trichodontiformes** : Trichodon.

Division **Ammodytiformes** : Ammodytes.

Division **Champsodontiformes** : Champsodon.

Division **Trachiniformes** : Percophis, Tra chinus, Uranoscopus.

Division **Gobiesociformes** (Xenopteri) : Gobie- sox.

Division **Nototheniiformes** : Notothenia.

Division **Callionymiformes** : Callionymus.

Section **Gobiiformes** : Gobius, Periophthalmus.

Section **Echeneiformes** (Discocephali): Echeneis, Opisthomyzon, Remora.

Section **Scorpaeniformes** (Scleroparei) : Agonus, Comephorus, Cottus, Cyclopterus, Dactylo- pterus, Hexagramma, Platycephalus, Scor- paena, Sebastes, Trigla.

Section **Blenniiformes** (Jugulares) : Anarhicas, Blennius, Clinus, Congrogadus, Dactylo- scopus, Fierasfer, Ophidium, Pholis, Stichaeus, Xiphidion, Zoarces.

Section **Batrachiformes** (Pediculati).

Subsection **Batrachoidea** : Batrachoides, Opsanus (Batrachus).

Subsection **Lophioidea** : Antennarius, Ceratias, Chaunax, Lophius, Mela- nocetus, Anchocephalus (Malthe).

Section **Scombriformes** : Blochius, Histiophorus, Luvarus, Palaeorhynchus, Scomber, Thunnus, Trichiurus, Xiphias.

Section **Kurtiformes** : Kurtus.

Section **Mastacembeliformes** (Opisthomi) : Mastacembelus.

Suborder **Gadiformes** (Anacanthini).

Division 1. Bathygadus, Macrurus.

Division 2. Gadus, Lota, Molva, Motella, Pseudophycis.

Branch **GNATHOSTOMATA**—*Continued*

Grade **Tetrapoda** (Cheiropterygii).

Subgrade **Anamnia**.

Class **Amphibia** (Batrachia).

Subclass **Stegocephalia** (Labyrinthodontia).

Order **Embolomeri**\*[1] : Baphetes, Cricotus, Diplovertebron (Gephy-rostegus), Eogyrinus (Anthracosaurus, Pteroplax), Orthosaurus (Loxomma), Palaeogyrinus, Pholidogaster, Pholiderpeton.

Order **Rhachitomi**\* (Temnospondyli) : Acheloma, Actinodon, Archego-saurus, Aspidosaurus, Cacops, Chelydosaurus, Dasyceps, Dwina-saurus, Eryops, Lydekkerina, Micropholis, Rhinesuchus, Trema-tops, Trimerorhachis, Zatrachis.

Order **Stereospondyli**\* : Anachisma, Bothriceps, Capitosaurus, Cycloto-saurus, Lyrocephalus, Mastodonsaurus, Metaposaurus, Tremato-saurus.

Order **Branchiosauria**\* (Phyllospondyli) : Branchiosaurus, Eugyrinus, Leptorophus, Melanerpeton, Micrerpeton, Micromelerpeton, Pelo-saurus.

Order **Ceraterpetomorpha**\* (Nectridea) : Batrachiderpeton, Cerater-peton, Diceratosaurus, Diplocaulus, Urocordylus, Ptyonius.

Order **Aistopoda**\* : Dolichosoma, Ophiderpeton.

Subclass and Order **Anura** (Salientia).

Suborder **Phaneroglossa**.

Section **Arcifera** : Bufo, Calyptocephalus, Ceratophrys, Cystignathus, Discoglossus, Hyla, Pelobates.

Section **Firmisternia** : Engystoma, Palaeobatrachus\*, Rana.

Suborder **Aglossa** : Hymenochirus, Pipa, Xenopus.

Subclass and Order **Urodela** (Caudata).

Suborder **Lysorophida**\* : Lysorophus.

Suborder **Hylaeobatrachia**\* : Hylaeobatrachus.

Suborder **Caducibranchiata** : Amphiuma, Amblystoma (Siredon), Cryptobranchus, Megalobatrachus, Molge (Triton), Plethodon, Salamandra, Spelerpes, Tylototriton.

Suborder **Perennibranchiata** : Necturus (Menobranchus), Proteus.

Suborder **Sirenoidea** (Meantes) : Siren.

Subclass and Order **Apoda** (Gymnophiones, Coeciliae) : Dermophis, Hypogeophis, Ichthyophis, Siphonops.

Subgrade **Amniota**.

Class **Reptilia**.

Group **Anapsida** or **Prosauria**.

Subclass and Order **Microsauria**\* : Dawsonia, Hylonomus, Petrobates, Seeleya.

Subclass and Order **Seymouriamorpha**\* : Conodectes (Seymouria), Karpinskiosaurus, Kotlassia.

---

[1] This Order may include some forms which should be placed in a basal group of Tetrapoda ancestral to both Anamnia and Amniota.

Grade **Tetrapoda,** Class **Reptilia**—*Continued*

 Subclass **Anapsidosauria.**

  Order **Cotylosauria*** : Captorhinus, Diadectes, Eunotosaurus (?), Labidosaurus, Limnoscelis, Pantylus, Pariotichus, Sauravus.

  Order **Pareiasauria*** : Anthodon, Bradysaurus, Elginia, Pareiasaurus, Propappus.

  Order **Procolophonia*** : Koiloskiosaurus, Procolophon, Sclerosaurus Thelegnathus.

 Group **Synapsida,** or **Reptilia Theropsida.**

 Subclass **Theromorpha.**

  Superorder **Theraptosauria.**

   Order **Pelycosauria*** : Clepsydrops, Dimetrodon, Sphenacodon.

   Order **Edaphosauria*** : Edaphosaurus, Naosaurus.

   Order **Poliosauria*** : Ophiacodon, Poliosaurus, Varanops, Varanosaurus.

   Order **Caseasauria*** : Casea.

  Superorder **Therapsida.**

   Order **Anningiamorpha*** : Anningia, Glaucosaurus (?), Mycterosaurus (?).

   Order **Dromasauria*** : Galechirus, Galepus.

   Order **Dinocephalia*.**

    Suborder **Tapinocephalia** : Delphinognathus, Deuterosaurus (?), Mormosaurus, Moschops, Rhopalodon (?), Tapinocephalus.

    Suborder **Titanosuchia** : Titanosuchus.

   Order **Dicynodontia** (Anomodontia)* : Dicynodon (Oudenodon ?), Endothiodon, Geikia, Gordonia, Placerias, Pristerodon, Procynodon.

   Order **Theriodontia*.**

    Suborder **Therocephalia** : Aelurosaurus, Alopecodon, Ictidosuchus, Lycosaurus, Lycosuchus, Pristerognathus, Scylacosaurus, Scymnosaurus.

    Suborder **Gorgonopsida** : Arctops, Gorgonops, Galesuchus, Scymnognathus, Theriodesmus (?).

    Suborder **Burnetiomorpha** : Burnetia.

    Suborder **Bauriamorpha** : Bauria, Microgomphodon, Sesamodon.

    Suborder **Cynodontia** : Cynognathus, Diademodon, Galesaurus, Gomphognathus, Nythosaurus, Thrinaxodon, Trirhacodon.

 Group **Parapsida.**

  Subclass and Order **Mesosauria** (Proganosauria)* : Mesosaurus, Stereosternum.

  Subclass **Sauropterygia.**[1]

   Order **Nothosauria*** : Lariosaurus, Neusticosaurus, Nothosaurus, Simosaurus.

   Order **Plesiosauria*** : Cryptocleidus, Elasmosaurus, Muraenosaurus, Peloneustes, Plesiosaurus, Pliosaurus, Polycotylus, Thaumatosaurus.

---

[1] The Sauropterygia are possibly related to the Chelonia (Broom).

Grade **Tetrapoda,** Class **Reptilia**—*Continued*

    Subclass and Order **Placodontia*** : Cyamodus, Placochelys, Placodus.

    Subclass and Order **Pleurosauria** (Protorosauria)* : Araeoscelis, Palaeohatteria (?), Pleurosaurus, Sauranodon.

    Subclass and Order **Ichthyosauria*** : Cymbospondylus, Ichthyosaurus, Mixosaurus, Ophthalmosaurus, Shastosaurus, Toretocnemus.

   Group **Eusauria** or **Reptilia Sauropsida.**

    Subclass **Testudinata.**

      Order **Chelonia.**

        Suborder **Triassochelydia*** : Triassochelys.

        Suborder **Amphichelydia*** : Baëna, Glyptops, Platychelys, Pleurosternum, Probaëna.

        Suborder **Pleurodira** : Bothremys*, Chelodina, Hydraspis, Miolania*, Pelomedusa, Podocnemis, Sternothaerus.

        Suborder **Cryptodira** : Archelon*, Chelone, Chelonides*, Chelydra, Dermochelys (Sphargis), Desmatochelys*, Emys, Eurysternum*, Platysternum, Protostega*, Psephophorus*, Testudo, Thalassemys.

        Suborder **Trionychoidea** : Conchochelys*, Plastomenus*, Trionyx.

    Subclass **Diapsida.**

      Superorder **Diaptosauria.**

        Order **Rhynchocephalia.**

          Suborder **Rhynchosauria*** : Howesia, Hyperodapedon, Mesosuchus (?), Rhynchosaurus.

          Suborder **Sphenodontia** : Homoeosaurus*, Sphenodon (Hatteria).

          Suborder **Champsosauria*** (Choristodera) : Champsosaurus, Simaedosaurus.

          Suborder **Thalattosauria** (?)* : Nectosaurus, Thalattosaurus.

          Suborder **Protorosauria** (?)* : Protorosaurus.

      Superorder **Lepidosauria** (Streptostylica).[1]

        Order **Lacertilia.**

          Suborder **Hydrosauria.**

            Tribe **Varanomorpha** : Megalania*, Palaeovaranus*, Varanus.

            Tribe **Dolichosauria*** : Acteosaurus, Dolichosaurus, Pontosaurus.

            Tribe **Aigialosauria*** : Aigialosaurus.

            Tribe **Mosasauria*** (Pythonomorpha) : Clidastes, Hainosaurus, Lestosaurus, Mosasaurus, Platecarpus.

          Suborder **Lacertae** : Agama, Amblyrhynchus, Anguis, Aniella, Dibama, Draco, Euposaurus*, Gerrhosaurus, Heloderma, Iguana, Lacerta, Scincus, Tejus, Zonurus.

          Suborder **Amphisbaenia** : Amphisbaena, Chirotes, Cremastosaurus*.

---

[1] The Lepidosauria are included in the Diaptosauria on the assumption that their monapsid skull has been derived from the diapsid type.

Grade **Tetrapoda,** Class **Reptilia**—*Continued*

Suborder **Geckones** : Eublepharus, Gecko, Ptychozoon, Uroplates.

Suborder **Chamaeleontes** (Rhiptoglossa) : Chamaeleo.

Order **Ophidia** : Boa, Coluber, Crotalus, Dipsas, Elaps, Eryx, Glauconia, Hydrophis, Ilysia, Naja, Python, Tropidonotus, Typhlops, Uropeltis, Vipera, Xenopeltis.

Superorder **Archosauria** (Thecodontia).

Order **Eosuchia*** : Palaeagama, Paliguana (?), Youngina.

Order **Proterosuchia*** : Proterosuchus.

Incertae sedis, Howesia, Mesosuchus.

Order **Parasuchia***.

Suborder **Pseudosuchia** : Aëtosaurus, Erpetosuchus (?), Euparkeria, Notochampsa, Ornithosuchus, Scleromochlus, Sphenosuchus.

Suborder **Erythrosuchia** (Pelycosimia): Erythrosuchus.

Suborder **Phytosauria** : Machaeroprosopus, Mesorhinus, Mystriosuchus, Parasuchus, Phytosaurus (Belodon), Rhytidodon, Stagonolepis.

Order **Crocodilia.**

Suborder **Mesosuchia*** : Atoposaurus, Bernissartia, Geosaurus, Goniopholis, Notosuchus, Pelagosaurus, Pholidosaurus, Steneosaurus, Teleosaurus.

Suborder **Eusuchia** : Alligator, Caiman, Crocodilus, Gavialis, Osteolaemus, Thoracosaurus,* Tomistoma.

Suborder **Thalattosuchia*** : Dacosaurus, Metriorhynchus.

Order **Saurischia*** (Dinosauria Theropoda and Sauropoda).

Suborder **Megalosauria** (Theropoda) : Ammosaurus, Anchisaurus, Ceratosaurus, Coelurus, Compsognathus, Creosaurus, Megalosaurus, Plateosaurus, Thecodontosaurus, Zanclodon.

Suborder **Cetiosauria** (Sauropoda, Opisthocoelia): Apatosaurus (Brontosaurus), Atlantosaurus, Camarosaurus (Morosaurus), Cetiosaurus, Diplodocus, Titanosaurus.

Order **Ornithischia** (Dinosauria Orthopoda, Predentata)*.

Suborder **Iguanodontia** (Ornithopoda) : Camptosaurus, Claosaurus, Hadrosaurus, Hypsilophodon, Iguanodon, Laosaurus, Nanosaurus, Trachodon.

Suborder **Stegosauria** : Polacanthus, Scelidosaurus, Stegosaurus.

Suborder **Ceratopsia** : Ceratops, Diceratops, Triceratops.

Order **Pterosauria***.

Suborder **Tribelesodontia** : Tribelesodon.

Suborder **Rhamphorhynchoidea** : Dimorphodon, Rhamphorhynchus, Scaphognathus.

Suborder **Pterodactyloidea** : Nyctosaurus, Ornithodesmus, Pteranodon, Pterodactylus.

Grade **Tetrapoda**—*Continued*

Class **Aves.**

Subclass **Archaeornithes** (Saururae) : Archaeopteryx*, Archaeornis*.

Subclass **Neornithes** (Ornithurae).

Section **Odontormae.**

Order **Ichthyornithes*** : Ichthyornis.

Section **Odontolcae*.**[1]

Order **Hesperornithes** : Hesperornis.

Section **Ratitae.**[2]

Order **Casuarii** : Casuarius, Dromaeus.

Order **Struthiones** : Struthio.

Order **Rheae** : Rhea.

Order **Dinornithes*** : Dinornis, Palapteryx

Order **Aepyornithes*** : Aepyornis.

Order **Apteryges** : Apteryx.

Section **Carinatae.**

Group *a.* **Palaeognathae.**

Order **Tinamiformes** : Cryptura, Rhynchotus, Tinamus.

Group *b.* **Neognathae.**

Order **Colymbiformes** : Colymbus, Podiceps.

Order **Sphenisciformes** : Aptenodytes, Eudiptes, Palaeeudyptes*.

Order **Procellariiformes** : Diomedea, Fulmarus, Procellaria, Puffinus.

Order **Ciconiiformes** : Ardea, Balaeniceps, Ciconia, Eudocimus, Fregata, Ibis, Nycticorax, Odontopteryx*, Palaelodus*, Pelecanus, Phaethon, Phalacrocorax, Phoenicopterus, Scops.

Order **Pelecaniformes** :

Order **Anseriformes** : Anas, Anser, Chauna, Cygnus, Fuligula, Mergus, Nesonetta, Palamedea, Somateria.

Order **Falconiformes** : Accipiter, Aquila, Buteo, Cathartes, Circus, Falco, Gyparchus, Gypaëtus, Gyps, Haliaëtus, Milvus, Pandion, Polyborus, Sarcorhamphus, Serpentaria, Vultur.

Order **Opisthocomi** : Opisthocomus.

Order **Galliformes** : Argusianus, Crax, Gallinuloides*, Gallus, Lagopus, Laphophorus, Megapodius, Meleagris, Numida, Ortalis, Palaeortix*, Pavo, Pedionomus, Perdix, Phasianus, Tetrao, Turnix (Hemipodius).

Order **Gruiformes** : Aphanapteryx*, Balearica, Cariama, Crex, Erythromachus*, Eurypyga, Fulica, Gallinula, Grus, Heliornis, Mesites, Notornis*, Ocydromus, Otis, Parra, Phororacus*, Rallus, Rhinochetus.

Order **Charadriiformes.**

Suborder **Limicolae** : Aegialitis, Charadrius, Chionis, Dromas, Gallinago (Capella), Glareola, Haematopus, Machetes, Numenius, Oedicnemus, Pluvianus, Scolopax, Thinocorys, Totanus, Tringa.

[1] Should perhaps be placed with the Colymbitormes.

[2] The true affinities of these flightless and ' palaeognathous ' Orders are still doubtful.

Grade **Tetrapoda,** Class **Aves**—*Continued*

  Suborder **Lari** : Alca, Anous, Larus, Megalestris, Mergulus, Rissa, Rhynchops, Sterna, Uria.

  Suborder **Pterocles** : Pterocles, Syrrhaptes.

  Suborder **Columbae** : Columba, Didunculus, Didus*, Ectopistes, Goura, Pezophaps*, Turtur.

 Order **Cuculiformes.**

  Suborder **Cuculi** : Coccystes, Crotophaga, Cuculus, Musophaga, Necrornis*, Turacus.

  Suborder **Psittaci** : Cacatua, Eos, Loriculus, Lorius, Melopsittacus, Nestor, Psittacula, Psittacus, Stringops.

 Order **Coraciiformes.**

  Suborder **Coraciae** : Alcedo, Buceros, Bucorvus, Coracias, Dacelo, Eurystomus, Merops, Momotus, Upupa.

  Suborder **Striges** : Asio, Bubo, Strix, Syrnium.

  Suborder **Caprimulgi** : Caprimulgus, Podargus, Steatornis.

  Suborder **Cypseli** : Collocalia, Cypselus, Lophornis, Panyptila, Patagona, Trochilus.

  Suborder **Colii** : Colius.

  Suborder **Trogones** : Haploderma, Harpactes, Trogon.

  Suborder **Pici** : Bucco, Capito, Dendrocopus, Galbula, Gecinus Indicator, Iynx, Picus, Pteroglossus, Rhamphastus.

 Order **Passeriformes.**

  Suborder **Anysomyodi** (Clamatores) : Cotinga, Dendrocolaptes, Eurylaemus, Formicaria, Philepitta, Pipra, Pitta, Rupicola, Xenicus.

  Suborder **Diacromyodi** (Oscines) : Ampelis, Atrichornis, Cardinalis, Certhia, Chelidon, Cinolus, Corvus, Hirundo, Fringilla, Icterus, Lanius, Loria, Loxia, Meliphaga, Menura, Mimus, Mniotilta, Muscicapa, Nectarinia, Oriolus, Paradisea, Parus, Passer, Pica, Pratincola, Prunella, Pycnonotus, Ruticilla, Serinus, Sitta, Sturnus, Sylvia, Tanagra, Troglodytes, Turdus, Vidua, Zosterops.

Class **Mammalia.**

 Subclass and Order **Multituberculata*** (Allotheria).

  Suborder **Tritylodontoidea** : Oligokyphus, Stereognathus, Tritylodon.

  Suborder **Plagiaulacoidea** : Bolodon, Ctenacodon, Hypsprymnopsis (Microlestes), Loxaulax, Microcleptes (Microlestes, in part), Neoplagiaulax, Plagiaulax, Ptilodus, Taeniolabis (Polymastodon).

 Subclass and Order **Triconodonta*** : Amphilestes, Phascolotherium, Triconodon, Trioracodon.

 Subclass **Pantotheria.**

  Order **Spalacotheria** (Symmetrodonta)* : Peralestes, Spalacotherium.

  Order **Amphitheria*** : Amblotherium (Dryolestes), Kurtodon, Phascolestes.

 Subclass and Order **Monotremata** (Ornithodelphia, Prototheria), Echidna, Ornithorhynchus.

Grade **Tetrapoda,** Class **Mammalia**—*Continued*

Subclass **Ditremata** (Theria).

Grade **Marsupialia** (Didelphia, Metatheria).

Order **Polyprotodontia.**

Suborder **Didelphoidea** : Amphiproviverra*, Borhyaena*, Dasyurus, Didelphys, Eodelphys*, Marmosa, Myrmecobius, Prothylacinus*, Thlaeodon*, Thylacinus.

Suborder **Notoryctoidea** : Notoryctes.

Suborder **Perameloidea** [1] : Perameles.

Order **Caenolestoidea** (Paucituberculata): Caenolestes, Epanorthus, Garzonia*.

Order **Diprotodontia** : Bettongia, Diprotodon*, Hypsiprymnus, Macropus, Petaurus, Phalanger, Phascolarctos, Phascolomys, Tarsipes, Trichosurus, Thylacoleo*.

Grade **Placentalia** (Monodelphia).

Order **Insectivora.**

Group *a.*

Suborder **Deltatheroidea*** : Deltatheridium, Deltatheroides.

Group *b.* **Zalambdodonta.**

Suborder **Centetoidea** : Centetes, Chrysochloris, Microgale, Necrolestes*, Potamogale, Solenodon, Xenotherium*, Zalambdalestes*.

Group *c.* **Dilambdodonta.**

Suborder **Erinacoidea** : Diacodon*, Erinaceus, Gymnura, Leptictis*, Palaeolestes*, Palaeoryctes*.

Suborder **Soricoidea** : Blarina, Crocidura, Myogale, Nectogale, Scalops, Sorex, Talpa.

Order **Tillodontia*** : Esthonyx, Tillotherium.

Order **Pholidota** (Nomarthra in part) : Manis.

Order **Xenarthra** (Edentata in part).

Suborder **Palaeanodonta*** : Metacheiromys, Palaeanodon.

Suborder **Loricata** (Hicanodonta) : Chlamydophorus, Dasypus, Doedicurus*, Glyptodon*, Panochthus*, Peltephilus*, Priodon, Tatusia, Tolypeutes.

Suborder **Pilosa** (Anicanodonta) : Bradypus, Cholaepus, Cycloturus, Glossotherium (Neomylodon)*, Megalonyx*, Megatherium*, Mylodon*, Myrmecophaga, Scelidotherium*, Tamandua.

Order **Taeniodontia*** (Ganodonta) : Conoryctes, Psittacotherium, Stylinodon.

Order **Rodentia.**

Suborder **Duplicidentata** : Lagomys, Lepus.

Suborder **Simplicidentata** : Arctomys, Bathyergus, Castor, Cavia, Cephalomys*, Chinchilla, Dasyprocta, Dipus, Dolichotis, Erethizon, Geomys, Gerbillus, Hydrochaerus, Hystrix, Mus, Myoxus, Octodon, Pedetes, Sciurus, Spalax, Spermophilus.

[1] Perhaps more closely allied to the Diprotodontia.

Grade **Tetrapoda,** Class **Mammalia**—*Continued*

Order **Carnivora.**

Suborder **Creodonta\*.**

Tribe **Procreodi** : Arctocyon, Chriacus, Claenodon, Deltatherium, Oxyclaenus.

Tribe **Acreodi** : Andrewsarchus, Coconodon, Dissacus, Mesonyx, Pachyaena.

Tribe **Pseudocreodi** : Hyaenodon, Limnocyon, Oxyaena, Proviverra, Palaeonictis, Patriofelis, Sinopa.

Tribe **Eucreodi** [1] : Didymictis, Miacis, Viverravus, Vulpavus.

Suborder **Fissipedia.**

Section *a.* Ælurictis, Acinonyx\* (Cynaelurus), Eusmilus\*, Felis, Lynx, Machairodus\*, Nimravus\*.

Section *b.* Arctogale, Cryptoprocta, Cynictis, Eupleres, Fossa, Genetta, Gulo, Hyaena, Latax, Lutra, Mephitis, Mellivora, Mustela, Palaeogale\*, Paradoxurus, Plesictis\*, Proteles, Viverra.

Section *c.* Aeluropus, Aelurus, Bassaris, Canis, Cercoleptes, Cynodictis\*, Daphaenus\*, Hemicyon\*, Hyaenarctos\*, Lycaon, Melursus, Nasua, Procyon, Otocyon, Ursus.

Suborder **Pinnipedia** : Cystophora, Halichaerus, Monachus, Otaria, Phoca, Trichechus.

Order **Artiodactyla.**

Suborder **Protartiodactyla\*** : Diacodexis (Pantolestes, Trigonolestes).

Suborder **Bunoselenodontia\*** : Ancodon, Anoplotherium, Anthracotherium, Dichobune (?), Merycopotamus.

Suborder **Bunodontia** (Suina) : Achaenodon\*, Chaeropotamus\*, Dicotyles, Elotherium\*, Entelodon\*, Hyotherium\*, Palaeochoerus\*, Phacochoerus, Platygonus\*, Potamochoerus, Sus.

Suborder **Selenodontia** (Ruminantia).

Section *a.* Dichodon\*, Caenotherium\*, Xiphodon\*.

Section *b.* **Oreodonta\*** : Agriochoerus, Merycochoerus, Mesoreodon, Oreodon, Protoreodon.

Section *c.* **Tylopoda** : Auchenia, Camelus, Poebrotherium\*, Protolabis\*, Stenomylus\*.

Section *d.* **Tragulina** : Gelocus\*, Blastomeryx\*, Cryptomeryx\*, Dorcatherium, Hyaemoschus, Hypertragulus\*, Leptomeryx\*, Lophiomeryx\*, Tragulus.

Section *e.* **Pecora** : Alces, Antilocapra, Bos, Capra, Cephalophus, Cervus, Elaphodus, Gazella, Giraffa, Moschus, Okapia, Ovibos, Ovis, Rangifer, Sivatherium\*, Protoceras\*.

Order **Cetacea.**

Suborder **Archaeoceti\*** : Agorophius, Pappocetus, Patriocetus, Protocetus, Prozeuglodon, Zeuglodon.

Suborder **Mystacoceti** : Balaena, Balaenoptera, Megaptera, Rhachianectes.

---

[1] Should probably be placed in the Fissipedia as ancestral forms.

Grade **Tetrapoda,** Class **Mammalia**—*Continued*

Suborder **Odontoceti** : Cogia, Delphinus, Grampus, Globiocephalus, Hyperoodon, Mesoplodon, Monodon, Orca, Phocaena, Physeter, Platanista, Pontoporia, Squalodon*, Steno, Ziphius.

Order **Amblypoda***.

Suborder **Taligrada** : Ectoconus, Mioclaenus, Pantolambda, Periptychus.

Suborder **Dinocerata** : Coryphodon, Eudinoceras, Prodinoceras, Uintatherium (Dinoceras).

Order **Condylarthra*** : Hyopsodus (?), Meniscotherium (?), Phenacodus Tetraclaenodon.

Order **Subungulata.**

Suborder **Hyracoidea** : Dendrohyrax, Hyrax (Procavia), Megalohyrax*, Sagatherium*.

Suborder **Embrithopoda*** : Arsinoitherium.

Suborder **Proboscidea** : Baritherium*, Dinotherium*, Elephas, Mastodon*, Moeritherium*, Palaeomastodon*, Stegodon*, Tetrabelodon*.

Suborder **Sirenia** : Desmostylus*, Elotherium*, Eosiren*, Halicore, Halitherium*, Manatus, Prorastomus*, Protosiren*, Rhytina.

Order **Notoungulata***.

Suborder **Typotheria** : Archaeohyrax, Archaeopithecus, Interotherium, Hegetotherium, Typotherium.

Suborder **Entelonychia** : Arctostylops, Homalodontotherium, Isotemnus, Leontinia, Notostylops, Palaeostylops.

Suborder **Astrapotherioidea** : Astrapotherium, Trigonostylops.

Suborder **Toxodontia** : Adinotherium, Nesodon, Notohippus, Toxodon.

Order **Pyrotheria*** : Pyrotherium.

Order **Perissodactyla.**

Suborder **Rhinocerotoidea** : Aceratherium*, Amynodon*, Aphelops*, Atelodus*, Baluchitherium*, Caenopus*, Ceratorhinus*, Coelodonta*, Diceratherium*, Elasmotherium*, Hyrachyus*, Hyracodon*, Metamynodon*, Rhinoceros, Teleoceras*.

Suborder **Tapiroidea** : Colodon, Helaletes*, Heptodon*, Homogalax*, Megatapirus*, Protapirus*, Tapirus.

Suborder **Hippoidea** : Anchilophus*, Anchitherium*, Eohippus (Proterohippus)*, Epihippus*, Equus, Hipparion*, Hippidium*, Hyracotherium* (Pliolophus), Merychippus*, Mesohippus*, Miohippus*, Orohippus*, Palaeotherium*, Paloplotherium*, Parahippus*, Plesippus*, Pliohippus*, Propalaeotherium*, Protohippus*.

Suborder **Chalicotheria*** (Ancylopoda) : Chalicotherium, Eomoropus, Macrotherium, Moropus, Schizotherium.

Suborder **Titanotheria*** : Brontotherium (Titanotherium), Eotitanops, Megacerops (Brontops), Palaeosyops, Protitanotherium, Telmatotherium.

Order **Litopterna*** : Adiantus, Diadiaphorus, Didolodus, Epitherium, Macrauchenia, Thoatherium.

Grade **Tetrapoda,** Class **Mammalia**—*Continued*

    Order **Tubulidentata** : Orycteropus.

    Order **Menotyphla** : Adapisorex (?)\*, Macroscelides, Mixodectes (?)\*, Plesiadapis\* (Nothodectes) (?), Ptilocercus, Tupaia.

    Order **Dermoptera** : Galaeopithecus.

    Order **Chiroptera.**

      Suborder **Megachiroptera** : Archaeopteropus\* (?), Cephalotes, Epomophorus, Harpyia, Notopteris, Pteropus, Xantharpyia.

      Suborder **Microchiroptera** : Desmodus, Emballonura, Glossophaga, Hipposiderus, Megaderma, Miniopterus, Molossus, Mormops, Mystacops, Natalus, Noctilio, Nycteris, Phyllostoma, Rhinolophus, Scotophilus, Thyroptera, Vespertilio, Vesperugo, Zanycteris\*.

    Order **Primates.**

      Suborder **Lemuroidea.**

        Series **Lemuriformes** : Adapis\*, Avahis, Cheiromys, Chirogale, Hapalemur, Indris, Lemur, Lepidolemur, Megaladapis\*, Microcoebus, Nesopithecus\*, Notharctus\*, Opolemur, Pelycodus\*, Propithecus, Protoadapis\*.

        Series **Lorisiformes** : Galago, Loris, Nycticebus, Perodicticus.

        Series **Tarsiiformes** : Anaptomorphus\*, Hemiacodon\*, Microchoerus\*, Necrolemur\*, Omomys\*, Tarsius, Tetonius\*.

      Suborder **Anthropoidea.**

        Section **Parapithecoidea\*** : Moeripithecus, Parapithecus.

        Section **Platyrrhina** : Ateles, Callithrix, Cebus, Hapale, Homunculus\*, Lagothrix, Midas, Mycetes, Nyctipithecus, Pithecia.

        Section **Catarrhina** : Australopithecus\*, Anthropopithecus, Cercocoebus, Cercopithecus, Colobus, Cynocephalus, Cynopithecus, Dryopithecus\*, Gorilla, Hylobates, Macacus, Mesopithecus\*, Nasalis, Pliopithecus\*, Propliopithecus\*, Semnopithecus, Simia Simopithecus\*, Sivapithecus\*, Theropithecus\*.

        Section **Bimana** : Eoanthropus\*, Homo, Pithecanthropus\*, Sinanthropus\*.

# EDWIN STEPHEN GOODRICH[*]
## 1868–1946

On January 6th of this year, 1946, our beloved and revered Professor Goodrich died at Oxford in his seventy-eighth year, scarcely three months after he had retired from his long tenure of the Linacre Chair. He is acknowledged on all hands to have been one of the great masters of Zoology. His influence will not die with his passing: his contributions to our science have been fundamental and have added so many different and vital parts to its permanent framework. As well as a great master he has been one of the great servants of Science: for a quarter of a century he has been the devoted editor of our Quarterly Journal.

Only a few weeks before he died he had corrected the proofs of the last part of that remarkable review of his 50 years' work on nephridia and coelomoducts which forms parts II, III, and IV of the previous volume. The last part was printed but not issued when he died, and before it appeared Dr. Bidder added to it the mourning notice which bore these words:

*Si monumentum quaeras, respice.*

The *Quarterly Journal of Microscopical Science* for the last fifty years is indeed his memorial; apart from his editorship since 1920, no fewer than forty-three of his research papers, from 1893 onwards, have been published in its pages.

Edwin Stephen Goodrich was born at Weston-super-Mare on June 21, 1868, the son of the Rev. Octavius Pitt Goodrich, and was the last male descendant of John Goodrich of Energlyn, Glamorganshire, who came from Nansewood, Virginia, U.S.A., in 1775. John Goodrich's forbear, also John, had gone to America in 1630 and settled in Nansewood in 1635; he in turn was descended from John, the elder brother of Thomas Goodrich who was Lord Chancellor of England, Bishop of Ely from 1534 to 1545, then Ambassador to France and again Bishop of Ely in 1551. With Professor Goodrich's death this branch of the family is now extinct.

His father having died, his mother Frances Lucinda Parker (who lived until 1936 reaching the age of 98) took the children

[*]Reprinted from Quarterly Journal of Microscopical Science, Volume 87, Part IV, 1946.

to the south of France at the end of the Franco-Prussian war and they settled at Pau. His elder brother returned for education to England, going to Charterhouse and Balliol, but he himself was considered too delicate and was brought up in France; he attended first a French Lycée and then an English school at Pau. So it came about that he spoke French as perfectly as English.

From his earliest years he had a taste for natural history and, inheriting a family gift for drawing, produced in his boyhood beautiful coloured studies of birds and butterflies. His keen artistic sense, as will be stressed later, was an important factor contributing to his great qualities as a teacher and master of his science; it also made him an accomplished landscape painter in water colour.

At the age of twenty Goodrich returned to England and entered the Slade School of Art at University College, London, in 1888. What a fortunate event for Zoology that was! Ray Lankester, then at the height of his powers as an inspiring teacher, was Jodrell Professor at London and lecturing in a nearby classroom; so Goodrich with his interest in natural history went to hear him. He immediately fell under his spell; he decided then and there that zoology was his real career and changed his course of studies from art to become a pupil under Lankester. At that moment a very important link in the chain of zoological history was forged. Lankester was at once greatly impressed by Goodrich's ability and when in 1891 he was appointed to the Linacre Chair at Oxford, he took Goodrich with him as his assistant. I am sure that in many Zoologists' minds the names of Lankester and Goodrich are closely linked—and with good cause. Lankester was the dominating force in the evolutionary comparative anatomy which arose and flourished after the publication of the *Origin of Species*. Goodrich more than anyone else has carried forward the torch, lit by Lankester, in this field of zoology; he has carried it from the last century up to nearly half of this and the flame burns as brightly in his last great paper just published, as it did in his early papers of the 'nineties. To say this is not to imply that Goodrich just continued lines of work started by Lankester—not at all: his genius and insight continually opened up new lines of work bringing sense and order where hitherto had been confusion in both vertebrate and invertebrate zoology. Our Journal has of course developed and kept its fame under the guidance of these two great leaders: when Lankester gave up his long editorship in 1920, Goodrich was his natural follower.

On coming to Oxford from London Goodrich entered Merton College as an undergraduate in 1892 and while acting as Assistant to Lankester read for the final honour school in Zoology; he was awarded the Rolleston Memorial Prize in 1894 and graduated with First-class Honours the following year.

An account of his scientific work will come later, but while we are being biographical it should be recorded that when still an undergraduate he had become a most active researcher. He was of course somewhat older than the average undergraduate; he was twenty-four when he entered Merton and in that year he published his first two papers. His third paper, and his first in this Journal, came in 1893, two more in 1894, and before he took his final schools he must have completed the two papers published in 1895 which included his ever famous dissertation 'On the Coelom, Genital Ducts and Nephridia'. His wide range of interest was already clearly shown: apart from this classic, which covered the whole range of the Metazoa, his early papers had dealt with cephalopods, polychaetes, oligochaetes, fossil mammals and museum reform.

After graduation he went with the Naples Scholarship for six months to the famous Stazione Zoologica and in 1898 he was awarded the Radcliffe Travelling Fellowship, whereby he visited India and Ceylon. In the following year he was appointed Aldrichian Demonstrator of Comparative Anatomy and in 1900 was elected a Fellow of Merton. Apart from his world-wide travels in vacations Goodrich remained at Oxford all his life. W. F. R. Weldon had become Linacre Professor in 1899 when Lankester went to be Director of the Natural History departments of the British Museum and was in turn succeeded in the chair by G. C. Bourne in 1906. During the first world war when Bourne and other members of the staff were away on war service, Goodrich carried on the teaching and administration of the department single-handed. A special Professorship of Comparative Embryology was made for him in 1919, and in 1921 he succeeded Bourne in the Linacre Chair, which he held until last year. All this time, until his death Goodrich remained a Fellow of Merton, becoming a Professorial Fellow when he took the Chair, and being elected an Honorary Fellow when he retired.

In 1913 he married Helen Pixell, the eminent protozoologist, and more will be said of this very happy partnership later. Here I want to refer to something that is so characteristic of his modesty: he would not take his D.Sc. degree until some years after his wife had taken hers and then only when persuaded to the extent of her paying the necessary University dues and providing the gorgeous and costly robes!

Many were the honours that came to him. He was elected a Fellow of the Royal Society in 1905, when still in his thirties, served on the Council twice (1923–5 and 1931–2) and as Vice-President during 1930–1, and was awarded the Royal Medal in 1936. From 1915 to 1923 he was Zoological Secretary of the Linnean Society of London, helping to keep it alive through those lean and difficult years of war; in 1932 he received the Society's Gold Medal. He was given an Honorary LL.D. by Edinburgh University and an Honorary Sc.D. by Dublin. He was Hon. Member of the New York Academy of Sciences, Member of the Royal Swedish Academy, Membre Correspondant de la Société de Biologie de Paris, Associé de l'Académie Royale de Belgique, Foreign Member of the Academy of Sciences of U.S.S.R., Leningrad, Hon. Fellow of the National Institute of Sciences of India, Member of the International Institute of Embryology of Utrecht and Member of the Royal Society of Sciences of Upsala.

On his seventieth birthday, in 1938, his colleagues and pupils expressed their admiration for his work by presenting him with a congratulatory volume of essays edited by Dr. (now Professor) G. R. de Beer and entitled *Evolution: Essays on Aspects of Evolutionary Biology*.

With this brief biographical summary let us now turn to consider his contributions to zoological knowledge and his influence as a teacher. Appended to this account of his work will be found a complete list of his publications arranged in chronological order, which was kindly prepared for me by Mrs. Goodrich; to her also I am much indebted for notes regarding his career.

Goodrich's first paper, published in the *Journal of the Marine Biological Association* in 1892 was a precise account of a large and rare squid *Ommastrephes pteropus* Stp. which had been captured off Salcombe; but he was not content with presenting just a careful description, for he added to it a valuable table giving the chief characters of all the genera of recent Oigopsid Cephalopoda in the form of a key. Four years later, in his tenth publication, he wrote a report on a collection of 162 Cephalopoda belonging to 28 genera, collected by H.M.S. Investigator in the Indian Ocean; he described and figured eleven entirely new species belonging to nine genera and recorded four genera not hitherto taken in the Indian region.

In 1892 he also published a note on a new species and genus of oligochaete *Vermiculus pilosus*, which he discovered at Weymouth, and in 1895 gave a full account of it in this Journal; he showed that it has a number of characters which place it in a very isolated position including a dense covering, from head to tail, of remarkable 'sense hairs'. He wrote further notes on oligochaetes with a description of a new species *Enchytraeus hortensis* in 1896, here paying particular attention to the coelomic corpuscles.

As soon as he came to Oxford he began to assist Lankester in an entire rearrangement of the zoological collections in the University Museum. He described these reforms in the now extinct monthly journal *Natural Science* in 1894. It is clear from his writing how enthusiastically he took up this task.

'Here', he writes, 'one need seek neither to attract the nursery-maid nor to amuse children, nor again need one trouble to satisfy the idle curiosity of the sightseer. There is, then, no necessity for tragic groups of stuffed animals, for birds perched on cardboard rocks among artificial flowers. On the contrary, the exhibits are to be strictly scientific, forming series at once instructive and interesting to the general educated public, and more especially to the real student of zoology. Surrounded as it is by the various chemical, physical, and biological laboratories, the central court is in the first instance a place of study. In such educational collections it is essential that each object should be exhibited for a definite purpose, should show what it is meant to show as clearly as possible, and should be fully labelled in language technical so far as is necessary for accuracy. The observer is not to be bewildered by a number of specimens, but rather impressed by a few well-chosen examples.'

He was responsible for the greater part of the vertebrate exhibits. As a Professor from another University remarked to me recently 'there is no other museum in which a student can learn so much sound comparative anatomy by walking round and studying the exhibits and their labels—thanks to Goodrich'.

This rearrangement of the museum led to Goodrich's first published work in palaeontology: his paper (1894) on the fossil Mammalia of the Stonesfield Slate. How characteristic of him is the manner in which he came to undertake it. In this paper he writes: 'Through the kindness of Professor Green and Professor Lankester, who placed the Oxford fossils in my hands for the purpose of displaying them in a museum case in a manner more worthy of their interest and value, I had the opportunity of examining and handling our six specimens.' These were the famous lower jaws of the first Mesozoic mammals to be discovered; they had been found about 1814 and examined and described by a succession of authors including Buckland, Cuvier, Owen and Osborn. Their particular interest apart from their early origin lay in the nature of their teeth and the light they shed on the evolution of mammalian dentition. Goodrich was not content simply to display the specimens with explanatory labels setting out the current theories concerning them; he must thoroughly re-examine them himself to see if they really did support the theories. We must remember that at this time he was still an undergraduate working for his schools. He also obtained access to the three other known English specimens: two in the British Museum and one at York. He states the 'Tritubercular Theory' advanced at that time by Osborn, Cope and other American palaeontologists and then characteristically writes: 'Let us now examine the facts.'

All through his life's work that phrase, or some other like it, recurs again and again; he states the generally accepted theory and then examines the facts: the actual specimens concerned. So often, as here, he proved the theory false, or else greatly enhanced its value. The then widely accepted American view was that the Tritubercular tooth, with cusps arranged in a triangle, was derived from a Triconodont type, with the three cusps in line, by the shifting outwards of the median cusp; the Triconodont condition was in turn considered the first step towards the more complex mammalian molar by being derived from the simple reptilian cone by the addition of an extra cusp in front and behind. 'Professor Osborn', writes Goodrich, 'in his illustrations of the theory . . . has made large use of the Mesozoic mammals found in England; one can therefore stand on firm ground while criticising his conclusions and his interpretations of the facts.' By carefully working away the matrix Goodrich exposed new cusps to some of the teeth and in some cases new teeth. His re-examination demolished the supposed evidence upon which Osborn's theory was based and led him to conclude 'that the common ancestor of Marsupial and Placental mammals had teeth with many cusps of the Tritubercular sectorial pattern' and that it 'seems extremely probable' that the molars of the earliest ancestral mammal 'were of an indefinite multituberculate pattern'.

In the meantime he had in 1893 published his discovery of the dorsal ciliated organ in Nereis and found it in other closely allied polychaetes but not in genera of other families; he states his reasons for considering it 'as a genital duct not fully developed'. He also gives a beautiful description of the nephridium of Nereis. This is the beginning of that magnificent series of studies on nephridia and coelomoducts to which he returned and added to so often throughout his life until the very end. When he wrote this, his first contribution to the subject, it was generally believed that genital ducts and nephridia were homologous structures; here he points out the difficulties of this view and with remarkable insight tentatively foreshadows the conclusions which he was subsequently to establish beyond doubt.

Two years later, in 1895, came his classic 'On the Coelom, Genital Ducts and Nephridia'. It is written with his typical lucidity and beautiful economy of words; in a text of only twenty-six pages, in which he refers to 116 other published researches, he compares all the main groups of the triploblastic Metazoa and shows the thread of homology running through them. The significance of this paper cannot be better expressed than in his own words taken from its introduction:

'An unprejudiced review of the well-established and recently ascertained facts concerning the development of the excretory organs and genital ducts of the Coelomata must, I think, inevitably lead us to the conclusion that we have been con-fusing two organs of totally different origin under the one name nephridium—the one organ the true nephridium, the other the morphological representative of the genital duct, which may be called the peritoneal funnel, to avoid confusion. Further, that while on the one hand in certain groups such as the Planaria, Nemertina, Hirudinea, Chaetopoda, Rotifera, Entoprocta, besides the genital ducts or peritoneal funnels, we find true nephridia in the adult; on the other hand, in such groups as the Mollusca, Arthropoda, Ectoprocta, Echino-derma, and Vertebrata, there are in the adult no certain traces of true nephridia. In these latter groups, as we shall see, the peritoneal funnels (primitive genital ducts) take on the excretory functions of the nephridia which they supersede.'

It will be remembered that at this time Goodrich had not yet discovered the nephridial nature of the excretory organs of Amphioxus.

He continues:

'In the following brief review of the various classes of Coelomata, I shall endeavour to show that the two kinds of organs can always be distinguished; that the first, the nephri-dium, is primitively excretory in function, is developed cen-tripetally as it were, and quite independently of the coelom (indeed, is probably derived from the epiblast), possesses a lumen which is developed as the hollowing out of the nephridial cells, and is generally of an intracellular character, is closed within, and may secondarily acquire an internal opening either into a blood space or into the coelom (true nephridial funnel as opposed to the peritoneal funnel); and that the second kind of organ, the peritoneal funnel, is primitively the outlet for the genital products, is unvariably developed centrifugally as an outgrowth from the coelomic epithelium or wall of the genital follicle, is therefore of undoubtedly mesoblastic origin, and possesses a lumen arising as an extension of the coelom itself.

'In the series of diagrams illustrating this paper, based on the most recent and accurate researches, it has been my constant endeavour to interpret the author's results correctly and not to distort the facts in favour of the theory here advocated.'

He then proceeds to compare the conditions found in the different coelomate Metazoa group by group.

In the following year (1896) he replies in the *Zoologischer Anzeiger* to a critical review of his paper by Bergh; in this he makes a dramatic reference to his discovery of solenocytes which he had not yet announced.

'The reviewer', he writes, 'appears still to hold the view that the nephridia of the Oligochaeta are homologous not with the nephridia (excretory organs) of the Platyhelminths and Nemertines, but with the follicle-ducts of the latter; I contend that recently ascertained facts concerning the anatomy and development of these organs render the theory untenable. It may be said that if the theory which I on the other hand advocate be true, I should be able to show an Annelid with an undoubted coelom into which the "true nephridia" do not open—to this I can answer, that I believe I am now in a position to supply this long sought link in the chain of argument (*Nephthys* and *Glycera*: as I hope to show in a forthcoming paper).'

There then followed that remarkable series of papers 'On the Nephridia of the Polychaeta', Part I in 1897 dealing with

Hesione, Tyrrhena and Nephthys, Part II in 1898 on Glycera
and Goniada, and Part III in 1900 dealing with the Phyllodocidae, Syllidae, Amphinomidae, &c., and general conclusions.
Here he describes and figures with superb drawings the minute
and delicate anatomy of the excretory and genital ducts of so
many different polychaetes. Here are his discoveries of the solenocytes of various kinds, the blind endings of excretory canals
comparable to the flame cells of the Platyhelminths but dif-
fering from them in the possession of fine straight tubes, enclosing the flagellum, running from the cells to the lumen of the
canal. Here he also describes the different conditions of combination of nephridium and genital duct or funnel that he calls
the nephromixium.

There is no need here to stress the immense amount of work
he has described in these and subsequent papers; as already
mentioned and as all will know, he had so recently completed,
just before he died, that magnificent review of all the work done
in this field since the publication of his paper of 1895. It is
written with the same economy of words, yet instead of twenty-
six it has 266 pages and refers to 430 other papers. It is more than
a review of past work for it contains many original and hitherto
unpublished observations; the most important of these is perhaps his study of the early stages of the nephridioblast in
Tubifex where he clearly shows that it was never a cell derived
from the coelomic epithelium as believed by Meyer. His own
work and that of others have fully confirmed the conclusions he
formerly reached regarding the nature of the two kinds of ducts;
in addition the gonocoel theory is accepted as the best explanation of the origin of the coelom. Professor de Beer in his Royal
Society obituary of Goodrich has well said: 'Even if he had
done nothing else this last paper would be sufficient to ensure
his lasting reputation as a zoologist.'

In spite of this so recent review of his, we must not leave the
subject of nephridia without recalling what is perhaps his most
exciting discovery: the solenocytes of Amphioxus. In 1890 both
Weiss and Boveri had independently discovered the excretory
organs of Amphioxus but had described them as tubules opening
into the coelomic cavities; they took them to be the primitive

homologues of the pronephric tubules of the higher chordates.
Goodrich in his third paper on the nephridia of the Polychaeta
(1900) records in a footnote how he was struck by the 'strange
resemblance between the solenocytes' (which he had discovered
in the Polychaetes) 'and the peculiar cells described by Boveri
as surrounding the openings of the excretory tubules in Amphioxus'. He goes on to say: 'Some years ago, I examined these
tubules in fresh specimens and came to the conclusion that the
resemblance is only superficial.' The following winter, however,
when working at Naples, he decided to re-examine them and
was now able to show that they were indeed true solenocytes
and there was in fact no funnel opening into the coelom at
all. They were not homologous with the kidney tubules of
vertebrates which he had shown to be coelomoducts but were
true nephridia and bore a remarkable resemblance to the
solenocytes he had described in Phyllodoce. It must have
given him great satisfaction to have had the opportunity of
personally demonstrating the correctness of his observations
to Professor Boveri who happened to be visiting Naples at
the time.

As will be seen from his list of publications he returned again
and again to the study of Amphioxus; he made many journeys
to obtain material to Sicily, Naples, Heligoland and Bermuda.
His proficiency in the Italian language, as well as French, was a
great help to him in his field work, for he was often out with the
fishermen in their small boats going from Messina to Cape Faro
at night or very early in the morning in search of Amphioxus.
Great was his disappointment to find that the plentiful supply
there earlier in the century had been exterminated by the earth-
quakes of 1912, probably by a wave of hot water, and had not
been replenished twelve years or more afterwards. Overcoming
the many difficulties, technical and otherwise, he produced
further detailed studies on the nephridia of Amphioxus and
their development in 1909, 1932, and 1934 as well as a short note
on 'Hermaphroditism in Amphioxus', 1912, and a paper on the
development of the club-shaped gland in 1930. Other beautiful
studies of solenocytes in larval forms must just be mentioned:
his account of the body cavities and nephridia of the Actinotrocha

larva of Phoronis (1903) and the nephridia of the larvae of Echiurus and Polygordius (1909).

He wrote two papers on Sternaspis (1898 and 1904) which, although originating in an examination of the genital organs and nephridia should be mentioned for their fine anatomical studies of the muscular and vascular systems. I cannot resist quoting from the first of these papers for quite another reason: it illustrates so well his characteristic combination of courtesy and directness in demolishing the false views of others. He begins the paper thus: 'In the beautiful works both of Professor Vejdovsky and M. Rietsch on Sternaspis we find certain statements which, if correct, would place that worm in a very exceptional position.' He then briefly describes the statements concerned and goes on: 'It was, therefore, with a view to either confirm or correct these descriptions that I began a study of *Sternaspis thalassemoides*, Otto, during a recent visit to Naples. I may say at once that they both proved to be erroneous.' His clear interpretations and drawings of his serial sections then supply the proof.

In 1898 with his remarkable morphological insight he cleared away much previous confusion in his essay on the segmentation of the Arthropod head and his thesis has well stood the test of time. His arguments in favour of there being six segments in the Crustacean head were largely based on evidence from the nervous system, for at that time distinct somites or coelomic cavities had not yet been traced with certainty in the development of the cephalic region. How pleased he must have been when Miss Manton in 1928 in her beautiful embryological study of Hemimysis clearly demonstrated six mesoblastic somites in the head.

To group after group of invertebrates he applied his skill; in the same year he solved a nice problem in the Mollusca. Again I cannot resist giving a quotation:

'Strange indeed, and happily unique in the annals of comparative anatomy, has been the history of our knowledge of the reno-pericardial canals of Patella. Although discovered more than thirty years ago, and investigated by many observers since, not only is their structure insufficiently known, but their very existence has been called in question and even positively denied!

'Wishing to find out definitely whether these ducts really existed or not, I undertook this work, which was carried out in Oxford, on material obtained from Plymouth and Naples. In this short paper I hope to establish clearly, and beyond the possibility of doubt, the fact that there are reno-pericardial canals leading from the pericardium to the right kidney and to the left kidney in Patella.'

And he did.

In the following year, 1899, he made a study of the coelom and vascular system of the Leech and in 1900 came his section on the Holothuroidea in the Echinoderm volume of Lankester's *Treatise on Zoology.*

Space will not permit more than a passing reference to his keen interest in the Archiannelids and the problem of their systematic position: whether they are to be regarded as primitive or secondarily simplified; he has studies on Saccocirrus (1901), Dinophilus (1909), Nerilla (1912), and Protodrilus (1921). In the Nerilla paper he sums up his conclusions: 'Taken as a whole the Archiannelida form a degenerating series which can only be read one way. But very possibly the group includes three such series starting from a common Chaetopod ancestor, Chaetogordius and Polygordius forming one, Saccocirrus and Protodrilus another, and Nerilla, Dinophilus and Histriobdella a third.' He also wrote three papers on new or little known Syllid worms (1900, 1930 and 1933).

In a paper in 1919 he showed that the slender pseudopodia usually described and figured as projecting from the leucocytes of invertebrates are in reality the radial folds of an extensive membrane which surrounds such cells and had hitherto escaped detection. In the same year he and Mrs. Goodrich collaborated in a most interesting study of the ecological interrelationships between leucocytes and parasitic protozoa, bringing out among other things the conclusion that most such protozoa must produce some secretion which causes leucocytes to avoid them;

together they also described (1920) a new species of Gregarine, *Gonospora minchinii*, inhabiting the egg of Arenicola. Here too may be a convenient place to refer to one of his very recent papers, 1942, on a new method of dissociating cells: by immersing small pieces of tissue, or whole small animals such as Hydra, in a saturated solution of boric acid in normal salt solution to which a trace of Lugol's solution of iodine has been added. The cells fall apart, or may be easily separated, retaining their characteristic form; he shows many beautiful examples such as ecto- and endodermal musculo-epithelial cells of Hydra, cells of the intestine and the nephrostome of Lumbricus, cells from various tissues of the frog and rabbit: all most valuable for class work.

During the recent war the importance of studying and controlling the insect pests infesting grain and other stored products has been fully realized and many have been engaged in such researches. In the previous war Goodrich was a pioneer in this field; he sought to find out how the presence of parasitic Hymenoptera (Chalcidae) may affect the various grain-infesting beetles. First he showed that some species of beetle were parasitised and others not, and that those which were, were attacked in the larval stage. He then showed that the Chalcids could not be effectively used in keeping down these beetles because, as he discovered, they themselves were in turn parasitised and kept in check by an acarid *Pediculoides ventricosus* Newport which had not hitherto been known to attack hymenoptera. Rarely in an official report (1921) do we see such a vivid description as he gives:

'In a grain of wheat are often found the shrivelled remains of the Calandra larva on which the hymenopteron larva has fed, the dead or dying Chalcid imago, and the Pediculoides attached to it. Thus the whole series of events is permanently recorded in chitin, and the complete tragedy can be unfolded, even from unpromising material, by soaking it in a strong solution of potash.'

Up to here, the only vertebrate work of his we have noted is his study of the fossil mammals of the Stonesfield Slate. If a

novice in Zoology should read this article thus far, he would get
the impression that Goodrich was mainly an invertebrate special-
ist; we must now correct that impression. Great as have been
his contributions to invertebrate Zoology, still greater are his
achievements among the vertebrates.

In 1901 in making a study of the pelvic girdle and fin of the
fossil fish Eusthenopteron he came to compare the pelvic girdles
and fins of all groups of fish. There was at that time considerable
confusion regarding the morphology of the pelvic supports; it
was commonly held for example that a true pelvic girdle was
present in the Selachii, Holocephali and Dipnoi but that the
supports in the Crossopterygii and Actinopterygii were derived
from the fin skeleton itself. 'Let us see what difficulties such
views lead us into', he says, and at once proceeds to one of his
masterly analyses of the different theories side by side with a
study of the actual specimens concerned. The logic of his argument inevitably leads us to the 'conclusion that the pelvic
supports, whether paired or unpaired, are homologous throughout the fish series'. He now became greatly interested in the
fins of fish and the importance of their differences in structure
in classification. In 1903 he published his beautiful studies of
the dermal fin rays of both living and fossil forms. Having clearly
distinguished the four different kinds: the ceratotrichia of the
Elasmobranchii and Holocephali, the actinotrichia and lepidotrichia of Teleostomes and the camptotrichia of the Dipnoi, he
then proceeds to discuss their origin and homologies. He shows
that the lepidotrichia are of quite a different nature from the
horny ceratotrichia and actinotrichia and are undoubtedly derived from modified body scales. Further, although not conclusively proved, he shows it likely that the camptotrichia of
the Dipnoi are homologous with the lepidotrichia of the Teleostomes but have sunk deeper and been overlaid by a secondary
extension of the body scales.

The two foregoing papers, important in clearing up much confusion, were but the prelude to his grand attack on the problem
of the origin and nature of the paired fins in 1906. It was a
major problem of the time, for there was little doubt that the
paired fins of fish and the limbs of the higher vertebrates were

homologous. Zoologists were divided into two camps: those who followed Gegenbaur in believing the paired fins to be derived from gill structures (the gill-arch theory) and those who followed Balfour, Thacker and Mivart in the view that they were derived from paired longitudinal fin folds of a similar nature to the median fins (the lateral fin-fold theory). 'Each of these theories', he says, 'may claim to have among its numerous supporters the names of some of the most eminent exponents of the morphology of the vertebrates.'

The literature on the subject had been extensive, but it practically came to an end when Goodrich stepped in and settled the matter for good and all. It is impossible in a brief review to do justice to his case, but let us just remind ourselves of some of the more telling points he made in this which was another of his classic papers. The paired fins develop on the whole just like median fins: the muscle buds grow out from the myotomes, divide into upper and lower halves to supply each side of the radials which are differentiated between them. There is a remarkable resemblance in detail of structure between the paired and unpaired fins. If the paired fins had developed from vertical gill septa they would in the first instance have hindered forward locomotion and the two pairs would have been close together one behind the other and so mechanically ineffective. In development the fin never appears as a dorso-ventral fold, but always as a longitudinal one. There is no evidence, either from primitive living fish or early fossil forms, of a more anterior pelvic fin which might be expected if it was derived from a gill arch; in those Teleosts where the pelvic fin is far forward, there is good evidence that this is a recent and secondary development. The presence of rudimentary muscle buds in front of the pelvic fins had been supposed to indicate a backward migration of the fin from a primitively more forward position; Goodrich, however, showed that rudimentary muscle buds may also be found *behind the fin*. The gill-arch theory does not account for the large number of segments often contributing to the muscle buds of the fins and the fact that usually more segments are concerned in the more primitive forms. And then the *coup de grâce:* the gill arches are morphologically in the wall of the alimentary canal and are supplied by visceral muscles innervated here by *dorsal roots* (vagus) whereas the paired fin muscles are derived from myotomes and innervated by somatic motor nerves from the *ventral roots*.

This same paper did much more than clear up the question of the paired fins; it dealt also with the development, structure and origin of the median fins. He showed how the 'concentration' of muscle buds and radials found in the fins (both median and paired) came about: the muscle buds having been nipped off from the myotomes, the body of the fish now grows faster than the fin so that the series of muscle buds no longer corresponds in length with the series of myotomes which gave rise to the buds but appears as a concentration.

His studies of the nerve supply of the muscle buds of fins and limbs led him to enunciate a general principle which is of great importance in helping the comparative anatomist in the correct interpretations of evolutionary morphological problems: that the motor nerves always remain faithful to their particular myotomes or their derivatives even, as he says 'throughout the vicissitudes of phylogenetic and ontogenetic modification'. It seemed to him, both on physiological and anatomical grounds, highly improbable that a motor nerve could forsake the muscle in connection with which it was originally developed to become attached to another muscle of different origin. All his work on the development of the limbs supported this. They are supplied by branches from a number of segmental nerves forming a plexus, but such a plexus can be shown to be 'brought about, not by the nerve deserting one muscle for the sake of another, but by the combination of muscles derived from neighbouring segments'. He tested this experimentally in the living skate by observing the separate contraction of the different muscle elements of the plexus when their corresponding nerves were stimulated by electrical and mechanical means.

All through Goodrich's work we see his curiosity being aroused by points which set him off on fresh lines of fruitful investigation; he had a remarkable gift for picking out problems of importance, the significance of which had been missed by others. We now come to the puzzle of Polypterus. In his paper of 1901 on the pelvic fins and girdles he draws attention to the position of this fish which for so long had been placed with the Crossopterygii and hints that he considers it not unlikely that it is really an Actinopterygian. In 1907 he read a paper to the Zoological section of the British Association on 'The Systematic Position of Polypterus' in which he develops the thesis more definitely. It had been placed in the Crossopterygii by Huxley on account of its lobate paired fins, paired gulars, rhomboid scales and outwardly diphycercal tail. Goodrich had already shown that internally its paired fins were of quite a different structure from those of the Crossopterygians to which they had but a superficial resemblance. He now showed the same thing for the scales, the two kinds look alike but those of Polypterus are not covered with cosmine but are of a true ganoid type resembling closely those of the fossil Palaeoniscoids. The paired gular plates might just as well be compared with the anterior members of the lateral series of plates of an Actinopterygian (such as the branchiostegal rays of Amia) as with the more median pair of gular plates of the Crossopterygians—indeed he pointed out that among the fossil Actinopterygians there are the Palaeoniscidae which in fact have just such anterior lateral plates enlarged. Again internally the caudal fin of Polypterus shows evidence of being a modified heterocercal tail. He now definitely believed it should be regarded as an Actinopterygian—but he was cautious about going further at that time, although reading between the lines one can sense his leaning to the belief that it is really a living Palaeoniscid. In his great book on the Cyclostomes and Fishes published in 1909 he still places Polypterus among the Crossopterygians but at their end, next to the Actinopterygians, and indicates his belief that they will be proved to belong to the latter; here however we see a certain caution owing to his having seen the resemblance of Polypterus to *Tarrasius problematicus* which was then regarded as an Osteolepidotid Crossopterygian. But I must cut a long, and exciting, story short. It was not until 1927 that Goodrich published his 'Polypterus a Palaeoniscid?' in which he fully gives the reasons with which he had 'ventured to suggest that the Polypterini are survivors of this large and varied group

hitherto supposed to be extinct'.  His brilliant pupil, the late Mr.
J. A. Moy-Thomas, now put the finishing touches to the story;
his tragic death in the war, such a great loss to Zoology, was a
personal grief which Goodrich felt very deeply.[1]  Moy-Thomas
published his study[2] of the development of the chondrocranium
of Polypterus in 1933 and compared it with the development
of the chondrocrania of other fish; he ended by saying 'the
view of Goodrich is thus afforded additional support'.  In the
following year he, Moy-Thomas, proved that *Tarrasius problematicus* was actually a Palaeoniscid.[3]  Goodrich's suspicions
were confirmed in both directions: Polypterus resembled both
Tarrasius and the Palaeoniscids for the now simple reason that
the two were shown to be of one and the same Actinopterygian
group.

In 1939 Moy-Thomas in his book *Palaeozoic Fishes* (p. 117)
definitely refers to 'Polypterus, itself a palaeoniscid derivative'
and ends his book with these words:

'The African *Polypterus* is probably directly descended from
the Palaeoniscids in the Cretaceous, and has retained the
Palaeoniscoid scales, but has become rather specialized in
other ways, especially in the nature of its fins.'

The puzzle of Polypterus, indeed an exciting story of detection,
is ended.  We have here a living fossil, almost as remarkable
as the living Coelocanth Latimeria, discovered not, as was
the latter, by its sudden appearance in a trawl, but by
the methods of comparative anatomy of which Goodrich was
the master: the comparison of both living and fossil forms
together.

Again one thing leads to another.  Both his work on the
dermal fin-rays of fish and his interest in the scales of Polypterus
led him on to another of his major contributions to vertebrate
morphology: his study 'On the Scales of Fish, Living and
Extinct, and their importance in Classification', published in
1908.  Here he gave us his beautiful drawings of sections of the

[1] See his obituary notice of Moy-Thomas in *Nature*, April 8, 1944.
[2] *Q.J.M.S.*, **76**. 209.
[3] *Proc. Zool. Soc. London*, 1934,  367.

different kinds of scale and his interpretations of them. William-son half a century earlier had shown that some of the so-called ganoid scales of Agassiz, those of fossil osteolepidotid fish such as Megalichthys were of what he called a cosmoid type, formed by a layer of fused denticles—the cosmine layer—becoming attached to an underlying bony plate, the so-called 'isopedin' layer. Goodrich largely confirmed Williamson's findings and called attention to his somewhat neglected work which had been hidden by the more recent and, as Goodrich showed, erroneous theories of Oscar Hertwig. He distinguished the cosmoid scales of Williamson from the true ganoid scales and further sub-divided the latter into those of the Palaeoniscoid type, found in the fossil Palaeoniscids and the living Polypterus, and those of the Lepidosteoid type found in Lepidosteus (and the Amioidei). The former he showed to be evolved from the cosmoid type by the addition of layers of ganoin on top: a sandwich of cosmine between the ganoin and bony isopedin plates. The Lepidosteoid scale he showed to be similar but lacking the intermediate layer. He went on to demonstrate the great value of these dif-ferent scales as an aid to classification.

This work in turn led to an interesting discovery he published in 1913 but which is best mentioned here: one concerning the structure of bone in fishes; a 'contribution to palaeohistology' he called it. In addition to the differences between the palaeonis-coid and lepidosteoid scales just referred to, it was now found that the bony layers of the latter were quite different from those of the former; in the lepidosteoid scale the layers of bone are traversed at right angles by peculiar tubules which in the living tissues are filled with the long protoplasmic processes of large cells situated on the surface of the scale. He now discovered that this condition was also present not only in those dermal bones of the skull originally derived from scales but in the *whole endoskeleton* as well, that is of those Actinopterygian fish which have Lepidosteoid scales (the Amioidei and Lepidosteoidei) and in those fish alone. He gives a list of the fish of many groups he has investigated. 'It follows that, from the examination of the minutest fragment of the skeleton of a living or extinct species of fish we can decide whether it belongs to these two orders or to some other group. The histological structure of the bone may therefore be of the greatest practical value for the identification of fragmentary specimens.' He had placed a new tool in the hands of the phylogenetic 'detective'.

In 1909 came his *magnum opus* on the 'Vertebrate Craniata: Cyclostomes and Fishes' forming Part IX of Lankester's *Treatise on Zoology*. All will know that it has been, and will continue to be for very many years, the standard text-book on the morphology of fish. While a literature of over 500 items is referred to, it is no mere compilation of the work of others; it is threaded through and through with his original observations on both recent and fossil forms, and the majority of the observations of others have been checked by him personally. Here, in addition to the results of his researches on scales and fins already referred to, are his masterly accounts of the skull and axial skeleton, the segmentation of the head, the nerve components, the nature and development of the coelomoducal kidneys, the vascular system and the air bladder; this is to mention only some of the many subjects all treated from the evolutionary point of view and clarified by his peculiar morphological insight. More than 150 of the illustrations are original, and many of them are those semi-diagrammatic but nevertheless accurate figures showing the three dimensions of space which are such a godsend to the student. Flesh and fossil, Science and Art have rarely been combined as here. It is superfluous to say more when the fame of the book is world-wide; I will just add a quotation from an appreciation of Goodrich by Dr. Julian Huxley in *The Times*:

> 'As an example of the international esteem in which he was held, I should like to record what Professor Berg, the leading Russian authority on fishes, said to me in Leningrad this summer, in asking me to take charge of a book for presentation to Goodrich: "Please tell him that, though neither I nor my colleagues have ever met him, we all regard ourselves as his pupils." '

Following a laudatory review of this book, 'W. E. A.' in *Nature*, 1909 (vol. 82, p. 152), among a very few 'points of minor importance which call for criticism', writes:

'On p. 116 we read, as one of the *primitive* characters of the Pisces (which group here does not include the Cyclostomes), that the pericardium may communicate with the abdominal coelome. In view of the fact that this communication in Elasmobranchs is formed secondarily in ontogeny after the two cavities have been completely separated from each other, it would have been better not to have included it in the list of characters "considered primitive" without a qualifying note.'

I mention this 'minor point' because it has an interesting outcome. Goodrich did not reply for nine years, not until he had characteristically had an opportunity of re-examining the facts, and when he did he made no reference to 'W. E. A.'s' criticism. In 1918 he published his study, with some of his best three-dimensional reconstructions of sections, 'On the Development of the Pericardiaco-peritoneal Canals in the Selachians'. I quote the two opening sentences of his summary:

'Balfour's suggestion that the canal leading in the adult Selachii from the pericardial to the peritoneal coelom, and opening into the latter by paired apertures, is a remnant of the wide communication between these cavities in the embryo is correct. The canal openings are not new formations as Hochstetter maintained, but are derived from the pericardiaco-peritoneal passages above the mesocardia lateralia.'

In 1910 he took part, with the other leading zoologists of the day, in the famous two days' debate, recorded in the *Proceedings of the Linnean Society*, on Gaskell's theory of the origin of the Vertebrates from Arthropod ancestors, which of course he opposed. The Vertebrates cannot be descended both from a form like Amphioxus and from an Arthropod; the supporters of Gaskell's heterodox views regarded Amphioxus not as a primitive form but as a secondarily simplified degenerate vertebrate. Although Gaskell's theory, that fascinating but gigantic folly of phylogenetic speculation, appears to-day to be dead and forgotten, there may still be a misguided few who prefer to regard Amphioxus as degenerate rather than primitive. If there

are, let them for a moment listen to Goodrich making some of
his telling points in the debate:

'Now, although *Amphioxus* is doubtless in some respects a
very specialized animal—as for instance in the possession of
an atrial cavity—yet it preserves many primitive characters.
Judging from its structure, we must conclude that the ancestral Vertebrate was still more uniformly segmented than the
primitive Craniate. The head-region was scarcely differentiated at all, there was no skull (probably no cartilaginous
axial skeleton at all), a quite rudimentary brain, no specialized cranial nerves, no cephalization due to the presence of
large paired organs of sense. It is possible that *Amphioxus*
is somewhat degenerate; but it cannot seriously be urged that
it once possessed in well-developed condition those paired
sense-organs which have so profoundly modified the structure
of the head-region in the Craniata. For it would be ridiculous
to suppose that the modified segments could be restored to
their original condition of uniformity with the trunk segments; no trace of the disturbance appearing in either adult
or embryo.

'Further, in *Amphioxus*, there is no dermal or epidermal
armour, and primitiveness is shown in the structure of the
endostyle, which becomes modified into the thyroid gland in
higher forms. Lastly the presence of true nephridia, a type of
excretory organ which has been lost in other Vertebrates,
links *Amphioxus* to the lower Invertebrate Coelomata.

'Thus can be traced an irreversible series of stages in the
differentiation of Vertebrate structure, at the bottom of which
we find a much simpler, but still essentially Vertebrate ancestor, probably already extinct in Silurian times.'

In the 1906 paper on the development of fins Goodrich first
pointed out a most important conclusion that I have not hitherto
referred to; I have delayed mention of it because it was in two
later papers, in 1911 and 1913 that he developed these conclusions to their full and surprising significance. In 1906 he had
shown that in the paired fins, as in the median ones, different
series of segments were involved in different species of fish. In

the course of evolution there had been a change in the position of the fins up and down the body; this he showed was not due to an actual migration of the fin material itself, but was brought about by the incorporation of fresh segments to the front of the fin and a reduction of those taking part behind or vice versa: so producing an apparent 'migration'. In 1911 in his paper 'On the Segmentation of the Occipital Region of the Head in the Batrachia Urodela' he showed the same thing taking place in the hind region of the head. The problem he tackled had arisen thus. The occipital region of the Amniota includes behind the vagus nerve four scleromeres enclosing three roots of the hypoglossal nerve, thus making at least five segments between the auditory capsule and the Atlas; in the fish the post auditory region while less definite always includes at least seven segments; but in the Batrachia the skull appears to end immediately behind the vagus foramen. He writes thus:

'These facts immediately suggest several questions:—Does the occipital region of the Amphibian really include fewer segments than that of the other Gnathostomes, or have certain segments been telescoped and practically crushed out? Are the hypoglossal segments of the Gnathostomes really represented by the first three trunk-segments of the Amphibian, or have these simply assumed the function originally fulfilled by others farther forward? Further, if the Amphibian head includes fewer segments, it may be asked whether this condition is primary, or due to the return of segments to the trunk which formerly held a place in the head.'

He now makes his careful and as usual beautifully illustrated study of the development of the Amphibian head and comes to this conclusion:

'Now, in the case of the fins of fishes, I have already shown that it is not possible to account for variation in position by the theory of inter- and excalation. Growth and transposition from one segment to another alone account for the facts. The same is probably true of the occipital condyle. There is not the slightest trace of the disappearance of segments behind

the vagus in the ontogeny of the Amphibia. We are familiar
with the variation in the extent of the gill-region in Vertebrates by mere growth. Obviously the hind limit of the series
of gill-slits varies backward or forward, according as certain
segments cease to develop gills or take on the function of gill-
formation. The posterior limit of the skull is doubtless
altered in the same way, and the position of the occipital
condyles may shift up or down the segmental series. There
should, therefore, be no theoretical objection to accepting the
anatomical and embryological evidence that the occipital
region of the head in Amphibia contains only three segments.
If segments could really disappear, leaving no trace behind,
it would be hopeless to attempt to homologise segments in
any two forms.'

This leads to his very important 1913 paper on 'Metameric
Segmentation and Homology' where he develops this thesis to
the full. As with fins, so with paired limbs. No one will deny
that the fore limbs or hind limbs are homologous throughout
the Tetrapods and that they can be traced back in an uninterrupted series to some common ancestral form; yet they are not
necessarily made up of the same segments. The hind limb of
the frog for instance occupies segments 8, 9, and 10, that of the
salamander 16, 17, and 18, and that of Necturus segments 20,
21, and 22. These and many other facts are considered and
lead him to give us this new conception of homology:

'In the Vertebrates, as in other animals, the organs and
parts of two individuals are to be considered as homologous
when they can be traced back to corresponding parts in a
common ancestor, and not because they occur on the same
segments. The homology is independent of the number and
ordinal position of the segments which take a share in the
formation of the organs. Any structure may apparently shift
from one segment to another; and this is brought about
neither by intercalation or excalation of segments, nor by
redivision, nor by migration, but by a process of transposition.
Organs may be homologous when they are composed of few
or of many, of the same or of different segments, or are

not segmented at all. There are degrees of homology; it may
be general or more special, complete or incomplete. The
homology of two organs is complete when all their parts have
been derived from corresponding parts in a common ancestor.'

When discussing vertebrate segmentation we should recall that
he made an even more detailed study of this in the head of
Scyllium in 1918.

In 1915 he published an account of a most delicate piece of
work on the development of the chorda tympani (that twig of
the hyomandibular branch of the facial nerve which supplies
the organs of taste and salivary glands in the region of the lower
jaw) in relation to the tympanic membrane and the structure of
the middle ear in reptiles, birds and mammals. Its position in
relation to the tympanic membrane had been a difficulty in
accepting the conclusions of Reichert that the auditory ossicles
of the mammal, stapes, incus and malleus, were derived from the
columella, quadrate and articular respectively. If the tympanic
membrane corresponded to the spiracle as had been thought,
how is it that the chorda tympani passes above and in front of
the former whereas it passes behind and under the spiracle?
Goodrich clears up the whole matter in confirmation of Reichert's
views. He shows that the tympanic membrane although now
actually occupying the former position of the original spiracle,
does not represent a covering of that opening; the tympanum
develops as a separate diverticulum of the spiracular cleft
(tympanic cavity) rather below and behind the spiracle proper
which is more and more reduced as the diverticulum (tympanum)
swells up to *take its place*. It swells up not only below and
behind the spiracle but also below and behind the chorda tympani, so now this nerve passes above and in front of it. The
difficulty is resolved. His paper is illustrated by plates of
superb reconstructions of sections in which the different elements are shown in shadings of five different colours.

There are too many good things to look at all at once. In
viewing any exhibition of works of art or science there comes a
time when we must stop; there is a limit to what we can appreciate at one time, even if the works are familiar to us. We have

the catalogue; we know where they are to be found for future study. We must leave ourselves time, and here space, to consider our general impressions.

But there is still his greatest work of all, and we must hurry through the gallery of his vertebrate studies to reach it. As we pass we just note 'The Classification of the Reptilia', 1916 (also 1942), in which he points out the systematic value of the fifth metatarsal which is hooked in some and straight in others, and a kindred study of syndactyly as a key to the phylogeny of the Marsupials, 1935. We see his notes on the reptilian heart, 1919, and on the blastocoelic and enteric cavities in Amphibia, 1935.

His 'Proboscis Pores in Craniate Vertebrates', 1917, is a suggestion of the homology of the connections linking the coelom of the premandibular somites with the hypophysis, as found in the development of Torpedo and of the duck, with the opening of Hatschek's pit in Amphioxus, the proboscis pores of Balanoglossus and the water pores of Echinoderms, all to be regarded as coelomoducts. Here too are further studies on the Cyclostomes and fish: on the head of Osteolepis, 1919, the pectoral girdle of young Clupeids, 1922, the cranial roofing bones in the Dipnoi, 1925, the relationship of the Ostracoderms to the Cyclostomes, 1930, the spinal nerves of the Myxinoidea, 1937, and on the denticles in fossil Actinopterygii, 1942. We see his work on the vertebrates, as on the invertebrates, going on to the very end.

We now come to his *maximum opus*, that masterpiece: *Studies on the Structure and Development of Vertebrates*. It is all that his Cyclostomes and Fishes volume is, only more so: full of his own original work and his careful checking of the work of others. He refers to no fewer than 1,186 other works and it is illustrated by 754 text-figures of which again so many are his own. 'This work has been written', he says, 'in the hope that it may help advanced students and others engaged in teaching and research.' Every serious student of the vertebrates will acknowledge how fully his hope has been realised. His book is indispensable and it cannot be an extravagant prophecy to say that it will still be so in a hundred years' time. A senior zoologist in a recent letter expresses the feelings of all: 'I never use his comparative morphology of the Vertebrates without an increasing admiration for the mind that conceived it or the hand that illustrated it.'

As with his Cyclostomes and Fishes volume it is so well known that any description of it in the space available would be superfluous. I prefer to use that space in quoting from his preface to show in his own words his grand conception; it will be useful too because so often the student dives at once into the text for the facts he wants and leaves the preface unread.

'It is not a complete treatise, but deals with certain subjects and problems of special interest and importance, some of which receive but scant notice in current text-books. My original intention was to cover the whole range of vertebrate morphology; but the preparation of this volume has taken so many years, that I thought it better to publish what is ready than to wait for the remainder which might possibly never be completed. The literature dealing with the Morphology of the Vertebrata is so vast, the accumulation of known facts so large, that students are apt to feel discouraged from the start, and to turn perhaps to some newer branch of zoological science. On the one hand, they may think that little remains to be done in so ancient a study; or, on the other hand, that its conclusions, for instance in Phylogeny, are so insecure that they afford little trustworthy evidence concerning the process of Evolution. It has, therefore, been my endeavour not only to give an account within reasonable compass of the facts already known and to discuss their significance, but also to point out where our knowledge is deficient; and where further research is desirable. During the last fifty years or so much has been accomplished, many old theories have been overthrown, some new conclusions have been firmly established; yet a great deal remains to be done, and new fields for research are continually being opened up.'

While not a complete treatise it deals very fully with the vertebral column, ribs and sternum, the median fins and paired limbs and limb girdles, the segmentation of the head, the skull, the skeletal visceral arches, the middle ear and ear ossicles, the visceral clefts and gills, the vascular system and the heart, the air bladder and the lungs, the subdivisions of the coelom and the diaphragm, and the excretory and genital ducts. The nervous system and sense organs are less fully dealt with; but here he gives important new views on the evolution of the autonomic system. In the detail in which he planned it, no one person could have done more.

Some of the younger generation whose main interest is focused on the rapidly growing physiological, genetical or ecological branches of zoology may be inclined to think of Goodrich as an out-of-date morphologist—out of date because they regard morphology as a worked-out mine with little more to yield. His pupils never thought this. While Goodrich was largely engaged in morphological studies, he was never a morphologist pure and simple, in the sense of one who delights in unravelling and describing details of bodily structures as an end in itself. This end is of course important, but he was primarily a comparative anatomist and there is a big difference between being that and being a pure morphologist. The former compares animal structures with a view to discovering the course of evolution, tracing lines of phylogeny and building a classification as far as possible upon true relationship. Goodrich's passionate interest was not just in the details of the different kinds of nephridia and coelomoducts or scales and fins which he discovered; it was always centred upon the homologies they might reveal linking group with group: their evolutionary significance. Let me again quote from the preface of his great book:

'The triumph of the doctrine of Evolution has owed much in the past to the study of the structure and development of the Vertebrates, and the correct interpretation of their morphology still plays an important part in the elucidation of the evolutionary process. No other group of animals presents us with so complete a record of the divergent phylogenetic lines along which they have evolved.'

The elucidation of the evolutionary process—meaning the elucidation of the paths the process has taken rather than the causes underlying it—that was what he strove for all the time and how remarkably successful was his quest. He had a genius for seeing the essentials and so selecting the profitable lines of attack. In that I think we see Goodrich the artist. Great landscapes are never photographic reproductions of nature; the artist emphasises those features which are essential to the beauty or character of his composition and lays less stress on others. Goodrich did not look at his animals with just the photographic eye of the pure morphologist. He saw much more; he had the insight enabling him to pick out from among the details those points which had significance for his picture; his evolutionary theme. Perhaps all great scientists are artists in their particular medium, but they become great only when, like Goodrich, they subject their artistic insight to the discipline and rules of the scientific method.

Goodrich never allowed himself to be carried away on wild flights of phylogenetic fancy; he was ever critical of those plausible speculations on descent which, often based only on flimsy similarities, bring discredit on the comparative method when they are held almost as creeds instead of being put forward as tentative hypotheses. He was always cautious. We have seen that in his 1907 paper on the phylogenetic position of Polypterus one can sense his leaning to the belief that it is a living Palaeoniscid; but he does not jump to this conclusion; he tests it step by step. In the paper of the following year on the scales of fish he writes: 'Not for a moment is it asserted that Polypterus is a living Palaeoniscid; but it is probably in the neighbourhood of this family that it will eventually find its place in the system of classification.' It was another twenty years before he allowed himself to write 'Polypterus a Palaeoniscid?' and still with a question mark; it was another ten years before it seemed certain.

The discoveries Goodrich continued to make should show that comparative anatomy is not yet a worked out field. It is true that to-day it does not have the same attraction that it had; the new growing branches of biology are discovering more and more about the causes underlying the evolution, development, mechanism and behaviour of living things, so that it is natural that they should draw towards them those most curious about the nature of life. But the work of the great comparative anatomists like Goodrich is not obsolete and dead; it has been providing a more and more reliable chart of the animal kingdom based on the course evolution has taken in the different phyla. It forms the essential background in the education of the zoologist, no matter in what particular field of research he intends to work. It makes sense of the diversity of form; it shows what achievements the process of evolution is capable of.

While his research was mainly concerned with tracing the course of evolution it would be the greatest mistake to suppose that he was not interested in the causes underlying the process. In 1912 he wrote a little book in the People's Series called *The Evolution of Living Organisms* (second edition 1920) and in 1924 enlarged it considerably under the title of *Living Organisms: their Origin and Evolution*. No clearer accounts of our knowledge of the process of evolution had been written at the time these books were published and in spite of recent additions to the theory of the subject his *Living Organisms* is still one of the best introductions to evolution for the student. In the original 1912 edition see how clearly he emphasised the importance of both heredity and environment:

'An organism is moulded as the result of two sets of factors: the factors or stimuli which make up its environment, the conditions under which it grows up; and the factors of inheritance, the germinal constitution, transmitted through its parent by means of the germcells. No single part or character is completely "acquired", or due to inheritance alone. Every character is the product of these two sets of factors, and can only be reproduced when both are present. Only those characters reappear regularly in successive generations which depend for their development on stimuli always present in the normal environment. Others, depending on a new or occasional stimulus, do not reappear in the next generation unless the stimulus is present. In popular language the former are said to be inherited, and the latter are said not to be inherited. But both are equally due to factors of inheritance and to factors of environment; in this respect the popular distinction between acquired and not acquired characters is illusory. In every case it is the capacity to acquire, to become modified or to respond, which is really transmitted ; the direction and extent of the modification depends on the stimulus. The presence of a given hereditary factor cannot be determined by mere inspection of the characters of an organism ; the factor may be present, but the corresponding character fail to show itself owing to the absence of the necessary stimulus. On the other hand, dissimilar stimuli acting on different factors may give apparently similar results. Heredity must be defined afresh as the transmission of the factors of inheritance, and not as the reappearance of characters in successive generations.'

In 1921 he was President of Section D (Zoology) of the British Association at its meeting in Edinburgh and chose for the title of his presidential address : 'Some Problems in Evolution'. Here we find he had already appreciated that the genes form an interacting system subject to selection, so foreshadowing the conception of the gene-complex which has been so much developed in recent years, for he says :

'Thus natural selection preserves those factorial complexes which respond in a favourable manner. In other words an organism to survive in the struggle for existence must present that assemblage of factors of inheritance which under the existing environmental conditions will give rise to advantageous characters.'

During Goodrich's tenure of the Linacre Chair the Oxford department expanded both in space and scope. New laboratories for both undergraduate teaching and graduate research were added and, more important, the staff increased. Under his headship the Oxford school widened with the rapid development of zoology because he chose for his new colleagues young zoologists, all of whom were his own pupils, enthusiastic in different fields of work. Alongside his own researches were developing under his encouragement the embryological and evolutionary studies of G. R. de Beer, the work on breeding seasons and later on cytology and histochemistry of J. R. Baker, the ecological population studies of C. S. Elton, the ornithological work of B. W. Tucker, the genetical and field evolutionary studies of E. B. Ford, the researches on nerve anatomy, physiology and regeneration of J. Z. Young and the work of the late J. A. Moy-Thomas on palaeozoic fish. More recently he had appointed H. K. Pusey, whose embryological evolutionary studies have been interrupted by war service, and P. B. Medawar who is subjecting the problems of 'growth and form' to mathematical treatment, and investigating the nature of the differences between individuals. In all this work, so much of it so different from his own, Goodrich took a great and sympathetic interest. While always ready to help with suggestions he never tried to divert the researches of his staff along lines other than of their own choosing.

He was from first to last a warm and valued friend of the marine biological stations at Naples and Plymouth; he worked repeatedly at each, and at home frequently obtained material from them.

In character Goodrich was quiet, reserved and unassuming; while those who did not know him well would have regarded him as somewhat shy and retiring, his close friends found in him a fund of amusing dry humour. In spite of his reserve he was a great teacher. We who have been his pupils will never forget his style in lecturing. As in writing, he had in speech that power of clear and logical presentation of complicated fact, and lucid explanation of theory. But the strength of his lectures was not in the spoken word; his speech was quiet, not forceful. The impression upon his students was made by a beautiful combination of verbal clarity with visual demonstration on the board. As he developed his exposition so also he developed drawings in coloured chalks; they were not just diagrams, they were not slow and laboured drawings, they were pictures, often optical sections in three-dimensional perspective, which grew before our eyes to build up the animal structures he was describing. Bones, blood vessels, nerves, were put in in just the right sequence to make understanding easy, put in, as he spoke, with the rapid sure touch of the artist. He made easy all those difficulties of visualising what is really happening in an animal's development when organs are being formed by the folding of surfaces or the nipping off of this or that bud or diverticulum; with a growing series of sketches giving all the impression of solidity, we could not fail to follow the changing and subtle relationships of form he was describing. His drawings had life and reality in them; they made his lectures vivid and unforgettable. Story has it that on one occasion his Honours class asked permission for the rubbing out of his drawings to be delayed while they had them photographed; all enquiries I have made to try to obtain that photograph have failed. I should much like to see it reproduced and placed on record.

Another feature of his lectures should be specially mentioned because it was so much a part of his character: his extreme modesty. When he was describing his own contributions to zoology, and we have seen how many and great they were, he never gave the slightest hint to the student that they were indeed his own discoveries.

He took the keenest and kindest interest in the practical work of his class; he was always tolerant and sympathetic to the young student in difficulties and always ready to show him how to make closer observations and better drawings of what he saw. He encouraged his pupils to go out into the field; when the course on Protozoa came round he used to offer a book prize in the Honours class for the student who had collected and made drawings of the largest number of specimens; it was keenly competed for.

A great deal of his time must have been taken up by editing the Quarterly Journal; so many have testified to the unstinted help and advice which he gave towards the improvement of the papers they had sent him for publication.

Apart from his teaching and research he took an active part in the work of the University, serving on many committees. He was always much interested in the affairs of his College and for a time was Garden Master and Librarian. One of the senior Fellows in a letter writes of his life at Merton as follows: 'He never had an enemy and he is the only one I can remember who, in that somewhat strange life of a college, never lost his temper or fell out with anybody. He was the gentlest and kindest of men, but quite inflexible in following the course he felt right.'

His advice was of the greatest value in all artistic and architectural questions. He made a collection of photographs of all views of the precious parts of the college buildings, details of old and decaying stone carvings, woodwork and in fact anything that he considered would form a useful record to be of service to succeeding generations of students. He himself designed many new details, for example: common room chairs, fireplaces and brackets for lights in the quadrangle; it was he also who rescued from a lumber attic the remains of Wren's chancel screen of carved wood and had it adapted, according to his own designs, to beautify the reading rooms below the library.

It was in painting and travel that he sought relaxation from his scientific work. He travelled extensively and always returned home with a series of striking water-colours. He delighted in the play of strong sunlight and shadow on buildings, the more delicately graded light and shade on Alpine snows, or the subtle colourings in reflections. His clear colours and bold draughtsmanship captured the atmosphere of Venice, southern Italy, Greece, Tunis and Egypt, far away Java and Malaya, and many another scene of his many vacational wanderings. His sense of composition was just as keen. Occasionally he had exhibited in Bond Street, but it was only his intimate friends who realized the full scope of his power and versatility with the water-colour brush.

In this impression of his character and work I have reserved till the end that which is most personal: his very happy partnership with his wife, Dr. Helen Pixell Goodrich. Except in the two papers already referred to, in which they collaborated, they worked independently while sharing common scientific interests. They were devoted companions in their happy home and their wanderings together abroad. It is his work we are reviewing, not hers, yet no tribute to his life and achievement would be complete without a tribute to her as well. I am sure he would like it to be said, and I am sure it is the truth, that for his continued achievements in zoology up to the very end of his life we have in no small measure to be grateful to her. Those who him knew well from early years at Oxford, and with whom I have discussed his life, have each stressed the noticeable change in health and happiness that came to him on marriage. Our deep sympathy goes out to her in her great personal loss and we admire her courage as she continues her work in his old department.

Edwin Goodrich has gone from us; his work and influence live on. All are agreed that he was the greatest comparative anatomist of his day; in the history of science his achievements will, I believe, rank as high as those of any predecessor in his field of work, surpassing even those of the great master who inspired him, Edwin Ray Lankester.

A. C. HARDY

## CHRONOLOGICAL LIST OF SCIENTIFIC WORKS PUBLISHED
## BY E. S. GOODRICH

1. 'Note on a large Squid (Ommastrephes pteropus, Stp.)', Journal of the Marine Biol. Association, **2**, 314–21, 1892.
2. 'Note on a new Oligochaete', Zool. Anz., **15**, 474–6, 1892.
3. 'On a new Organ in the Lycoridea, and on the Nephridium of Nereis diversicolor, O. F. Mull', Q.J.M.S., **34**, 387–402, 1893.
4. 'On the Fossil Mammalia from the Stonesfield Slate', Q.J.M.S., **35**, 407–32, 1894.
5. 'Some Reforms in the Oxford University Museum', Nat. Sc., **5**, 128–31, 1894.
6. 'On the Structure of Vermiculus pilosus, Goodrich', Q.J.M.S., **37**, 253–67, 1895.
7. 'On the Coelom, Genital Ducts, and Nephridia', Q.J.M.S., **37**, 477–510, 1895.
8. 'Nephridia and Genital Ducts', Zool. Anz., **19**, 494–5, 1896.
9. 'Notes on Oligochaetes, with the description of a new species', Q.J.M.S., **39**, 51–69, 1896.
10. 'Report on a Collection of Cephalopoda from the Calcutta Museum', Trans. Linn. Soc., **7**, 1–24, 1896.
11. 'On the Nephridia of the Polychaeta. Part 1. On Hesione, Tyrrhena, and Nephthys', Q.J.M.S., **40**, 185–95, 1897.
12. 'Notes on the Anatomy of Sternaspis', Q.J.M.S., **40**, 233–45, 1898.
13. 'On the Relation of the Arthropod Head to the Annelid Prostomium', Q.J.M.S., **40**, 247–68, 1898.
14. 'On the Reno-Pericardial Ducts of Patella', Q.J.M.S., **41**, 323–8, 1898.
15. 'On the Nephridia of the Polychaeta. Part II. On Glycera and Goniada', Q.J.M.S., **41**, 439–57, 1898.

16. 'On the Communication between the Coelom and the Vascular System in the Leech, Hirudo medicinalis', Q.J.M.S., **42**, 477–95, 1899.

17. 'Observations on Syllis vivipara, Krohn', Proc. Linn. Soc., **28**, 105–8, 1900.

18. *The Holothurioidea* in the *Treatise on Zoology*, vol. iii, London, 1900.

19. 'On the Nephridia of the Polychaeta. Part III. The Phyllodocidae, Syllidae, Amphinomidae, etc., with Summary and Conclusions', Q.J.M.S., **43**, 699–748, 1900.

20. 'On the Structure and Affinities of Saccocirrus', Q.J.M.S., **44**, 413–28, 1901.

21. 'On the Pelvic Girdle and Fin of Eusthenopteron', Q.J.M.S., **45**, 311–24, 1901.

22. 'On the Excretory Organs of Amphioxus', Proc. Royal Soc., Lond., **69**, 350–1, 1901.

23. 'On the Structure of the Excretory Organs of Amphioxus'. Part I. Q.J.M.S., **45**, 493–501, 1902.

24. 'On the Body Cavities and Nephridia of the Actinotrocha Larva', Q.J.M.S., **47**, 103–21, 1903.

25. 'On the Dermal Fin Rays of Fishes—Living and Extinct', Q.J.M.S., **47**, 465–522, 1903.

26. 'On the Branchial Vessels of Sternaspis', Q.J.M.S., **48**, 1–10, 1904.

27. 'The development and origin of the Median and Paired Fins of Fish', Q.J.M.S., **50**, 333–76, 1906.

28. 'On the Systematic Position of Polypterus', Report of British Association, 545–6, 1907.

29. 'On the Scales of Fish, Living and Extinct'. Proc. Zool. Soc. Lond., 751–74, 1908.

30. *The Vertebrata Craniata* (*Cyclostomes and Fishes*). Volume IX of the 'Treatise on Zoology', Lond., 1909.

31. 'On the Nephridia of Dinophilus and the Larvae of Echiurus, Polygordius, and Phoronis', Q.J.M.S., **54**, 111–18, 1909.

32. 'On the Structure of the Excretory Organs of Amphioxus, Part 2. The Nephridium in the Adult. Part 3. Hatschek's Nephridium', Part 4. 'The Nephridium in the Larva', Q.J.M.S., **54**, 185–205, 1909.

33. 'Origin of Vertebrates' (Discussion, Session 122), Proc. Linn. Soc. London, 24–6, 1910.

34. 'On the Segmental Structure of the Motor Nerve-plexus', Anat. Anz., **36**, 109–12, 1910.

35. 'Segmentation of Occipital Region of the Head in the Batrachia Urodela', Proc. Zool. Soc. Lond., 101–20, 1911.

36. *The Evolution of Living Organisms*. Edinburgh, 1912.

37. 'Nerilla, an Archiannelid', Q.J.M.S., **57**, 397–425, 1912.

38. 'Hermaphroditism in Amphioxus', Anat. Anz., **42**, 318–20, 1912.

39. 'Nephridia of the Alciopinae', Zool. Jahr. Suppl. 15, **2**, 185–90, 1912.

40. 'The Structure of Bone in Fishes: a Contribution to Palaeohistology', Proc. Zool. Soc. Lond., 80–5, 1913.

41. 'Metameric Segmentation and Homology', Q.J.M.S., **59**, 227–48, 1913.
42. 'The Chorda Tympani and Middle Ear in Reptiles, Birds and Mammals', Q.J.M.S., **61**, 13–160, 1915.
43. 'Classification of the Reptilia', Proc. Roy. Soc. B, **89**, 261–76, 1916.
44. 'Proboscis pores in Craniate Vertebrates, a Suggestion Concerning the Premandibular Somites and Hypophysis', Q.J.M.S., **62**, 539–53, 1917.
45. 'Development of the Pericardiaco-peritoneal Canals in Selachians', Jour. Anat., **53**, 1–13, 1918.
46. 'Development of the Segments of the Head in Scyllium', Q.J.M.S., **63**, 1 30, 1918.
47. 'Note on the Reptilian Heart', Jour. Anat., **53**, 298–304, 1919.
48. 'Restorations of the Head of Osteolepis', Jour. Linn. Soc. Lond., **34**, 181–8, 1919.
49. 'The Pseudopodia of the Leucocytes of Invertebrates', Q.J.M.S., **64**, 19–26, 1919.
50. 'Leucocytes and Protozoa' (with H. Pixell Goodrich), Contributions to Medical and Biological Research (Sir W. Osler's 70th birthday), 958–72, 1919.
51. *The Evolution of Living Organisms.* Edinburgh, 2nd edition, 1920.
52. 'Gonospora minchinii, n.sp., a Gregarine inhabiting the egg of Arenicola' (with H. Pixell Goodrich), Q.J.M.S., **65**, 157–62, 1920.
53. 'Note on the Hymenoptera parasitic on Beetles infesting Grain', Reports of Grain Pests (War) Committee, Royal Soc., No. 9, 1–11, 1921.
54. 'Some Problems in Evolution', Rep. Brit. Assoc. Zoological President's address, 1921, also Nature, **108**, 404, 1921.
55. 'On a new Type of Teleostean Cartilaginous Pectoral Girdle found in young Clupeids', Jour. Linn. Soc. Lond., **34**, 505–9, 1922.
56. *Living Organisms: their Origin and Evolution.* Oxford, 1924.
57. 'Origin of Land Vertebrates', Nature, Lond., **114**, 935–6, 1924.
58. 'Cranial roofing-bones in the Dipnoi', Jour. Linn. Soc. Lond., **36**, 79–86, 1925.
59. 'The Blastocoelic and Enteric Cavities in Amphibia', Q.J.M.S., **69**, 745–6, 1925.
60. 'Polypterus a Palaeoniscid?', Palaeobiologica, **1**, 87–92, 1927.
61. 'The problem of the sympathetic nervous system from the morphological point of view', Proceedings of the Anatomical Society of Great Britain and Ireland, in Journ. Anat., **61**, 499, 1927.
62. 'A new Hermaphrodite Syllid', Q.J.M.S., **73**, 651–66, 1930.
63. 'The Development of the Club-shaped Gland in Amphioxus', Q.J.M.S., **74**, 155–64, 1930.
64. *Studies on the Structure and Development of Vertebrates.* London, 1930.
65. 'On the Relationship of the Ostracoderms to the Cyclostomes', Proc. Linn. Soc. Lond., 45–9, 1930.
66. 'The Scientific Work of Edwin Ray Lankester', Q.J.M.S., **74**, 363–81, 1931.

67. 'Notes on Protodrilus', Q.J.M.S., **74,** 303–19, 1931.
68. 'On the Nephridiostome of Lumbricus', Q.J.M.S., **75,** 165–79, 1932.
69. 'The Nephridia of Asymmetron and Branchiostoma Compared', Q.J.M.S., **75,** 723–34, 1932.
70. 'Notes on Odontosyllis', Q.J.M.S., **76,** 319–29, 1933.
71. 'The early development of the Nephridia in Amphioxus: Introduction and Part I, Hatschek's Nephridium', Q.J.M.S., **76,** 499–510, 1934.
72. 'The early development of the Nephridia in Amphioxus: Part II. The Paired Nephridia', Q.J.M.S., **76,** 655–74, 1934.
73. 'Syndactyly in Marsupials', Proc. Zool. Soc. Lond., 175–8, 1935.
74. 'Mouth and Anus', Q.J.M.S., **77,** 659–61, 1935.
75. 'On the Spinal Nerves of the Myxinoidea', Q.J.M.S., **80,** 153–8, 1937.
76. 'The Hind Foot of Youngina and the fifth Metatarsal in Reptilia', Jour. Anat., **76,** 308–12, 1942.
77. 'A New Method of Dissociating Cells', Q.J.M.S., **83,** 245–58, 1942.
78. 'Denticles in fossil Actinopterygii', Q.J.M.S., **83,** 459–64, 1942.
79. 'The Study of Nephridia and Genital Ducts since 1895', Q.J.M.S., **86,** 113–392, 1945.

# CHAPTER I

## VERTEBRAL COLUMN, RIBS, AND STERNUM

## THE ENDOSKELETON IN GENERAL

THE entire body of a vertebrate is supported by a framework of connective tissue which packs and binds the various parts together, delimits spaces, and serves for the attachment of muscles. Doubtless primitively the vertebrates had an elongated body stiffened by the notochordal rod, and moved by a side-to-side bending more especially of the caudal region. Correlated with this mode of progression is the segmentation of the somatic or body-wall muscles, entailing the corresponding segmentation

1

of the peripheral nervous system and the skeleton. The parts of the endoskeleton of cartilage or bone may be looked upon as local specialisations of the general connective tissue system developed in those regions where the stresses are most pronounced and where the muscular attachments need most support. Although this primitive segmentation may be much modified in the adult, especially of the higher forms, and even scarcely recognisable, yet it is always distinctly shown in the embryo and persists more or less completely in lower forms. Now, in such

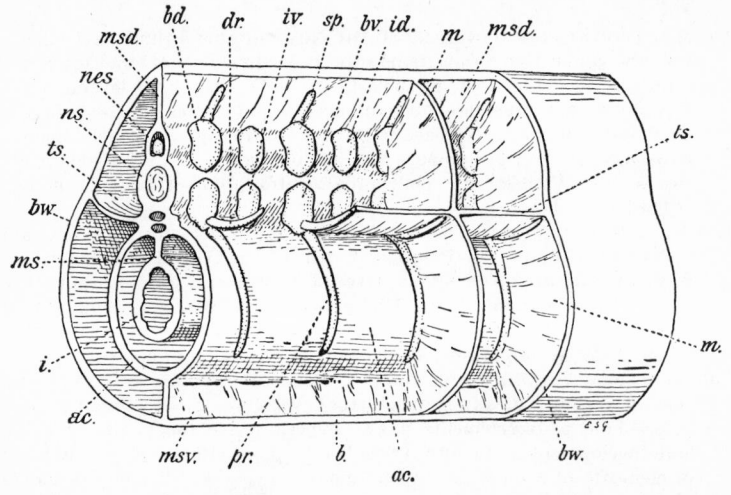

Fig. 1.

Diagram of the connective-tissue system in the trunk of a Craniate Vertebrate, showing the relation borne by the axial skeleton to the transverse and longitudinal septa. *ac*, wall of splanchnocoel ; *bd*, basidorsal ; *bv*, basiventral ; *bw*, cut body-wall ; *dr*, dorsal rib ; *i*, intestine hanging in the coelom ; *iv*, interventral ; *m*, transverse septum (myocomma) ; *ms*, mesentery ; *msd*, median dorsal septum ; *msv*, median ventral septum ; *nes*, neural tube ; *ns*, notochordal sheath ; *pr*, ventral or pleural rib ; *sp*, supraneural spine ; *ts*, horizontal septum. Oblique view of left side, from which the septa have been partially removed. (From Goodrich, *Vert. Craniata*, 1909.)

primitive forms, the connective tissue surrounds the somatic muscle segments or myomeres, forming not only closed boxes in which they lie, but also a lining to the skin outside and to the body-cavity or coelom within. Connective tissue sheaths also surround the notochord, the neural canal enclosing the central nervous system, and the alimentary canal hanging in the coelom. Moreover, since the mesoblastic segments and the coelomic cavities are of paired origin, the body is divided into right and left halves by a longitudinal vertical median septum continuous with the sheaths enclosing the nervous system, notochord, and gut ; this septum remains as a median dorsal and median ventral septum separating the myomeres, and as a median mesentery suspending the gut. The ventral mesentery below the gut disappears almost completely (p. 620), but the dorsal mesentery usually remains. Thus is formed a system of longitudinal septa and tubular coverings, and of transverse septa (myosepta, myocommata) intersegmental in position between the myomeres, Fig. 1.

Before dealing with the endoskeleton in further detail, something

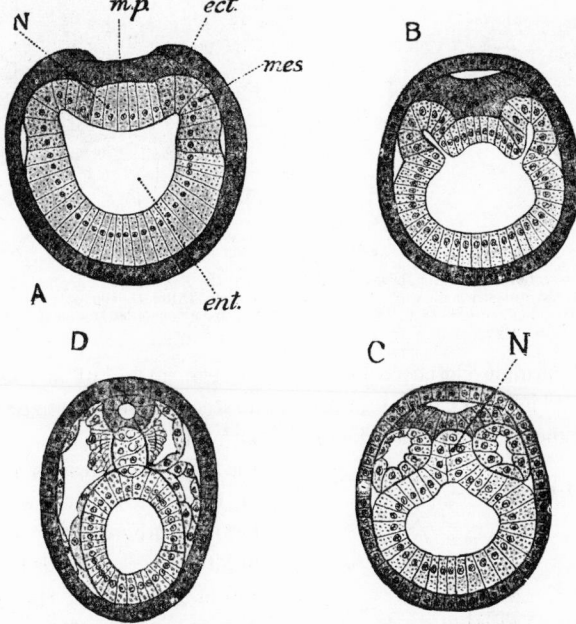

Fig. 2.

Transverse sections of young *Amphioxus* illustrating the origin of the mesoderm. (After Hatschek.) *ect*, Ectoderm; *ent*, enteric cavity; *m.p*, medullary plate; *mes*, mesoderm; *N*, notochordal rudiment. The dark tone indicates ectoderm, the pale tone endoderm, and the medium tone mesoderm. (From J. G. Kerr, *Zoology*, 1921.)

must be said about the embryonic origin of the connective tissue and the development of the mesoblast in Vertebrata. In general terms the middle or mesoblastic germ layer may be described as arising from paired outgrowths of the roof of the archenteron near the blastopore. These outgrowths develop on either side of a median longitudinal band which gives rise to the notochord, and when the notochordal band and the right and left mesoblastic rudiments become separated off, the archenteric walls meet below them to complete the hypoblastic lining of the gut.[1] In

[1] As the embryo elongates backwards the three germ-layers, epiblast, hypoblast, and mesoblast (ecto-, endo-, mesoderm) become differentiated from the indifferent tissue proliferating forwards from the lip of the blastopore.

Cephalochorda the lateral outgrowths destined to give rise to all the mesodermal tissues develop as a series of paired segmental pouches from before backwards, Fig. 2. They soon become nipped off from the archen-

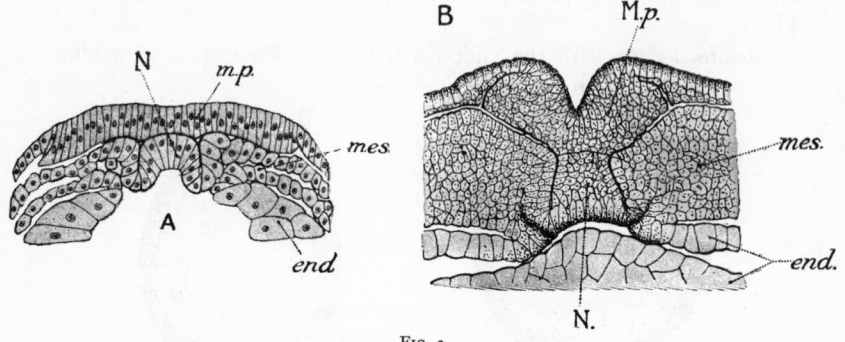

FIG. 3.

Transverse sections through embryos of (A) *Triton* and (B) *Rana temporaria* showing continuity of endoderm and mesoderm on each side of the notochord. (After O. Hertwig, 1882 and 1883.) *end*, Endoderm; *m.p*, medullary plate; *mes*, mesoderm; *N*, notochordal rudiment. (From J. G. Kerr, *Embryology*, 1919.)

teric wall forming closed coelomic sacs or segments; but in *Amphioxus* the first, and in other Craniates the first and second pairs tend to be delayed in development and to remain longer in continuity with the fore-gut. From

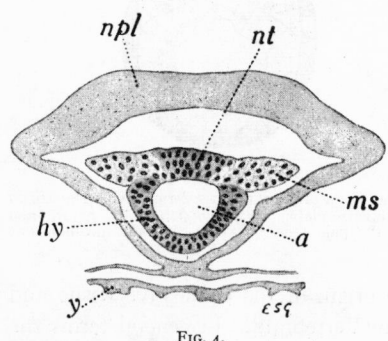

FIG. 4.

*Scyllium canicula*, Stage B. Transverse section through head. *a*, Archenteron; *hy*, hypoblast; *ms*, first outgrowing mesoblastic somite; *npl*, neural plate; *nt*, notochordal plate; *y*, hypoblastic layer of yolk sac.

the first few backwards, the origin of the sacs as hollow pouches becomes progressively obscured; in later stages towards the hinder end of the growing embryo they first appear as practically solid outgrowths. Each coelomic sac becomes subdivided into a dorsal somite (future myotome and sclerotome) and a ventro-lateral chamber. The series of ventro-lateral cavities of *Amphioxus* soon combine to form a continuous longitudinal splanchnic coelom, with an outer wall (somatopleure) and an inner wall (splanchnopleure), by the breaking down of the transverse partitions. In the Gnathostomata the mesoderm is of essentially similar origin, but distinct hollow pouches are not clearly formed; paired grooves, however, of the archenteric wall near the blastopore have been found by Hertwig and G. Schwink in Amphibia, Fig. 3, and by others in Selachii, indicating a folding off of the mesoblast. Similarly there is distinct evidence of paired segmental outgrowths in the first two or three segments of Selachian embryos, Fig. 4, and still more obvious pouches occur in this region in *Petromyzon* where, consequently, the mesoblast is at first completely segmented as in Cephalochorda (Kupffer, 55 ; Hatschek, 43 ; Hatta, 44 ; Koltzoff, 361).

It is very improbable that the formation of coelomic sacs as hollow pouches is of any phylogenetic significance and represents an adult ancestral condition ; nevertheless this mode of separating off the mesoblastic building material seems to have been established at an early stage in the history of the Vertebrate phylum. Since it occurs also in the development of related groups such as Echinodermata and Enteropneusta the origin of the mesoblast from paired pouches is probably an embryonic device inherited from the ontogeny of the remote common ancestor of all these coelomate phyla. It may, therefore, be considered as an ancient and so far primitive mode of development which has become modified and obscured in the higher Vertebrates ; for in them not only do the coelomic sacs develop by the secondary hollowing out and subdivision of continuous mesoblastic bands, but the ventral lateral-plate region and its contained splanchnocoel never show distinct signs of segmentation except to a slight extent in Cyclostomes.

In *Amphioxus* all the coelomic segments except the first pair become subdivided into dorsal and ventral portions. The adjacent walls of the latter soon fuse and break down and there is so formed a continuous splanchnocoel as mentioned above. From the dorsal portions or somites are formed the hollow myotomes and sclerotomes. Most of the adult myomere is developed from the inner wall of the myotome, but its outer wall also contributes muscle cells (Sunier, 86, E.S.G.). The sclerotome arises by outfolding from the inner wall of the base of the somite, and grows up between the myomere and axial organs. While the cavity of the myotome or myocoel is soon obliterated, that of the sclerotome (sclerocoel) persists in the adult, Fig. 707. The splanchnocoel forms the adult perivisceral coelom behind, and the right and left suprapharyngeal coelom in front ; from which extend coelomic canals down the primary gill-bars to a median subpharyngeal or endostylar coelom. Segmental coelomic canals also pass down the inner side of the metapleural folds to the genital coelomic chambers (Legros, 844). The thin layers of connective tissue seem to develop from the surface of all these mesoblastic structures derived from the original coelomic sacs. The mesoblastic bands of the Craniata become differentiated into dorsal segmental somites and ventral unsegmented lateral plate, Figs. 5 and 12. The segmental somite becomes further differentiated into myotome, sclerotome, and nephrotome or stalk connecting it with the lateral plate (Chapter XIII.). A cavity (myocoel), continuous through the nephrotome with the splanchnocoel, extends at first into the myotome, but disappears later. The definitive myomere or muscle segment (' somatic ' muscle) is usually developed from the inner wall of the myotome, though in Dipnoi the outer so-called cutis layer may also contribute muscle (Kerr, 840). The bulk of the axial connective tissue is derived from the sclerotome, an outgrowth or proliferation from the ventral inner region of the myotome. Mesenchyme cells may also be proliferated from the nephrotome, the

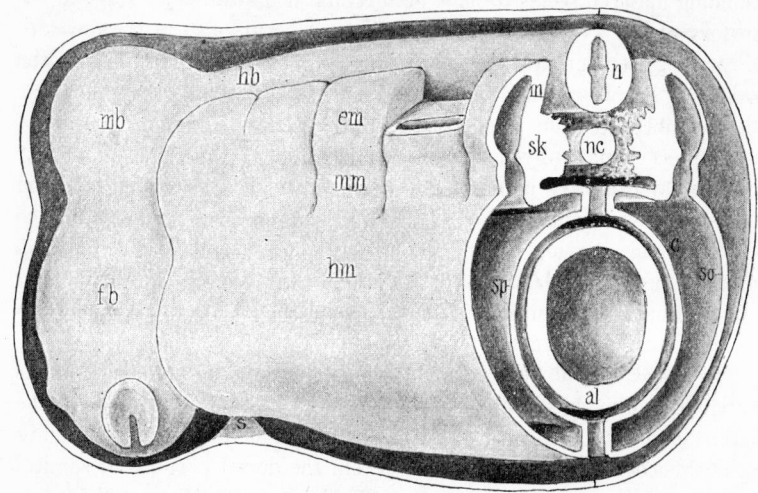

Fig. 5.

Stereogram of head region of craniate embryo, showing segmentation of mesoblast (from J. S. Kingsley, *Comp. Anat. of Vertebrates*, 1926). *al*, Alimentary canal; *c*, coelom; *em*, epimere (myotome); *fb*, fore-brain; *hb*, hind-brain; *hm*, hypomere (lateral-plate); *m*, myomere; *mb*, mid-brain; *mm*, mesomere (nephrotome); *n*, spinal cord; *nc*, notochord; *s*, stomodaeal region; *sk*, sclerotome; *so*, *sp*, somatic and splanchnic walls of coelom approaching above and below *al* to form mesenteries.

outer cutis layer of the myotome, and the outer surface of the somatopleure. All these cells scatter and multiply, filling the spaces between the various layers and organs. During this process the original segmentation of the sclerotomes is lost, the later segmentation displayed by the skeleton being, so to speak, reimposed upon the mesenchyme by the myomeres.

The Acrania and Cyclostomata illustrate the segmental structure in its least modified condition. In the Gnathostomata the myomeres become subdivided into dorsal (epiaxonic) and ventral (hypoaxonic) portions by an additional longitudinal horizontal septum stretching from the base of the notochordal sheath to the body wall surface,[1] completing

[1] In Pisces and aquatic Amphibia this horizontal septum reaches the surface at the level of the main ' lateral line '.

the system of chief membranes in which the various parts of the skeleton arise, Fig. 1.

The axial skeleton of the trunk first develops in connexion with the covering of the notochordal axis and the transverse septa. Speaking generally, where these septa meet the longitudinal sheaths neural arches develop above and haemal arches below, while vertebral centra appear round the notochord itself. Thus, since the myomeres mark the segments of the body, these skeletal segments of the vertebral column alternate with them, and become intersegmental in position, Fig. 1.

The right and left neural arches tend to meet and fuse above the neural canal, and the haemal arches to meet and fuse below the caudal artery and vein in the tail region. Interneural and interhaemal elements may also appear. Dorsal ribs develop where the transverse septa meet the horizontal septum, and ventral ribs where they meet the coelomic wall. Such is the fundamental plan of the axial skeleton in the Gnathostomes.

## THE NOTOCHORD AND ITS SHEATHS

The notochord is perhaps the most constant and characteristic feature of the Vertebrata, or Chordata, as they are often called. Essentially a rather stiff but flexible rod lying below the central nervous system and between the paired series of muscle segments, it not only forms the chief skeletal axis in the more primitive Cephalochorda and Cyclostomata, but always serves as the foundation of the vertebral column in higher Craniata. Indeed it must surely have been one of the chief factors in the development of the fundamental plan of structure of early vertebrates as free-swimming segmented animals moving by a lateral bending of the body.

The presence of the notochord not only in all the Vertebrata, but also in the degenerate Ascidians, shows that it is an extremely ancient organ; yet we have little real evidence as to its origin. We may, however, conjecture that it arose simply as a longitudinal thickening of the wall of the gut. The interesting suggestion made by Bateson, that an anterior diverticulum of the oesophagus in the Enteropneusta represents the notochord, rests on a very slender foundation, and in any case *Balanoglossus* differs too widely from the true Chordata for much help to be derived from this comparison.

The notochord invariably develops from the dorsal wall of the archenteron as a thickening or upfolding which (except at its extreme anterior end) becomes nipped off from before backwards, and continues to grow at its posterior end as the embryo lengthens. The growing point is situated just in front of the neurenteric canal at a point representing the original dorsal lip of the blastopore; thus, when a primitive streak is established the notochordal cells may no longer arise from the wall of the gut itself, but directly from the undifferentiated tissue of the streak.   In front the

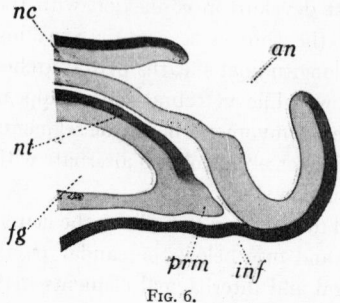

FIG. 6.

Median sagittal section through head-region of embryo *Torpedo marmorata*, 2·8 mm. long (after Dohrn, 1904). *an*, Anterior neuropore; *fg*, fore-gut; *inf*, beginning of hypophysial invagination; *nc*, nerve-cord; *nt*, notochord; *prm*, premandibu-lar mesoblast joining paired somites.

notochord always extends to near the extremity of the archenteron, to the wall of which it may remain for some time attached at a place im-mediately behind the hypophysis and below and behind the infundibu-lum, Figs. 6, 7, and 234.   Never, in Craniates, does the notochord pass beyond this region.   Here, then, is a meeting-point of these three struc-tures, hypophysis, infundibulum, and notochord, constant throughout the Craniata from Cyclostomes to man (p. 214).   This disposition is probably fundamental and primitive, and the growth forward of the notochord beyond the brain and mouth in *Amphioxus* would then be a secondary

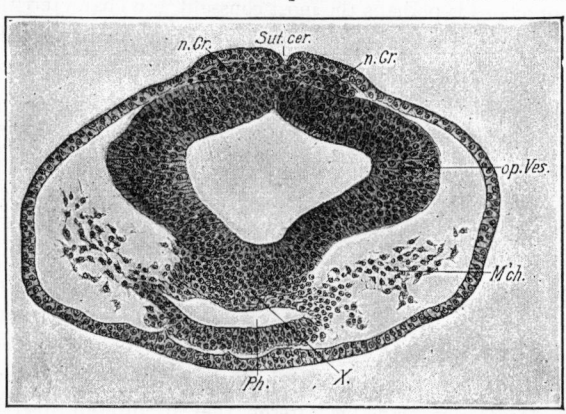

FIG. 7.

Transverse section of fore-brain and optic vesicles of chick embryo of 7 somites (from F. R. Lillie, *Develt. Chick*, 1919).   *M'ch*, Mesenchyme; *n.Cr*, neural crest; *op.Ves*, optic vesicles; *Ph*, pharynx; *Sut.cer*, anterior cerebral suture; *X*, mass of cells in which anterior end of intestine and notochord fuse.

adaptation to its well-known habit of burrowing rapidly in the sand (Willey, 94).

Soon after the separation of the notochord from the wall of the archen-teron the cells become flattened and arranged in a single row like a pile of coins (Boeke, 8).   In *Amphioxus*, although the nuclei may divide and become distributed, the flattened cuticularised cells retain this original disposition; there is no special covering epithelium, but a dorsal and ventral strand of superficial cells. But in the Craniata, after repeated division of the nuclei, the cells multiply, become cuticularised and vacuolated, forming the characteristic notochordal tissue of polygonal cells. At the periphery, however, an epithelium is formed of cells rich in protoplasm, which apparently secrete the covering sheaths.

The history of the two sheaths present in the Craniata, and secreted by the notochordal epithelium, is of considerable interest. Their origin and structure has been worked out chiefly by Kölliker (54), Hasse (39-42), v. Ebner (20), Klaatsch (53), Schneider (81), Schauinsland (78), and others, and is now well understood. At an early stage the notochordal epithelium secretes a thin covering membrane in which intercrossing elastic fibres become differentiated; this is the elastica externa. Next is secreted, also by the notochordal epithelium, an inner and usually thicker fibrous sheath.[1] The fate of these true notochordal sheaths varies in different groups, and their structural importance is inversely proportional to the development of the mesoblastic vertebral column outside.

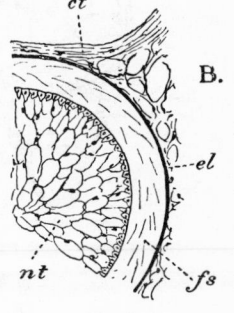

Fig. 8.

Ammocoete larva of *Petromyzon fluviatilis*, L. Portion of a transverse section of the notochord, enlarged. *ct*, Connective tissue; *el*, elastica externa; *fs*, fibrous sheath; *nt*, notochord. (From Goodrich, *Vert. Craniata*, 1909.)

In the Cyclostomata, where the large notochord forms the main axial support in the adult without a trace of centra, and remains as a continuous unconstricted rod stretching from the infundibular region to the tip of the tail, the fibrous sheath is quite thick, Figs. 8 and 30. But in most of the living Gnathostomata (all Teleostomi with the exception of the Chondrostei, and especially in the Tetrapoda) it remains comparatively thin and frequently disappears. In the Tetrapods, indeed, the sheaths together with the notochord are reduced to a mere vestige in the adult.

In the Elasmobranchii mesoblastic cells, from the skeletogenous layer originally outside the sheaths, make their way through the thin elastica externa and invade the underlying fibrous sheath in every segment at four points in its circumference corresponding to the bases of the dorsal and ventral arches, Figs. 9 and 22. These cells penetrate in large numbers, arrange themselves in concentric layers, and contribute matrix to the ever-widening fibrous sheath in which the centra are thus eventually

---

[1] There is still some doubt as to the share taken by the chordal epithelium in the formation of the sheaths; Tretjakoff, one of the most recent writers on this subject, believes the elastica externa to be of mesoblastic origin (87-89).

formed (p. 21). Next to the notochord is generally seen a clear cell-less layer, often called the ' elastica interna ' ; but apparently it is usually only the last-formed layer of the fibrous sheath, and the true elastica interna, when present, is an extremely thin layer of fibres near the

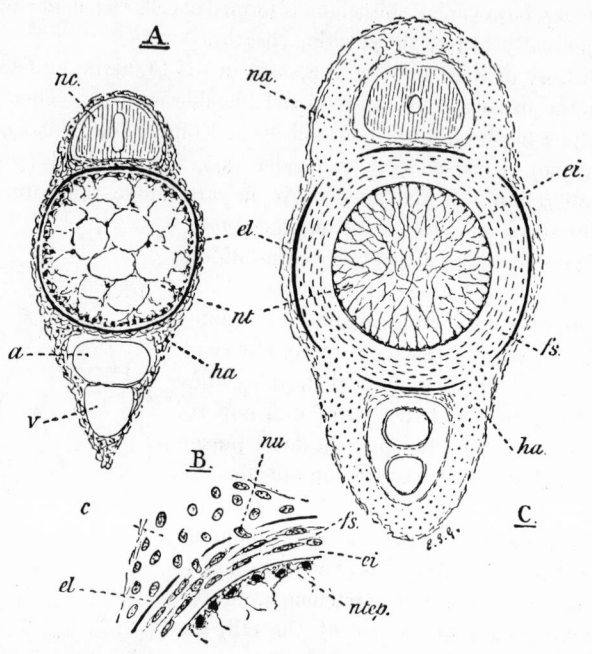

FIG. 9.

*Scyllium canicula*, L. A, Transverse section of the vertebral column of the tail of a young embryo before invasion ; B, the base of the neural arch in an older embryo showing invasion ; C, of a later stage : all magnified. *a*, caudal artery ; *c*, cartilage ; *ei*, ' elastica interna ' or inner layer of the fibrous sheath ; *el*, elastica externa ; *fs*, fibrous sheath which becomes invaded by mesoblastic cells ; *ha*, haemal arch ; *na*, neural arch ; *nc*, nerve-cord ; *nt*, notochord ; *ntep*, notochordal epithelium ; *nu*, nuclei of mesoblastic cells passing through the broken elastica externa ; *v*, caudal vein. (From Goodrich, *Vert. Craniata*, 1909.)

notochord.[1] The centrum may develop as a cartilaginous ring in continuity with the arches, and carrying on its outer surface the remains of the ruptured elastica. Or cartilage may spread from the base of the arches both inside and outside ; the elastica then becomes embedded in the centrum and eventually disappears as a rule. Such centra, in which

[1] There has been much controversy concerning the presence of a distinct elastica interna inside the fibrous sheath of the Craniata. O. Schneider has recently shown that such a thin layer of elastic fibres exists in the Elasmobranchs, in Acipenser, and in some but not in all Teleosts, and in the form of scattered fibres in the Cyclostomes. It has been described by many observers in fishes.

the invaded fibrous sheath takes a share, are called chordal centra, as distinguished from the usual perichordal centra developed outside the unbroken elastica externa.

A similar invasion of the thick fibrous sheath through the elastica takes place in the Dipnoi ; but the invasion is less thorough, and although a small amount of cartilage is formed at the base of the arches by the

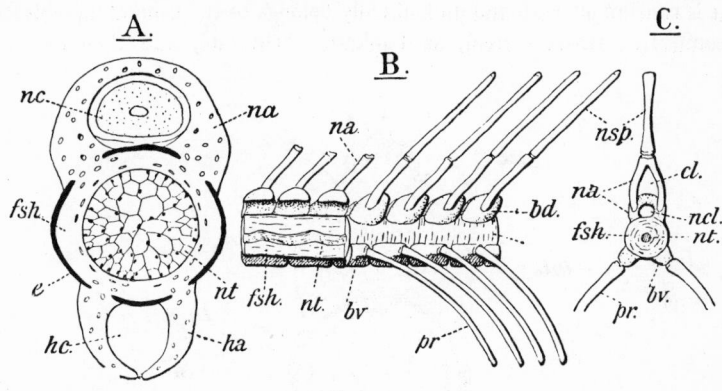

FIG. 10.

A, Transverse section of vertebral column of a young *Protopterus*, showing the invasion of the fibrous notochordal sheath by the mesoblastic cells ; B, left-side view of a portion of the vertebral column (abdominal region) of *Ceratodus Forsteri*, Krefft., of which the anterior half has been cut longitudinally ; C, view of the same cut across. *bd*, Basidorsal cartilage ; *bv*, basiventral cartilage ; *cl*, canal for ligament ; *e*, elastica externa ; *fsh*, fibrous sheath ; *ha*, haemal arch (basiventral) ; *hc*, haemal canal ; *na*, neural arch ; *nc*, nerve-cord ; *ncl*, neural canal ; *nsp*, supraneural spine ; *nt*, notochord ; *pr*, pleural rib. (From Goodrich, *Vert. Craniata*, 1909.)

mesoblastic cells, true complete centra are not developed at all events in living genera, Fig. 10.

True centra are not formed in the living Holocephali, although the fibrous sheath is invaded by cells. The cells gather into a middle zone in the sheath, and a series of calcified rings are here developed which are more numerous than the segments, Fig. 31. The extinct *Squaloraja*, from the Lower Lias, had vertebral rings much better developed and more like centra, Fig. 32.

The Chondrostei also have a well-developed fibrous sheath, Fig. 34. No centra are formed in living genera ; but, as first discovered by Schneider, the fibrous sheath is invaded through the ruptured elastica, in spite of many statements to the contrary (E.S.G.).

The concurrence of this invasion in such diverse groups of fish naturally suggests the question whether it is a primitive condition in Pisces, or a secondary modification of no phylogenetic significance, and connected with the thickening of the sheath. No definite answer can as yet be given ; but whichever it should be, there can be little doubt that the centra themselves were originally formed outside the elastica externa. In this connexion it should not be forgotten that the occipital region of the skull is always so developed, even in the Selachian, and that where, as in Holocephali, Dipnoi, and Chondrostei, several anterior vertebral rings may merge into the occipital region, these are perichordal in structure.

The notochord in *Amphioxus* is surrounded by a strong sheath ; but it is continuous with and undoubtedly belongs to the general mesoblastic connective tissue system, as Lankester held (56), and therefore not

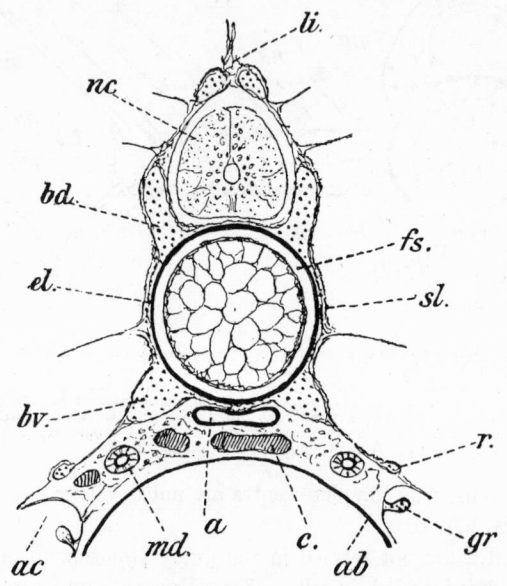

Fig. 11.

Transverse section of the vertebral column in the trunk of a very young trout (*Salmo*), enlarged. *ab*, Dorsal wall of air-bladder ; *ac*, abdominal coelom ; *bd*, basidorsal cartilage ; *bv*, basiventral cartilage ; *c*, posterior cardinal vein ; *el*, elastica externa ; *fs*, fibrous sheath surrounding notochord ; *gr*, genital ridge ; *li*, dorsal longitudinal ligament ; *md*, mesonephric duct ; *nc*, nerve-cord ; *r*, rib ; *sl*, skeletogenous tissue. (From Goodrich, *Vert. Craniata*, 1909.)

homologous with either of the true sheaths described above. Whether there is really a very thin separate sheath between it and the notochord, as described by v. Ebner (20) and Klaatsch (53), is doubtful. If present it probably corresponds to the elastica externa.

The vertebral centra in Teleostomes and Tetrapods are formed from the mesoblastic skeletogenous layer surrounding the notochordal sheaths, and belong to the perichordal type, Fig. 11. In these forms, then, the centra typically lie outside the notochord and its sheaths ; the latter remain intact, although they often become much constricted and even obliterated in the adult.[1] Probably all the Osteichthyes, as well as the Tetrapods, have vertebral columns really belonging to this type; for though the fibrous sheath is invaded in modern Dipnoi and Acipenseroidei, as mentioned above, yet the cartilaginous elements representing the centra in these fish are placed outside the sheaths.

A remarkable alteration of the notochord takes place in the middle of the vertebra in Amphibia, *Sphenodon*, and many Lacertilia, Figs. 56, 58, 268. It consists in the late appearance of a zone of cartilage-like tissue, which may constrict the ordinary notochordal tissue to a mere thread (Gegenbaur, 29, in Urodela, Apoda, and Lacertilia; Goette, 1875, in Anura). About the origin of this ' chordal cartilage ' there has been much controversy, some believing it to be produced by invading mesoblastic cells (Lwoff, 56; Zykoff, 99; Gadow, 26; Tretjakoff, 89), others holding that it is formed from modified notochordal cells which secrete a matrix resembling that of true cartilage (Field, 21; v. Ebner, 20; Klaatsch, 53; Kapelkin, 52; Schauinsland, 78). There can be little doubt that the latter is the correct interpretation. There is good evidence that the notochordal sheaths remain unbroken, that mesoblastic cells do not pierce them, and that the notochordal tissue becomes converted into the chordal ' cartilage '.

## THE VERTEBRAL COLUMN

The structure and development of the vertebral column in the Craniata may now be considered. Great diversity occurs in the various groups not only in the number of elements serving to arch over the neural canal and to enclose the haemal canal, but the vertebral centra themselves may vary greatly. They may be of more or less complex build, may be well developed, vestigial, or altogether absent, and even may be more numerous than the segments in which they lie. Yet it is probable that the vertebrae are fundamentally homologous throughout the Craniata. The older authors roughly identified arches and centra in fishes and land vertebrates; but recently attempts have been made to compare in detail different types of vertebral column and refer them to a single scheme of homologous parts. It is doubtful whether such a proceeding is altogether justifiable, since at least some of the types may have been independently evolved. Moreover, there is danger of adopting too uniform and artificial a scheme for the whole length of the column, forgetting that the arrangement of the dorsal elements may never have

---

[1] According to Tretjakoff, the fibrous sheath may possibly be slightly invaded in Amphibia (89).

corresponded exactly to that of the ventral elements, and that the anterior region may never have exactly resembled the posterior. Nevertheless

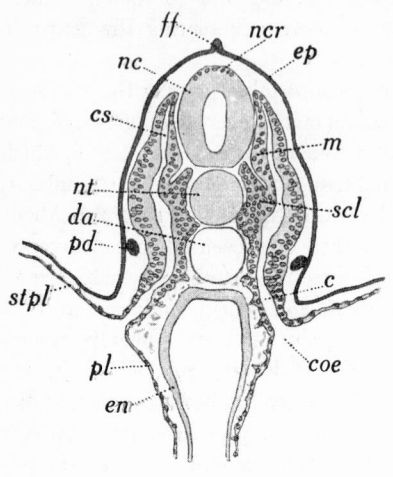

FIG. 12.

*Scyllium canicula*; transverse section through trunk of embryo, stage H. *c*, Coelomic canal between ventral splanchnocoele, *coe*, and dorsal myocoele, *cs* ; *da*, dorsal aorta ; *ep*, epidermis ; *en*, endodermal gut ; *ff*, ectodermal fin fold ; *m*, myotome ; *nc*, nerve cord ; *ncr*, neural crest ; *nt*, notochord ; *pd*, pronephric duct ; *pl*, splanchnopleure ; *scl*, sclerotome ; *stpl*, somatopleure.

considerable success has already been achieved, notably by Cope (13), Hay (45), Goette (31-4), and more especially by Gadow and Abbott (27), and Schauinsland (78).

**Selachii.**—It is convenient to begin with an account of the vertebral column of the Selachii, and its structure is best understood by describing its development. The sclerotomes which yield the mesoblastic tissue of which it is composed are of course strictly segmental in origin (p. 6), and grow so as to surround both the notochord in its sheaths (p. 9) and the neural canal, Figs. 12, 14, 15, 16. Between successive sclerotomes extend upwards small segmental blood-vessels, arteries from the dorsal aorta, and veins from the cardinals. These primitive vessels are, therefore, intersegmental in

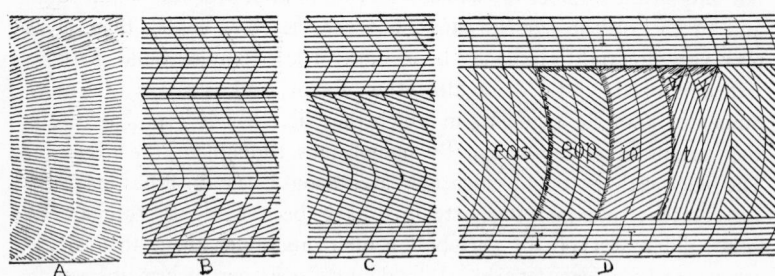

FIG. 13.

Scheme of arrangement of *myomeres* and muscle fibres in left-side view of trunk of : A *Petromyzon*, B *Selachian*, C *Teleost*, D Urodele (from J. S. Kingsley, *Comp. Anat. of Vertebrates*, 1926). *eop*, *eos*, Deep and superficial external oblique ; *io*, internal oblique ; *l*, longissimus dorsi ; *r*, rectus abdominis ; *t*, transversus ; *v*, subvertebral.

position ; and when, as soon happens, the limits between consecutive sclerotomes become obscured as the cells become distributed along the column to form a continuous covering of skeletogenous tissue or membrana reuniens, the blood-vessels even in the adult serve to show the original limit between the segments (Rabl, 71-2; Schauinsland, 78). Outside this sclerotomal tissue develop the segmental myotomes, giving rise to myomeres which soon become bent first in < shape, then in ≳ shape, so that their disposition no longer corresponds to the original vertical intersegmental divisions still indicated by the intersegmental vessels, Figs. 13 and 15. Moreover, the myocommata are set obliquely to the long axis, each myomere being partly covered by the one in front.

In the course of development the posterior half of each sclerotome becomes denser than the anterior, and through the anterior half of looser tissue pass the ventral and dorsal nerve-roots, the latter bearing a ganglion. The anterior half may be called the cranial half, the posterior the caudal half-sclerotome. Primitively, no doubt, the dorsal roots are intersegmental and the ventral roots segmental in position; but, owing to relative shifting of parts and obliquity of septa, the ganglia appear to move forward and come to occupy a position opposite the middle of the segment to which they belong, Figs. 15, 16.

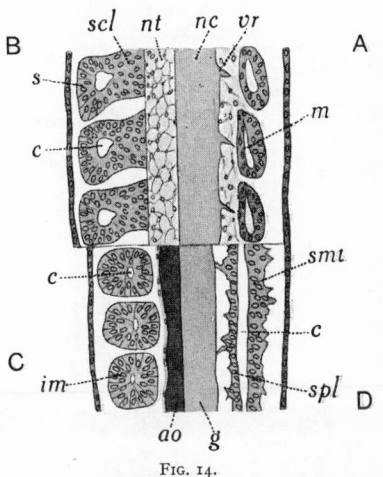

FIG. 14.

*Scyllium canicula.* Longitudinal frontal sections of trunk of embryo, stage I. A, Most dorsal, D, most ventral; B, through sclerotomes, *scl*, and scleromyocoeles, *c*; C, through nephrotomes and nephrocoeles, *c*; D, through ventral lateral plate and splanchnocoele, *c*; *ao*, dorsal aorta; *g*, gut wall; *im*, intermediate mass (nephrotome); *nc*, nerve cord; *smt*, somatopleure; *spl*, splanchnopleure. Other letters as in Figs. 12 and 15.

The main branch of the mixed spinal nerve passes out in the transverse septum posterior to its myomere. Into this septum also grows outwards a prolongation of the ventral region of the posterior dense half of the sclerotome to form the rudiment of the rib (p. 71). Dorsally to the notochord now appear two condensations of the sclerotomal mesenchyme on each side of the neural canal in each segment. The posterior and larger rests on the elastica externa and is the rudiment of the cartilaginous neural arch which takes up an approximately intersegmental position, between the intersegmental vessels behind and the dorsal root in front. The anterior and smaller rudiment does not usually reach the elastica, is situated behind the intersegmental vessels between the ventral and the dorsal nerve-roots, and gives rise to the interneural or 'intercalary' cartilaginous arch.[1] Ventrally to the notochord on each side in each segment appear a pair of rudiments corresponding to those above. The posterior and larger gives rise to the haemal or 'transverse process' bearing the rib in the trunk or the haemal arch in the tail. The anterior rudiment is far less regularly developed and in many forms vestigial or absent; in some Selachii and in certain regions of the column it may be well developed and persist

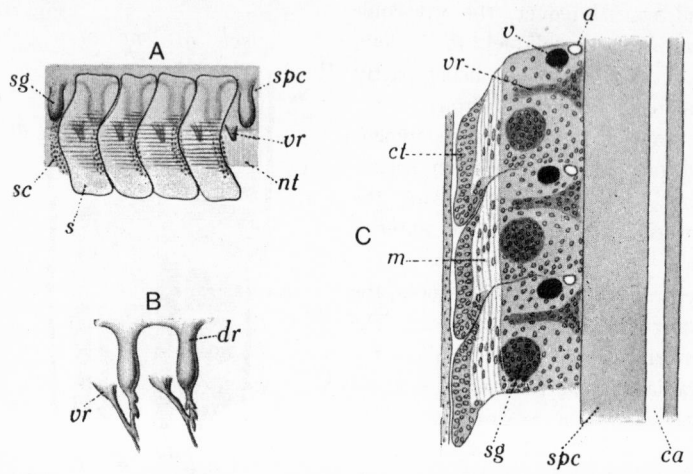

Fig. 15.

*Scyllium canicula.* A, Left side view of myotomes, etc., of trunk of embryo stage J. B, Reconstruction of spinal nerve roots of later stage. C, Longitudinal frontal section of trunk of embryo, stage K, left side only complete; *a,* segmental artery; *ca,* neural canal; *ct,* outer 'cutis' layer of myotome; *dr,* dorsal root; *m,* myomere; *nt,* notochord; *s,* segmental myotome; *sc,* scleromere; *sg,* spinal ganglion; *spc,* spinal cord; *v,* segmental vein; *vr,* ventral root.

as a separate 'intercalary' cartilage. It is in connexion with the posterior dorsal and ventral paired elements that the centrum of the vertebra is developed. These four cartilages spread at their bases over the elastica externa, Fig. 22, and it is at these four points in the circumference, chiefly if not entirely, that the piercing of the elastica takes place, allowing the mesoblastic cells to invade and spread throughout the fibrous sheath (p. 9). Chondrification now extends in the sheath forming rings of cartilage in continuity with the neural and haemal elements outside; thus are formed the 'chordal' centra constricting the notochord inter-

[1] Van Wijhe has recently shown that at an early stage of the development of the column of Acanthias the arcualia are represented by four continuous bands of cartilage along the notochordal sheath, which subsequently break up into separate basidorsal and basiventral elements (v. Wijhe, **93**). Similar bands of early cartilage have been described by de Beer in Heterodontus (**7**); it would seem, however, that the continuity is better ascribed to the temporary fusion of rudiments set very close together than to the arcualia having been evolved from an originally continuous cartilaginous band.

segmentally, but allowing it to continue growing segmentally. The fibrous sheath between the consecutive cartilaginous centra remains to form the intervertebral fibrous rings, Figs. 17-21.

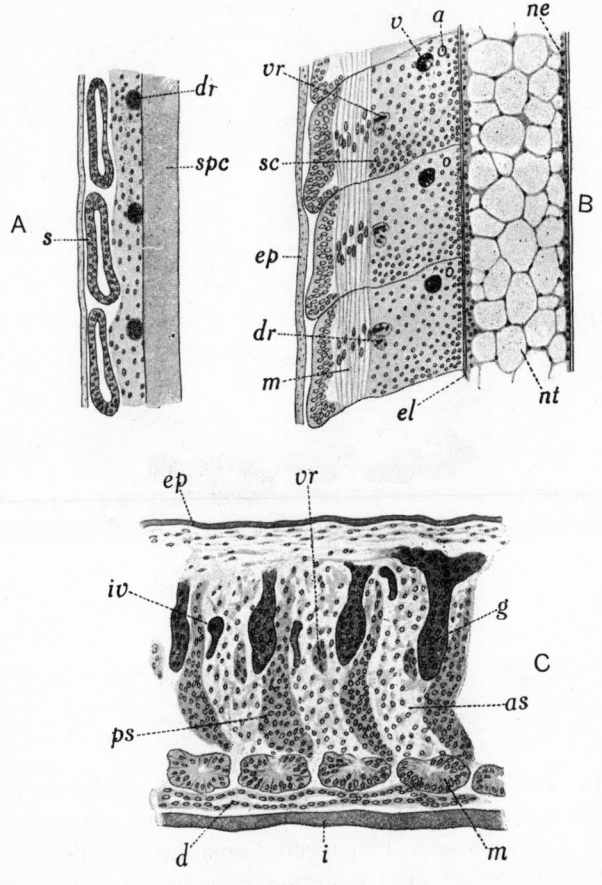

FIG. 16.

*Scyllium canicula*, embryo stage K ; longitudinal frontal section more dorsal in A, more ventral in B. *dr*, Dorsal root; *el*, elastica externa ; *ep*, epidermis ; *m*, myomere ; *ne*, notochordal epithelium ; *s*, dorsal region of myotome; *sc*, denser posterior region of sclerotome ; *spc*, spinal cord ; *vr*, ventral root. Other letters as in Fig. 17. C, Sagittal section to left of middle plane, stage J. *d*, Primary (mesonephric) duct ; *g*, ganglion ; *i*, intestinal wall ; *iv*, intersegmental vein ; *m*, mesonephric tubule rudiment ; *vr*, ventral root ; *as* and *ps*, anterior and posterior halves of sclerotome ; much denser latter half will give rise to basalia.

The important conclusion is reached with regard to the vertebral column in Selachii that four paired elements in each segment contribute to its development. To these may be applied the terms introduced by Gadow and Abbott: the paired elements above and below the notochord are called the dorsal and ventral arcualia respectively ; the larger posterior arcualia in each segment are the basalia (basidorsalia and basiventralia); the smaller anterior arcualia are the interbasalia (interdorsalia and inter-

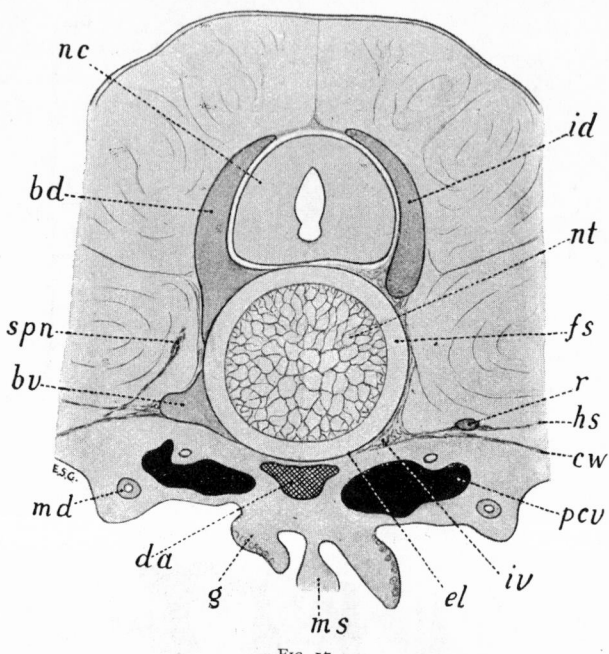

FIG. 17.

Transverse section through the anterior trunk region of an embryo *Scyllium canicula* about 32 mm. long. Being slightly oblique the section cuts basidorsal, *bd*, and basiventral, *bv*, on left, and interdorsal, *id*, and interventral, *iv*, on right. *cw*, Connective tissue of splanchnocoelic wall ; *da*, dorsal aorta ; *el*, elastica externa ; *fs*, fibrous sheath ; *g*, gonad ; *hs*, horizontal septum ; *md*, Müllerian duct ; *ms*, mesentery ; *nc*, nerve cord ; *nt*, notochord ; *pcv*, posterior cardinal vein ; *r*, dorsal rib ; *spn*, spinal nerve.

ventralia). The basidorsal (neural arch) and the basiventral (haemal arch) are derived from the 'caudal' or posterior denser half of the sclerotome, and the interdorsal and interventral from the 'cranial' or anterior half of the sclerotome.[1] The segmentation of the sclerotomes is early

[1] For the theory of Gadow and Abbott (**27**), that each scleromere or vertebral segment is formed on each side of the ventral half of one sclerotome combined with the dorsal half of the sclerotome of the segment next following (each sclerotome being obliquely and not vertically divided), there seems to be no good evidence. These authors were apparently misled by the secondary bending of the myomeres causing the septa to pass obliquely across the column ; while the original segmentation is better indicated by the intersegmental vessels as explained above. The evidence seems to be clear that the basidorsal and basiventral of each vertebral segment are derived from the posterior region of the same sclerotome. Nevertheless Marcus and Blume (**62**) have revived Gadow's theory in dealing with the Apoda.

lost, but the original limits between them are shown by the inter-segmental blood-vessels. The bases of the basidorsals and basiventrals spread over the elastica externa but do not as a rule meet round it, and the chordal centra are developed in continuity with them as complete rings. Since the basalia (and centra) take up a position between consecutive myomeres, they become connected with the intersegmental myocommata, while the interbasalia become segmentally placed. The

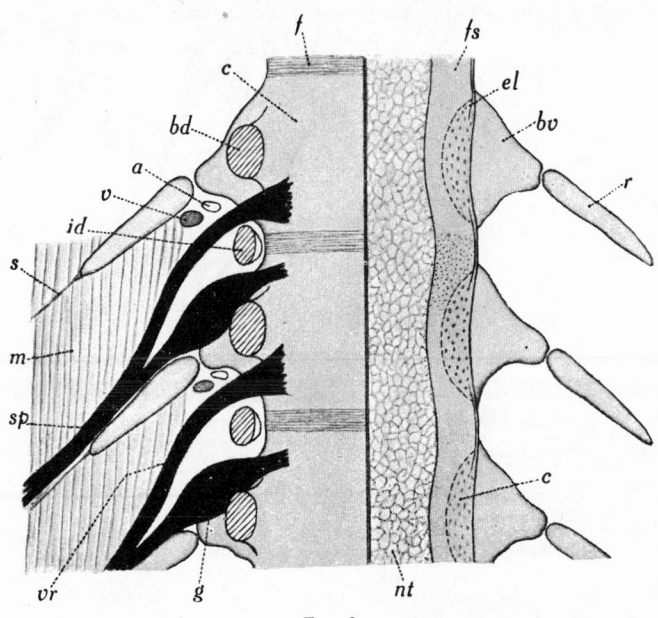

Fig. 18.

*Scyllium canicula.* Reconstruction of vertebral column, etc., of advanced embryo ; dorsal view. On left, arcualia cut through ; on right, deeper cut through notochord. *a,* Intersegmental artery ; *bd,* basidorsal ; *bv,* basiventral ; *c,* centrum developing in fibrous sheath ; *el,* interrupted elastica externa ; *f,* intervertebral ligament ; *fs,* notochordal fibrous sheath ; *g,* ganglion on dorsal root ; *id,* interdorsal ; *m,* myomere ; *nt,* notochord ; *r,* rib ; *s,* intersegmental septum ; *sp,* spinal mixed nerve ; *v,* intersegmental vein ; *vr,* ventral root.

finished column thus consists of vertebral centra alternating with muscle segments, two myomeres being connected to each vertebra, an adaptation for the bending of the vertebral column seen in Gnathostomes generally.

The structure of the vertebral column in adult Selachians has been studied by Kölliker (54), Goette, Hasse (38), and others. Lately Ridewood has extended and corrected earlier observations, and provided a sounder interpretation of results (76). The column forms a flexible skeletal covering not only to the notochord but also to the neural canal above, and the haemal canal below in the caudal region. There are no

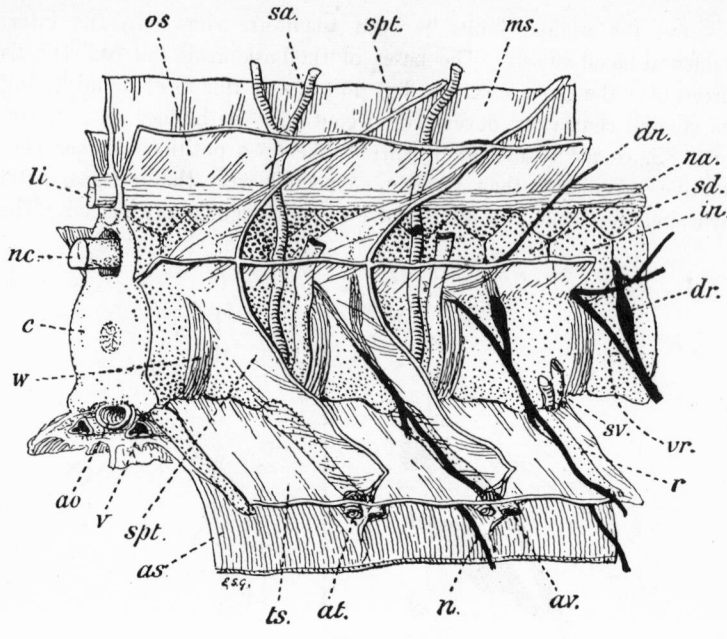

FIG. 19.

*Scyllium canicula*, L. Left-side view, enlarged, of a portion of the vertebral column and ribs with the connective tissue septa, to show their relation to the blood-vessels and nerves. *ao*, Dorsal aorta ; *as*, abdominal wall ; *at*, artery ; *av*, vein ; *c*, centrum ; *dn*, dorsal nerve ; *dr*, ganglion of dorsal root ; *in*, interdorsal ; *li*, dorsal ligament ; *ms*, median dorsal septum ; *n*, ventral branch of spinal nerve ; *na*, basidorsal ; *n.c*, nerve-cord ; *r*, rib ; *s.a*, segmental dorsal artery ; *sd*, supradorsal ; *spt*, vertical transverse septum passing between successive myotomes ; *sv*, segmental dorsal vein ; *ts*, chief transverse horizontal septum in which lie the ribs ; *os*, oblique upper longitudinal septum, a similar lower septum occurs between it and the transverse horizontal septum ; *v*, posterior cardinal vein ; *vr*, ventral spinal root ; *w*, intervertebral ligament. (From Goodrich, *Vert. Craniata*, 1909.)

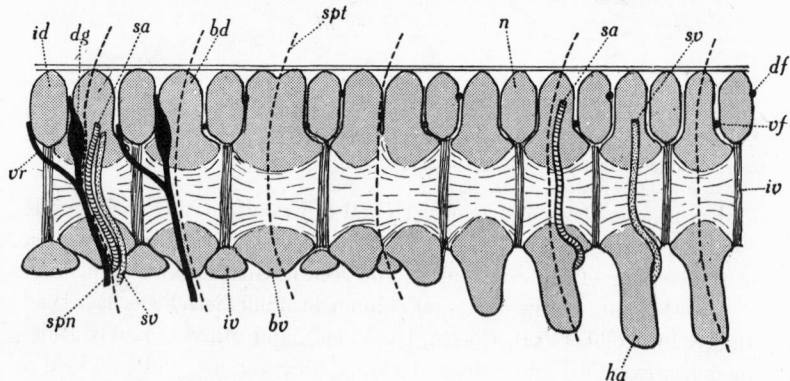

FIG. 20.

Diagram illustrating structure of vertebral column and transition to diplospondylous condition in caudal region of a *Selachian*. Cartilage stippled. *bd*, basidorsal ; *bv*, basiventral ; *df*, foramen for dorsal root ; *dg*, spinal ganglion on dorsal root ; *ha*, haemal arch, prolongation of basiventral ; *id*, interdorsal ; *iv*, interventral ; *n*, secondary intercalated interneural ; *sa*, segmental artery ; *spn*, mixed spinal nerve ; *spt*, position of intersegmental septum ; *sv*, segmental vein ; *vf*, foramen for ventral root ; *vr*, ventral root.

articular joints between the centra and no articular processes between the arches, the consecutive centra being firmly united by fibrous rings and the arcualia by fibrous tissue. The dorsal and ventral nerve-roots escape through foramina situated respectively either in front and behind each interdorsal (Scyllioidei) or through the basidorsal and interdorsal, which have grown backwards so as to enclose them (Goodrich, 35; v. Wijhe, 93; de Beer, 7). Above the column runs the strong longitudinal elastic ligament found in all Craniates. Below this there is usually a series of small median supradorsal cartilages (sometimes wrongly called neural spines, p. 87) wedged between the tips of the basidorsals and inter-dorsals, and forming keystones to the arches; or the basidorsals and -interdorsals fuse above the neural canal as in *Squalus*. In the caudal region the interventrals are reduced or gener-ally lost, and the right and left basiventrals fuse below the caudal vessels, and are pro-longed as broad median spines supporting the ventral caudal fin. The basiventral may some-

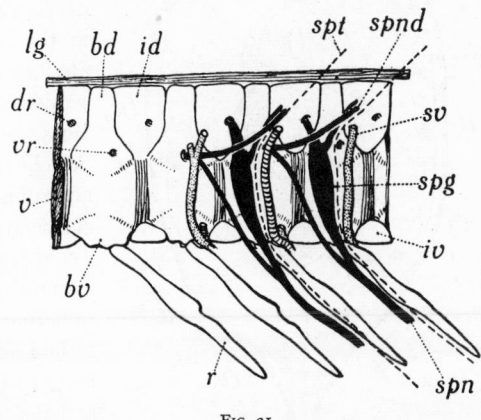

FIG. 21.

*Squalus acanthias.* Left-side view of portion of vertebral column of mid-trunk. *bd*, Basidorsal; *bv*, basiventral; *dr*, dorsal root foramen; *id*, interdorsal; *iv*, interventral; *lg*, dorsal ligament; *r*, dorsal rib; *spg*, spinal ganglion; *spn*, mixed spinal nerve; *spnd*, dorsal branch of spinal nerve; *spt*, course of intersomitic septum; intersegmental vein (corresponding artery shown in next segment); *v*, intervertebral disc; *vr*, ventral root foramen.

times show a ventral prolongation at the side of the aorta in addition to the more dorsal process supporting the dorsal rib (*Cetorhinus, Laemargus,* etc.). In such a form as *Lamna* the basiventrals and interventrals together with cartilages apparently representing the ribs form in the trunk con-tinuous outstanding flattened flanges in the horizontal septum, Fig. 25. As a rule the interventrals are irregularly developed, vestigial, or absent.

The most important modifications occur in the structure and develop-ment of the centra. To what may be termed the chordal centrum, formed in the fibrous sheath and growing by expansion into typically biconcave or amphicoelous cartilages in continuity with the basalia, may be added later on cartilage developed at four points between the bases of these arches from skeletogenous tissue outside the elastica externa. These are the four intermedialia (dorsal, ventral, and two lateral) of Ridewood, which grow by addition of new layers peripherally, forming wedges between the arches and burying the remains of the elastica deeper and deeper in the centrum. Eventually the elastica may be absorbed and the limits between the components of the cartilaginous centrum be lost, Figs. 28, 29.

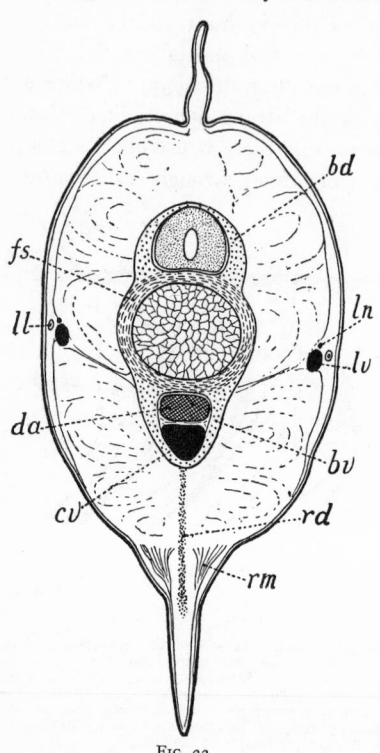

FIG. 22.

Transverse section of the tail of *Scyllium canicula*, late embryo. *bd*, Basidorsal; *bv*, basiventral; *cv*, caudal vein; *da*, caudal artery or dorsal aorta; *fs*, fibrous sheath of notochord invaded by mesoblastic cells; *ll*, lateral-line canal; *ln*, lateral-line nerve; *lv*, lateral cutaneous vein; *rd*, procartilaginous rudiment of radial of anal fin; *rm*, radial muscles.

Besides the usual crust of calcification extending over the surface of the cartilages, special much denser calcifications are deposited in the centra, except in degenerate forms, giving rise in transverse section to characteristic patterns. Hasse attempted to classify the Selachii into three main groups according to these patterns: Cyclospondyli with a simple cylinder, Tectospondyli with concentric cylinders, and Asterospondyli with radiating lamellae, Fig. 23. But a rigid adherence to his definitions leads to a very artificial grouping, and the types are by no means so distinct as he supposed. The calcifications increase with age, and radiating lamellae occur in nearly all the families.

The primary cartilaginous centrum becomes differentiated into outer, middle, and inner zones, and calcification starts early in the middle zone forming a simple cylinder or double cone expanded at both ends. Such a primary cylinder with an outer strengthening of calcification derived from the outer zone is found in the Squalidae, Figs. 24 and 29. To the primary cone may be added successive concentric cylinders developed in the outer zone as in *Squatina* (tectospondylous type), Fig. 26. The outer zone in *Pristis* and *Rhynchobatus* is occupied by a solid calcification. To the primary cones are frequently added longitudinal radiating lamellae spreading in the outer zone. Four such diagonal lamellae occur in most Scyllioidei (not, however, in the common Dog-fish, *Scyllium,*

[*Scylliorhinus*] *canicula*). The lamellae may become more numerous, subdividing from their outer ends as in Notidani and Heterodonti.

Another set of calcifications may develop either as radiating lamellae (*Stegostoma, Lamna*) or as concentric lamellae (*Cetorhinus*) in the four intermedialia. They extend inwards and in some forms reach to near the primary cylinder, Figs. 25, 28.

Degeneration of the vertebral column occurs in several groups of the Selachii. It is usually more pronounced anteriorly, the caudal region

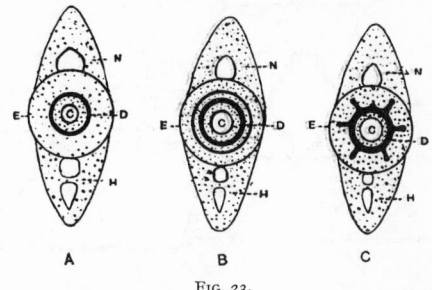

A          B          C

Fig. 23.

Diagrammatic transverse sections of vertebrae of Selachians. A, Cyclospondylous; B, tectospondylous; C, asterospondylous condition (after Hasse, from A. Sedgwick, *Zoology*, 1905). C, Notochord; D, central calcareous ring; E, elastica externa; H, haemal arch; N, neural arch.

retaining a more primitive structure. In the Notidani, *Echinorhinus,* and *Laemargus* (*Somniosus*), for instance, the centra become narrower

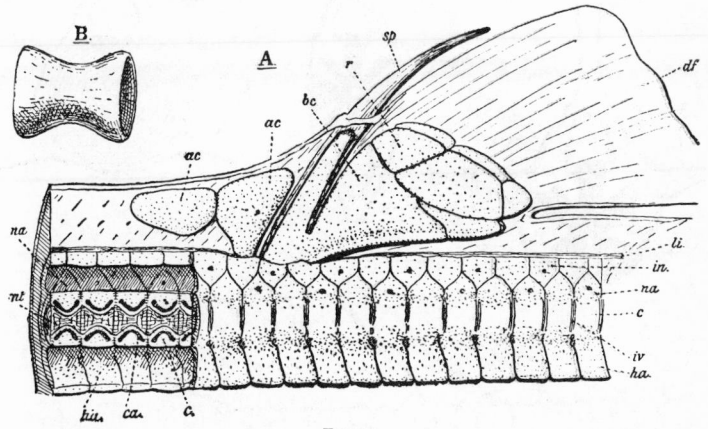

Fig. 24.

*Squalus vulgaris*, Risso. A, Dorsal fin and portion of the vertebral column, which has been cut through longitudinally in front. B, Calcified cylinder of a centrum. *ac*, Anterior cartilages (either modified radials or neural spines); *bc*, basal cartilage; *ca*, calcified cylinder; *df*, dorsal fin; *ha*, haemal arch; *in*, interdorsal; *iv*, intervertebral ligament; *li*, dorsal ligament; *na*, neural arch; *nt*, notochord; *sp*, fin spine, with base cut away to expose cartilage core; *r*, radial. The cartilage is dotted. (From Goodrich, *Vert. Craniata*, 1909.)

and the intervertebral rings wider, until the vertebral constrictions are reduced to septa separating large blocks of swollen partially liquefied notochord. In *Chlamydoselachus* the notochord is no longer constricted anteriorly, Fig. 27.

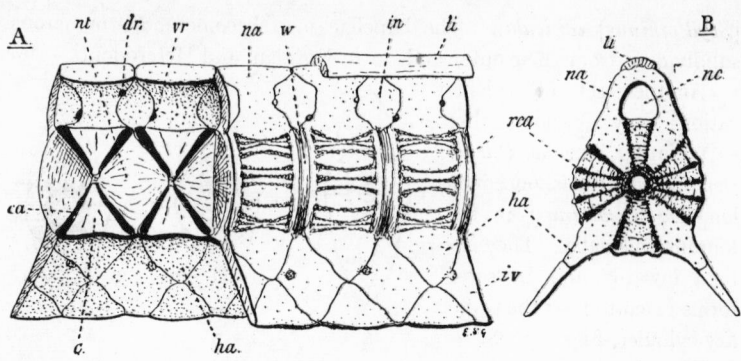

FIG. 25.

*Lamna cornubica*, Gm. A, Portion of the vertebral column of the trunk, partly cut longitudinally (right-side view); B, transverse section of the same through the middle of a centrum. *c*, Centrum; *ca*, calcareous constricted ring; *dr*, foramen for dorsal nerve-root; *ha*, basiventral; *in*, interdorsal; *iv*, interventral; *li*, ligament; *na*, basidorsal; *nc*, neural canal; *nt*, notochord; *rca*, radial calcifications; *vr*, foramen for ventral root; *w*, intervertebral ligament. (From Goodrich, *Vert. Craniata*, 1909.)

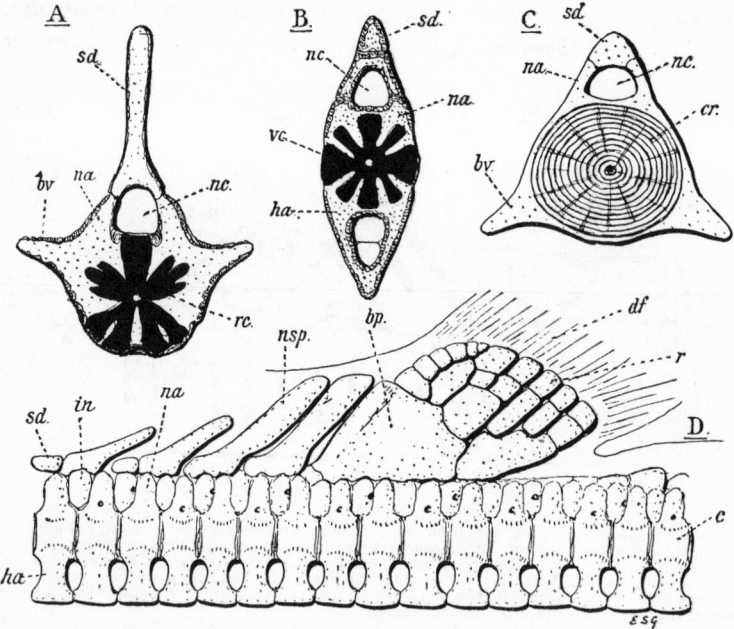

FIG. 26.

Transverse section through the centre of A, a trunk vertebra of *Raja*. B, A caudal vertebra of *Rhinobatus granulatus*, Cuv.; C, a trunk vertebra of *Rhina squatina*, L.; D, left-side view of a portion of the vertebral column, and of the skeleton of the first dorsal fin of *Rhina squatina*, L. *bp*, Basal; *bv*, basiventral (haemal arch); *c*, centrum; *cr*, calcareous ring; *df*, dorsal fin; *ha*, haemal arch; *in*, interdorsal; *na*, basidorsal (neural arch); *nc*, neural canal; *nsp*, supraneural spine (or anterior radial); *r*, distal end of radial; *rc* and *vc*, radiating calcification (black); *sd*, supradorsal. (From Goodrich, *Vert. Craniata*, 1909.)

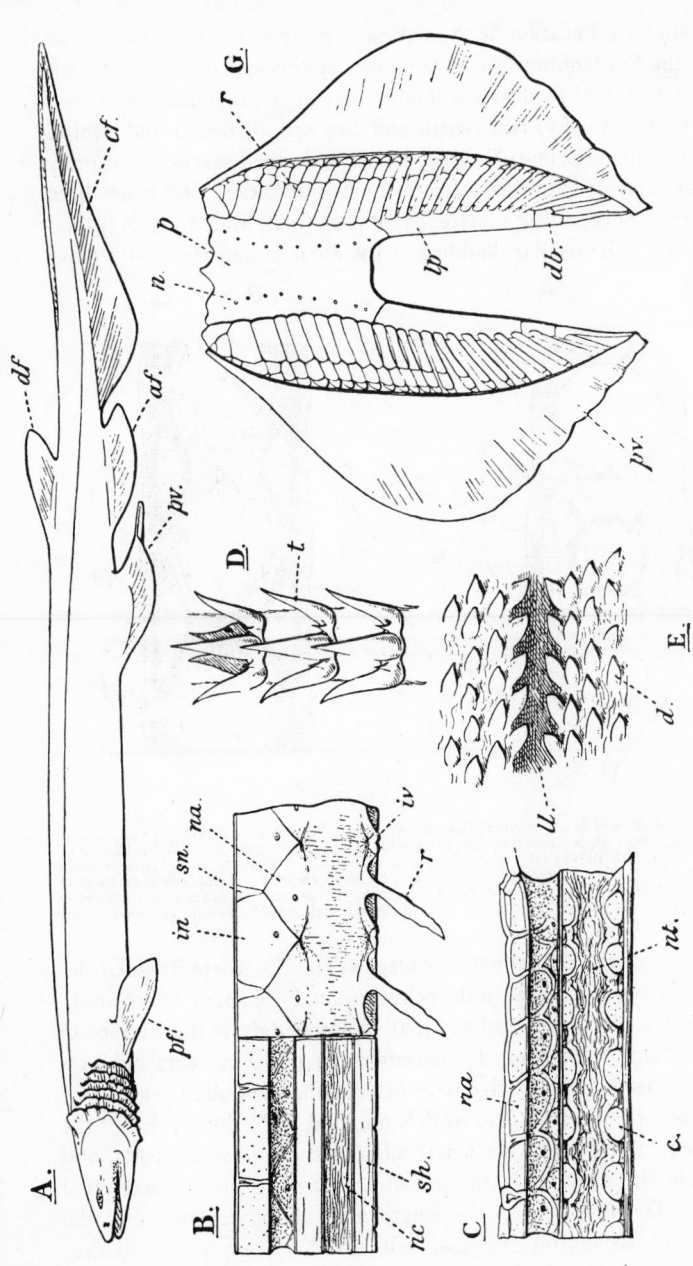

FIG. 27.

*Chlamydoselachus anguineus*, Garman. A, Left-side view of male; B, portion of vertebral column of trunk, part of which has been cut longitudinally (right-side view); C, longitudinal section of more anterior region; D, three teeth; E, lateral line; G, pelvic fins and girdle (ventral view). B, C, D, and E are modified from Garman. *af*, Anal fin; *c*, centrum; *cf*, caudal fin; *d*, denticle; *df*, dorsal fin; *in*, interdorsal; *iv*, interventral; *ll*, lateral-line groove; *p*, proximal segment of basipterygium; *n*, nerve foramen; *na*, neural arch; *nc*, notochord; *nt*, notochordal sheath; *sn*, supraneural; *t*, tooth.   (From Goodrich, *Vert. Craniata*, 1909.)

A strange modification of the normal structure occurs in the caudal region of the Elasmobranchs. It is known as diplospondyly, for here the number of vertebral segments is double that of the myomeres and their nerves; that is to say, two centra and two sets of dorsal and ventral arcualia correspond to one pair of myomeres and spinal nerves. Naturally this exceptional structure has attracted much attention, and it has been studied most successfully of late by Mayer (128), Ridewood (75), and Sečerov (84). The regular doubling of the arcualia and the centra takes

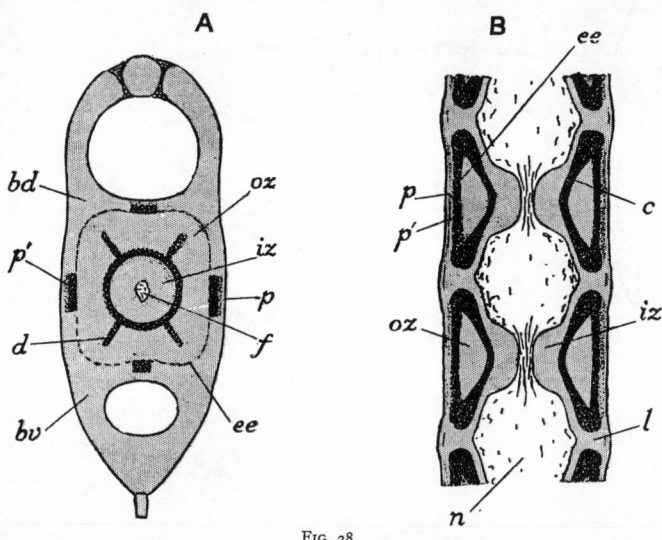

Fig. 28.

A, Transverse section of caudal vertebra from region of second dorsal fin of late embryo of *Mustelus vulgaris*, 286 mm. long ; B, horizontal section of vertebrae from same region (from W. G. Ridewood, *Tr. Roy. Soc.* 1921). *bd*, Basidorsal ; *bv*, basiventral ; *d*, diagonal calcified lamella ; *ee*, membrana elastica externa, outer limit of notochordal sheath ; *f*, funiculus chordae ; *iz*, inner-zone cartilage of sheath ; *l*, intervertebral ligament ; *n*, remains of notochord ; *ox*, and *oz*, outer-zone cartilage of sheath ; *p*, cartilaginous part of intermediale of perichondrial origin outside sheath ; *p'*, calcified part of same.

place throughout the caudal region, except at the tip, where irregularities occur, and the transition zone in the pelvic region, Figs. 20, 24, 26. A study of development shows conclusively that diplospondyly is due neither to a mere splitting of the ready-formed rudiment of the vertebra nor to a reduction by fusion of successive pairs of myotomes and disappearance of alternate pairs of nerves as held by Schauinsland. The duplication of the skeletal parts is related to the lengthening of the caudal segments, and judging from the structure of the transitional region seems to take place as follows. The first step is the lengthening of the centrum and the basidorsal and basiventral ; these arcualia are then transversely divided, and later a new interdorsal appears between the basidorsals. Lastly a centrum is formed in relation to each set of basalia. As the caudal segment lengthens the originally intersegmental vessels become separated. The artery remains in front, and the vein is shifted to the middle of the segment; the new interdorsal lies between them (E.S.G.). The transition may be abrupt as in *Squalus*, short but gradual as in *Scyllium*, or long as in *Hexanchus*, where several centra bear double sets of arches. The same phenomenon occurs in the Holocephali; but in these fish towards the tip of the tail the arcualia become small and very numerous, leading to an obviously secondary condition misleadingly called poly-spondyly. It is by lashing the tail from side to side that fish propel themselves, and 'diplo-spondyly' seems to secure greater flexibility for this purpose.

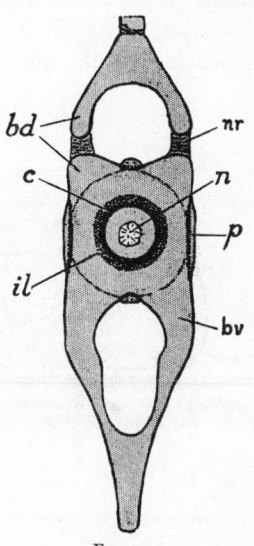

FIG. 29.

Transverse section of caudal vertebra of *Squalus acanthias* (from W. G. Ridewood, *Tr. Roy. Soc.* 1921). *c*, Primary double cone, calcification of middle zone of noto-chordal sheath; *il*, investing layer calcification; *nr*, nerve foramen; other letters as in Fig. 28.

The extreme tip of the column is much specialised. Here the arcualia become irregular and replaced by blocks of cartilage which tend to fuse to a continuous rod completely en-veloping and replacing the posterior extremity of the notochord. A similar modification is found to some extent in all Pisces, excepting those specialised Teleostei in which the verte-bral column is truncated in the adult (p. 113).

**Cyclostomata.**—We may now review the structure and development of the vertebral column in the Craniata generally. Dealing first with the Cyclostomata we find a per-sistent unconstricted notochord enclosed in the typical sheaths: elastica externa, and thick fibrous sheath. The mesoblastic cells outside form a connective tissue covering to the notochord and enclosing the neural canal as well as a longitudinal median dorsal space filled with fatty tissue above, and a haemal canal below in the tail, Fig. 30. There is no trace of centra;[1] but in the Petromyzontia the axial skeleton is represented by paired rods or arches resting on the notochordal sheath on either side of the neural canal (Parker, 67; Schneider, 81; Schauinsland, 78; Tretja-koff, 87-8).

Throughout the greater length of the trunk there are two pairs of such arches in every segment not meeting above, but passing vertically

[1] The doubtful traces described by Schauinsland in anterior segments scarcely deserve the name.

upwards in the anterior trunk region. They alternate regularly with the dorsal and ventral root nerves ; the posterior arch being approximately intersegmental, just behind the dorsal nerve and about on a level with the intersegmental blood-vessels, and the anterior arch just behind the ventral nerve. Schauinsland compares the posterior pair to the basidorsals and the anterior pair to the interdorsals of Gnathostomes. But in the Selachian it is the basidorsal or neural arch which lies between a dorsal nerve root in front and a ventral root behind, so it is more probable that the anterior cartilage (cranial of Schauinsland) is the

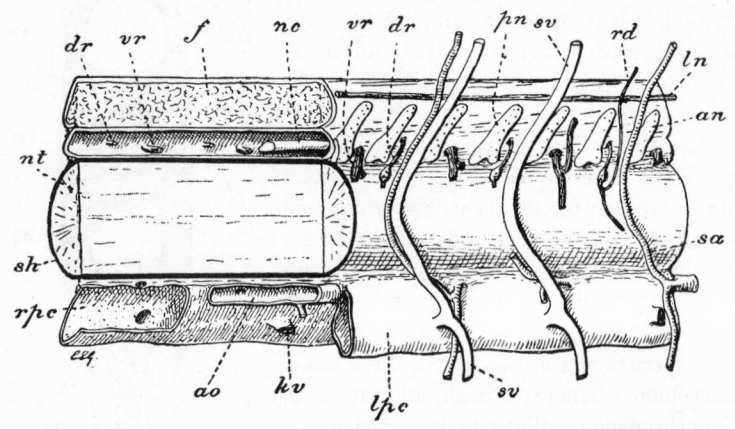

FIG. 30.

*Petromyzon marinus*, L. Left-side view of a portion of the notochord and neighbouring organs ; the left half has been removed by a median longitudinal section in the anterior region. *an*, neural arch (basidorsal ?) ; *ao*, dorsal aorta ; *dr*, dorsal nerve-root ; *f*, fatty tissue ; *kv*, kidney vein ; *ln*, lateral-line nerve ; *lpc*, left posterior cardinal vein ; *nc*, nerve-chord ; *nt*, notochord ; *pn*, interneural arch (interdorsal ?) ; *rd*, ramus dorsalis ; *rpc*, right posterior cardinal ; *sa*, segmental artery ; *sh*, notochordal sheath ; *sv*, segmental vein ; *vr*, ventral nerve-root. (From Goodrich, *Vert. Craniata*, 1909.)

homologue of the Gnathostome basidorsal ; moreover, it is the larger and more important of the two arches in *Petromyzon*. In the anterior region the anterior arches tend to fork at their base over the ventral nerves which they come to surround. (The first arch, perhaps formed of two fused arches, encloses the motor nerve to the fourth metaotic myomere and also the dorsal nerve in front of it in *P. fluviatilis*.) In the caudal region the arches dwindle in size, become irregular, tend to fuse to a continuous covering of the tip of the notochord, and come into connexion with the dorsal median fin supports. These are slender cartilaginous rods, Fig. 99, which in the hinder region of the caudal fin fork at their bases over the neural canal like neural arches and fuse to a longitudinal plate on each side. Similar median fin-supports occur in Myxinoidea (p. 97), but there are no true vertebral elements, Fig. 100. In this respect these Cyclostomes are possibly degenerate.

**Chondrichthyes.** — The diagram given in Fig. 20 illustrates the general morphology of the vertebral column in Selachians. Each vertebral segment is composed typically of paired basidorsals and interdorsals above and paired basiventrals and interventrals below, the basidorsals and basiventrals (intersegmental or vertebral in position) alone rest on the notochordal sheath, and the chordal centrum is formed intersegmentally in continuity with them as a complete ring. Typically, also, the basalia do not meet round the notochord, but perichordal cartilage may be added to the chordal centrum from skeletogenous tissue between their bases. Nevertheless, although the possession of chordal centra is so characteristic of the Selachii, it is not impossible that this condition is secondary and that they have been derived from ancestors with perichordal centra derived chiefly from the bases of the arcualia as in other Pisces. In this connexion it should be noticed that near the skull the basidorsals tend to meet the basiventrals forming a perichordal investment, and that in such an archaic form as Heterodontus they do so throughout the column.

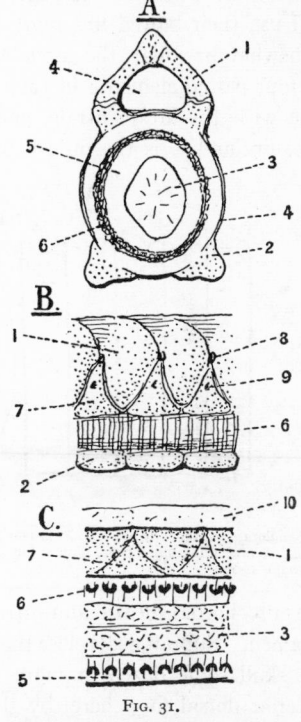

FIG. 31.

*Chimaera monstrosa*, L. Vertebral column : A, transverse section ; B, side view ; and C, longitudinal median section. (All after Hasse, slightly modified.) 1, Interdorsal ? ; 2, basiventral ; 3, notochord ; 4, elastica externa and connective tissue ; 5, fibrous sheath ; 6, calcified ring ; 7, basidorsal ? ; 8, dorsal nerve-root foramen ; 9, ventral nerve-root foramen ; 10, supradorsal. (From Goodrich, *Vert. Craniata*, 1909.)

The Holocephali (Hasse, 38 ; Klaatsch, 53 ; Schauinsland, 78), closely related to the Selachii, have a persistent and unconstricted notochord, Fig. 31. The thick fibrous sheath is invaded by mesoblastic cells through the ruptured elastica externa. Typical chordal centra are not developed ; but the cells spreading throughout the sheath form complete rings, which acquire a calcified bone-like structure in *Chimaera*, and are much more numerous than the segments. Such rings do not occur in *Callorhynchus* ; while in the extinct *Squaloraja* of the Lower Lias they are, on the contrary, very strong and closely packed, Fig. 32. It is possible that the Holocephali are descended from early ancestors with chordal centra like those of the Selachii, and that the rings have been formed by their duplication or subdivision. Their reduced condition or absence in modern forms is doubtless due to degeneration in fish which live in deep waters and use their paired fins more than their tails for swimming. Though somewhat irregular, the arcualia are developed, much as in Selachians, as four paired elements in each trunk segment. The basiventrals may fuse with the interventrals, and there are no ribs. As interpreted by Schauinsland it is the interdorsal only which reaches and spreads over

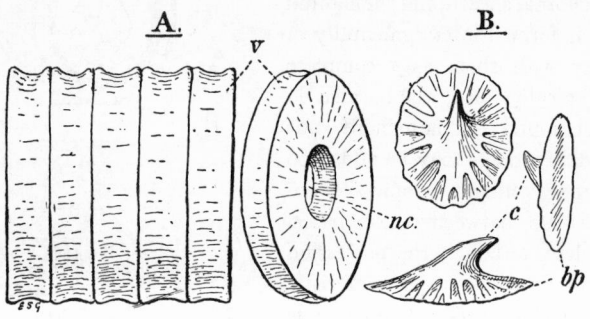

FIG. 32.

*Squaloraja polyspondyla*, Ag. Enlarged views of, A, vertebral rings; B, denticles. *bp*, Basal plate; *c*, projecting spine; *nc*, cavity for notochord; *v*, vertebral ring. (From Goodrich, *Vert. Craniata*, 1909.)

the notochordal sheath, and surrounds from behind the ventral nerve-root foramen. Supradorsals close the neural tube above. Immediately behind the skull some dozen or more vertebral segments are fused below the anterior dorsal fin; here, by the fusion of the dorsal with the ventral arcualia round the notochord and of the consecutive cartilages with each other, is formed a rigid continuous perichordal cartilage enclosing both nerve-cord and notochord, and stretching upwards into a process articulating with the cartilage of the fin-base. Numerous nerve apertures betray its compound nature, and in the extinct *Squaloraja* and *Myriacanthus* other traces of segmentation appear in it (Dean, 17). The same doubling of the skeletal elements takes place in the segments of the tail region as in Selachians.

The structure of the vertebral column in the extinct groups of Chondrichthyes is but imperfectly known. The Pleuracanthodii, Cladoselachii, and Acanthodii seem all to have had a persistent unconstricted notochord without centra. Basidorsals and basiventrals bearing ribs are well developed in *Pleuracanthus*, but the interdorsals and interventrals are small (Brongniart). Basidorsals and basiventrals have been described in *Cladoselache* (Dean, 154) and in Acanthodians.

**Dipnoi.**—Modern Dipnoi have a persistent notochord provided with an elastica externa and a thick fibrous sheath. The latter is invaded by mesoblastic cells (p. 11) to a considerable extent, yet complete chordal centra are never formed so as to constrict the notochord as in Selachians, Figs. 10 and 33. But in *Ceratodus* it is pushed alternately from above and below by the cartilaginous masses growing inwards from the basidorsals and basiventrals (Goodrich, 35). Well-developed somewhat irregular interdorsals appear in the tail of *Ceratodus*, but elsewhere they are probably fused

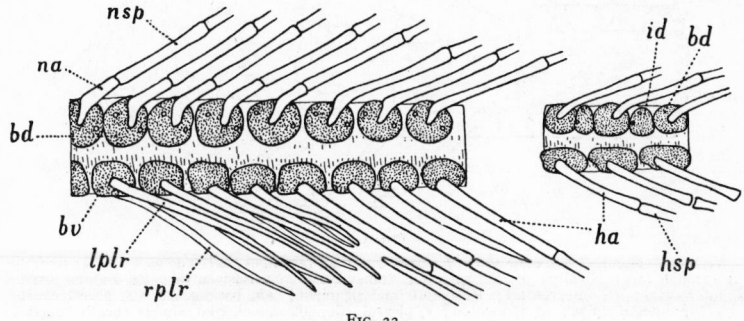

FIG. 33.

*Ceratodus Forsteri.* Left-side view of vertebral column of posterior trunk, anterior and middle caudal regions. *bd,* Basidorsal cartilage ; *bv,* basiventral cartilage ; *ha,* haemal arch ; *hsp,* infra-haemal spine ; *lplr,* and *rplr,* left and right pleural ribs ; *na,* neural arch ; *nsp,* supraneural spine.

with the bases of the large basidorsals. Similarly the large basiventrals probably include the interventrals. The basidorsals meet above and below the longitudinal ligament ; and since, except at the extreme ends of the column, they do not meet the basiventrals the notochordal sheath remains exposed at the sides. The enlarged bases of basidorsals and basiventrals remain cartilaginous, but the slender neural and haemal arches are ossified. The vertebral column of the modern genera is probably degenerate.

**Teleostomi.**—The centra of the Teleostomi are of the perichordal type (p. 12). Usually well developed in the higher forms, they strongly constrict the notochord and its sheaths. No centra, however, occur in living Chondrostei, where the notochord is persistent and unconstricted, passes uninterruptedly into the base of the skull, and is surrounded by a thick fibrous sheath (slightly invaded, p. 11). An absence of centra is characteristic of some of the earlier and extinct groups of Teleostomes which apparently retained an unconstricted notochord (Coelacanthini, Pycnodontidae). In many of the extinct Osteolepidoti centra seem to have been absent, though they occur as ossified rings in *Megalichthys*, and as paired wedge-shaped pieces in Eusthenopteron (Bryant, 465). In many of the earlier Amioidei the centra are absent (*Hypsocormus, Caturus* (A. S. Woodward, 663)) or but slightly developed as thin rings. They rarely occur in Palaeoniscoidei, where, however, traces of centra have been described in some genera (*Pygopterus, Phanerosteon* (Traquair 616,

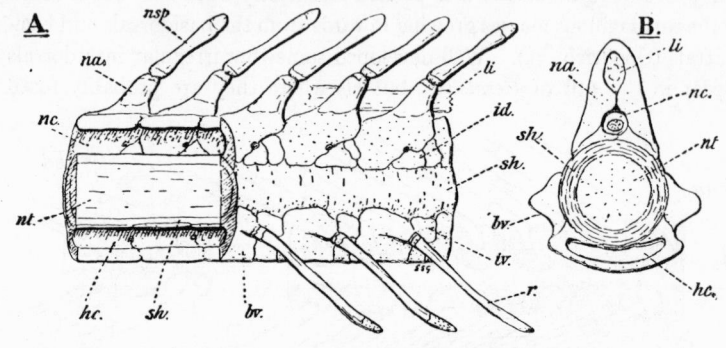

FIG. 34.

Vertebral column of *Acipenser sturio*, L., from the trunk region. A, Left-side view of a piece partly cut through longitudinally; B, the same cut transversely. *bv*, Basiventral; *h.c*, haemal canal; *id*, interdorsal; *iv*, interventral; *li*, longitudinal ligament; *na*, basidorsal; *n.c*, neural canal; *n.sp*, supraneural spine; *nt*, notochord; *r*, pleural rib; *sh*, notochordal fibrous sheath bounded outside by the elastica externa. (From Goodrich, *Vert. Craniata*, 1909.)

Fritsch, 23)). The absence or slight development of centra in these various groups is probably due to degeneration.

The vertebrae of the adult Polypterini are very thoroughly ossified. The larva of *Polypterus* shows cartilaginous basidorsals and basiventrals, but no interbasals. Anteriorly the basiventrals seem to be subdivided into separate elements bearing the dorsal and the pleural ribs (Budgett, 10, p. 73).

The arcualia, on the other hand, are usually well formed and occur as ossified basidorsals (neural arches) and basiventrals (haemal arches) in Coelacanthini, some Osteolepidoti, and the Actinopterygii generally. The modern Chondrostei have basals and interbasals well represented. The large and partly ossified basidorsals meet below and above the dorsal ligament, and may bear supraneural spines. Interdorsals are present, wedged between their bases. Below basiventrals alternate with interventrals and their haemal processes enclose the dorsal aorta, Figs. 34 and 132*a*. As a sign of degeneration it may be noted that these cartilages are often irregular and tend to be secondarily subdivided.[1]

[1] In the Belonorhynchidae, which are probably Chondrostei related to the Acipenseridae (Stensiö, 134), there are no centra; but the early Triassic

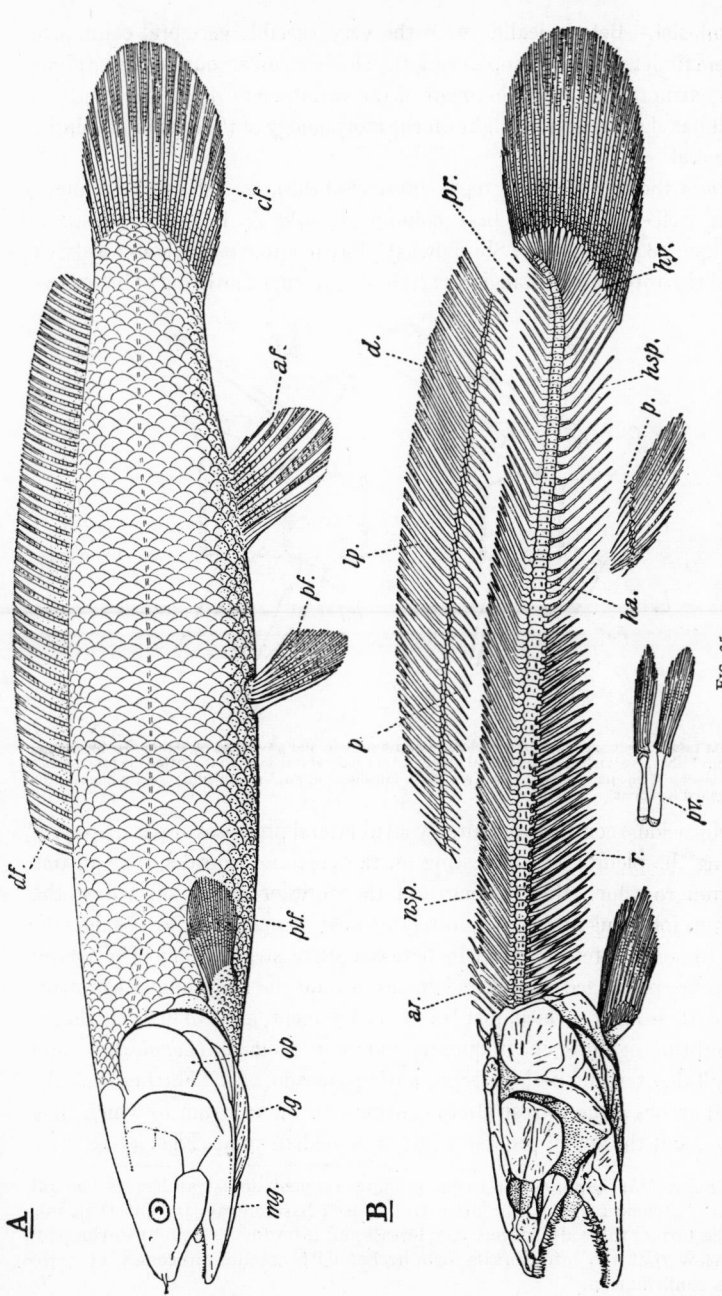

FIG. 35.

*Amia calva*, L. A after Brown Goode, slightly altered; B after Franque, slightly altered. *af*, Anal fin; *ar*, anterior dorsal radials (?); *cf*, caudal fin (hypochordal); *d*, distal segment of dorsal radial; *ha*, haemal arch; *hsp*, haemal spine; *hy*, hypural arches; *lg*, lateral gulars; *lp*, lepidotrichia; *mg*, median gular; *nsp*, neural spine; *op*, operculum; *p*, proximal segment of radial; *pf*, pelvic fin; *pr*, posterior dorsal radials; *pvf*, pectoral fin; *pv*, pelvic bone; *r*, pleural rib. (From Goodrich, *Vert. Craniata*, 1909.)

**Holostei.**—Before dealing with the very variable vertebral column in the remainder of the Actinopterygii, the Holostei, an account must be given of the structure and development of the vertebrae in *Amia*, the study of which has shed important light on the morphology of the vertebral column in general.

*Amia*, the only surviving representative of the large Sub-order Amioidei, has a well - ossified vertebral column remarkable in several respects (Franque, 1847; Zittel, 98; Shuffelt, 85). Passing from before backwards, we find in the anterior trunk region vertebral segments consisting of biconcave

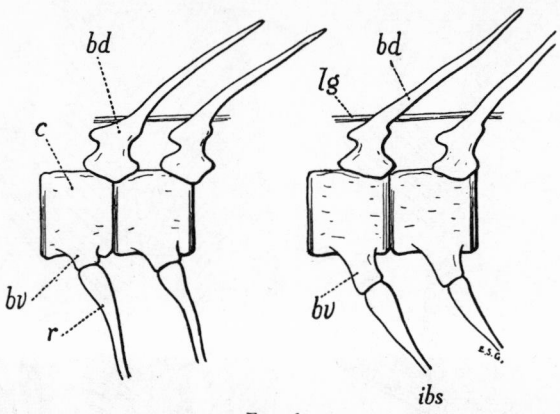

FIG. 36.

*Amia calva.* Left side view of vertebrae 7 and 8 on left, and 30 and 31 on right. In the former the pleural rib, *r*, is attached to the lateral process of the basiventral, *bv.* In the latter the basiventrals join to enclose a haemal canal and bear a median infrahaemal, *ibs.* *c*, Centrum; *bd*, basidorsal; *lg*, longitudinal ligament.

(amphicoelous) centra with paired ventro-lateral processes or parapophyses bearing the pleural ribs. Resting on the posterior dorsal surface of one centrum to which they belong and the anterior dorsal surface of the centrum following are the separately ossified neural arches or basidorsals, thus to some extent wedged in between successive centra. The neural arches are prolonged into paired spines beyond the longitudinal ligament, and on their inner surface, just below the ligament, are two little cartilages of doubtful significance, frequently found in Holostei (*Lepidosteus*, and many Teleostei) and perhaps representing supradorsals. Farther back the neural arches come to rest almost entirely on the centrum to which they belong, and the spinal processes fuse to a median spine, Figs. 35-40.

---

form *Saurichthys ornatus* has twice as many ossified dorsal arches as ventral arches. Stensio believes the latter to be fused basiventrals and interventrals and the former to be alternately basidorsals and interdorsals equally developed. This view that the interdorsals form arches with spinous processes, etc., requires confirmation.

In the caudal region below each pair of neural arches is a pair of haemal arches, separately ossified and at first bearing a separate median

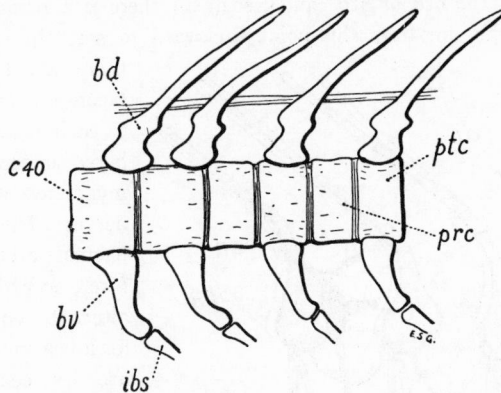

FIG. 37.

*Amia calva*: left side view of caudal vertebrae. *c40*, centrum of fortieth vertebra; *ibs*, median infrahaemal; *prc*, precentrum; *ptc*, postcentrum.

haemal spine, which soon becomes continuous with the fused arches farther back. Finally, in the posterior upturned region the haemal

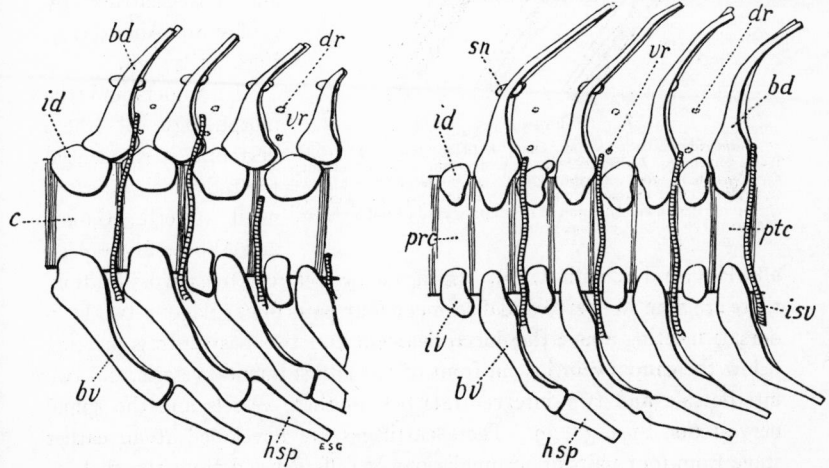

FIG. 38.

*Amia calva*, about 45 mm. long, cartilaginous stage: left side view of anterior (on left) and posterior caudal regions of vertebral column. *bv*, basiventral; *hsp*, infrahaemal spine. Other lettering as in Figs. 37, 39.

arches themselves fuse with their centra, Fig. 35. Throughout the column dorsal and ventral spinal nerve-roots issue through the gap between successive pairs of neural arches which are intersegmental in position and have the transverse septa attached to them, Fig. 39.

At about the 6th or 7th caudal segment there is a remarkable and sudden change, for from this point backward to near the extreme tip

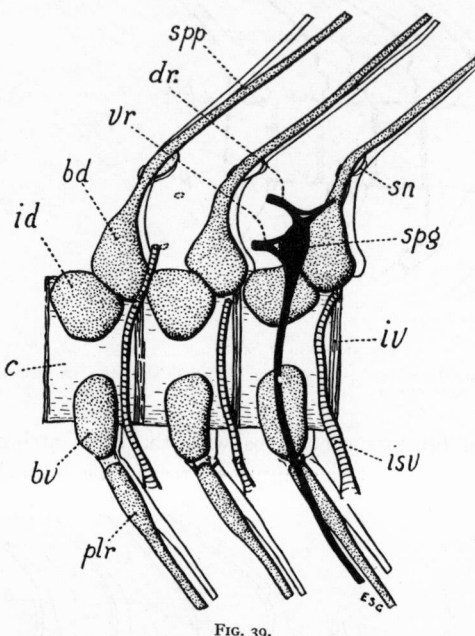

there are two similar biconcave bony centra to each segment of the body, as shown by the myomeres and spinal nerves. The neural and haemal arches, there-fore, occur on every alternate centrum.[1] The arch-bearing and the arch-less centrum have been called respectively centrum and intercent-rum by Schmidt (80), pleuro- and hypo-cent-rum by Hay (45), pre- and post-centrum by Gadow and Abbott (27), Figs. 35, 37, 38.

To understand the morphology of these vertebrae it is essential to study their develop-ment (Goette, Gadow and Abbott, and especi-

Fig. 39.

*Amia calva*, about 45 mm. long; left-side view of 3 anterior trunk vertebrae. *bd*, Basidorsal; *bv*, basiventral; *c*, bony centrum; *dr*, dorsal nerve-root; *id*, interdorsal; *isv*, intersegmental artery; *iv*, intervertebral ligament; *plr*, left pleural rib; *sn*, supradorsal; *spg*, spinal ganglion; *spp*, paired spinal process of neural arch; *vr*, ventral nerve-root. Cartilage dotted.

ally Hay, and Schauinsland). In the young, before extensive ossification, there are seen in every caudal segment four pairs of cartilages : two basi-dorsals meeting above the dorsal ligament and two basiventrals meeting below the caudal vein just in front of the intersegmental vessels, and two interdorsals and two interventrals behind these vessels and the spinal nerve-roots, Figs. 38, 39. These cartilages are developed at an earlier stage from four pairs of accumulations of cells derived from the skeleto-genous layer. The interventrals disappear as separate elements in the anterior caudal region, becoming fused with the basiventrals from this

[1] Many irregularities may occur in the fusion of the elements of the vertebral column. In the tail an arch-bearing centrum may occasionally fuse with the arch-less centrum in front, or that behind, or with both.

point forwards.    Passing towards the head the interdorsals become
wedged from in front below the basidorsals which succeed them.    Ossification begins, according to Hay, as a thin layer on the neural arches,
and on the bases of the interdorsals, basiventrals, and interventrals of
the tail.    Later the separate ossifications on the interdorsals and basi-

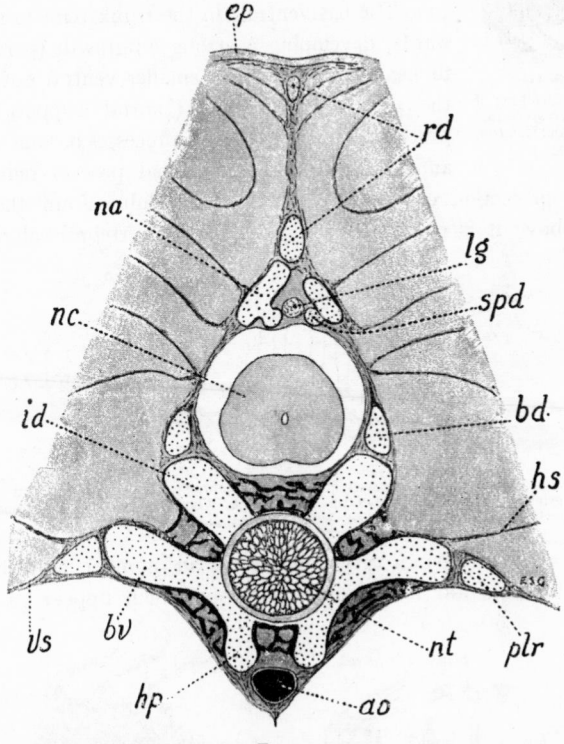

FIG. 40.

Transverse section of *Amia calva*, about 60 mm. long, anterior trunk region.  *ao*, Dorsal aorta ;
*bd*, basidorsal ; *bv*, basiventral ; *ep*, epidermis ;  *hp*, haemal process ;  *hs*, horizontal septum ;  *id*,
interdorsal ; *lg*, longitudinal ligament ;  *na*, dorsal end of neural arch (basidorsal) ;  *nc*, nerve cord ;
*nt*, notochord surrounded by fibrous sheath and elastica externa ;  *plr*, pleural rib ;  *rd*, radial ;  *spd*,
supradorsal ; *vs*, wall of splanchnocoele.   Cartilage dotted, bone in black.

ventrals of the trunk region spread and join to a complete cylindrical
centrum.    In that region of the tail where two ' centra ' exist in each
segment, separate ossifications appear at the base of each of the four
paired cartilaginous elements, and also on the projecting neural and
haemal arches.    The ' post-centrum ' is formed by the fusion to a
complete ring of the basal ossifications of the basidorsals and basiventrals ; the arch-less ' pre-centrum ' by the fusion to a complete ring

of the basal ossifications of the interdorsals and interventrals. Thus the adult bony centra are of compound origin.

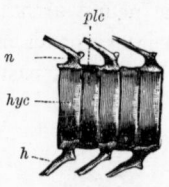

As the bony centra thicken outwards the bases of the cartilaginous elements remain embedded in the bone, and show in transverse section as cartilaginous wedges reaching to near the notochordal sheath, Fig. 40. The basiventrals in the trunk tend to spread upwards, developing a strong outgrowth (parapophysis) to bear the ribs and a smaller ventral outgrowth at the side of the aorta ('aortal support', haemal process). Later these two processes become separated, and the cartilaginous haemal process remains as a ventral projection of the centrum in the adult. From the account given above it is clear that the parts of the vertebral column of the

FIG. 41.

Caudal vertebrae of *Eurycormus speciosus*, Wagn. (From K.Zittel, *Palaeontology*.)

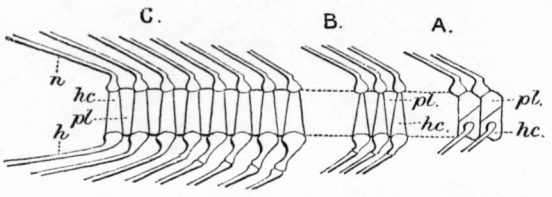

FIG. 42.

*Eurycormus speciosus*: A, Foremost abdominal vertebrae; B, posterior abdominal vertebrae; C, caudal vertebrae. U. Jurassic: Bavaria. (From A. S. Woodward, *Vertebrate Palaeontology*, 1898.) *h*, Haemal arches; *hc*, 'hypocentra'; *n*, neural arches; *pl*, 'pleurocentra'.

adult *Amia* correspond very imperfectly in number and disposition to the fundamental four paired elements which appear as separate

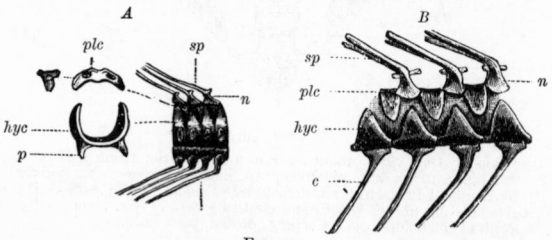

FIG. 43.

Vertebrae of *Euthynotus* (*A*), and *Caturus furcatus*, Ag. (*B*). *c*, Rib; *hyc*, hypocentrum; *n*, neural arch; *p*, parapophysis; *plc*, pleurocentrum; *sp*, cleft neural spine. (From K. Zittel, *Palaeontology*.)

cartilages in the young. In the formation of a complete single vertebral segment the basal elements become associated and fused with the inter-basal elements lying anteriorly to them. If this association holds good in other Teleostomes (which has not yet been satisfactorily proved), there is a fundamental difference between the vertebra of a Teleostome

and that of a Tetrapod, since, in the latter, the basal elements combine
with the interbasal elements lying behind them.

Certain Jurassic Amioids have, as in *Amia*, two complete centra in
each caudal segment, but farther forward these become reduced to
alternate dorsal and ventral crescents which remain distinct even near the
skull although combining to form one vertebral segment, Fig. 44 (Zittel,
98; Woodward, 663, 665; Schmidt, 80; Goette, 32; Hay, 45). *Caturus*
shows perhaps the most primitive condition (Zittel); here each vertebral

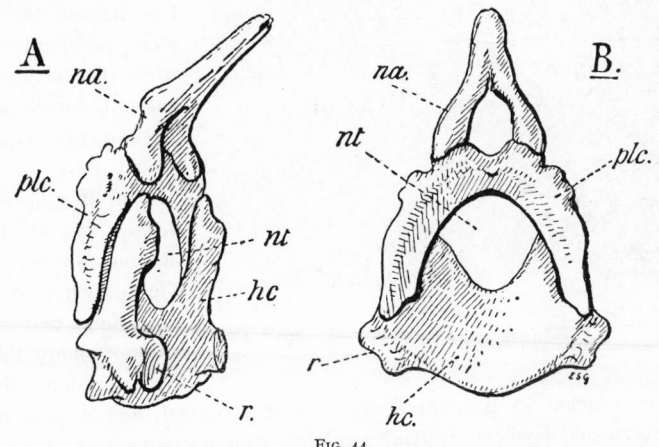

FIG. 44.

Vertebra of *Osteorhachis leedsi*, A. S. W.; Oxford Clay, Peterborough. A, Oblique side view
from behind; B, front view. *hc*, hypocentrum; *na*, neural arch; *nt*, aperture for notochord;
*plc*, pleurocentrum; *r*, parapophysis for rib. (From Goodrich, *Vert. Craniata*, 1909.)

segment of both trunk and tail shows an anterior dorsal and a posterior
ventral crescent embracing the notochordal space, Figs. 43 B, 44. Between
the former interdorsal crescents are wedged the neural arches; while the
ventral (basiventral) crescents bear parapophyses in the trunk and haemal
arches in the tail. But in the mid-caudal region of *Caturus heterurus* the
four typical elements are separately ossified in each segment (E.S.G.).[1]
*Eurycormus* has in the tail alternate arch-bearing and arch-less centra
round the notochord; but in the trunk the interdorsal anterior elements
remain crescentic, and the neural arches tend to shift on to them, Figs.
41 and 42. The fusion of the interdorsal anterior crescent with the posterior
crescent or ring would give rise to the condition seen in the trunk of
*Amia*. In *Hypsocormus* only the arches are ossified, Figs. 45, 46.

[1] In the posterior caudal region of this fish the interdorsal and interventral
elements are no longer ossified, and each vertebral segment has a dorsal crescent
formed by the basidorsals and a ventral crescent by the basiventrals, recalling
the structure of the vertebral column in Pycnodontidae.

In conclusion it may be said that the bony vertebral segment of the Amioidei seems to have been laid down on the four original paired elements

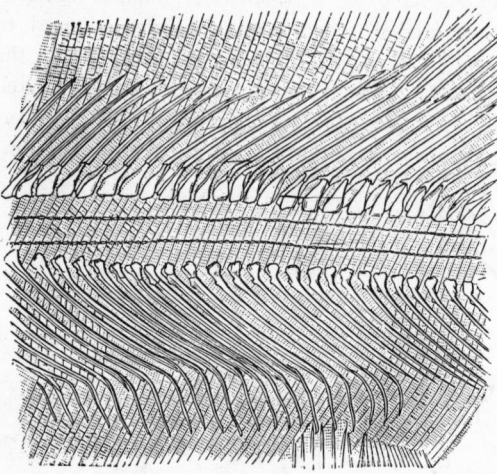

already recognised in the Selachian; that from the basidorsals are developed the neural arches and from the basiventrals the haemal arches and parapophyses, while the cartilaginous interdorsals and interventrals remain small (the interventral disappearing in the trunk) and become buried in the growing bony centrum; that an anterior bony crescent develops dorsally in relation to the interdorsal and interventral, and a posterior bony crescent develops ventrally related to the basiventral; that in the tail the two crescents form complete rings in the more advanced

FIG. 45.

*Hypsocormus insignis*, Wagn. Portion of trunk. Upper Jurassic (Lithographic Stone); Eichstädt, Bavaria. (From K. Zittel, *Palaeontology*.)

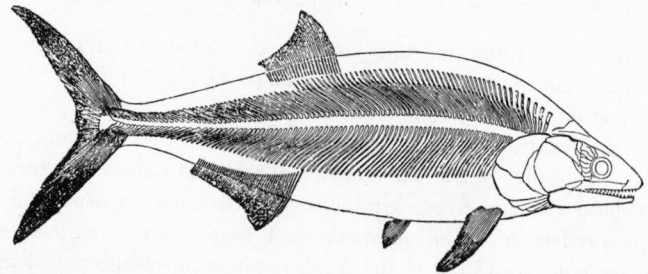

FIG. 46.

*Hypsocormus insignis*: restoration, scales omitted. U. Jurassic: Bavaria. (From A. S. Woodward, *Vertebrate Palaeontology*, 1898.)

Amioids; and lastly that in the anterior tail and trunk-region of *Amia* they are represented by a single centrum (showing, however, no signs of a compound origin in the adult). In the Aspidorhynchidae, according to Zittel (98), annular centra occur bearing neural and haemal arches.

The vertebrae of *Lepidosteus* are unique among fishes in being opisthocoelous, the centrum having a convex anterior face fitting into a concavity of the centrum in front (Gegenbaur, 30; Balfour and Parker, 2; Gadow and Abbott, 27; Schauinsland, 78). The notochord becomes completely constricted intervertebrally. The neural arches are continuous with the centra, and in the trunk separate neural spines rest on the dorsal ligament below which are supradorsal cartilages. The development has been studied by Balfour and Parker, and Gadow and Abbott. The notochordal sheaths are thin and in later stages the notochord is almost obliterated. In the young separate basidorsals and basiventrals appear, the latter meeting below the haemal canal in the caudal region. The slight vertebral constriction of the notochord due to these basalia is soon obliterated by the pronounced intervertebral constriction brought about by the development of a wide cartilaginous ring formed apparently by the coalesced interdorsals and interventrals. As usual in the Holostei, supradorsal cartilages appear at the sides of the dorsal ligament

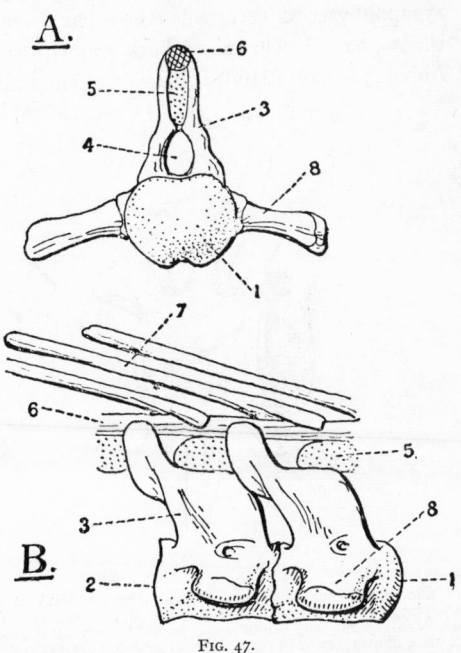

FIG. 47.

*Lepidos eus osseus*, L. A, Vertebra from in front; B, vertebral column of trunk, right-side view. (After Balfour and Parker.) 1, Convex anterior surface of centrum; 2, concave posterior surface of centrum; 3, neural arch (basidorsal); 4, neural canal; 5, supradorsal cartilage; 6, longitudinal ligament; 7, neural spine; 8, transverse process of centrum (parapophysis). (From Goodrich, *Vert. Craniata*, 1909.)

between the neural arches. The opisthocoelous joint is carved out of the intervertebral ring which becomes divided into anterior and posterior portions; these are ossified in continuity with the outer vertebral cylinder, Fig. 47.

The Teleostei usually have well-developed amphicoelous bony centra strongly constricting the notochord and its sheaths, Fig. 11. These remain thin vertebrally but thicken intervertebrally, contributing to the usual strong intervertebral ligament an inner layer or ligamentum intervertebrale internum of Kölliker (1864). The vertebrae show great variety in detail within the group, but the centra are always simple and interseg-mental in the adult.

Special intervertebral articulations are formed by anterior processes from the neural or haemal arches which rest on corresponding processes in front, and these may be supplemented or replaced by dorsal and ventral processes from the centra themselves, analogous to the pre- and post-zygapophyses of Tetrapods (Gegenbaur, 270; Goette, 32; v. Ebner, 20; Ussow, 90; Bruch, 1862; Lotz, 57; Grassi, 37; Scheel, 79; Gadow and Abbott; Schauinsland). Basidorsal and basiventral cartilages rest on the

### A.     B.

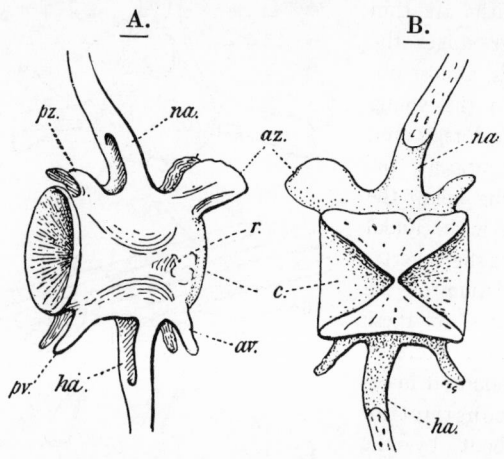

FIG. 48.

Caudal vertebrae of *Thynnus vulgaris* (Cuv. and Val.) A, Right-side view; B, left-side view of the same cut in half. *av*, Anterior ventral process; *az*, anterior "zygapophysis"; *c*, centrum; *ha*, haemal arch; *na*, neural arch; *pv*, posterior ventral process; *pz*, posterior "zygapophysis"; *r*, place of attachment of rib. (From Goodrich, *Vert. Craniata*, 1909.)

notochordal sheath in the young, Fig. 11; but interbasals do not usually appear at all, though traces of interventrals occasionally have been found (*Salmo fario*, Schauinsland). Supradorsal cartilages usually appear between the neural arches as in other Holostei, Figs. 48, 49, 50.

According to Schauinsland the vertebra is really formed by the coalescence of an anterior half (developed in relation to the basalia) and a posterior half (developed in relation to the interbasalia) derived from the sclerotome of the segment behind. He claims that in *Fistularia* where the nerves issue through the neural arches these two halves develop similar arches both dorsal and ventral. Though this interpretation of the bisegmental origin of the Teleostean vertebra is possibly correct, the absence of clearly developed interbasals in the types hitherto studied makes it difficult to verify.

The Teleostean bony centrum itself usually shows no trace of compound origin, but develops as a cylinder embracing the arcualia. The bases of the basalia do not, as a rule, join round the notochord to form a complete vertebral ring, and may remain as four conspicuous radiating cartilages in the adult centrum (as in *Esox*, Fig. 49 B). Following the general tendency towards a reduction of cartilage in the Holostei, and the direct development of bony tissue without a preceding cartilaginous

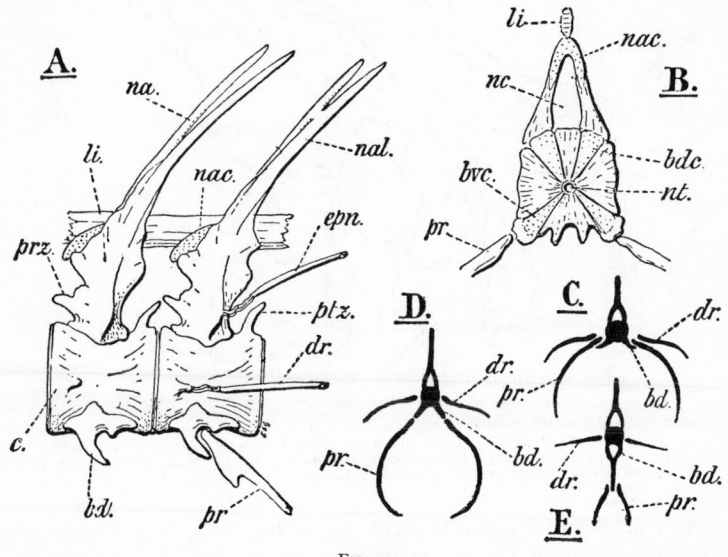

Fig. 49.

A, Left-side view of two trunk vertebrae of *Esox lucius*, L. B, Vertical median section of the same ; D, C, and E, *Thynnus vulgaris*, Cuv. ; C, anterior trunk region ; D, posterior trunk region ; E, caudal region. *bd*, Basiventral (haemal arch) ; *bdc*, basidorsal cartilage ; *bvc*, basiventral cartilage ; *c*, centrum ; *dr*, dorsal rib (epipleural) ; *epn*, epineural ; *li*, longitudinal ligament ; *na*, basidorsal (neural arch) ; *nac*, supradorsal cartilage ; *nal*, left neural arch ; *nc*, neural canal ; *nt*, notochord ; *pr*, pleural rib ; *prz*, anterior articulating process ; *ptz*, posterior articulating process. (From Goodrich, *Vert. Craniata*, 1909.)

stage, the bony centrum appears early as a thin cylinder which thickens rapidly outwards. Later on a thin layer of cartilage may extend from the basalia between the bone and the elastica externa as in *Amia*—a vestige perhaps of an ancestral cartilaginous centrum. In *Rhodeus*, however, the basidorsals join the basiventrals at the sides, forming a cartilaginous ring of considerable thickness interrupted above and below (Scheel, **79**).

Ossification may extend from the centrum over the basalia, the neural and haemal arches being then continuous with the centrum as in most of the higher Teleostei and the tail region of even the lower forms. But in the trunk of some of the Cypriniformes, Esociformes, and Clupeiformes

the basiventrals and even the basidorsals (*Esox*) may be separately ossified and remain distinct in the adult—presumably a more primitive but
less efficient condition, Fig 49.

Concerning the general morphology of the vertebrae in the Teleostomi
it may be said that, although the four fundamental paired elements may

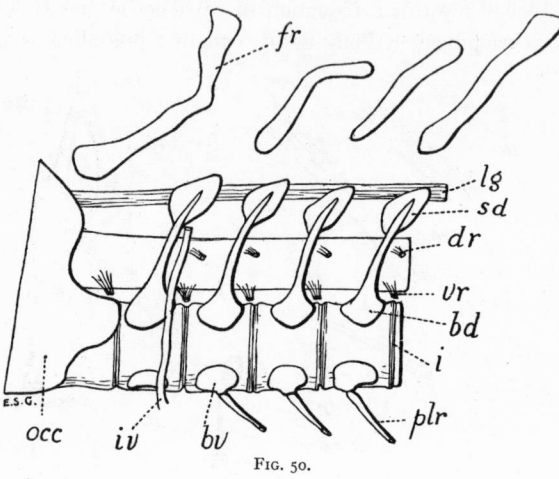

FIG. 50.

Anterior region of vertebral column of *Salmo truta*, 35 mm. long.  Left-side view.  *bd*, Basidorsal;
*bv*, basiventral; *dr*, dorsal nerve-root; *fr*, radial (?); *i*, intervertebral ligament between thin bony
centra; *iv*, intersegmental artery; *lg*, longitudinal ligament; *occ*, occipital cartilage; *plr*, pleural
rib; *sd*, supradorsal cartilage; *vr*, ventral nerve-root.

often be made out as separate cartilages in the young, they tend to take
less and less share in the formation of the adult centrum.  The latter in
the form of an intersegmental biconcave bony cylinder develops chiefly
in the skeletogenous layer surrounding the notochordal sheaths; this is
in accordance with the general tendency throughout the endoskeleton of
these fishes for the cartilage to be reduced even in development, and for
the bone to be formed more and more directly and precociously from
skeletogenous tissue.

Reviewing the structure of the vertebrae in Pisces generally, it appears
that although the four fundamental paired arcualia may be traced with
considerable certainty in all the large groups, yet the part played by
the individual elements varies greatly.  For instance, in the Selachii the
interdorsals take no share in the formation of the centrum, but in the
trunk of *Amia* they contribute greatly to its structure while the basidorsals are excluded.  Again, in the Teleostei, it is the basidorsal which
together with the basiventral is the important element.  The interdorsal, extending primarily between the ventral and dorsal roots of a

spinal nerve are liable to be interrupted and hindered in development ; hence the main element of the neural arch is always the basidorsal.  It will be gathered from the above account that a good deal more work is required before the history of the centrum in the various groups can be satisfactorily described.

## THE VERTEBRAL COLUMN OF TETRAPODA

The morphology of the vertebral column of the Tetrapoda may be studied from two points of view : with the help of comparative anatomy and palaeontology we may attempt to reconstruct its phylogenetic history in the adult, or we may try to determine the homology of its parts by following their development in existing forms.  The interpretation of the embryological facts is, however, difficult, since most modern Tetrapods are specialised and have departed along divergent lines from the primitive structure.

In adaptation to progression by means of walking limbs there is an increasing tendency for the body of the terrestrial vertebrates to become differentiated into well-defined head, neck, trunk, and tail regions, mainly determined by the position of the limbs and their girdles.  The slender neck lifts and moves the head, the trunk contains the coelomic cavities and viscera, and the tail becomes narrow and tapering.  Corresponding variations of structure occur in the vertebral column which becomes differentiated into regions whose limits are arbitrarily defined for descriptive purposes.  The cervical vertebrae are typically very movable and bear small ribs.  Between pectoral and pelvic regions are the trunk vertebrae (' dorsal ', or thoracico-lumbar vertebrae) with ribs well developed anteriorly where they reach the sternum, but dwindling posteriorly.  The pelvic girdle becomes attached to the sacral vertebrae by means of stout, short, sacral ribs.  In Mammalia and some of the higher Reptilia a few of the trunk vertebrae in front of the sacral may lose their ribs more or less completely, and are then distinguished as lumbar from the more anterior thoracic vertebrae.  In the tail the ribs tend to disappear and the vertebrae become simplified and reduced towards the tip.  In no region of the column is there any trace of separate supraspinal elements above the neural arches, or of infraspinal elements below the haemal arches, such as occur in Pisces.

In general build a typical trunk vertebra consists of a body or centrum and a neural arch, with which are associated a pair of ribs (p. 75).  The two halves of the arch join above the longitudinal ligament to a median dorsal spine, and bear paired pre- and postzygapophyses with which they articulate with neighbouring arches,[1] and paired lateral transverse processes (diapophyses). The capitulum of the rib articulates at the anterior intercentral region, and the tuberculum at the end of the diapophysis. The arch and ribs are essentially intersegmental; the fibrous intervertebral discs uniting consecutive centra are segmental. The spinal nerves issue behind the neural arches.[2] Muscular segments

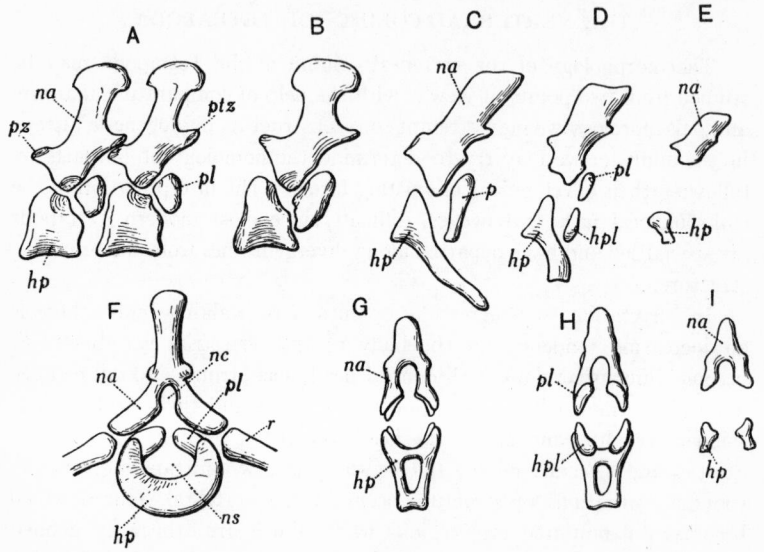

FIG. 51.

Diagram of rhachitomous vertebrae of *Archegosaurus* (chiefly from Jaekel, 1896). Left-side view of anterior thoracic A, posterior trunk B, anterior caudal C, and more posterior caudal vertebrae D and E. F anterior view of A. G anterior and H posterior view of D. I anterior view of E. *hp*, Hypocentrum (basiventral); *hpl*, hypocentrum pleurale (interventral); *na*, neural arch (basidorsal); *nc*, neural canal; *ns*, space for notochord; *pl*, pleurocentrum (interdorsal); *ptz*, postzygapophysis; *pz*, prezygapophysis; *r*, rib.

and vertebrae alternate, and as always in vertebrates one muscular segment is connected to two vertebral segments.

**Amphibia.**—Important evidence regarding the morphology of the

[1] Additional articular processes have been developed in various groups with long flexible vertebral column. A projecting zygosphene above the prezygapophysis fitting into a zygantrum above the postzygapophysis occurs not only in all Ophidia, but also in certain Lacertilia (Iguanidae, Mosasauridae), and in some Stegocephalia (*Urocordylus, Diplocaulus*, etc.). Similar hyposphenes and hypantra occur below the zygapophyses in the Cotylosaurian *Diadectes*. The more specialised Pterodactyls develop accessory articulating processes below the centrum.

[2] Although the spinal nerves issue between the cartilaginous neural arches, in the adult they may pierce the arches in many cases owing to secondary overgrowth of bone.

Tetrapod vertebra has been obtained from the fossil Stegocephalia (Owen;
v. Meyer; Cope, **12, 13**; Fritsch, **23**; Gaudry, **28**; Zittel, **98**; Jaekel, **51**;
Schwarz, **83**; Williston, **95**; Watson, **631, 643, 644,** and others). The
vertebrae of the earlier and more primitive forms are found to consist of several elements contributing to the formation of amphicoelous
centra constricting the notochordal space. Such vertebrae have been
called temnospondy-
lous by Cope, who
divides them into
rhachitomous and
embolomerous types.
*Archegosaurus* affords
a good example of
the rhachitomous
structure, Fig. 51.
Each typical trunk
vertebra consists of
a neural arch of two
halves fused above
to a median neural
spine, a large cres-
centic anterior wedge
partially surrounding
the space for the noto-
chord from below
(hypocentrum of
Gaudry, intercen-
trum of Cope), and a
pair of posterior dor-
sal elements (pleuro-
centra of Gaudry)
which together par-

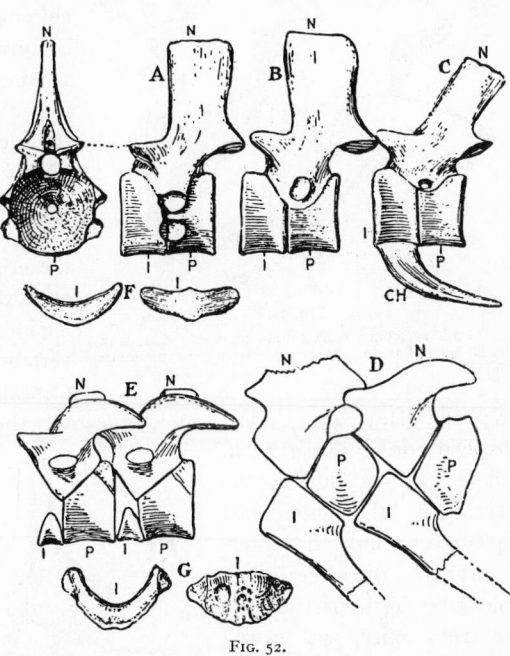

FIG. 52.

Vertebrae of *Cricotus*, A, anterior and left-side views of dorsal
(thoracic); B and C, left side views of anterior and median caudals.
D, Left-side view of caudals of *Eryops*. E, Left-side view of thoracics
of *Conodectes*. F, Dorsal intercentrum (hypocentrum) of *Dimetrodon*,
and G of *Trimerorhachis* from in front and below. (From Williston,
*Osteology of Reptiles*, 1925.) N, Neural arch; I, hypocentrum; P, pleurocentrum; CH, chevron.

tially surround the notochordal space from above. The intercentrum
and pleurocentra, together with the bases of the arches wedged in between
them, make up the amphicoelous body of the vertebra. Passing forwards
the hypocentrum is seen to increase somewhat in size. Passing backwards to the tail region the hypocentrum is seen to diminish in size
and to become incompletely divided into two wedges which send down
long processes meeting below, enclosing the haemal canal and fusing to
a median haemal spine. Still farther back the neural arch and the
hypocentrum are represented by small paired elements. The pleuro-

centra are elongated in the pelvic region almost surrounding the notochord, and in the tail become divided into paired dorsal pleurocentra

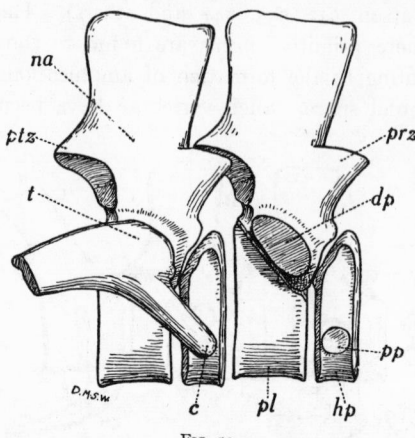

FIG. 53.

Trunk vertebrae of *Eogyrinus*, right-side view, drawn by D. M. S. Watson. *hp*, Hypocentrum; *prz*, prezygapophysis.

and paired ventral hypocentra
pleuralia (Fritsch). Both these
disappear towards the end
of the tail. Most of the rhachitomous vertebral columns
conform to this structure; but
separately ossified hypocentra
pleuralia have only been
recorded in *Archegosaurus*,
*Chelydosaurus*, and *Spheno-
saurus*.

It would appear, then, that
the original four paired arcualia already described as entering into the composition of the
vertebra of most fish can be
identified in that of the Stego-
cephalia (Hay, 45; Gadow, 26)[1], and that they may be separately
ossified and so preserved in
these fossils. But in the
Tetrapod the interdorsal
(pleurocentrum) and interventral (hypocentrum
pleurale) form part of the
centrum only, the neural
arch being formed from the
basidorsals alone above and
the haemal arch from the
basiventrals alone below.
There are no separate arches
developed from the inter-
basals; see, however, p. 51.

In the embolomerous type
each vertebra consists of the
neural arch and two complete
amphicoelous discs surround-
ing the notochordal space, Figs. 52 A, 53, 54. The hypocentrum has

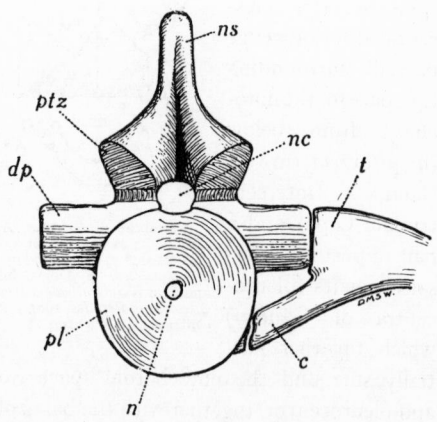

FIG. 54.

Trunk vertebra of *Eogyrinus*, posterior view, drawn by D. M. S. Watson. *c*, Capitulum; *dp*, transverse process of neural arch; *nc*, neural canal; *n*, canal for notochord; *ns*, neural spine; *pl*, pleurocentrum; *ptz*, postzygapophysis; *t*, tuberculum of rib.

[1] The interpretation of the constitution of the vertebral column of Tetrapods adopted in this volume differs from that of Gadow.

grown round dorsally to form the anterior disc, and the pleurocentra have fused and grown round ventrally (or combined with the hypocentra pleuralia) to form the posterior disc. In the anterior segments the hypocentral disc is somewhat wedge-shaped, and in the tail it is prolonged ventrally to form the haemal arch. Since the embolomerous vertebra occurs only in primitive Carboniferous and Lower Permian forms (*Cricotus*, Cope ; *Diplovertebron*, Fritsch ; *Orthosaurus*, *Eogyrinus*, Watson), Williston and Watson believe it to be the most primitive type. Its exact phylogenetic relationship to the rhachitomous type is, however, still obscure ; and on general grounds we should expect to find the four paired elements separately and more equally developed in the ancestral vertebral column.

The later and more specialised large Stegocephalia such as *Mastodonsaurus* have vertebrae belonging to the so-called stereospondylous type. Here the neural arch rests on an amphicoelous centrum notched or pierced for the notochord and composed of a single bone. Apparently the stereospondylous has been derived from the rhachitomous type by the enlargement of the hypocentrum to form the whole body, while the other elements, if present, remain small and unossified.

The Branchiosauria, a specialised group of small Stegocephalia with a somewhat degenerate and weakly ossified endoskeleton, have so-called

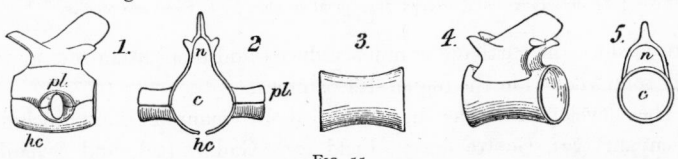

FIG. 55.

Diagrams of Branchiosaurian (1, 2) and Microsaurian (3, 4, 5) vertebrae. 1, Vertebra of *Branchiosaurus*, lateral aspect. 2, The same, end view. 3, Vertebra of *Hyloplesion*, inferior aspect. 4, The same, lateral aspect. 5, The same, end view (after A. S. Woodward, *Vertebrate Palaeontology*, 1898). *c*, Notochordal canal ; *hc*, hypocentrum ; *n*, neural canal ; *pl*, transverse process.

phyllospondylous vertebrae, Fig. 55. The centrum is preserved in the form of a thin bony cylinder composed of four pieces belonging to the neural arches above and hypocentra below. These basidorsal and basiventral ossifications meet half-way, sharing in the formation of a large ' transverse process ', and enclosing a wide space in which doubtless lay cartilage and notochord. Another and highly specialised group of extinct Amphibia, the snake-like Aistopoda or Dolichosomatidae (Huxley, 1871 ; Fritsch, 23 ; Schwarz, 83) have numerous amphicoelous vertebrae ossified in one piece and closely resembling those of modern Apoda, to which this family is probably related, Fig. 323a. The more normal Urocordylidae (Huxley ; Fritsch) have vertebrae also ossified in one piece and very similar to those of modern Urodela.

Coming now to the modern Amphibia we find that their bony verte-brae, whether of the trunk or the tail, are all of one piece, the centrum being continuous with the neural arch and in the caudal region with the haemal arch as well. There are never any separate ' chevron bones ', an important fact distinguishing them from the Amniota. Thus there are in the adult no separate bony elements corresponding to those seen in primitive Stegocephalia, nor is it easy to recognise the elements in the

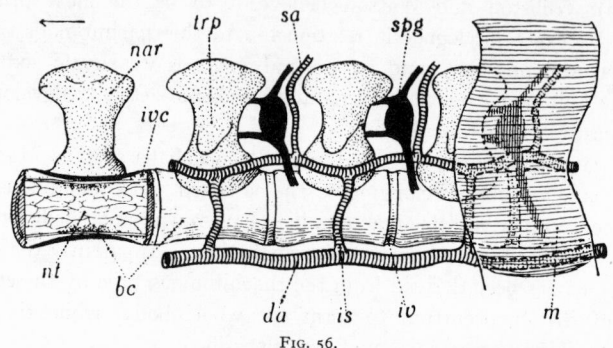

FIG. 56.

Larva of *Amblystoma*. Diagram of reconstructed left-side view of four vertebrae (3-6), showing relation to nerves (black), arteries (cross-lined), and myomere, *m*. First vertebra cut to remove left half. *bc*, Bony cylinder of centrum ; *da*, median dorsal aorta ; *is*, intersegmental artery to longitudinal anastomosis ; *iv*, intervertebral disc ; *ivc*, intervertebral cartilage ; *nar*, neural arch ; *nt*, notochord with notochordal ' cartilage ' ; *sa*, dorsal segmental artery ; *spg*, spinal ganglion ; *trp*, transverse process.

embryo since the cartilage is much reduced and ossification sets in very early somewhat as in the higher Teleostomes.

The development has been studied by many authors, including Gegenbaur (29), Goette (32-3), Field (21), Gadow (26), and Schauins-land (78). In the Urodela, as in other Craniates, the notochord secretes an elastica externa and an inner fibrous sheath ; these remain thin, are not invaded (p. 9), and are of little structural importance in the adult. The cartilaginous elements develop in the continuous mesoblastic skeletogenous layer derived from the sclerotomes which soon become confluent. This layer, surrounding neural canal, notochord, and caudal haemal canal, passes laterally into the transverse intersegmental septa, and here (in the intersegmental or vertebral zones) appear a pair of cartilaginous basidorsals above and a pair of basiventrals below. The former join to a neural arch dorsally,[1] and the latter to a haemal arch ventrally in the tail. The base of the basidorsal does not join that of the basiventral at the side ; but soon these arcualia become embedded in

[1] The spinal nerve-roots issue behind these arches ; but in the adult, owing to their enclosure by backwardly growing bone, they may pass through the neural arches.

the bony cylindrical centrum which develops round the notochord and extends over the arches in each vertebra ; it is wider at each open end than in the middle, where it constricts the notochord. This cylinder first appears as a thin layer of cell-less bone and was mistaken by Hasse (39) for a chordal sheath ('cuticula sceleti'). Unossified connective tissue unites consecutive centra in the intervertebral (segmental) zones ; and here the skeletogenous tissue thickens to form intervertebral cartilaginous rings between the notochordal sheath and the expanded ends of the bony cylinders, Figs. 56, 57. The intervertebral cartilage spreads and thickens, usually constricting the notochord intervertebrally. The modern Urodela

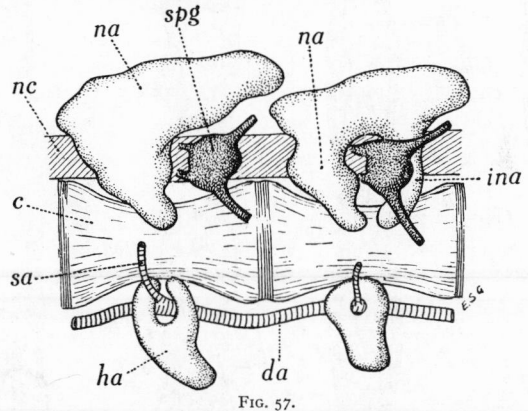

FIG. 57.

Reconstruction of two caudal vertebrae of the larva of *Amblystoma tigrinum*. *c*, Bony centrum ; *da*, dorsal aorta ; *ha*, cartilaginous haemal arch ; *ina*, cartilaginous interneural, and *na*, neural arch ; *nc*, nerve-cord ; *sa*, segmental artery ; *spg*, spinal ganglion.

have become more or less readapted to an aquatic life, and their vertebral column tends to remain correspondingly undeveloped. Thus in such forms as *Proteus, Ranidens,* and *Necturus,* the intervertebral cartilaginous ring is little developed, remains undivided, and the notochord is continuous ; but in more terrestrial Salamandridae the ring enlarges, strongly constricts or even obliterates the notochord, and becomes divided transversely so as to form an opisthocoelous joint between consecutive vertebrae, Fig. 58 (Wiedersheim, 311 ; Gadow, 26).[1]

Gadow's description of the development of the intervertebral ring from four primary rudiments (interdorsals and interventrals) has not

[1] Schauinsland's claim to have found vestigial interdorsal arches in the caudal region of *Amblystoma* needs confirmation (small vestiges have been described by Marcus and Blume in *Hypogeophis*, 62). Neither interdorsal nor interventral arches persist separately in any known Tetrapod, where these elements if represented at all form part of the centrum and its arches.

been confirmed ; nevertheless his comparison of the ring with the interbasals and the cartilages of the neural and haemal arches with the basals
is probably well founded.

The Apoda possess well-ossified amphicoelous vertebrae which differ

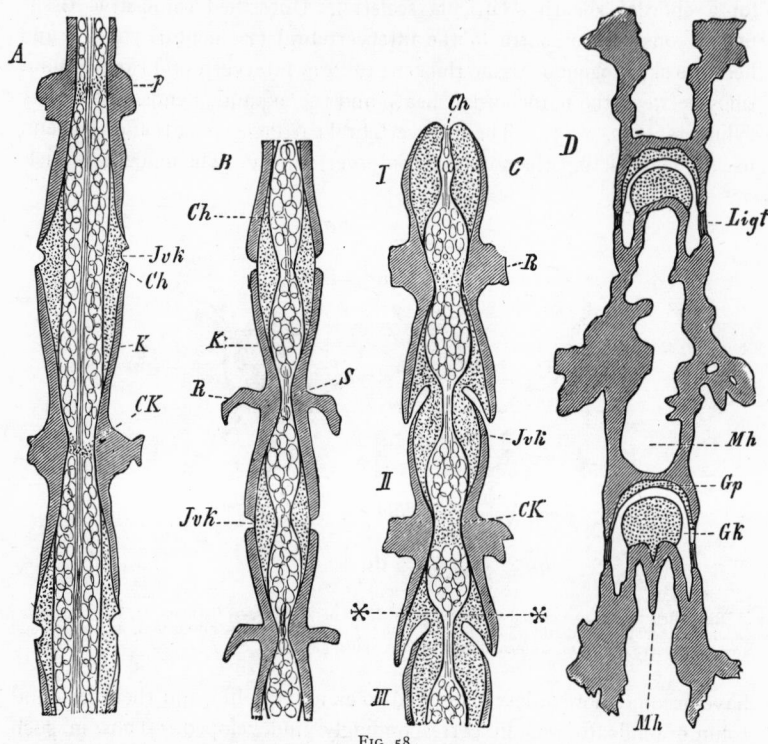

FIG. 58.

Longitudinal section through the vertebral centra of various Urodeles. A, *Ranodon sibericus*;
B, *Amblystoma tigrinum* ; C, *Gyrinophilus porphyriticus* (*I, II, III*, the three anterior vertebrae);
D, *Salamandrina perspicillata*. *Ch*, Notochord ; *CK*, intravertebral cartilage and fat-cells ; *Gp*,
concave posterior face, and *Gk*, convex anterior face of centrum with articular socket and head ;
*Jvk*, invertebral cartilage ; *K*, superficial bone of centrum ; *Ligt*, intervertebral ligament ; *Mh*, marrow
cavity ; *R*, transverse process ; *S*, intravertebral constriction of notochord in *Amblystoma*, without
cartilage and fat-cells ; **, intervertebral cartilage. (From Wiedersheim, *Comp. Anatomy.*)

little in development from those of Urodela, except that the intervertebral
cartilage is almost if not quite lost (Peter, **68** ; Marcus and Blume, **62**).

Of all vertebrates the Anura have the shortest vertebral column ; it
consists of not more than nine free vertebrae and a rigid bony rod, the
urostyle or os coccygeum, representing the postsacral vertebrae. The
well-ossified free vertebrae have a low neural spine and usually large
' transverse processes ' (much dilated on the sacral vertebra of Discoglossidae and Pelobatidae, and other Arcifera). Their articular surfaces

are either opisthocoelous as in Cystignathidae and Discoglossidae, or procoelous as in Bufonidae, Ranidae, etc., while the last free vertebra may have two convexities articulating with the urostyle. The development of the vertebral column is very specialised, and varies from the ' perichordal ' type seen in *Rana* and *Bufo* to the ' epichordal' type of *Pelobates Bombinator* and *Pipa* (Gegenbaur, **29** ; Goette, **32** ; Gadow, **26** ; Ridewood, **74** ; Schauinsland, **78**).   In the former, cartilage first appears as a series of intersegmental basidorsals which fuse at their bases to two continuous longitudinal rods above the notochord.   Ingrowths of the cartilage now take place intervertebrally, probably representing interdorsals, and constricting the notochord.   Later a continuous median rod of cartilage, sometimes indistinctly paired, appears below the notochord, and eventually becomes subdivided into vertebral pieces ; it is taken to represent the basi- and interventrals. Ossification spreads round the notochord and arches at each vertebra connecting the dorsal with the ventral cartilages which become included in the finished vertebra. The intervertebral cartilage surrounds and completely constricts the notochord, a remnant of which may sometimes remain vertebrally as in *Rana*.   This intervertebral cartilage becomes ossified, and according as it attaches itself chiefly to the centrum in front or behind gives rise to a pro- or opisthocoelous joint. In the ' epichordal' type the ventral cartilaginous elements are still further reduced, and the notochord in extreme cases is only enclosed below by the overgrowth of the bony cylinder of the centrum.

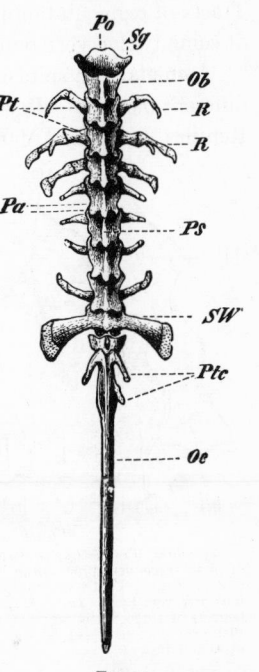

FIG. 59.

Vertebral column of *Discoglossus pictus*. *Ob*, Upper arch of first vertebra ; *Pa*, articular processes ; *Po*, anterior process of first vertebra ; *Ps*, neural spine ; *Pt*, transverse processes of trunk vertebrae ; *Ptc*, transverse processes of caudal vertebrae (urostyle, *Oc*) ; *R*, ribs ; *Sg*, condylar facets of first vertebra ; *SW*, sacral vertebra. (From Wiedersheim, *Comp. Anatomy*.)

In the swimming tail of the tadpole larva no vertebrae are developed, but only the notochord with its sheaths and an enveloping skeletogenous layer.   The whole  structure degenerates and is absorbed at metamorphosis.

That the urostyle is formed of fused post-sacral vertebrae is indicated in the adult by nerve apertures and sometimes, as in *Discoglossus*, by 'transverse processes' and vestiges of neural arches anteriorly, Fig. 59. It develops from two dorsal longitudinal cartilaginous rods, which later join, and a similar ventral rod; these eventually surround and obliterate the notochord, and enclose in front a narrow vestigial dorsal spinal canal. Traces of segmentation indicate that the urostyle is formed by the fusion of some twelve vertebrae (Gadow, 26).

**Amniota.**—In spite of various modifications in details in adaptation to different modes of life which need not be described here, the vertebrae of Reptiles, Birds, and Mammals conform in essentials to the fundamental plan of structure described above (p. 45). It is characteristic of the Amniote vertebra that in addition to the neural arch and body or centrum, which ossify separately, there is an anterior ventral element, the hypocentrum or intercentrum as it is often called, Fig. 61. In the caudal region it gives rise to the 'chevron' bones enclosing the haemal canal. The hypocentrum is particularly large in the very primitive reptile *Conodectes* (*Seymouria*), where the vertebra approaches the embolomerous type, but it remains unossified dorsally, never completely surrounding the notochord (Williston, 95; Watson, 643).

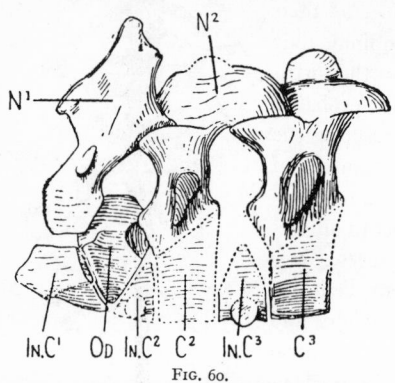

FIG. 60.

*Seymouria* (*Conodectes*) *bayloriensis*, left-side view of first three vertebrae (from D. M. S. Watson, *P.Z.S.*, 1918). $C^2$, $C^3$, centra (pleurocentra) of 2nd and 3rd vertebrae; $In.C^1$, $^2$, $^3$, intercentra (hypocentra) of three vertebrae; $Od$, odontoid process = pleurocentrum of atlas; $N^1$ and $N^2$, neural arches of atlas and axis.

Three important points remain to be discussed bearing on the general morphology of the vertebral column of Tetrapods. They are: (1) the structure of the atlas and axis and significance of its parts; (2) the possible identification of the primitive four paired elements seen in Pisces, and the share these take in the building up of the vertebra; (3) the relation of these elements to the embryonic sclerotomes and body segments.

Taking the last point first, we find, owing to the fact that in Amniotes the sclerotomes are more definite in structure and retain their segmentation longer than in most other Craniates, their relation to the developing vertebrae can be more easily traced, Fig. 62.

The sclerotome is large and arises ventrally from the inner wall of the primitive hollow somite (whose outer wall forms the cutis layer), while only a portion of the inner wall thickens to form the myotome. The

sclerotomes enlarge, forming blocks closely packed together and reaching
to the notochord. Each is developed from the somite as a saccular outgrowth, whose thickened anterior and posterior walls together with
immigrating cells reduce the cavity or sclerocoel to a narrow space
dividing the block into an anterior and a posterior half, except for the
thin original inner wall applied to the notochord (Corning, 15, Männer, 60,

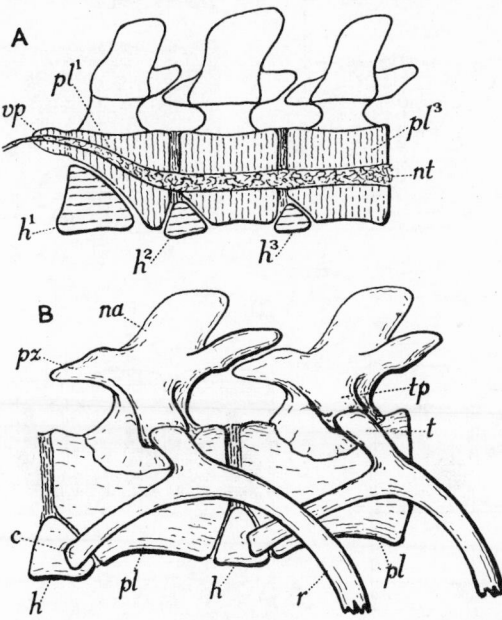

FIG. 61.

A, Diagrammatic longitudinal section of atlas, axis, and third cervical vertebra of a primitive
*Tetrapod* to show composition of centra and of odontoid process. *h*, Hypocentrum; *nt*, notochord;
*pl*, pleurocentrum; *vp*, vestigial pleurocentrum at end of odontoid process, and belonging to last
occipital segment. B, Diagrammatic left-side view of two thoracic vertebrae of a primitive *Tetrapod*,
showing relation of rib to vertebra. *c*, Capitulum; *na*, neural arch; *pz*, prezygapophysis; *t*,
tuberculum; *tp*, transverse process.

Schauinsland, 78, Higgins, 48, in Reptiles; O. Schultze, 82, in Birds; O.
Schultze, 82, Bardeen, 3, in Mammals). The narrow space just mentioned
may be called the sclerocoelic cleft; it is the 'Intervertebralspalte' of
v. Ebner, who first pointed out its significance as marking the position
of the future intervertebral joint. In Reptiles it is clearly developed,
is at first in communication with the myocoel, and may persist for a
considerable time. But, according to O. Schultze, in Birds it develops
later and only secondarily opens into the myocoel, while in Mammals,
though the division of the sclerotome is visible, the cavity is only virtual.
In Amniotes generally it is of course cut off from the myocoel when the

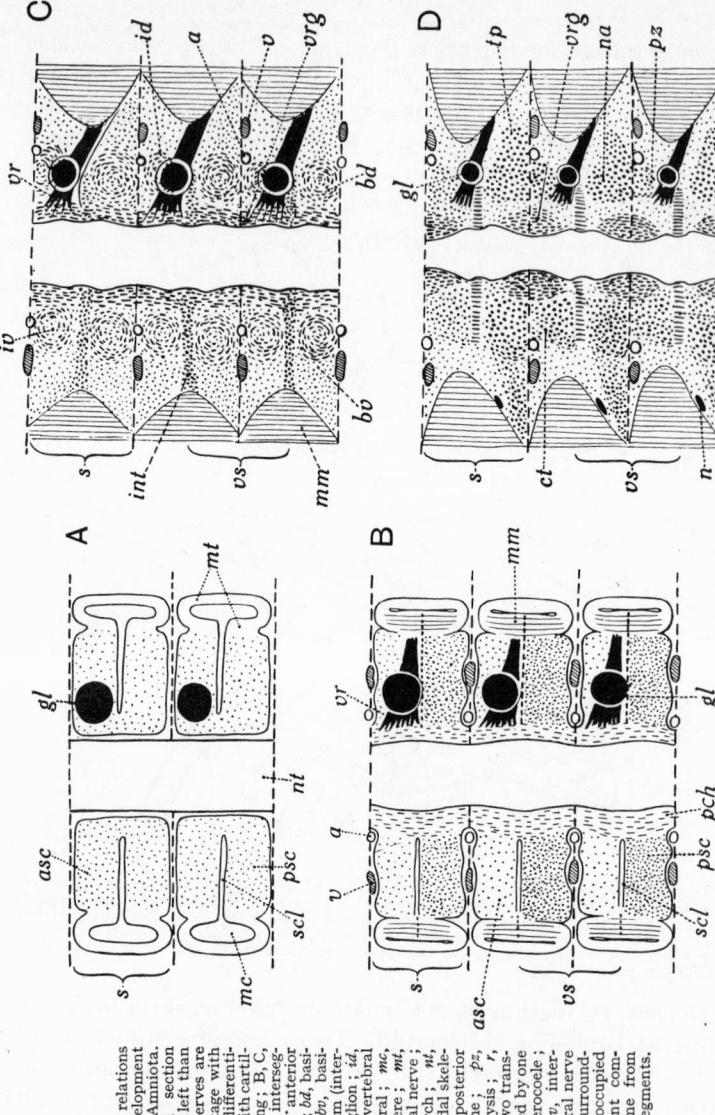

FIG. 62.

Diagrams illustrating relations of *sclerotomes* and development of *vertebral column* in Amniota. Longitudinal horizontal section taken at a lower level on left than on right, where spinal nerves are shown. A, Youngest stage with sclerotomes becoming differentiated; D, oldest stages with cartilaginous elements appearing; B, C, intermediate stages; *a*, intersegmental artery; *asc*, anterior (cranial) half-sclerotome; *bd*, basidorsal (neural arch); *bv*, basiventral; *ct*, pleurocentrum (interdorsal?); *gl*, spinal ganglion; *id*, interdorsal; *int*, intervertebral ligament; *iv*, interventral; *mc*, myocoele; *mm*, myomere; *mt*, myotome; *n*, mixed spinal nerve; *na*, base of neural arch; *nt*, notochord; *pch*, perichordal skeletogenous layer; *psc*, posterior (caudal) half-sclerotome; *pz*, region of postzygapophysis; *r*, rib; *s*, region between two transverse broken lines occupied by one body segment; *scl*, sclerocoele; *tp*, transverse process; *v*, intersegmental vein; *vr*, ventral nerve root; *vrg*, vertebral ring surrounding notochord; *vs*, region occupied by one vertebral segment composed of a half-sclerotome from each of two consecutive segments.

myotome is developed, and ultimately disappears. The posterior half
of the sclerotome usually becomes denser than the anterior half, which
is to a considerable extent invaded dorsally by the developing spinal
ganglion. Thus, owing to the sclerotomes retaining their individuality for
a considerable time, stained longitudinal sections of embryos show alternating light and dark half-sclerotomes. During subsequent development

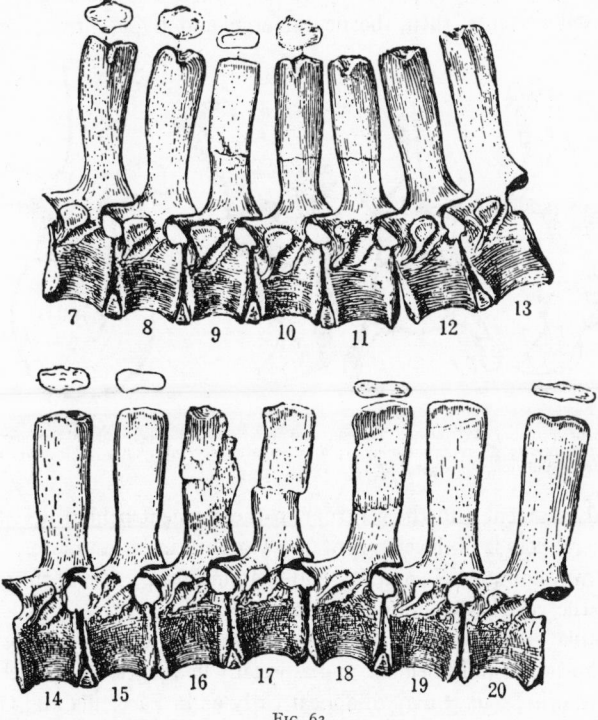

FIG. 63.

*Ophiacodon mirus*; left-side view of seventh to twentieth vertebrae showing pleurocentra and
hypocentra. (From Williston, *Osteology of Reptiles*, 1925.)

each light anterior half-sclerotome of segment B fuses with the dark
posterior half-sclerotome of segment A in front of it to give rise to a
complete vertebral segment. The vertebrae then come to alternate with
the original segmental somites. The sclerocoelic clefts are intervertebral,
the intersegmental vessels vertebral in position.

Meanwhile the adjacent sclerotomes early fuse at their inner ends
next to the notochord, where a continuous skeletogenous perichordal
layer is formed which spreads over the neural canal above and the caudal
haemal canal below. The myotome grows inwards as a wedge between

the two halves of a sclerotome, and the denser half-sclerotome grows outwards in the intermuscular septum. Cartilages then appear : the neural arch develops in the dorsal region and the hypocentrum (inter-centrum, or haemal arch in the tail) in the ventral region of the posterior half-sclerotome of segment A, while the centrum (pleurocentrum) develops in the anterior half-sclerotome of segment B. These three cartilaginous elements may ossify separately, but may later become fused. In the completed vertebra, then, the neural arch and hypocentrum belong to

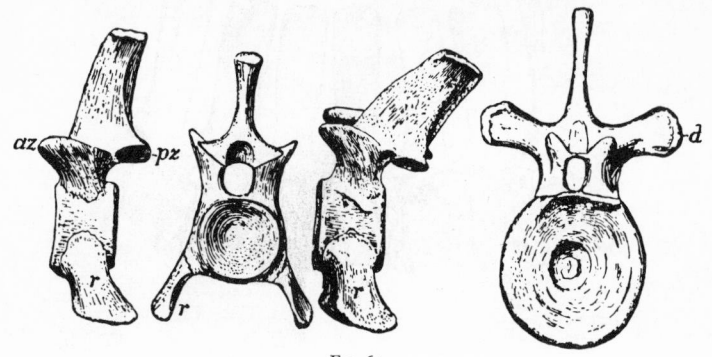

FIG. 64.

Plesiosaur vertebrae : *Polycotylus*. Left-side and posterior views of cervical and thoracic vertebrae. *az*, Prezygapophysis; *pz*, postzygapophysis; *d*, articulation for tuberculum on transverse process; *r*, rib. (From Williston, *Osteology of Reptiles*, 1925.)

one body segment and the centrum to the segment behind it.[1] Such is the general course of development of a vertebra in an Amniote.

We may now attack point (2), and examine more in detail the morphology of the vertebral column in various groups.

**Reptilia.**—In the Reptilia the neurocentral suture may persist as in many Crocodilia and Chelonia, and especially in aquatic forms such as the Ichthyosauria ; but it may disappear early as in Lacertilia and Ophidia. A hypocentrum is always present in the atlas (p. 66) and in primitive forms on all or nearly all vertebrae throughout the column, as in *Sphenodon* and Geckones among living forms. But usually they disappear as separate bones more or less completely in the more specialised and modern Reptiles, except in the tail, where they persist as originally paired elements prolonged ventrally to form haemal arches and spines (chevron bones). Rarely they are paired in the cervical region (Chelonia, Plesiosauria, *Procolophon*). Although the hypocentrum belongs to the centrum behind it, it is usually wedged in between two consecutive centra in the region of the intervertebral connective tissue disc. Secondarily it may

[1] See, however, p. 61.

fuse either with its own centrum or that in front, and even be carried
at the end of the hypapophysis of the anterior centrum (Osborn, **65**).

The early primitive Reptiles, such as the Cotylosauria, possess amphicoelous centra (pleurocentra) pierced by the constricted but continuous
notochord. Such 'notochordal' amphicoelous centra
are present in *Sphenodon* and the Geckones among
modern forms, Fig. 65.

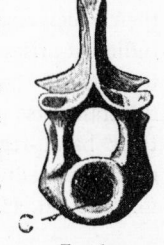

The Geckones (Gadow, **27**) seem to combine primitive
with degenerate characters : hypocentra are present, the
centra are amphicoelous cylinders constricting the notochord vertebrally ; but the cartilage is little developed,
forms an almost continuous tube, and there are no distinct intervertebral joints.

FIG. 65.

Vertebra of
*Sphenodon*, showing
the amphicoelous
centrum (*C*). (After
Headley.)

But from the middle Permian onwards the Reptilian
hollow centra tend to be replaced by solid centra with
shallow excavations (platycoelous) or flat faces (amphi-
platyan). The typical reptilian vertebra is procoelous,
with a concavity in front and a convexity behind, Figs. 66, 67. Such
centra appeared about the middle of the Jurassic epoch and occur in
Lacertilia, Ophidia, Crocodilia, and Pterosauria. Rarely opisthocoelous
centra are found, with an anterior convexity and posterior concavity, as

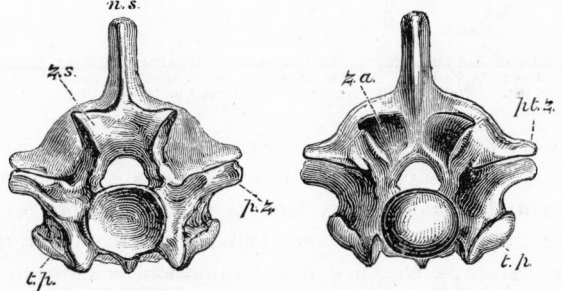

FIG. 66.

Vertebra of *Python*, anterior and posterior views. *n.s*, Neural spine ; *p.z*, prezygapophysis ;
*pt.z*, postzygapophysis ; *t.p*, transverse processes ; *z.a*, zygantrum ; *z.s*, zygosphene. (After Huxley.)
(From Parker and Haswell, *Zoology*.)

in the cervical region of Dinosaurs. The first caudal centrum is biconvex
in modern Crocodilia. More or less amphicoelous vertebrae persist among
modern Chelonia, but in this order the vertebral articulations become
very specialised and all types occur. In the trunk their neural arches are
intercentral in position, resting partly on their own and partly on the centrum in front. In the Edaphosauria the neural arch may be immensely
developed, apparently to support a membranous fold of skin, Fig. 68.

The early development of the reptilian vertebra and its relation to the sclerotomes has been studied by Corning and Brünauer in Snakes, by Männer in Snakes and Lizards, by Higgins in the Alligator, and by Schauinsland in *Sphenodon* and other forms. Although their observations do not agree in every detail, and some points are not yet quite established, their chief results may be summarised as follows. The neural arch rudiment arises in the denser posterior (caudal) half of the original sclerotome (see p. 57), chondrifies separately, and grows out laterally to form the transverse process. The right and left cartilages meet dorsally, while their basal regions expand and clasp the developing centrum. The neurocentral division may be lost in the cartilage, but is plain, at all events for a period, as a neurocentral suture when ossification has set in. The

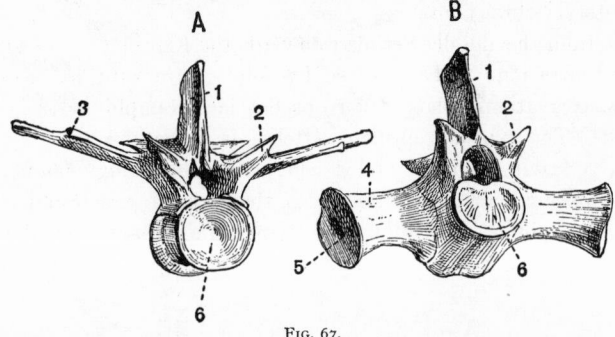

FIG. 67.

Anterior view of A, a late thoracic, and B, first sacral vertebra of a young *Crocodilus palustris* (from S. H. Reynolds, *Vertebrate Skeleton*, 1913). 1, Neural spine; 2, prezygapophysis; 3, facet for articulation with capitulum of rib; 4, sacral rib; 5, surface united with ilium; 6, concave anterior face of centrum.

exact history of the hypocentral structures, their relation to the half-sclerotomes, is less easily made out, owing perhaps to their taking up an intercentral position. They form a 'hypochordal bridge' from the united ventral regions of the same half-sclerotomes as give rise to the neural arches, are paired at first, but as a rule become united by bone into a single wedge below the intervertebral membranous joint. In the tail the originally paired cartilages unite below the haemal canal, and sometimes are joined by bone above it. The centrum itself appears as a chondrification in the now thickened perichordal layer, apparently developed from the anterior cranial half-sclerotomes of the segment behind (p. 57). Generally it appears ventrally at first (Brünauer, 9), but soon grows round the notochord to a complete ring slightly posterior to the neural arch. These rings spread along the perichordal layer, and slightly constrict the notochord vertebrally. The regions of the perichordal layer between the cartilaginous centra form the intervertebral ligaments.

In Reptiles with procoelous vertebrae the central cartilage develops greatly posteriorly, and eventually completely obliterates the notochord intervertebrally. The bulk of this posterior region of the centrum forms

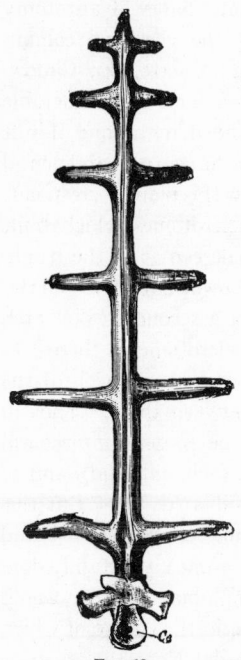

FIG. 68.

*Naosaurus claviger*: restoration of dorsal vertebra, anterior aspect. Permian, Texas. (After A. S. Woodward, *Vertebrate Palaeontology*, 1898.) *ce*, Centrum.

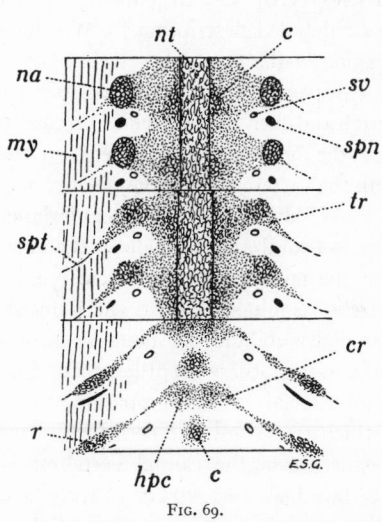

FIG. 69.

Longitudinal horizontal (frontal) sections of the mid-trunk region of an embryo *Lacerta* sp., taken at three successive levels, the upper being most dorsal and the lower most ventral. They show the cartilaginous elements beginning to appear. *c*, Body of vertebra (pleurocentrum); *cr*, capitulum of rib; *hpc*, intercentral vestige (hypocentrum); *my*, myomere; *na*, base of neural arch; *nt*, notochord with its sheaths; *r*, rib; *spn*, spinal nerve; *spt*, intersegmental septum; *sv*, segmental blood-vessel; *tr*, transverse process.

the convexity of the adult vertebra. A vestige of the notochord may sometimes remain near the middle of the centrum.

An important question remains to be considered concerning the origin of the neural arches—namely, whether only one or both half-sclerotomes share in their formation, or in other words whether in the Amniote there is any trace of an interneural arch (interdorsal arch). Although the bulk of the material forming the neural arch in Reptiles is undoubtedly derived, as described above, from the posterior caudal half-sclerotomes of segment Λ, there is reason to believe that the anterior cranial half-sclerotomes of segment B (see p. 58) also contribute tissue to build up the posterior dorsal region of the arch with its postzygapophyses (Goette, Schauinsland in *Sphenodon*, Higgins in *Alligator*, Piiper in Birds).

The structure and development of the caudal vertebrae in Rhyncho-cephalia and the Lacertilia throws some light on this question. It is well known that in *Sphenodon* and most modern Lacertilia the tail can be easily broken off. The break takes place at definite planes of autotomy corresponding to the myosepta and penetrating the vertebral column itself (Hyrtl, '52 ; Gegenbaur, '62 ; H. Müller, '64 ; Goette, 34 ; Gadow, 26 ; detailed description by Woodland, 97). Throughout a considerable region of the tail each vertebra is transversely divided by a zone of soft tissue passing approximately through the middle of the centrum and neural arch and even the transverse process (*Anguis*). Now this plane corresponds to the original division between the two half-sclerotomes which built up the vertebra and have not become as firmly coalesced as in the trunk.

As Männer (60) and Schauinsland (78) have shown, not only does the main neural arch develop in the anterior half, but a second weaker arch in the posterior half (original cranial half of a sclerotome) ; these two arches combine to form the foundation of the bony neural arch of the caudal vertebrae, the plane of autotomy being between them. Thus in the tail of these Reptiles there would seem to be present interneural (interdorsal) arches comparable to those of fishes (Schauinsland), and of which traces are also occasionally found in Amphibia (p. 51). But this structure of the caudal vertebrae is quite peculiar to *Sphenodon* and certain Lacertilia, and can hardly be truly primitive since it certainly does not occur in early unspecialised Reptiles and Amphibia. Rather would it seem to be a comparatively recent specialisation in the course of which possibly the interdorsal arch has been reinstated. Nevertheless it is possible that the portion of the neural arch bearing the posterior zygapophyses is derived in the Amniota from the half-sclerotome behind that which produces the main part of the arch (see below, in Birds). Further research is necessary to decide this difficult point.

**Aves.**—The avian vertebral column has been greatly modified in adaptation to flight. The thoracic vertebrae show a strong tendency to become rigidly ankylosed in certain regions ; the last thoracic, lumbar, and caudal vertebrae become assimilated to the sacral vertebrae between the expanded ilia. Most remarkable is the shortening of the tail. The Jurassic Saururae (*Archaeopteryx* and *Archaeornis*) still have an elongated tail with free vertebrae (only the anterior four or five have transverse processes) ; but in the Ornithurae, including all modern birds, it is reduced to a vestige with but a few free vertebrae, the remainder being fused into a characteristic pygostyle (urostyle) (W. Marshall, 63). In the embryo this bone is seen to correspond to a varying number of vertebrae at first laid down as separate cartilages.

*Archaeopteryx* and *Archaeornis* have retained the amphicoelous centra of their reptilian ancestor. Similar articulations occur only in Ichthyornis, the toothed Carinate of the Cretaceous (Marsh), Fig. 70. Opisthocoelous vertebrae occur in some Carinates such as Penguins, Auks, Parrots, Darters, and Cormorants; and procoelous vertebrae more rarely in the tail (Parker). But the characteristic and usual articulation is saddle-shaped (heterocoelous), Figs. 71, 72.

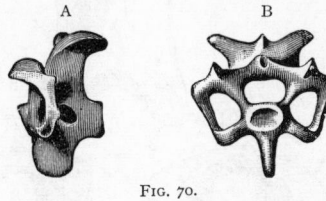

Separate hypocentra (intercentra) are found only in the tail of birds, where they may be paired and produce 'chevron bones'.

Fig. 70.

*Ichthyornis dispar*, Marsh. Lateral (A) and anterior (B) aspect of cervical vertebra, $\frac{2}{1}$. (After Marsh.) (From K. Zittel, *Palaeontology*.)

The development of the avian vertebrae has been well described by Froriep (24), and more recently by T. J. Parker (66), Schauinsland (78), Lillie (845), Sonies (385), and Piiper (70). The posterior half-sclerotomes, distinguished in early stages by their denser structure, give rise to skele-togenous tissue in which appear a prochondral neural arch and a ventral subchordal crescent ('hypochordalen Spange' of Froriep). A hypocentral cartilage develops in the crescent, and a neural arch cartilage dorsally.

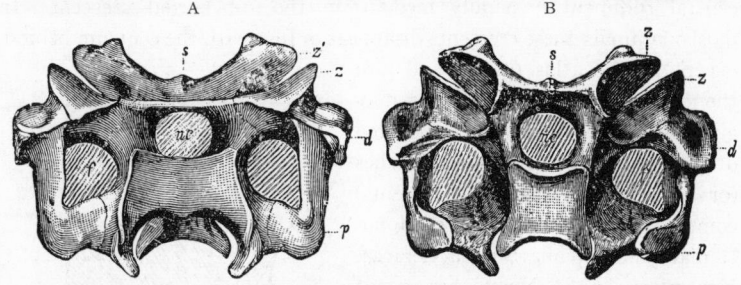

Fig. 71.

*Hesperornis regalis*, Marsh. Upper Cretaceous: Kansas. Anterior (A) and posterior (B) aspect of thirteenth cervical vertebra, $\frac{1}{1}$. *d*, Transverse process; *f*, costal canal for vertebral artery; *nc*, neural canal; *p*, parapophysis; *s*, rudimentary neural spine; *z*, *z'*, anterior and posterior zygapophyses. (After Marsh.) (From K. Zittel, *Palaeontology*.)

In the perichordal layer derived from the anterior half of the sclerotome behind appears the cartilaginous centrum. At first ventral it soon surrounds the notochord and grows forwards. Later the four cartilages of a vertebra join and fuse, and the notochord is obliterated by the centrum. Each half-sclerotome does not develop a dorsal arch and ringlike centrum which later combine to form the adult vertebra, as described by Schauinsland (Sonies, 385, E.S.G.). The composition of the avian vertebra, according to the latest researches of Piiper, is shown in Fig. 73, and according to this author both the half-sclerotomes contribute to the neural arch.

**Mammalia.**—The development of the mammalian vertebrae has been described by Froriep (24), Macalister (59), Weiss (91), Bardeen (3), and others ; it resembles that in Birds, and agrees closely with that shown in the diagram above, Fig. 62, p. 56. The denser posterior half-sclerotome surrounds as usual neural canal and notochord (and haemal canal in the tail), and spreads outwards in the myoseptum.

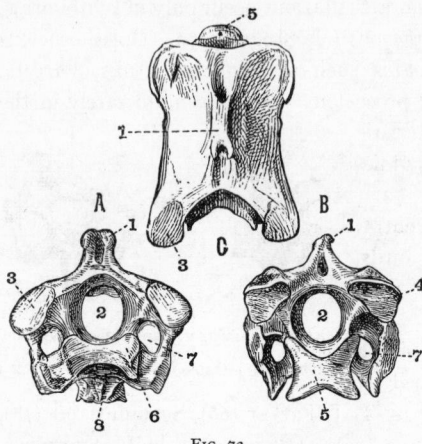

Fig. 72.

Third cervical vertebra of *Struthio camelus*. A, Anterior; B, posterior; and C, dorsal view. (From S. H. Reynolds, *Vertebrate Skeleton*, 1913.) 1, Neural spine ; 2, neural canal ; 3, prezygapophysis ; 4, postzygapophysis ; 5, posterior articular surface of centrum ; 6, anterior articular surface of centrum ; 7, vertebrarterial canal ; 8, hypapophysis.

Paired neural arch rudiments appear in the dorsal region, and a ventral hypocentral rudiment (generally median) in the subchordal crescent. In most mammals these crescents disappear or fuse with the centrum behind, except in the atlas (p. 66) and also the caudal region, where they may give rise to the ' chevrons ' of paired origin. Such Y-shaped haemal arches (or sometimes median crescents) commonly occur in the tails of Monotremata, Marsupialia, Sirenia, Cetacea, Xenarthra, and Nomarthra ; but hypocentra rarely survive elsewhere in the adult except in the lumbar region of Insectivora. The centrum arises from usually paired chondrifications in the perichordal region of the anterior half-sclerotome of the next segment behind. These soon fuse round the notochord, which is

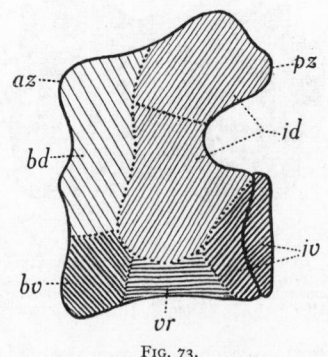

Fig. 73.

Diagram of the constitution of the *vertebra of a bird* (after Piiper, 1928). *az*, Anterior zygapophysis ; *bd*, basidorsal ; *bv*, basiventral ; *id*, interdorsal ; *iv*, interventral including intervertebral disc ; *pz*, posterior zygapophysis ; *vr*, vertebral ring.

completely obliterated, excepting for a small vestige (nucleus pulposus) in the middle of the intervertebral ligament, Fig. 74. In some mammals this ligament is formed secondarily after a temporary fusion of the

centra into a continuous cartilaginous rod (O. Schultze, **82**; Schauinsland, **78**).

From the account given above of the structure and development of
the vertebrae in the various groups of Tetrapoda, it appears that they
may all be derived from an ancestral form and made up as follows : paired
anterior dorsal elements combine to a neural arch (p. 47) ; paired anterior
hypocentra remain separate, combine to a median hypocentrum, or join

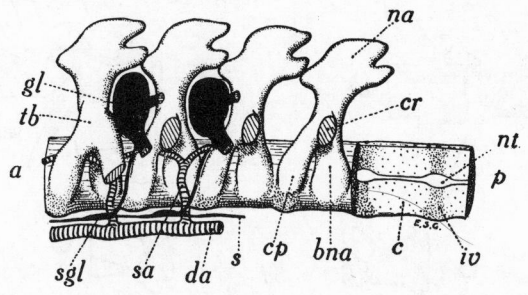

Fig. 74.

*Trichosurus vulpecula*, embryo 13·5 mm. long.   Reconstruction of developing vertebral column in
thoracic region, left-side view.   *a*, Anterior ; *bna*, base of neural arch ; *c*, pleurocentrum ; *cp*, capitulum of rib ; *cr*, cut shaft of rib ; *da*, dorsal aorta ; *gl*, spinal ganglion ; *iv*, intervertebral procartilage (hypocentral region) ; *na*, neural arch ; *nt*, notochord ; *p*, posterior ; *s*, longitudinal sympathetic nerve ; *sgl*, sympathetic ganglion ; *tb*, tubercular region of rib continuous with transverse
process of arch.

to a haemal arch in the tail ; and paired posterior pleurocentra (p. 47)
tend to surround and combine to a ' centrum ' behind.   The relation of
these elements to the sclerotomes and body-segments has already been
sufficiently explained above (p. 54), and the homology of the anterior
dorsal elements with the basidorsals, and anterior ventral elements with
the basiventrals of fishes may be considered as established.   But the
nature of the ' centrum ' of the Amniote is not so well understood.
Gadow considers it to be formed by the interventrals (**26**).   On the other
hand, Cope and others would derive it from the pleurocentra of temnospondylous Stegocephalia, in which case it would represent the interdorsals.
This interpretation is more plausible since interventrals are known for
certain only in the caudal region of certain Stegocephalia among Tetrapods
(p. 48).   Possibly it is a combination of both interventral and interdorsal
elements.   However this may be, there can be little doubt that in all
Tetrapods with well-developed vertebrae the basidorsals and basiventrals
of one segment join the pleurocentra of the segment next behind to form
a complete vertebra.

This result brings us to an important conclusion, first indicated by

Cope, that there has been a divergence between the Amphibia on the one hand and the Amniota on the other in the building up of the vertebra. For whereas in the former the hypocentrum gains in importance (at all events in most Stegocephalians) and the pleurocentra become relatively small, in the Amniote on the contrary the pleurocentra more and more form the bulk of the centrum or body of the vertebra, and the hypocentra take up an intercentral position or disappear.

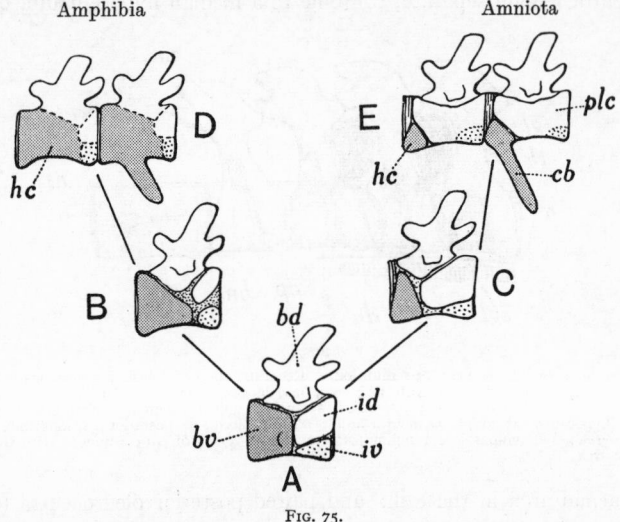

FIG. 75.

Diagram illustrating supposed divergence in development of vertebral elements leading from a primitive ancestral Tetrapod A to a typical Amphibian D, and a typical Amniote E. In D and E a caudal vertebra has been added to the trunk vertebra. *bd*, Basidorsal (neural arch); *bv*, basiventral = *hc*, hypocentrum; *cb*, chevron = intercentrum (shaded); *id*, interdorsal = *plc*, pleurocentrum; *iv*, interventral (coarsely dotted).

The structure of the vertebra, then, is a valuable guide to phylogeny, Fig. 75.

**Atlas and Axis.**—Another striking difference distinguishes the Amphibia from the Amniota. It is the specialisation of the first two cervical vertebrae in the Amniota to form a characteristic atlas and axis complex concerned with the articulation of the skull, Figs. 61 A, 76. The Amphibian second cervical differs in no special respect from the third and succeeding vertebrae, and the skull articulates with the anterior face of the first vertebral body expanded to receive it. When the typical paired amphibian condyles develop they fit into corresponding depressions in the centrum of this 'atlas' which in modern forms usually has a projection between them (see further, p. 68), Figs. 85, 267.

It is a significant fact that in the Amniota the atlas is permanently temnospondylous (p. 47). Its three elements, neural arch, hypocentrum, and pleurocentrum (all of paired origin), are separate in primitive early Reptiles ; its neural arch differs little from the succeeding ones in *Seymouria*, Fig. 60. Even in living Reptiles, Birds, and Mammals the pleurocentrum is separate from the other two elements (Gadow, **26** ; Osborn, **65**). This pleurocentrum becomes more or less closely attached to or fuses with the pleurocentrum (centrum) of the axis vertebra to form its odontoid process (dens epistrophei), Fig. 61. Thus, in Amniotes, the neural arch and hypocentrum of the atlas tend to combine to a ring supporting the

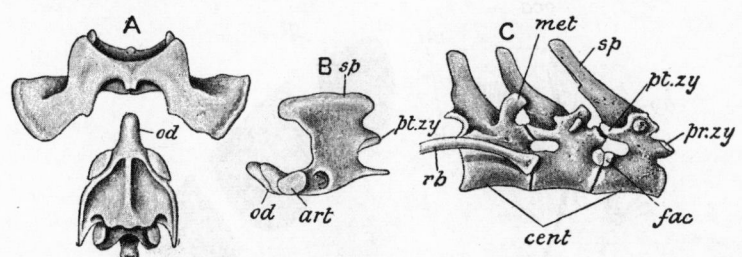

FIG. 76.

*Lepus cuniculus.* A, Atlas and axis, ventral aspect. *od,* Odontoid process of axis. B, Lateral view of axis ; *art,* articular facet for atlas ; *od,* odontoid process ; *pt.zy,* postzygapophysis ; *sp,* neural spine. C, Thoracic vertebrae, lateral view. *cent,* Centrum ; *fac,* facet for rib ; *met,* metapophysis ; *pr.zy,* prezygapophysis ; *pt.zy,* postzygapophysis ; *rb,* rib ; *sp,* spinous process. (From Parker and Haswell, *Zoology.*)

skull and movably articulated to the compound second cervical or axis vertebra (epistropheus). For the reception of the occipital condyle a depression is formed by the hypocentrum below, the expanded bases of the neural arch at the sides and the tip of the odontoid process between them. In the case of the mammal the hypocentral articulation with the basioccipital is reduced or lost, and the articulation becomes bicondylar.

It may be noted that in a primitive Reptile like *Ophiacodon* the pleurocentrum of the atlas is large and in the form of a disc pierced by the notochord much as in an embolomerous Stegocephalian (Williston, **95**) ; but in specialised forms it tends to become reduced to a mere process of the axis centrum concealed from without, Figs. 78, 79, 80. The hypocentrum of the atlas tends to become more closely united with its neural arch, and finally fuses with it to a complete ring, as in Birds and Mammals ; though in *Thylacinus* a separate bony hypocentrum persists in the adult.

It would be interesting to determine the exact position of the occipital joint in relation to the sclerotomes and original segmentation. According to Barge (**4**) it corresponds in Amniotes (Sheep) to the limit between the last occipital and first cervical segments.   That is to say, the hind-most region of the skull cartilage is derived from the posterior (caudal) half of the last sclerotome of the head ; while the neural arch and hypo-centrum of the atlas is from the posterior half of the next sclerotome (first cervical).   The axial ring comes to articulate directly with the occipital condyles since the cranial half-sclerotome between them fails to develop a pleurocentrum of any size, Fig. 77.

In the Urodela the occipital joint is probably not strictly intersegmental, but appears to correspond to the articulation formed between vertebrae

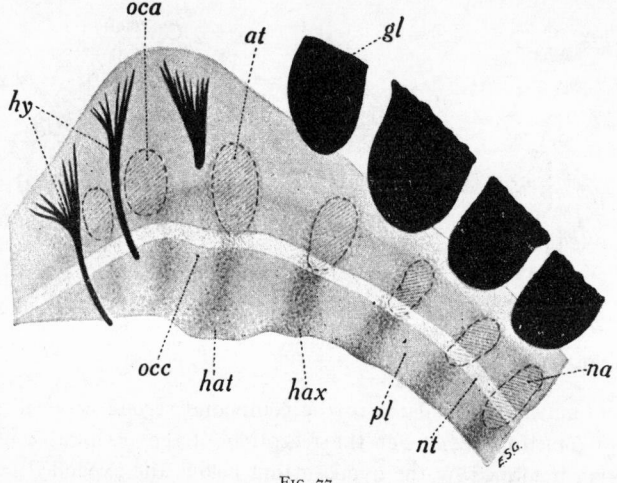

FIG. 77.

*Trichosurus vulpecula.* Embryo 7·25 mm. long.   Partially reconstructed thick longitudinal sagittal section of occipital and anterior cervical region, left-side view.   Two hypoglossal, *hy*, and the first cervical ventral nerve roots are shown ; also part of the cervical ganglia, *gl* ; *at*, base of arch of atlas vertebra ; *hat*, procartilage rudiment of hypocentrum of atlas ; *hax*, same of axis ; *na*, neural arch ; *nt*, notochord ; *oca*, occipital arch ; *occ*, posterior pleurocentral cartilaginous rudiment belonging to occipital region ; *pl*, pleurocentrum of third cervical vertebra.

in the intervertebral cartilage.   The cartilage in which the occipital joint arises belongs to the anterior (cranial) half-sclerotome of the first cervical segment (Fortman, 22).

**The Proatlas.**—There occurs in many Amniotes, overlying the neural canal between the occipital region of the skull and the arch of the atlas, a pair of small bones (or a single bone) having the appearance of a vestigial neural arch, Figs. 78, 79, 80.   They have been found in many Cotylosauria, Theromorpha, Rhynchocephalia, Dinosauria, and Crocodilia, and even in the Mammal *Erinaceus,* and may articulate with the skull in front and the atlas arch behind (Albrecht, 1 ; Dollo, 18 ; Hayek, 46, 47 ; Howes and Swinnerton, 49 ; Schauinsland, 78 ; Gadow, 26 ; Williston, 95).

Whether paired or single, the bones develop from paired cartilages, and were named ' proatlas ' by Albrecht [1] under the impression that they are the vestiges of a vertebra more or less completely crushed out between the skull and the atlas. Albrecht's theory, at first accepted by many (Baur, 6 ; Dollo, and others), is now discredited. It has been suggested that the proatlas is a ' neomorph ' of no special morphological significance, or that it is the vestige of the neural arch of a vertebral segment, of which the remainder is included in the occipital region. Barge (4) considers it to be the arcual of the anterior (cranial) half of the sclerotome which produces the arch of the atlas. On the whole this seems the most plausible explanation of its presence.

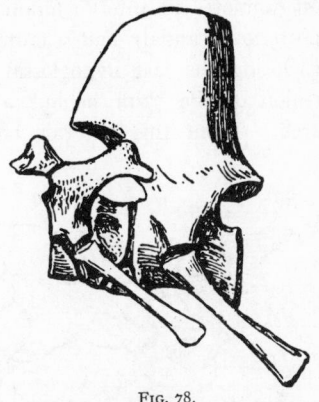

Fig. 78.

*Ophiacodon*; left-side view of proatlas, atlas, axis, and ribs. (From Williston, *Osteology of Reptiles*, 1925.)

In connexion with the proatlas, Schauinsland points out that the tip of the odontoid process chondrifies

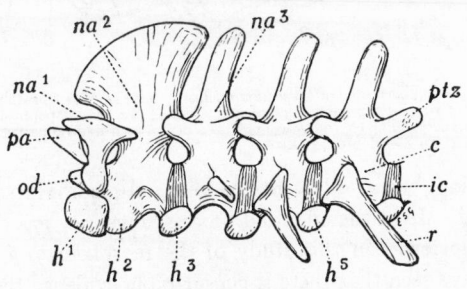

Fig. 79.

*Sphenodon punctatum* ; left-side view of anterior vertebrae, diagrammatic. *c*, Body of vertebra (pleurocentrum) ; *h*, hypocentrum ; *ic*, intervertebral disc ; *na*, arch ; *od*, odontoid process or first pleurocentrum ; *pa*, ' proatlas ' ; *ptz*, postzygapophysis ; *r*, rib.

separately in Sphenodon (78). Gaupp (512) believes the odontoid process in Echidna to contain the elements of two centra, and much the same

---

[1] Misled by the fact that the first spinal nerve (the ' suboccipital ' nerve between skull and atlas) has disappeared in the adult Anura, Albrecht erroneously concluded that the first or atlas vertebra in Amniotes corresponds to the second in Amphibia. But a ' suboccipital ' nerve exists in other Amphibia, and embryology shows that no segment has been lost in this region. The question is further complicated by the fact that in Urodela the first spinal nerve may secondarily become overgrown by the bone of the neural arch, and so pass through it.

result has been reached by de Burlet in Bradypus (11), by Hayek in
Reptiles, Birds, and Mammals (46-7). There is reason to believe that in
all Amniotes an anterior (cranial) half-sclerotome is present between the
posterior (caudal) half-sclerotome, which gives rise to the cartilage
enclosing the last hypoglossal nerve-root and completes the occipital
region of the skull behind, and that which gives rise to the atlas
arch. From this anterior half-sclerotome the 'proatlas' arch may

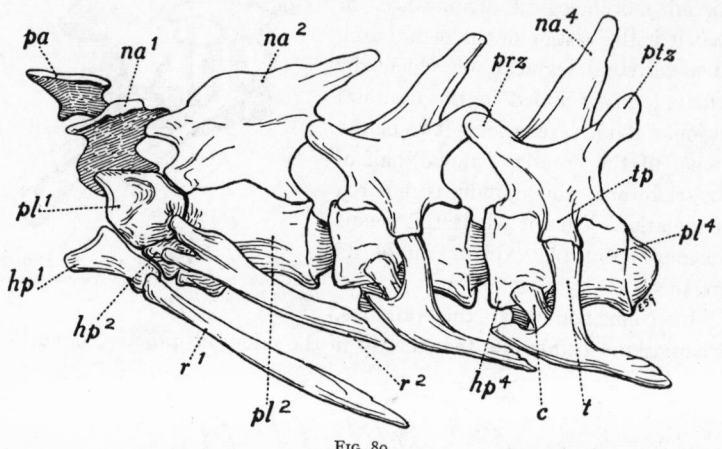

FIG. 80.

Anterior four cervical vertebrae of *Crocodilus niloticus*; left-side view. *c*, Capitulum; *hp*, hypocentrum; *na*, neural arch; *pa*, proatlas; *pl*, pleurocentrum; *prz*, prezygapophysis; *ptz*, postzygapophysis; *r*, rib; *t*, tuberculum; *tp*, transverse process; neural arch 1 and proatlas of left side removed
to expose pleurocentrum 1 = odontoid process.

perhaps develop, but at all events its vestigial pleurocentrum appears to
be added to the tip of the odontoid process, Figs. 61, 77.

**General Review.**—In this study of the morphology of the vertebral
column we have seen that there is considerable evidence that throughout
the Gnathostomes four paired elements or arcualia are concerned in the
building up of a vertebral segment. Of these the basidorsals and basiventrals are the more important, originate in the posterior (caudal) half of
the sclerotome, and give rise to the bulk of neural and haemal arch
respectively. The interdorsal and interventral elements develop in the
anterior (cranial) half of the sclerotome. But, while the morphological
position of the basalia (especially basidorsals) near the middle of the
vertebra, where comes the septum between two consecutive myomeres, is
constant from Selachians upwards, that of the interarcuals varies considerably, and the homology of the parts supposed to represent them is
by no means so clearly established. For instance, in Petromyzon and
the Selachii the interdorsal is primarily between the dorsal and ventral

nerve-root of a segment; but in other groups, where the interdorsals appear to be represented only by their bases closely applied to the notochord and the arches proper are little or not at all developed, the relation to the roots seems to vary. Moreover, if, as Schauinsland supposes, the interdorsal arch is occasionally developed in Urodeles (p. 51, and Fig. 57), then it passes behind both roots of the spinal nerve, which may become enclosed between the basidorsal and interdorsal arches of one vertebra, Fig. 57. On the other hand, if both these elements can combine to form the adult neural arch in Amniota, as held by Schauinsland and others (see above, p. 62), then in these Tetrapods both roots of the spinal nerve pass posteriorly to the interdorsal (p. 64, and Fig. 73).[1] Not only is the relation of the nerves to the cartilages different in these various groups, but the relation of the interdorsal to the intervertebral joint is also variable: it lies above it in Selachians, behind it in some Teleostomes, in front of it in Amniotes. In the modern Amphibia it would appear that the joint forms across the interarcuals. These are some of the obscurities which future research may clear up.

## THE RIBS

Ribs first make their appearance in the Gnathostomata, and it is now recognised that, as already mentioned above (p. 7, and Fig. 1), they are of two kinds[2]: upper dorsal ribs extending outwards in the horizontal septum at its intersection with the transverse myosepta, and lower ventral or pleural ribs extending downwards where these myosepta join the coelomic wall (A. Müller, 1853; Goette, 31-3; Rabl, 71; Baur, 100-2; Hatschek, 109). Both kinds are originally connected proximally with the basiventral, but while the former passes between the epiaxonic and the hypoaxonic muscles, the pleural rib passes below (internal to) the myomeres. Several important questions arise in connexion with the morphology of ribs: (1) whether they were derived phylogenetically from the axial skeleton as held by Gegenbaur (1870) or are independent structures which have become secondarily connected with it (Bruch, '67; Kölliker, '79; Hasse and Born, '79); (2) what relation have the two kinds to each other and to the haemal arches; (3) whether the bicipital ribs of Tetrapods are strictly homologous with one kind of rib or are a combination of both.

[1] These variations in relative position may be due to the cutting through, so to speak, of the interdorsal arch by the nerve-roots.

[2] The earlier view of Gegenbaur and others, that all ribs and haemal arches are homologous structures, was abandoned when it was shown that dorsal and pleural ribs may coexist in the same segment of the trunk, and dorsal ribs and haemal arches in the same segment of the tail.

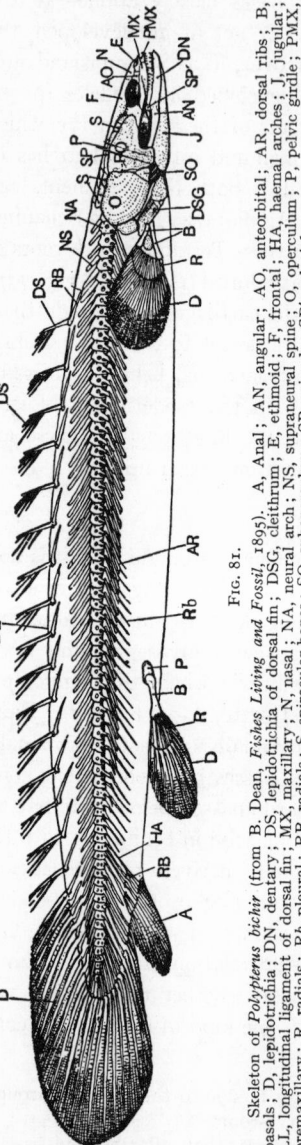

Fig. 81.

Skeleton of *Polypterus bichir* (from B. Dean, *Fishes Living and Fossil*, 1895). A, Anal; AN, angular; AO, anteorbital; AR, dorsal ribs; B, basals; D, lepidotrichia; DN, dentary; DS, lepidotrichia of dorsal fin; DSG, cleithrum; E, ethmoid; F, frontal; HA, haemal arches; J, jugular; LL, longitudinal ligament of dorsal fin; MX, maxillary; N, nasal; NA, neural arch; NS, supraneural spine; O, operculum; P, pelvic girdle; PMX, premaxillary; R, radials; Rb, pleural; RB, radials; S, spiracular bones; SO, suboperculum; SP, spiracle; SP', splenial.

Before attempting to answer these questions we must examine the structure and development of the ribs in the various groups, beginning with the Pisces.

**Pisces.**—The Selachii have well-developed ribs in the trunk which dwindle in size anteriorly, being usually absent in the first few segments. They also dwindle posteriorly, and are absent in the tail region except for vestiges in the most anterior caudal segments. These ribs are of the dorsal type, and are attached to the basiventrals provided with outer processes ('parapophyses') for the purpose. In development (Balfour, 1878; Göppert, 107; Schauinsland, 78) they arise in the distal region of the tissue which grows out into the myoseptum from the posterior (caudal) half of each sclerotome, Fig. 16. At first basiventral and rib rudiments are in perfect blastematous and even procartilaginous continuity. In some cases true cartilage may appear independently in the rib; but often it appears to develop continuously from basiventral to rib, and then the rib becomes secondarily detached, a fibrous joint appearing, which separates it from the basiventral or 'basal stump'. In the caudal region the haemal arches are developed in continuity with the basiventrals. Dorsal ribs and haemal arches may be considered as independent extensions of the basiventrals, the former developed in the trunk, the latter in the tail. Both may be present in the intermediate region (Balfour, 2). As pointed out by Schauinsland in *Laemargus*, a haemal process may be present on the inner side of the haemal arch in Selachians supporting the membrane which separates the aorta from the caudal vein. On passing forwards towards the trunk the closed arch opens out, the basiventrals spread dorsalwards and tend to separate into a pair of haemal processes protecting the aorta, and a more dorsal outstanding part supporting the rib (see also p. 21).

The condition of the ribs in the Polypterini is very instructive (Dollo, 104; Hatschek, 109; Göppert, 107; Budgett, 10). In *Polypterus* each segment of the vertebral column in the mid-trunk bears two almost equally developed pairs of bony ribs. The upper dorsal pair is articulated to the middle of the centrum; the lower ventral or pleural pair is secondarily attached farther forward and even intercentrally. The dorsal ribs increase in length forwards and disappear in the tail; the pleural ribs increase in length backwards, bend downwards, and, coming together ventrally, pass into the haemal arches in the tail, Fig. 81. Budgett has shown that in the young larva the upper ribs appear as prolongations of a series of lateral cartilages at the side of the notochord, and the pleural ribs as prolongations of a similar series of more ventral cartilages. Both lateral and ventral cartilages are situated vertebrally (in the same transverse plane as the basidorsals), and are no doubt of basiventral origin. It is clear that in *Polypterus* the haemal arches are serially homologous with the pleural ribs and basiventral bases of support. This conclusion is amply borne out by observations on the structure and development of these parts in certain other Teleostomes and in the Dipnoi.

The ribs in the lower Teleostomes (Chondrostei, Amioidei, Lepidosteoidei) appear to be all of the pleural type, and passing backwards the basiventrals and ribs of the trunk are seen to correspond to the basiventrals and haemal arches of the tail (Goette, 31-3; Balfour, 2, and others).[1] But the majority of the Teleostei, in addition to these pleural ribs, have upper ribs in the horizontal septum. The pleural ribs are usually very well developed and may almost meet ventrally. Proximally they are articulated to rib-bearing processes of the basiventrals which may be separately ossified as in *Esox* and *Cyprinus*. The upper ribs ('epipleurals') are usually attached by ligament to the sides of the centra, but sometimes to the pleural ribs themselves, in the anterior region.

[1] In spite of what has been said above, it is not impossible that the upper dorsal ribs of Selachians are really homologous with the pleural ribs of Teleostomes, as held by Balfour. In *Lepidosteus* the free ends of the ribs are embedded in the muscles and therefore in a somewhat intermediate condition. If, in phylogeny, pleural ribs have been derived from 'dorsal ribs', the dorsal ribs of the Teleostomes must have appeared as a new set of extensions in the horizontal septum. A closer study of the more primitive fossils might throw light on this difficult question.

Frequently they persist in the caudal region. Passing backwards to the tail the pleural ribs are seen to persist as such in its anterior region. The haemal arch is formed by the prolongation and meeting of two processes of the basiventrals which may be continued into a median spine. This condition of the posterior pleural ribs, very conspicuous in many

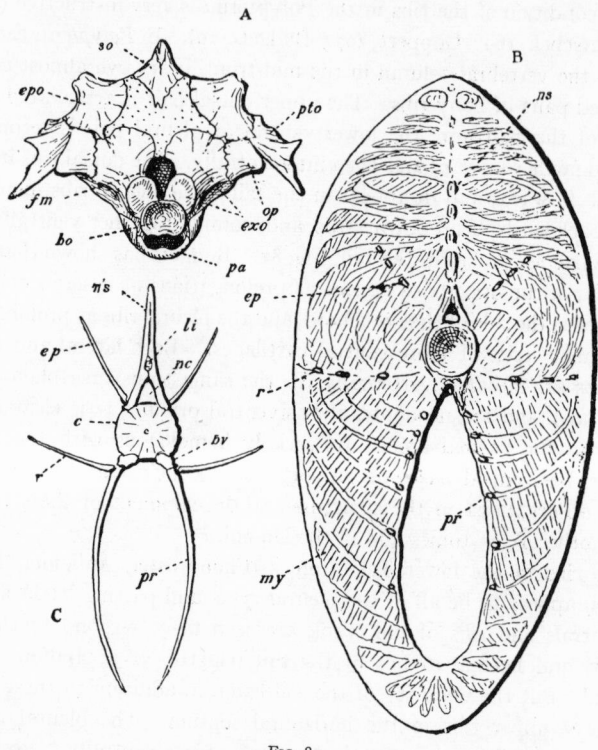

Fig. 82.

*Salmo salar*, L. (After Bruch.) A, Skull from behind; B, transverse section of the trunk; C, transverse section of a trunk vertebra. *bo*, Basioccipital; *bv*, basiventral; *c*, centrum; *ep*, epipleural; *epo*, epiotic; *exo*, exoccipital; *fm*, foramen magnum; *li*, longitudinal ligament; *my*, myotome; *nc*, neural canal; *ns*, neural spine; *op*, opisthotic; *pa*, parasphenoid below the myodome; *pr*, pleural rib; *pto*, pterotic; *r*, rib; *so*, supraoccipital. (From Goodrich, *Vert. Craniata*, 1909.)

of the higher Teleosts, may be related to the secondary shortening of the abdominal cavity and shifting forwards of the anus. On the whole, the evidence is against the conclusion of Goette and Balfour that the pleural rib enters into the formation of the haemal arch in Teleostei, Figs. 49, 141.

It may be added that pleural ribs develop in Teleostomes as extensions of the basiventral rudiment, continuous with it in the procartilaginous stage. The rib and basiventral often chondrify separately, but may become continuous. Later a fibrous joint is formed separating the rib from the process which bears it (Goette, Göppert). The upper rib cartilage arises separately, and is only connected with the basiventral by ligament.

The slender 'intermuscular bones' frequently present in the myosepta of Teleosts, extending from the centrum ('epicentrals') or neural arch ('epineurals'), were distinguished by J. Müller as ossified tendons from the true ribs preformed in cartilage ; but in Salmonidae the epineurals are at first cartilaginous, Fig. 82.

The Dipnoi, which in so many respects approach the Tetrapoda, differ from them markedly in the absence of upper or dorsal ribs and the presence of pleural ribs in the trunk, Figs. 10, 33. They articulate with the cartilaginous basal stumps (basiventrals) and are separately ossified. A very characteristic feature, seen even in Devonian forms, is the persistence and enlargement of the anterior pleural ribs giving rise to the so-called 'cranial ribs' attached to the skull and belonging to those vertebral segments which have been fused to its occipital region, Figs. 315-17.

Concerning the phylogenetic derivation of the ribs, since they are connected with the column, and always arise at least in blastematous continuity with it, we may conclude that they belong to the axial skeleton and are derivatives of the basiventral element. This conclusion is also borne out by what we know of the structure and development of the ribs in Tetrapods.

**Tetrapoda.**—The ribs of the Tetrapoda, in spite of the fact that they extend ventralwards to enclose the thoracic cavity and may even meet below, are of the upper or dorsal type, situated primarily in the septum between epiaxonic and hypoaxonic muscles. It is unnecessary, now, to enter in detail into the controversies carried on in the past as to their homology. Claus, 1876, pointed out that the coexistence of ribs and haemal arches in the tail of Amphibia and Reptilia disposed of the view that dorsal ribs, pleural ribs, and haemal arches are all homologous structures. Later Hoffmann urged that the ribs of Amniota are connected intervertebrally with the column (110). As indicated above (p. 15, and Fig. 62), it is now generally accepted that the ribs develop in the intersegmental septa from tissue derived from the posterior (caudal) half-sclerotome, and therefore from the same half-sclerotome as the hypocentrum and neural arch to which they belong.

In a typical primitive Tetrapod the rib is bicipital, the ventral head or capitulum being articulated to the hypocentrum below, the dorsal head or tuberculum to the extremity of the transverse process (diapophysis) of the neural arch above, Fig. 61. The shaft of the rib passes outward in the myoseptum. Between capitulum, tuberculum, and vertebra is enclosed a space, the 'vertebrarterial canal', through which runs a longitudinal vertebral artery joining successive segmental arteries.

The origin of the bicipital rib is an interesting problem which has not yet been satisfactorily solved.[1] If the upper rib is an outgrowth of the basiventral, or is at all events primitively related to it, its connexion with the transverse process of the neural arch must be secondary, and the tubercular head must have been added to secure better articulation to the vertebral column. It is not easy to see how the intermediate stages could have been useful. But the double head might also have been evolved by the spreading upwards of the original basal articulation from the hypocentrum to the arch and its subsequent subdivision into two accompanied by the forking of the proximal end of the rib itself. Such, for instance, is the view of Williston (95), who points out that apparently primitive single-headed (holocephalous) ribs occur in Temnospondyli among the Stegocephali and in some early Reptilia, Figs. 52, 84. This theory, however, is difficult to reconcile with the fact that typical bicipital ribs already occur throughout the vertebral column of *Seymouria*, perhaps the most primitive of all known reptiles, and in the earliest known Embolomeri, such as *Eogyrinus* (Watson, 644), Figs. 53, 54, 83. The ribs of this carboniferous Stegocephalian are of peculiar interest since even the sacral ribs are of considerable length, being scarcely yet modified to support the ilium, and bicipital. There can be little doubt that they represent an early stage in the evolution of the Tetrapoda before the typical short one-headed sacral rib had become developed.

This evidence, combined with that of the widespread occurrence of

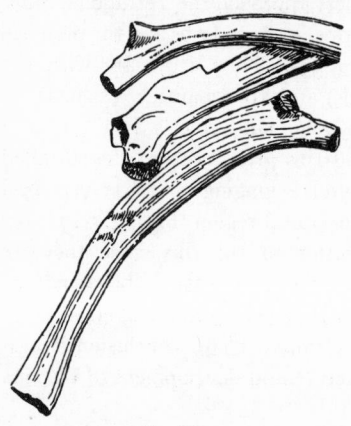

FIG. 83.

*Eogyrinus Attheyi*; typical dorsal, last dorsal, and first sacral rib. (From D. M. S. Watson, *Tr. Roy. Soc.*, 1926.)

---

[1] The theory put forward by A. Müller, '53, and supported by Dollo (104), that bicipital ribs are formed by the coalescence of dorsal and ventral ribs, is not supported by the study of their development, and seems to have been finally disposed of by the discovery of the coexistence with haemal arches of typical bicipital ribs in the anterior caudal segments of *Conodectes* (*Seymouria*) (Williston, 95; Watson, 643).

bicipital ribs among Reptiles, Birds, and Mammals, strongly favours the view that separate capitular and tubercular heads were present on the ribs of the ancestral Tetrapod. The holocephalous condition present always in the sacrum (except in certain Embolomeri mentioned above), and sometimes throughout the length of the column (Temnospondyli, Cotylosauria, many Theromorpha, Rhynchocephalia, Lacertilia, Ophidia, etc.), would then be secondary. Sometimes it appears to be due to the loss of the tubercular articulation as in Monotremes and some other Mammals; or to the fusion of the two heads to one as in *Sphenodon* (Howes and Swinnerton, 49), Ophidia, and most Lacertilia. But a

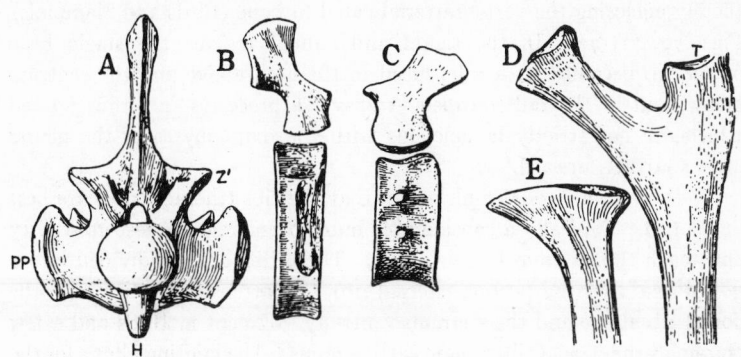

FIG. 84.

Vertebra: A, of *Clidastes*, posterior cervical from behind; B, of *Cymbospondylus*, anterior dorsal from right (after Merriam); C, of *Ichthyosaurus*, middle dorsal from left (after Broili). D, anterior dorsal rib of *Dimetrodon*, and E, of *Diadectes*. (From Williston, *Osteology of Reptiles*, 1925.)

detailed study of the articulation of the ribs in Reptiles remains to be made.

The Tetrapod rib chondrifies separately, and although its capitular region is always developed in blastematous continuity with the hypocentral blastema (hypochordal Spange of Froriep), yet its point of attachment may shift in the adult (Hoffmann, 110; Howes and Swinnerton, 49; Schauinsland, 78, in Reptiles; Froriep, 24, in Birds; Schultze, 82; Bardeen, 3, in Mammals). In primitive Stegocephalia and Reptilia, where the hypocentrum is large, the capitulum is articulated to it; but when the hypocentrum is reduced or disappears as such, the rib comes to articulate either in the intercentral region on facets belonging to two consecutive centra (as in some Mammals), Fig. 76, or on the centrum belonging to its arch (as in the majority of Reptiles and in Birds). A parapophysis may be developed on the centrum to support it. The tubercular articulation may also shift downwards on to the centrum, as in *Ichthyosaurus*, and a second more dorsal parapophysis be formed for it on the centrum, Fig. 84.

In the Archosauria there is a tendency for the capitulum of the trunk ribs to shift upwards on to the transverse process of the arch, at the tip of which it finally meets the tuberculum in the posterior segments. This peculiar mode of articulation is typically developed in Crocodilia, Fig. 67.

The rib of the atlas is generally lost ; but it remains in Archosauria (including modern Crocodilia) and some early Reptiles (Theromorpha such as *Ophiacodon*), Figs. 78, 80. As the neck region becomes more fully differentiated the cervical ribs tend to become shortened and reduced. In most Amniotes, however, they retain two heads and often become fused to the centrum below and the arch above, thus completely enclosing the vertebrarterial canal in bone (Birds and Mammals), Figs. 70, 71, 72. In the sacral and caudal regions the single head of the rib becomes, as a rule, fused to the arch above and the centrum below, and in the tail so-called ' transverse processes ' are thus formed which are not strictly homologous with the diapophyses of the neural arches farther forward.[1]

It is in the anterior trunk region that the ribs (thoracic ribs) are best developed. Typically a considerable number encircle the visceral cavity and reach the sternum below (p. 81). These ribs become divided into a dorsal and a ventral portion (sternal rib), the latter articulating with the dorsal rib above and the sternum ventrally. Except in Birds and a few Mammals the sternal ribs remain cartilaginous. The jointing allows for the expansion and contraction of the thoracic cavity for respiratory purposes (p. 84). The ribs of the Chelonia are highly modified. The cervical ribs have been lost except in the primitive *Triassochelys*, where they are small and bicipital. The ribs of the trunk in Chelonia are greatly modified owing to the formation of a dorsal carapace. The sternum is lost, the ribs stretch outwards, and eight pairs contribute usually to the carapace. The capitulum is suturally attached to the arch and two consecutive centra. In Ophidia, where there is no sternum, and also in the snake-like Lacertilia (where the sternum is reduced or absent), the ribs are well developed and tend to become uniform along the whole elongated trunk.

No modern Amphibian has typical ribs (Mivart, 1870 ; Göppert, **106, 108,** and others). They are absent on the atlas, but usually

---

[1] Ossified, or more usually cartilaginous, lateral projections known as uncinnate processes occur on the trunk ribs of some Temnospondyli among Stegocephalia, and possibly are represented by the distal dorsal process of the ribs of Urodela. Uncinnate processes occur also in fossil and living Archosauria (Sphenodon, Crocodilia), and in Birds. They chondrify separately, and do not unite with the ribs in Reptiles ; but in Birds, where they ossify, they fuse with the ribs.

present on all the presacral, sacral, and even anterior caudal vertebrae. Much reduced in all Anura, they may disappear altogether in the more specialised forms such as *Rana*. Even in Urodeles they are scarcely bent downwards to encircle the body cavity, never join the sternum, and often end in the horizontal septum at the level of the lateral line. The ribs in Urodeles sometimes fork distally, and usually are provided proximally with two heads attached to the bifurcated extremity of a ' transverse process ' of peculiar structure and doubtful homology, Fig. 85. This rib-bearing process in the adult has a strong dorsal limb continuous with the neural

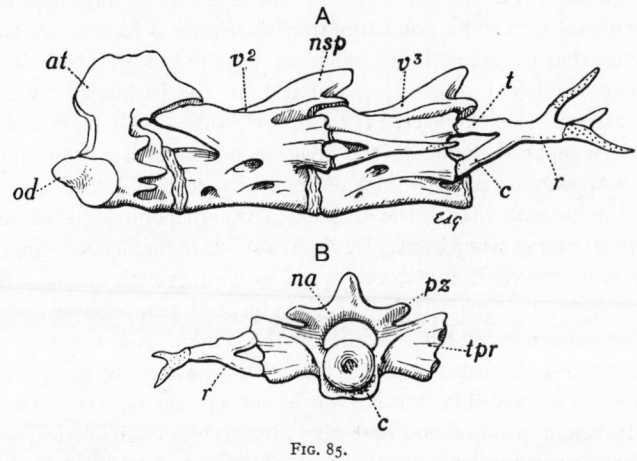

FIG. 85.

*Necturus maculatus.* A, Left-side view of first three vertebrae ; B, posterior view of fourth cervical vertebra.   *at,* Neural arch of first cervical vertebra ; *c,* ventral process of rib (capitulum ?); *na,* neural arch ; *nsp,* neural spine ; *od,* anterior process of first centrum ; *pz,* postzygapophysis ; *r,* rib ; *t,* dorsal process of rib (tuberculum ?); *tpr,* transverse process or 'rib-bearer', pierced at base for artery ; *v²,³,* second and third vertebrae.

arch, and a slender ventral limb continuous with the centrum below (the ventral limb may be reduced to a slender bone or even to a ligament in some genera). The two limbs meet distally, thus enclosing the vertebral artery ; and the rib having no connexion with the vertebrarterial canal, is carried away distally from it. The development of Amphibian ribs has been studied in detail by Göppert (108), Mayerhofer (112), Gamble (105), and others. As in other Tetrapods it arises in blastematous continuity with the basiventral or ' basal stump ', but at a higher level than usual owing to the more dorsal attachment of the horizontal septum. In *Necturus* the cartilaginous basiventral stretches outwards and upwards below the vertebral artery and may form the main portion of that part of the ' transverse process ' which bears the capitulum of the rib. In others, such as *Salamandra*, this basiventral bar is scarcely preformed in cartilage and is represented by a ligament which ossifies directly. Göppert concluded that the original connexion of the rib was by means of its ventral capitular head with an outgrowth of the basiventral passing below the vertebral artery, that this parapophysis tends to become reduced and that an upgrowth of the basiventral, distal to the artery, joins the neural arch above, forming the main part of the rib-bearer (Rippenträger) and affording further support to the rib. The upper branch of the rib would then be secondary. This theory of a special ' rib-bearer ' has been generally accepted, but is of very doubtful value. The view that the dorsal limb of the rib-bearer is only secondarily attached to the neural arch and is not a true transverse process rests on the slender evidence that in some forms, such as Triton and *Necturus*, its cartilaginous rudiment is early separated from the basidorsal by a thin layer of bone (Knickmeyer, 111 ; Göppert, 106). This may well be a secondary separation due to the great reduction of cartilage and premature appearance of bone ; for, in many Urodeles, the cartilage occurs in continuity with that of the arch like a true diapophysis, especially in the caudal region (*Amphiuma*, Davison, 16). Gamble, indeed, finds that in *Necturus* the rib-bearer develops not as an upgrowth but as a downgrowth from the arch which meets the ventral parapophysis. In the anterior segments the rib is borne by the combined extremities of the rib-bearer and the basal stump ; while more posteriorly the rib-bearer enlarges, grows ventrally, and intervenes between the basiventral and the rib. It would seem, then, that the rib was originally articulated as usual by its capitulum to the basiventral below and by its tuberculum to the basidorsal above, that it has been carried outwards at the extremity of a process formed by the combination of the parapophysis with the diapophysis ; and that, as the portion of this ' transverse process' derived from the diapophysis increased more and more at the expense of the parapophysis, the attachment of the capitulum shifted on to it, Figs. 85, 626.

This conclusion is borne out by observations on the structure and development of the bicipital ribs of the Apoda, where the tuberculum abuts against an outgrowth of the neural arch, and the capitulum against a more ventral cartilage representing the basiventral (Göppert, Marcus and Blume, 62).

The reduced single-headed rib of Anura is attached to a ' transverse process ', apparently a lateral outgrowth of the neural arch, but passing below the vertebral artery. It is doubtful, however, whether the vertebral artery in the various groups is strictly homologous and constant in position (Schöne, 114), and the evidence does not allow us to decide whether the process represents a parapophysis which has shifted dorsally, or a true diapophysis.

In conclusion it may be pointed out that the ribs of Gnathostomes are extensions outwards in the myosepta of the basiventrals; that in the Chondrichthyes the ribs are of the upper or dorsal type, situated in the horizontal septum; that in Tetrapods the ribs are of the same type although they may bend ventrally and surround the coelomic cavity of the trunk; that the Osteichthyes are provided with ribs of the lower or pleural type situated internally to the musculature in the wall of the coelom; and that in some (Polypterini and Teleostei) both types of ribs may apparently coexist. That the haemal arches are derived from the basiventrals seems certain; but it is not clear that the pleural ribs always share in their formation (Teleostei), although this seems to be their fate in the lower Teleostomes and Tetrapods.

Further research is necessary to determine whether the pleural ribs of Osteichthyes have or have not been phylogenetically derived from ancestral dorsal ribs.

## THE STERNUM

A typical sternum is found among living Gnathostomes only in Amniota, where it occurs as a median ventral endoskeletal plate in the thoracic region. It serves for protection of the organs in the thoracic cavity, for the attachment of pectoral limb muscles, and in respiratory movements, the first and a varying number of more posterior thoracic ribs being articulated to it ventrally. In Reptiles it is usually in the form of a shield-shaped cartilage narrowing behind and prolonged into paired slender processes joined to ribs. In flying Birds the plate develops a median keel affording greater surface of attachment for the powerful wing muscles, Figs. 86, 192. An analogous but smaller keel may arise on the sternum of Pterodactyles and Chiroptera. Paired ossifications may occur in the sternum of Ornithischian Dinosaurs; and in Aves the whole sternum becomes completely ossified from similar paired centres, Figs. 86, 188.

The mammalian sternum is in the form of a comparatively narrow longitudinal bar of cartilage which becomes more or less completely segmented and ossified into median sternebrae alternating and articulating with the ventral ends of the sternal ribs. The anterior segment (manubrium sterni), however, is longer and projects beyond the articulation with the first rib. Behind the sternum usually expands into a xiphisternal cartilaginous plate or is continued into two diverging processes.[1] When a dermal interclavicle is present it is applied to the ventral surface of the sternum.

In all Amniotes a close relation is early established between the sternum and anterior ribs which together come to encircle the thoracic cavity. But in no modern Amphibian does such a connexion exist. The

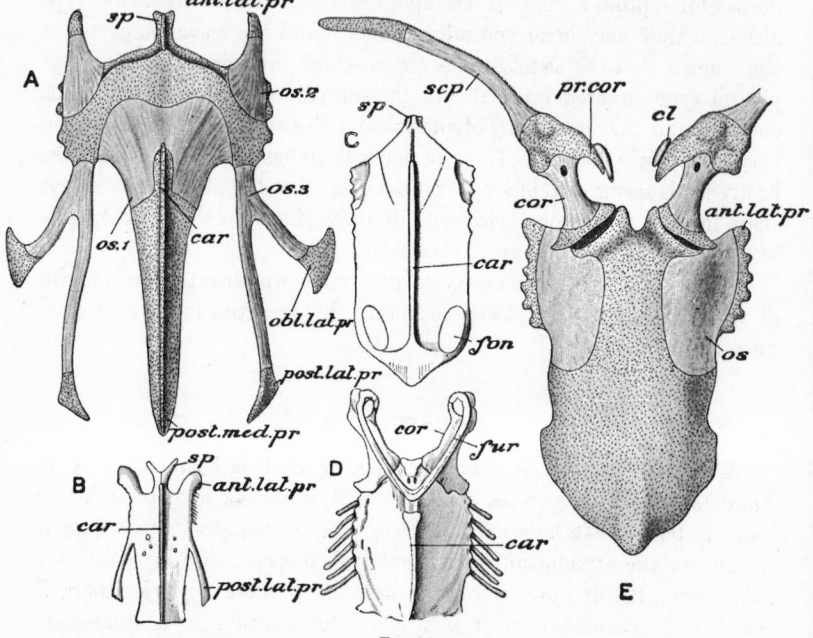

FIG. 86.

Sterna of various birds. A, *Gallus* (common fowl, young); B, *Turdus* (thrush); C, *Vultur* (vulture); D, *Procellaria* (petrel); E, *Casuarius* (cassowary). *ant.lat.pr*, Anterior lateral process; *car*, carina; *cl*, clavicle; *cor*, coracoid; *fon*, fontanelle; *fur*, furcula; *obl.lat.pr*, oblique lateral process; *os*, paired ossification of sternum in E; *os*. 1, carinal ossification in A; *os*. 2, *os*. 3, lateral ossifications; *post.med.pr*, posterior median process; *post.lat.pr*, posterior lateral process; *pr.cor*, procoracoid; *scp*, scapula; *sp*, spina sterni. (A and E after W. K. Parker; B, C, and D from Bronn's *Thierreich*.)

sternum is absent in Apoda, where it has no doubt been lost, and in Urodela is represented by a median plate of cartilage wedged in between the posterior ventral ends of the coracoids, and widely separated from the short ribs, Fig. 87. A somewhat similar plate occurs in arciferous Anura; and in Firmisternia there may be, in addition to this posterior sternum (ossified in part), a similar median plate and ossification ('omosternum') attached to the anterior border of the girdle, Fig. 87. Whether this anterior 'prezonal' element is of the same nature as the 'postzonal' sternum of these and

[1] The Mammalian sternum is sometimes described as composed of anterior presternum (manubrium), middle mesosternum (several sternebrae), and posterior xiphisternum (behind last sternal rib).

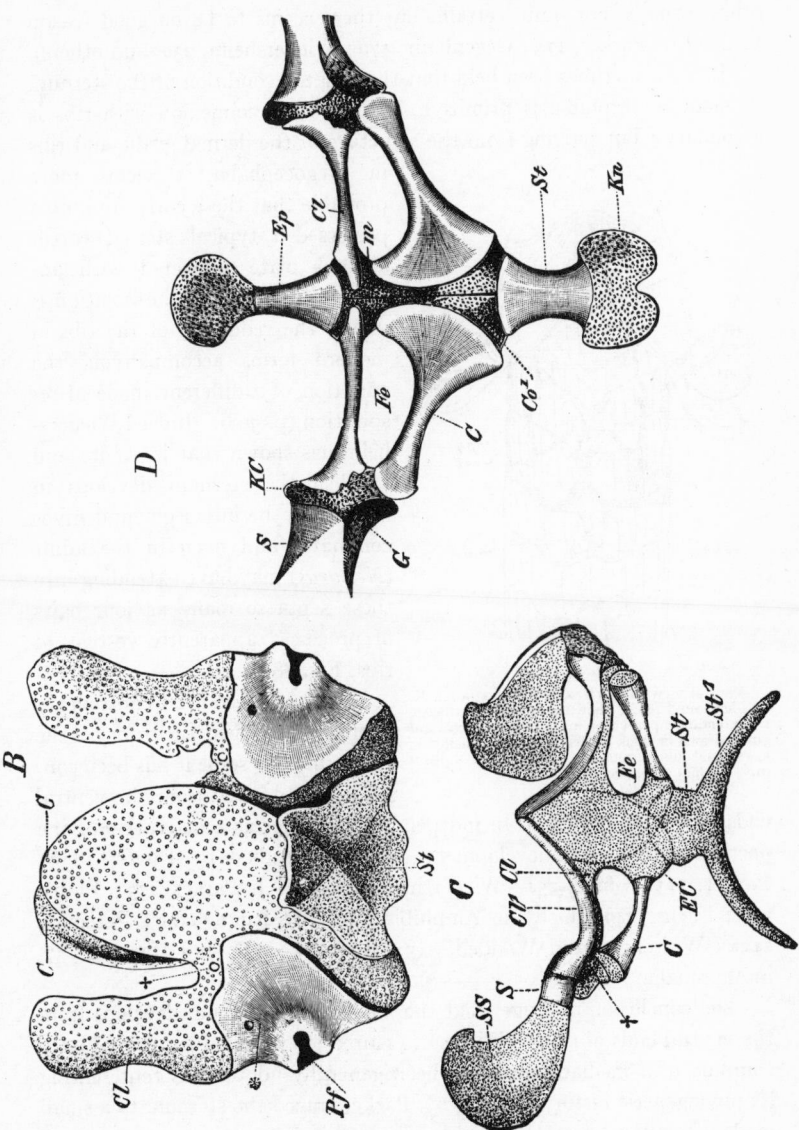

FIG. 87.

Pectoral arch of various amphibians. From the ventral side. B, Axolotl (*Amblystoma*); **C**, *Bombinator igneus*; D, *Rana esculenta*. C, coracoid; Cl, procoracoid; Cl¹ (Cl in D), clavicle; EC, Co¹, epicoracoid; Ep, omosternum; Fe, fenestra between procoracoid and coracoid bars; Kn, cartilaginous xiphisternum; †, Pf, G, glenoid cavity for the humerus; S, scapula; SS, supra-scapula St, St¹, sternum. *, † (in B) indicate nerve-apertures. (From Wiedersheim, *Comp. Anatomy*.)

other forms is not quite certain, but there seems to be no good reason to deny it (Parker, 113; Gegenbaur, 170; Wiedersheim, 230, and others).

It has sometimes been held that the isolated condition of the sternum in modern Amphibia is primitive, and that the connexion with ribs is secondary; but judging from the structure of the dermal girdle and ribs in Stegocephalia, it seems more probable that these early Amphibia possessed a typical sternal cartilaginous plate connected with anterior ribs, and that the isolation is due to the reduction of the ribs in modern forms accompanying the adoption of a different mode of respiration (p. 598). Indeed Wiedersheim has shown that in Anura and Urodela the sternum develops in relation to the intersegmental myocommata, and even in the adult (*Necturus*) may have extending into these septa so many as four pairs of processes, apparently vestiges of ribs, Fig. 88.

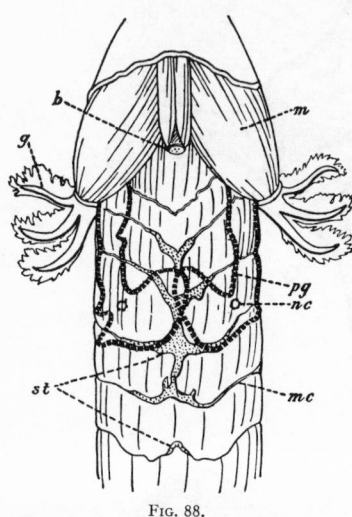

Fig. 88.

Ventral view of *Necturus maculatus* (after R. Wiedersheim, 1892), showing sternal cartilages, *st*, extending up myocommata, *mc*, and pectoral girdle drawn in thick broken line, *pg*; *b*, basihyal; *g*, external gill; *m*, muscle; *mc*, transverse septum (myocomma); *nc*, nerve foramen.

There has been much controversy about the phylogenetic history of the sternum. By some it has been considered as derived from the ventral ends of ribs, by others as of independent origin or as a derivative of the pectoral girdle. Its development has been studied by Dugés, 1835; Parker, 113; Götte, 254; Wiedersheim, 230; T. J. Parker, 113; Braus, 238; Fuchs, 249, chiefly in Amphibia; and by Ruge, 112b; Paterson, 112a; Whitehead and Waddell, 115; Krawetz, 273; and Hanson, 257, in Mammalia.

The conclusion of Ruge, that the mammalian sternum develops from the ventral ends of ribs which fuse to paired longitudinal bands and later combine to a median plate, has been generally adopted as representing its phylogenetic history. But T. J. Parker traced the sternum to a small median cartilage, first described by Haswell, between the ventral ends of the coracoids in *Notidanus* (113), and Howes distinguished an anterior 'coracoidal' from a posterior 'costal' element (263-4). No true sternum has been found in any Dipnoan or Teleostome; but infracoracoid cartilages sometimes occur in Pisces (pp. 166, 171), and may fuse to a median piece. There is no convincing evidence, however, that such coracoidal derivatives have given rise to even a part of the sternum of Tetrapods, as held by these authors and recently by Hanson.

On the other hand, from the work of Paterson, Krawetz, Whitehead and Waddell, and Hanson, it appears that in mammals the paired sternal bands first appear as procartilaginous rudiments independently of ribs with which they later become connected, and that Ruge missed the early stages,

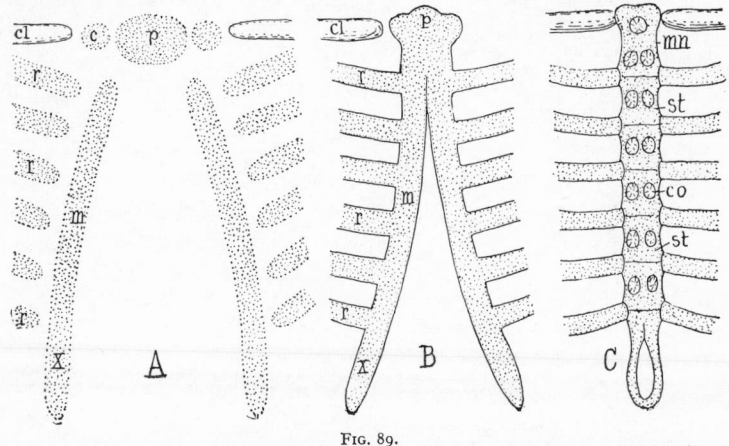

FIG. 89.

Scheme of development of *mammalian sternum*. A, Precartilaginous, early stage ; B, cartilage, halves beginning to unite ; C, beginning of ossification. c (?) Coracoid procartilage ; *cl*, clavicle ; *co*, centres of ossification ; *m*, longitudinal mesosternal element ; *mn*, manubrium ; *p*, pro- or presternum ; *r*, ribs ; *st*, sternebrae ; *x*, xiphisternum. (From J. S. Kingsley, *Vertebrate Skeleton*, 1925.)

Fig. 89. In front of the bands appears a separate median rudiment of the ' prosternum ', an element of doubtful origin which contributes to the formation of the manubrium sterni. It is this prosternal rudiment which has been claimed as of coracoidal origin ; but it possibly represents a vestige of the interclavicle. In addition, paired cartilaginous rudiments may combine with it as in Marsupials, or remain separate as in many lower Mammals, and give rise to small cartilages or bones in adult Insectivores and Rodents (omosternal elements of Parker ; praeclavium). The origin and significance of these paired structures, however, are insufficiently known, and worthy of further study.

In Reptiles and Birds the sternum also develops from paired longitudinal bands, at first widely separated but later fusing from before backwards. These rudiments are continuous with the ribs even in early procartilaginous stages (Juhn, **271** ; Bogoljubsky, **273**).

It may be concluded that the true sternum of the Amniota is of paired origin, and is closely associated with the ventral end of ribs if not actually derived from them ; that it belongs to the axial rather than to the appendicular skeleton ; that the sternum of modern Amphibia is probably of the same nature, and has become secondarily isolated owing to the reduction of the ribs ; and, finally, that the pectoral girdle has probably contributed little or nothing to its development.

# CHAPTER II

## MEDIAN FINS

## THE MEDIAN ENDOSKELETAL FIN-SUPPORTS AND NEURAL SPINES

AN important question relating to the morphology of the skeleton of the median fins of Fishes concerns the significance of the so-called 'neural spines'. There has been some confusion about the use of this term and the parts to which it has been applied. Doubtless, strictly speaking, the

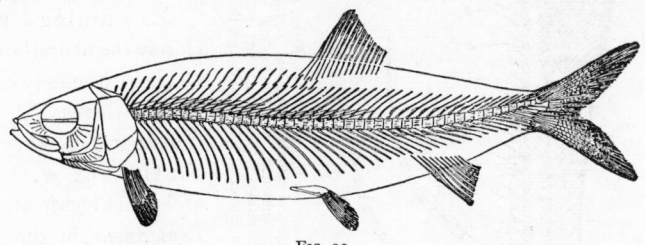

FIG. 90.

*Leptolepis dubius*: restoration, scales omitted. U. Jurassic: Bavaria. (From A. S. Woodward, *Vertebrate Palaeontology*, 1898.)

name neural spine should only be given to the median dorsal process projecting above the longitudinal ligament and formed by the fusion of the right and left half of the neural arch. Such a true neural spine is found in Amniotes and Amphibia, but does not occur either in Chondrichthyes or in Dipnoi. The neural arches of Teleostomes, however, are often prolonged dorsally far beyond the ligament as slender rods, which remain separate as a rule in the anterior segments but fuse to a median

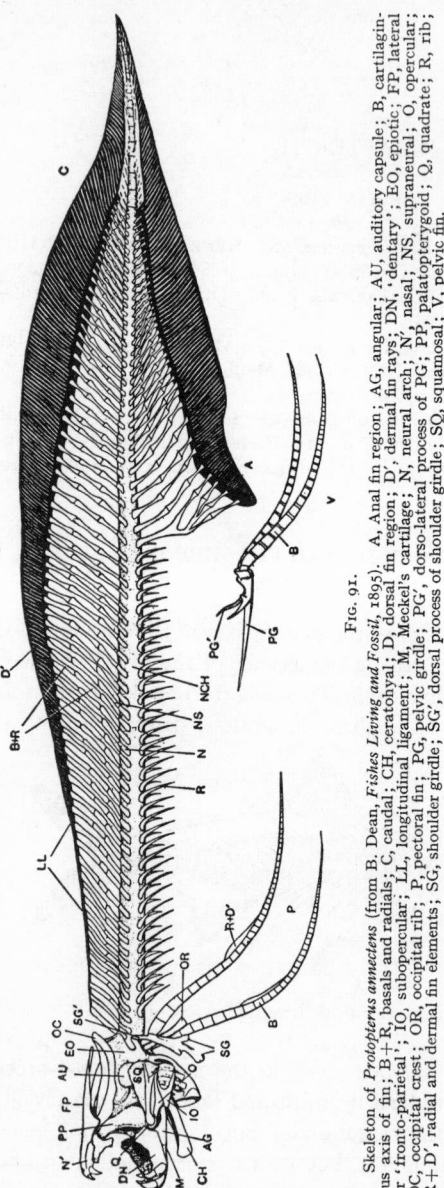

FIG. 91.

Skeleton of *Protopterus annectens* (from B. Dean, *Fishes Living and Fossil*, 1895). A, Anal fin region; AG, angular; AU, auditory capsule; B, cartilaginous axis of fin; B+R, basals and radials; C, caudal; CH, ceratohyal; D, dorsal fin region; D', dermal fin rays; DN, 'dentary'; EO, epiotic; FP, lateral or 'fronto-parietal'; IO, suboercular; LL, longitudinal ligament; M, Meckel's cartilage; N, neural arch; N', nasal; NS, supraneural; O, opercular; OC, occipital crest; OR, occipital rib; P, pectoral fin; PG, pelvic girdle; PG', dorso-lateral process of PG; PP, palatopterygoid; Q, quadrate; R, rib; R+D', radial and dermal fin elements; SG, shoulder girdle; SG', dorsal process of shoulder girdle; SQ, squamosal; V, pelvic fin.

rod in the caudal region. This kind of neural spine is little developed in Chondrostei, but more so in Holostei, and most of all in the higher Teleostei. Probably such spines are merely analogous to the true neural spine of Tetrapods, and may have been independently developed in the Pisces, Figs. 35-9, 49.

Corresponding to the dorsal neural spines similar haemal spines may be developed in the caudal region of Pisces (Chondrichthyes and Teleostomes) from the haemal arches; to determine their exact homology is a difficult task (see pp. 101, 110).

Examining more closely the neural 'spines' of Teleostomes we find that, whereas in the caudal region they are continuous with the arches in Chondrostei and *Lepidosteus*, in the more anterior segments they become separated off above the longitudinal ligament from the true neural arches below— these separate pieces may be called supraneural

spines or supraneurals. Such separate supraneurals occur possibly in some Selachii, especially near the base of the dorsal fins. Separate supraneurals are well developed in the lower Amioidei (Eugnathidae, Pachycormidae) and lower Teleostei (Leptolepidae, Fig. 90), but tend to disappear in the higher forms. Rods persisting near the head in modern forms (*Amia*, many Teleosts, Figs. 35, 50) are probably radials.

Similarly the haemal arches meet ventrally to form median haemal spines, and in the anterior caudal region become separated off to form what may be called infrahaemal spines or infrahaemals. In Teleostomes, such as *Amia*, Figs. 35-8, the gradual transition from haemal spine to infrahaemal spine can easily be seen. There can be no doubt, then, that there is no fundamental difference between the fused and the free pieces ; neural and supraneural spines are homologous elements, and the same may be said of haemal and infrahaemal spines.

But in the Dipnoi, where supraneurals and infrahaemals are most regularly developed, they form the basal piece of a segmented skeletal rod extending and supporting the base of the median dorsal and median ventral fins respectively. Towards the head, where the dorsal fin is reduced, this rod becomes two-jointed, and finally is formed of a single piece. A similar reduction occurs towards the tip of the tail, Figs. 33, 91.

The study of the ' neural spines ' in living and fossil fishes brings us to the consideration of an important question regarding the general morphology of the median fin-supports or radials and their relation to the axial skeleton : whether they are only secondarily connected with the vertebral column, or were primarily derived from it.

Thacher (219) and others considered that the radials are special structures developed to support the median fins, comparable to the radials of the paired fins, therefore forming part of the appendicular skeleton and only coming into secondary connexion with the axial skeleton.[1] On the contrary, Gegenbaur, 1870, and Cope (152) regarded the median fin radials as derivatives of the axial skeleton which may become secondarily separated off and specialised. Gegenbaur, indeed, considered them to be merely extensions of the neural and haemal spines. According to Cope the several pieces of each ray were simultaneously developed in lines of

---

[1] Schmalhausen (133), after a careful study of the development and structure of the median fins of fishes, adopts Thacher's view that the radials have secondarily become connected with the axial skeleton, especially in the tail. He bases his conclusion chiefly on embryological grounds. But here, as so often when dealing with ontogeny, the evidence may be read either way. The fact that the distal ends of the caudal haemal arches may sometimes chondrify separately and later become fused, may be considered either as a repetition of phylogeny, or as an indication that they are tending to become free and would fail to fuse if the process were carried further.

maximum strain, extended originally from neural arch to fin-base, and
became differentiated into proximal neural spine, middle 'axonost',
and distal 'baseost'. The axonost afterwards being separated from

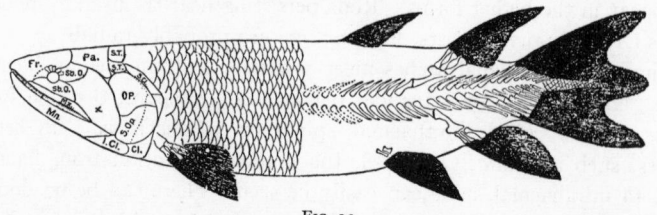

FIG. 92.

*Eusthenopteron foordi.* Restoration by J. F. Whiteaves, scales omitted in caudal region to expose
axial skeleton and bases of median fin. U. Devonian: Scaumenac Bay, Canada. (From A. S. Woodward,
*Vertebrate Palaeontology*, 1898.) *Cl*, Cleithrum ; *Fr*, frontal ; *I.Cl*, infracleithrum ; *Mn*, mandible ;
*Mx*, maxillary ; *OP*, operculum ; *Pa*, parietal ; *S.Cl*, supraclavicle ; *S.Op*, suboperculum; *S.T*, supratemporal; *Sb.O*, suborbital ; *x*, cheek-plate.

the spine, became the 'interspinal' of Cuvier, which together with the
baseost supports the fin-base.

In support of this theory of the derivation of the median fin-supports
from the axial skeleton it may be pointed out that the separation of the
radials from the vertebral column is clearly related to the need for the

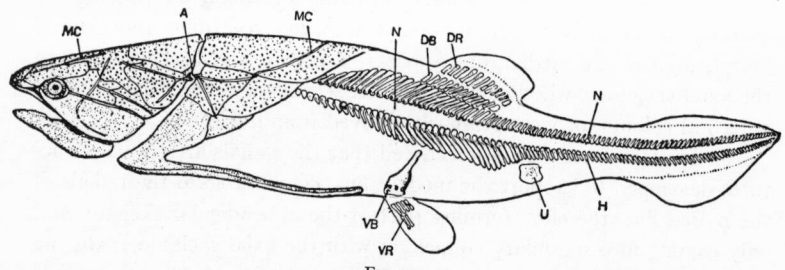

FIG. 93.

*Coccosteus decipiens.* Left-side view, restored (after A. S. Woodward, from B. Dean, *Fishes Living
and Fossil*, 1895). A, Articulation of head with trunk ; DB, cartilaginous basals ; DR, cartilaginous
radials of dorsal fin ; H, haemal arch and spine ; MC, lateral line canals ; N, neural arch and spine ;
U, median plate ; VB, pelvic girdle ; VR, radials of pelvic fin.

independent action of well-developed and isolated median fins in the
more active fishes. It generally accompanies the necessary concentration
of the radials at the base of dorsal and anal fins. Originally they were
of necessity strictly segmental as in Dipnoi ; but, when concentration
occurs, some if not all of the radials must become detached from their
corresponding neural arches (p. 118). Yet even in Selachians, where
the fin-skeleton is usually well separated from the column, it may rest
directly on the dorsal ligament in some sharks (as in *Squalus*, Fig. 24),
and especially in Rhina and other Rajiformes (*Raja*, Fig. 136). Moreover,

in the practically continuous dorsal fin of the Pleuracanthodii the radials
are closely connected with the neural arches
much as in Dipnoi, Fig. 94 (Fritsch, 23;
Brongniart, 149, etc.). Little is known
about the median fin-supports of the Osteolepidoti; in *Eusthenopteron*, however, not
only are they articulated to the arches in
the dorsal and ventral caudal fins, but also
some of them in the dorsal and anal, Fig. 92.
The Coelacanthini also have caudal radials
resting on the neural and haemal spines;
but those of the dorsal and anal fins are
extremely concentrated to single pieces
separated from the axial skeleton, Fig. 95.

The radials of the Actinopterygii seem
never to be so closely connected with the
distal ends of the spines as those of the
Dipnoi, though they may reach them and
often even overlap them (interspinous
bones, Fig. 141).

Generally, and probably primitively,
the radials are subdivided into three pieces
(dorsal fin of Pleuracanthodii, etc.). In
Selachii these may be of approximately
equal length, Fig. 132; but specialisation
leads to the further subdivision of the
elements or to their fusion (Mivart, and p.
119). The radials of the Holocephali remain
unsegmented, and those of the Dipnoi
have segments. The Teleostomi also have
their radials usually subdivided into three
pieces (Thacher, 219; Bridge, 118; Schmalhausen, 133); but while the proximal piece
becomes the main support (interspinal,
axonost), the middle piece is shortened, and
the distal element further reduced in size.
In the higher forms the bases of the

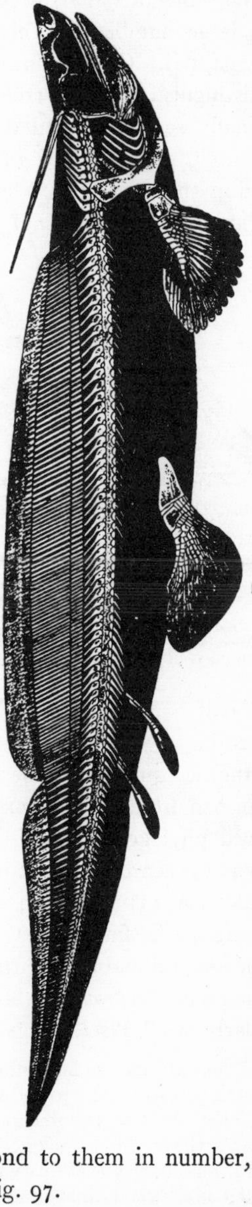

FIG. 94.

*Pleuracanthus Decheni.* Lower Permian of Bohemia; skeleton and outline restored. (After A. Fritsch, modified; from *Brit. Mus. Guide.*)

paired lepidotrichia, which come to correspond to them in number, are
firmly fixed to these rounded distal pieces, Fig. 97.

In the paired fins there are typically two radials to each segment (p.
125), and in the median fins also there may be two to each body-segment,

one opposite the neural arch and the other between two arches. Such a double series of radials occurs in the median fin of Pleuracanthodii and in a large number of Teleostomes (Chondrostei, and many Teleostei, Figs. 94, 96). Owing, however, to concentration it is not always easy to distinguish between true duplication and mere crowding together of originally segmental radials such as occurs, for instance, in *Scyllium* (Goodrich, **172**) and *Salmo* (Harrison, **179**). Both processes may be combined in the same fin. Whether the double number is due to secondary duplication of the original radial, or to the development of a radial in

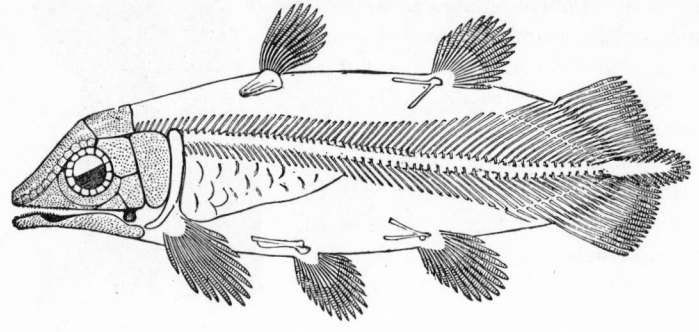

FIG. 95.

*Undina gulo.* Restoration, omitting scales and supraclavicle. L. Jurassic: Dorsetshire. (From A. S. Woodward, *Vertebrate Palaeontology*, 1898.) The extent of the ossified air-bladder is indicated beneath the notochordal axis in the abdominal region.

each half of a segment (corresponding to basalia and interbasalia), is uncertain.

Another question to be considered is how can a true radial be distinguished from a distal extension of a neural spine. If the former is derived phylogenetically from the latter no hard and fast line can be drawn between them; but it may be held that a supporting rod is a true radial when it is related to a pair of radial muscles (p. 114). These right and left special fin-muscles, whose fibres run parallel to the rods and not to the longitudinal axis of the body as in the myomeres, are present in the median fins of *Petromyzon* both on the trunk and tail,[1] Fig. 98, and occur regularly in all Pisces, Figs. 102, 130.[2] Their distal ends are attached

[1] Their absence in Myxinoidea and at the extreme end of the tail of *Petromyzon* is probably due to reduction and degeneration.

[2] They tend to become modified or reduced in the caudal fin. Schmalhausen's theory that the median fins of the Dipnoi are not true dorsal and ventral fins, but caudal fins which have grown forward, is manifestly contrary to palaeontological, anatomical, and embryological evidence. His contention that the Dipnoan fin-muscles are not true radial muscles because they do not develop from muscle-buds cannot be accepted. Median fin-muscles like

chiefly to the skin and dermal rays.    In the Selachii each muscle becomes subdivided into inner and outer regions, and they are further
specialised in Teleostomes.    Those of the Holostei become differentiated

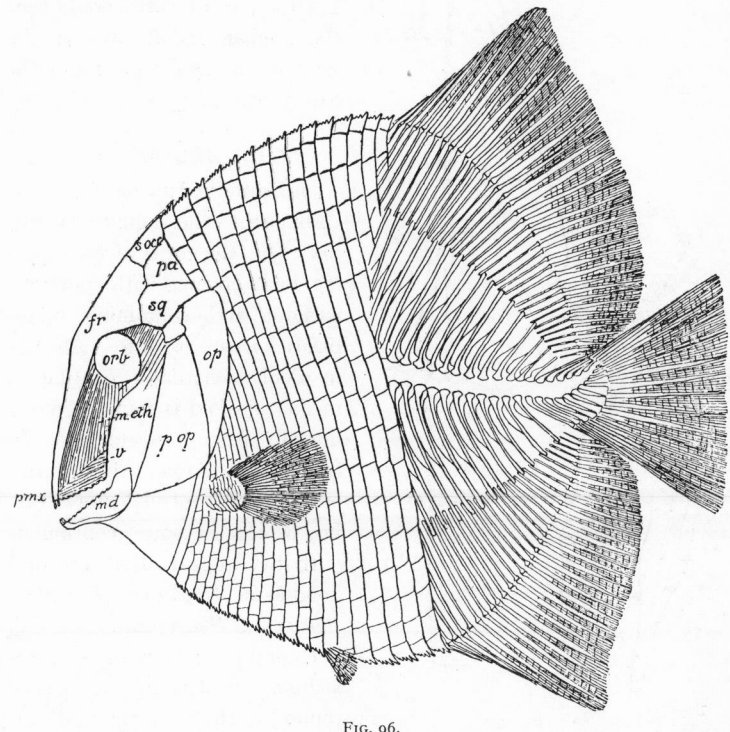

FIG. 96.

*Mesodon macropterus.*   Restoration, with cheek-plates removed.   U. Jurassic: Bavaria.   (From A. S.
Woodward, *Vertebrate Palaeontology*, 1898.)   *fr*, Frontal ;   *m.eth*, mesethmoid ;   *md*, mandible, showing
narrow dentary in front ;   *op*, operculum ;   *orb*, orbit ;   *p.op*, preoperculum ;   *pa*, parietal ;   *pmx*, premaxillary ;   *s.occ*, supraoccipital ;   *sq*, squamosal ;   *v*, prevomer.   The caudal region is destitute of
scales.

into an elaborate system of mm. inclinatores, erectores, and depressores
serving to move and fold the fins (Harrison, **179** ; Schmalhausen, **133**).

In conclusion, it would appear that the evidence is not yet sufficient
to enable us to assert that the radials of the median fins were derived
from the axial skeleton.    Should future evidence prove the correctness
of this theory we may be compelled to adopt some such view as that

paired limb-muscles may arise either from typical muscle-buds (p. 114) or
from proliferations of the myotomes (anal fin of Selachians, etc.).    Ceratodus
has typical radial muscles in its median fins (Goodrich, **122**) ; but they are
reduced and degenerate in the fins of the more sluggish Protopterus and
Lepidosiren.

foreshadowed by Owen in describing his 'archetype': namely, that the skeleton of the paired limbs was also originally related to the axial skeleton by means of the ribs. For there can be little doubt that the median radials are of the same nature as the radials of the paired fins (p. 132).

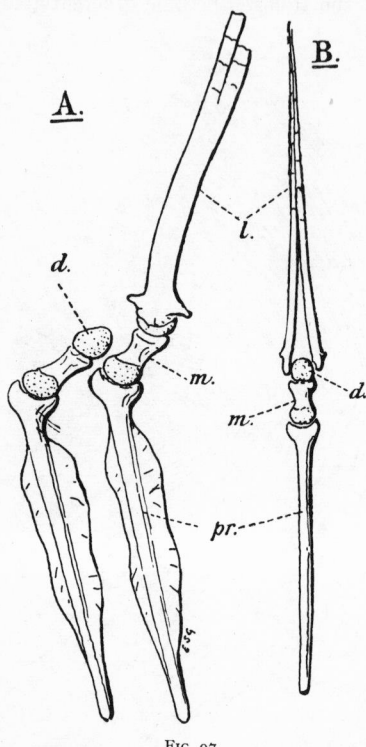

Fig. 97.

*Esox lucius*, L. A, two radials of the dorsal fin, left-side view; B, radial and dermal ray from in front. *d*, Distal cartilage; *m*, median segment, and *pr*, proximal segment of radial; *l*, lepidotrich, broken short in A. (From Goodrich, *Vert. Craniata*, 1909.)

### THE MEDIAN FINS

Longitudinal median fins occur throughout the aquatic vertebrates in the form of outstanding folds covered with epidermis without and containing mesoblastic tissue within. Already in Cephalochorda a continuous median fin-fold is found running dorsally from head to tail. In front it passes round the anterior end into a ventral 'subrostral' fin, which becomes continuous with the right fold of the oral hood as in *Amphioxus* (*Branchiostoma*) and *Heteropleuron*, or with both oral hood folds as in *Asymmetron*. Posteriorly it passes round the tip of the tail and runs forward ventrally to the atriopore, passing to the right of the anus. In the postanal region the median fins are usually expanded to a caudal fin; but in *Asymmetron* the pronounced ventral expansion is farther forward. In both *Heteropleuron* and *Asymmetron* the right metapleural fold is continued into the median fin behind the atriopore (Lankester, Andrews, Willey, Kirkaldy, **127**). The dorsal fin-fold is strengthened by a series of 'fin-rays' (some 250 in *Amphioxus*), more numerous than the segments (about 5 per segment). They dwindle and disappear before reaching the anterior and posterior ends of the body. Each 'fin-ray' consists of a mass of gelatinous tissue projecting into a box formed of a double layer of epithelium apparently derived from the sclerotomes (Stieda, 1873; Hatschek, **124**). A similar series of rays supports the ventral fin behind the anus; but between anus and atriopore the rays are for the most part in pairs, suggesting that in this region the fin is formed by the coalescence of paired folds.

Speaking generally, the median fins of the Craniata are similar longitudinal folds into which extends the median connective tissue septum dividing the body into right and left halves.[1]  In this septum are developed supporting endoskeletal rods or radials (fin-supports, pterygiophores,

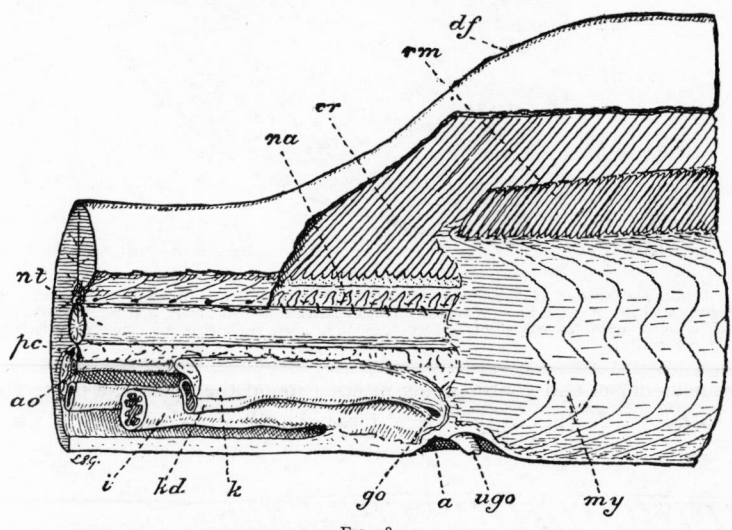

Fig. 98.

*Petromyzon marinus*, L.  Left-side view of the trunk region near the base of the dorsal fin; the skin and muscles have been partially removed.  *a*, Anus; *ao*, dorsal aorta; *cr*, cartilage rays supporting fin; *df*, dorsal fin; *go*, left genital aperture into urinogenital sinus; *i*, intestine; *k*, mesonephros, and *kd*, its duct; *my*, myotome; *na*, neural arch; *nt*, notochord; *pc*, posterior cardinal vein; *rm*, radial muscles of fin; *ugo*, urinogenital opening on papilla.  (From Goodrich, *Vert. Craniata*, 1909.)

somactidia), primarily segmental, and the nature of which is discussed above (p. 89).  Special paired radial muscles, parallel to and corresponding to the radials, serve to move the fin.  Although the median fins appear in the young as continuous dorsal and ventral folds, these usually become subdivided and specialised into separate dorsal, caudal, and postanal fins.  As a rule the subdivision is most complete in the most actively swimming forms, and the fins vary much in shape and extent according to the habits of the fish (Osburn, **202**; Gregory, **123**; Breder, **117**).

**Cyclostomata.**—The Cyclostomes possess median fins, better developed

---

[1] The median fin-folds of larval Anura and of aquatic Urodela have no special muscles, endoskeletal radials, or dermal rays.  These fins are possibly new structures reacquired in adaptation to their aquatic habits, and not directly derived from the median fins of fishes.

in the active Petromyzontia than in Myxinoidea, where they form con-

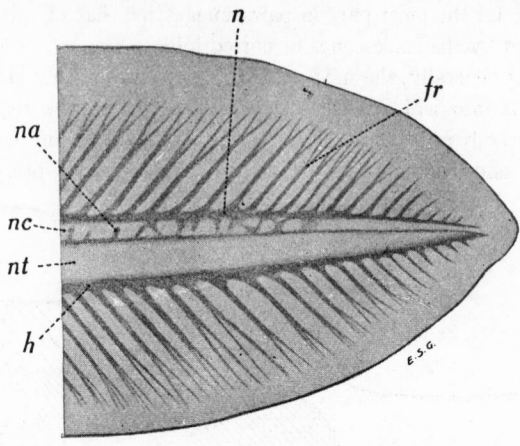

Fig. 99.

*Petromyzon marinus.* Left-side view of end of tail showing the cartilaginous endoskeleton. *fr*, Fin-ray (radial); *h*, fused bases of ventral fin rays forming a haemal canal; *n*, fused bases of dorsal radials in the membranous wall of the neural canal, *nc*; *na*, vestigial neural arch; *nt*, notochord. (Cp. Fig. 101.)

tinuous dorsal and ventral folds meeting round the tip of the tail. The ventral fold reaches to the cloacal pit, and in Myxinoids divides into two

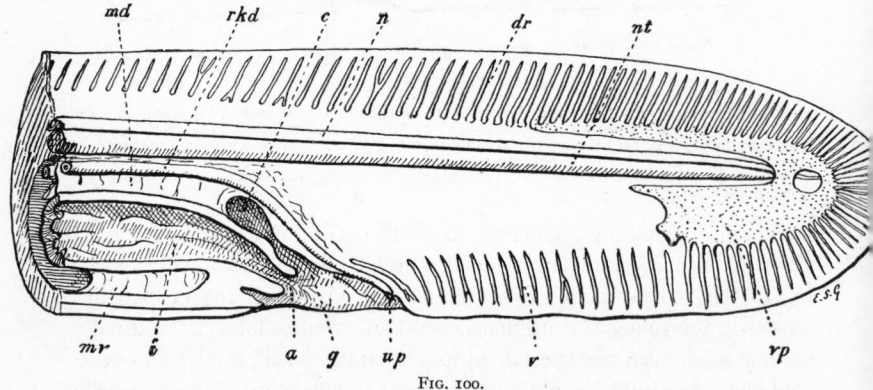

Fig. 100.

Tail of *Myxine glutinosa*, L., cut so as to show the skeleton and the opening of the intestine, etc.; left-side view. *a*, Anus; *c*, gap behind mesentery leading from right to left coelomic cavities; *dr*, cartilage radials of dorsal median fin; *g*, median opening through which the genital cells escape; *i*, intestine; *md*, dorsal mesentery; *mv*, ventral mesentery; *n*, nerve-cord; *nt*, notochord; *rkd*, left kidney duct; *up*, urinary papilla; *v*, cartilage radials of ventral median fin; *vp*, cartilaginous plate. (From Goodrich, *Vert. Craniata*, 1909.)

ridges passing on either side and meeting again in front to a small median fold which extends forwards to near the branchial apertures.

There is a continuous median fin in the Ammocoete larva, but in the adult Petromyzontia the dorsal fold is subdivided and expanded into two dorsal fins separate from the caudal. These dorsal fins are supported by cartilaginous unsegmented median rods, with tapering and branching distal ends reaching to near the margin, and with bases resting on the axial membranous covering of the neural tube. They are about three to

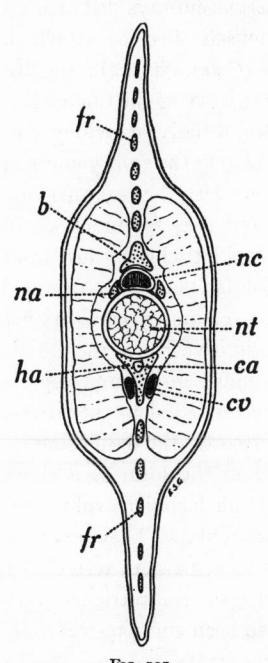

FIG. 101.

*Petromyzon merinus.* Transverse section of tail. *b*, Base of dorsal fin-radial; *ca*, caudal artery; *cv*, caudal vein; *fr*, cartilaginous fin-ray or radial; *ha*, base of ventral fin-radial; *na*, neural arch; *nc*, nerve cord; *nt*, notochord with sheaths.

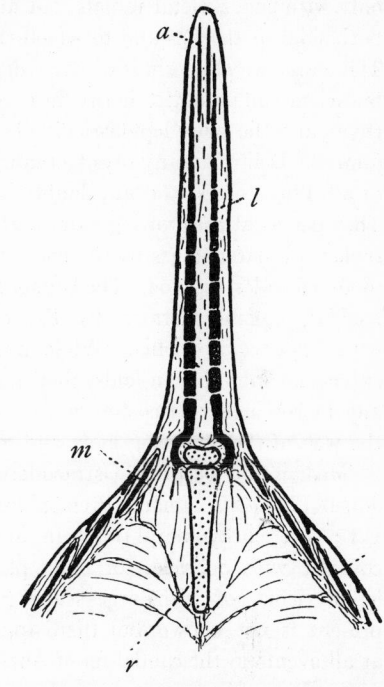

FIG. 102.

Diagram of a section through the dorsal fin of a Teleost. *a*, Actinotrich; *l*, lepidotrich; *m*, radial muscle; *r*, endoskeletal fin-radial; *s*, scale. (From E. S. Goodrich, *Quart. Jour. Micr. Sci.*, v. 47, 1903.)

four times as numerous as the segments, Fig. 98. In both Myxinoidea and Petromyzontia similar cartilaginous rays support the dorsal and ventral lobes of the caudal fin extending round the tip of the notochord; they tend to fuse at their base, forming plates partially enclosing both spinal cord and notochord, Figs. 99, 100, 101. Since these rods are unsegmented, no distinction can be drawn in Cyclostomes between true fin radials and axial rods (p. 92), but radial muscles occur in the dorsal fins of Petromyzontia. All these cartilaginous structures are differentiated in the skeletogenous tissue surrounding the axial nerve chord and notochord and extending into the fin-folds in the embryo (Schaffer, **132**).

Very similar unsegmented branching median rods springing from the axial skeleton seem to have been present in the Devonian *Palaeospondylus* (Traquair, 137-8), and afford evidence of its relationship with the Cyclostomes.

**Pisces.**—Both the median and the paired fins of Pisces are provided not only with endoskeletal radials, but also with dermal fin-rays disposed on both sides of the fins and to which the radial muscles become attached. There are two chief kinds of these dermotrichia (Goodrich, 122) : the unbranched and unjointed horny fin-rays, or ceratotrichia, of the Chondrichthyes, and the bony lepidotrichia of Teleostomes, usually branching and jointed. Delicate horny rays (actinotrichia) develop in the embryonic fins of all Teleostomes, and are doubtless homologous with the ceratotrichia. They persist at the growing margin of the fins ; but they are functionally replaced in later stages by the more superficial lepidotrichia formed from modified scales, Fig. 102. The Dipnoi also have jointed bony rays (camptotrichia), possibly formed by the combination of outer lepidotrichia with deeper ceratotrichia. While in the more primitive Pisces the radials extend far into the fin-folds, they tend in the higher forms, and especially in the higher Teleostomes, to become more restricted to their base, the web of the fins being more and more supported by the dermotrichia.

Median fins occur in Ostracodermi, usually in the form of a short dorsal (*Thelodus*, among Pteraspidomorphi ; Cephalaspidomorphi, Fig. 151 ; Pterichthyomorphi) or an anal fin (Anaspida). They may be covered with denticles, or bony plates in rows somewhat resembling lepidotrichia, or with large scales (whether deeper ceratotrichia were present is not known, but there appear to have been endoskeletal rods, at all events in the caudal fin of Anaspida (Kiaer, 126)).

## THE CAUDAL FIN

The study of the general homology of the skeleton of the median fins has a bearing on our interpretation of the structure of the caudal fin in fishes, a subject of very considerable interest from the point of view not only of morphology, but also of evolution in general. For the development of the caudal fin in the higher fishes affords a most striking instance of so-called recapitulation ; as in other cases, however, it may be interpreted as a repetition of the developmental stages of the ancestor and not of adult phylogenetic stages.

The structure and development of the caudal fin of aquatic Vertebrates has been studied by many authors. Though L. Agassiz, in his great work on Fossil Fishes, 1833, introduced the terms heterocercal and homocercal to indicate externally asymmetrical and symmetrical caudal fins, and McCoy later the term diphicercal for the truly symmetrical form, it was not till Huxley, 1859, studied the development of the tail in *Gasterosteus* that the full significance of the false or secondary symmetry of the homocercal type became apparent. Kölliker then described the anatomy of the tail in 'Ganoids', and Lotz in Teleosts, while A. Agassiz (1878) and Huxley (125) completed our knowledge of the development, and Ryder (130), Emery (121), Gregory (123), and Dollo (119-120) have since made important contributions. Recently Whitehouse (139-140), Totton (136), Regan (129), and Schmalhausen have studied the question in further detail. Three main types have been distinguished: (1) Protocercal (diphycercal)[1]: primitively symmetrical externally and internally, with continuous dorsal epichordal and ventral hypochordal fin-folds equally developed respectively above and below the notochordal axis which is straight. (2) Heterocercal: the posterior end of the notochord is bent upwards, the ventral hypochordal lobe of the fin being more developed than the epichordal, and the caudal fin consequently asymmetrical both externally and internally. (3) Homocercal: the caudal fin is externally

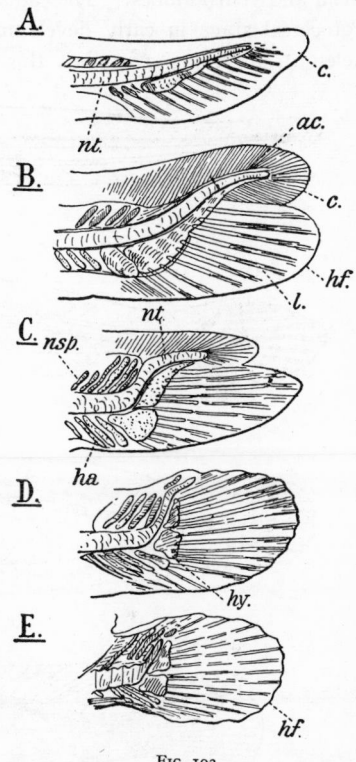

FIG. 103.

Successive stages in the development of the homocercal tail of the Flounder, *Pleuronectes flesus*, L., showing the disappearance of the axial lobe, *c*, and growth of the hypochordal fin, *hf*. *ac*, Actinotrichia; *ha*, haemal arch; *hy*, hypural cartilage; *l*, dermal ray; *nsp*, neural spine; *nt*, notochord. (After A. Agassiz.) (From Goodrich, *Vert. Craniata*, 1909.)

symmetrical but internally asymmetrical, and the notochordal axis upturned and shortened, Fig. 105. As the later types have been derived from the earlier, intermediate forms occur which bridge over the gaps between them and do not quite fit these definitions.

[1] The term diphycercal having been somewhat loosely applied to secondarily symmetrical as well as to primitively symmetrical tails, it is better to use the term protocercal only for the latter (Whitehouse).

A protocercal fin is found in the Acrania (Cephalochorda), the extinct *Palaeospondylus*, and Cyclostomata, Fig. 98. It is adapted for propulsion by an undulating lateral motion of the body. When radials are developed, as in Cyclostomes, they are symmetrically disposed in the dorsal and ventral lobes.[1] The caudal fin of all Pisces passes through a protocercal stage in early development (before the appearance of the skeleton), Figs. 103, 104; but this structure is probably not retained

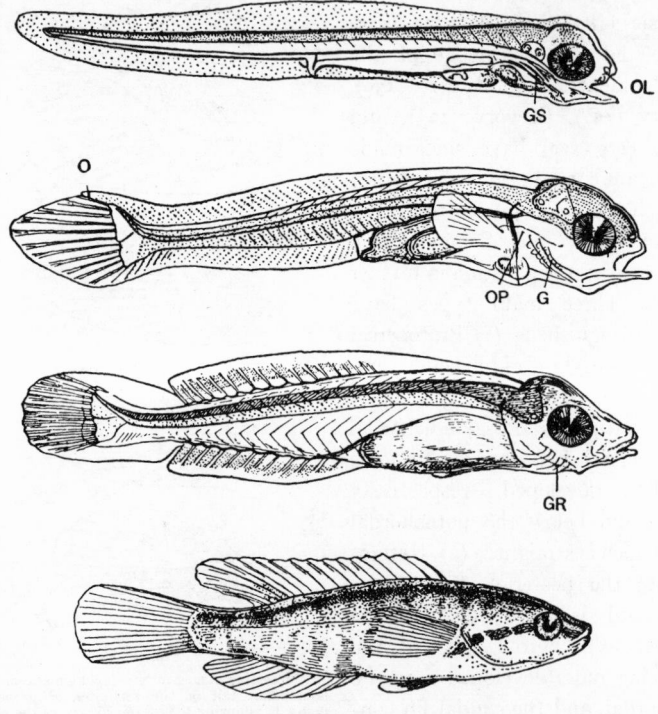

FIG. 104.

Larvae of Teleost, *Ctenolabrus* (after A. Agassiz, from B. Dean, *Fishes Living and Fossil*, 1895). G, Gill-arches; GR, branchiostegal rays; GS, gill-slit; O, region of upturned notochord; OP, opercular fold; OL, olfactory pit.

unmodified in any living fish, although persisting in aquatic Amphibia. The tail of the majority of the lower Pisces is frankly heterocercal. In the typical heterocercal tail of a shark (or Teleostome) the centra remain separate on the upturned axis, except at its extreme tip where they may be represented by a cartilaginous rod (p. 27). Dermal fin-rays are

[1] Even in Cyclostomes the dorsal and ventral lobes are not quite equal. The structure of these fins has already been described above (p. 95).

present in both lobes; especially well developed in the hypochordal lobe, they may become highly modified and reduced in the epichordal lobe. This lobe is supported by a series of closely set radials resting on but mostly separate from the neural arches, Figs. 105, 132 A. Usually, except near the tip, the radials are twice as numerous as the centra, thus corresponding to interbasals as well as basals. The larger hypochordal lobe is strengthened by what appear to be broad prolonga-

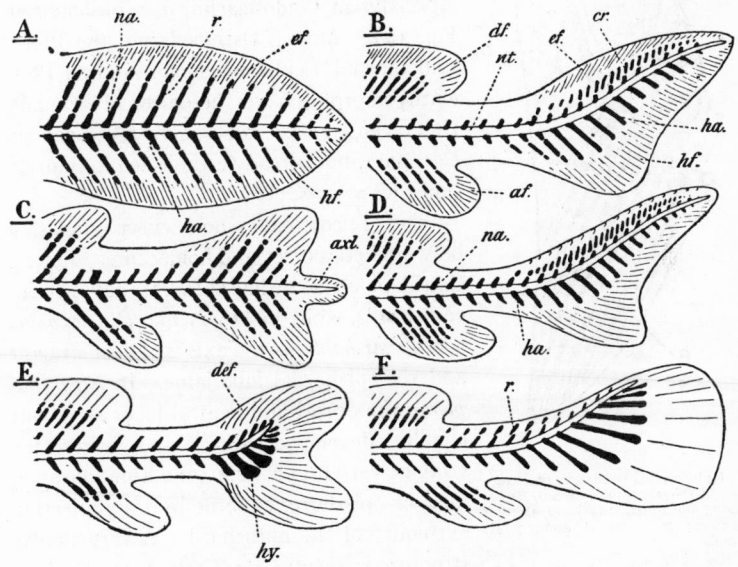

FIG. 105.

Diagrams showing the modifications of caudal fins, and the relations of the endoskeletal radials of median fins to the axial skeleton. A, Protocercal (diphycercal) type, with equal dorsal and ventral lobes (Dipnoi); B, heterocercal type (Selachii); C, modified diphycercal (Coelacanthini); D, heterocercal (Chondrostei); E, homocercal type (Teleostei); F, abbreviate heterocercal type (Amioidei). af, Anal fin; axl, axial lobe; cr, epichordal radial; def, dorsal lobe partly formed by epichordal lobe; df, dorsal fin; ef, epichordal lobe; ha, haemal arch; hf, hypochordal lobe; hy, hypural arch; na, neural arch; nt, notochord; r, radial. The endoskeleton is black. (From Goodrich, *Vert. Craniata*, 1909.)

tions of the haemal spines, known as hypurals. There is good evidence that these represent combined true radials and haemal spines (p. 89), and separate radials often persist anteriorly (Whitehouse, Schmalhausen). Special radial muscles are absent in the dorsal but present in the ventral lobe. Heterocercy is related to fast swimming and active motion, and useful perhaps to counteract the heaviness of the head. The caudal fin, the chief organ of propulsion, is separated from the more anterior dorsal and anal fins, and the enlarged hypochordal lobe enables the fish to rise rapidly. But in many Selachians heterocercy seems to have been secondarily reduced, the ventral lobe diminishes, and the axis tends to become straight (*Scyllium, Chlamydoselachus*). The Holocephali may be typically heterocercal (Callorhynchus), but in many genera inhabiting the deeper waters the caudal fin is much elongated and may almost return to a symmetrical condition (*Harriotta*). In Pleuracanthodii also heterocercy is but feebly developed; in Acanthodii, however, and especially in Cladoselachii, it is pronounced, Fig. 106. Among Ostracodermi, the Pteraspidomorphi, Cephalaspidomorphi, and Pterichthyomorphi have heterocercal caudals. Heterocercy was not only prevalent in Devonian, but already established in Silurian times (*Pteraspis*, etc.).[1]

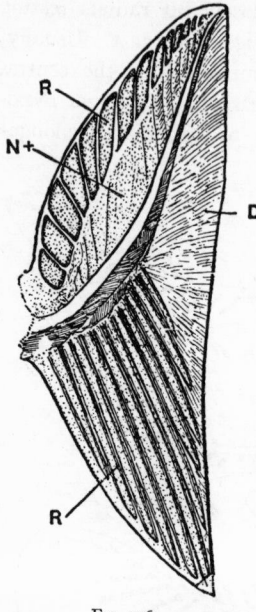

FIG. 106.

Heterocercal caudal fin of *Cladoselache fyleri* (from B. Dean, *Fishes Living and Fossil*, 1895). D, Dermal fin-rays; N+, neural arches; R, radials.

The Teleostomes show every gradation between heterocercy and homocercy. Among Osteolepidoti, some like *Osteolepis* have heterocercal tails, while in others like *Glyptopomus* and *Tristichopterus* the axis is almost straight and the epichordal lobe large. In *Eusthenopteron* the dorsal and ventral lobes are about equally developed above and below the straight vertebral column, and a middle axial lobe, or opisthure, is borne by the projecting extremity of the notochord. A very similar structure is seen in the Coelacanthini, where the notochord is straight and the opisthure distinct, Fig. 95. It is generally held that these more or less symmetrical tails have been secondarily derived from a more primitive heterocercal type; but the evidence is uncertain, Figs. 107-109.

Still more difficult to interpret is the symmetrical tail of modern Dipnoi. Here neither in ontogeny nor in the adult is there any evidence of heterocercy. The posterior extremity of the notochord remains straight, though it, as in many other fishes, undergoes degeneration, becoming enclosed in a cartilaginous rod representing the modified vertebral elements, Figs. 110, 91. Balfour, indeed, considered that the true caudal had degenerated and been replaced by the extended dorsal

---

[1] According to Kiaer's recent account (126) the tail of the Anaspida was of the reversed heterocercal type, with the axis bent downwards, a very small hypochordal and a large epichordal lobe. Such a ' hypocercal ' tail is unique among fishes, but is paralleled by the analogous caudal fin of Ichthyosauria.

and anal fins (116), while Schmalhausen on the contrary believes the
median fins of modern Dipnoi to be formed by the forward growth of the

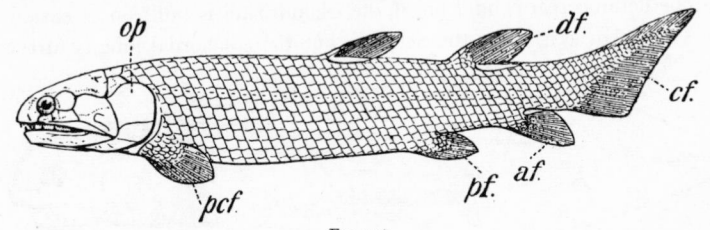

FIG. 107.

*Osteolepis macrolepidotus*, Ag.; restored. (After Traquair.)  *af*, Anal fin; *cf*, caudal fin; *df*,
second dorsal fin; *op*, opercular; *pcf*, pectoral fin; *pf*, pelvic fin. (From Goodrich, *Vert. Craniata*,
1909.)

caudal; neither of these views has good evidence in its favour. Dollo
(119) derives the continuous median fins of modern Dipnoi from the

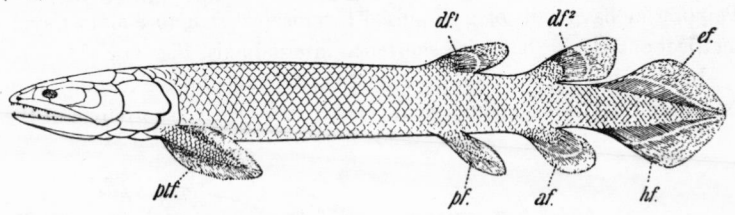

FIG. 108.

Restoration of *Glyptopomus Kinnairdi*, Huxley; Devonian.  (After Huxley, modified.)  *af*, Anal,
*df*, dorsal; *ef*, epichordal; *hf*, hypochordal; *pf*, pelvic, and *ptf*, pectoral fin.  (From Goodrich,
*Vert. Craniata*, 1909.)

condition seen in *Dipterus*, where the dorsal and anal fins are separate
and short, and the caudal is heterocercal, through such intermediate
forms as *Uronemus*, *Phaneropleuron*,
and *Scaumenacia* described by Traquair, in which the median fins become
more and more elongated until they
meet and finally fuse into continuous
fins as in modern Dipnoi, Figs. 111, 112.
This view is now generally accepted;
but although *Dipterus* is the earliest
known Dipnoan, yet the occurrence
of *Scaumenacia* already in the Devonian suggests that the continuous
fins may after all be primitive. What-

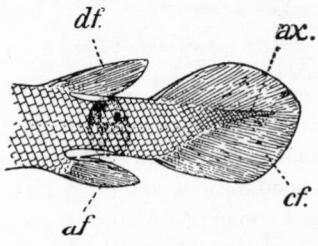

FIG. 109.

Tail of *Diplopterus Agassigii*, Traill. (After
Traquair.) *ax*, Extremity of axis; *af*, anal
fin; *cf*, hypochordal fin; *df*, dorsal fin. (From
Goodrich, *Vert. Craniata*, 1909.)

ever conclusion is reached with regard to the primitive type of caudal
fin in Dipnoi and Teleostomi, it is clear that it must be admitted that

either the symmetrical or the asymmetrical form has been independently acquired in various groups.

The heterocercal caudal fin of the Chondrostei is built on essentially the same plan as that of the Selachii, but the epichordal lobe is further

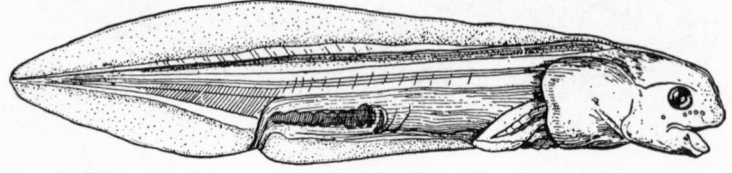

FIG. 110.

Larva of *Ceratodus forsteri*. (After R. Semon, '93, from B. Dean, *Fishes Living and Fossil*, 1895.)

reduced and the lepidotrichia generally remain only as a double series of pointed scales often fused to ∧ shaped fulcra, Figs. 113, 132*a*. The Polypterini have tails of a disguised heterocercal structure almost symmetrical outwardly, but with shortened internal axis, Fig. 114.

In the Holostei a progressive modification takes place leading from the heterocercal to the homocercal type, by the relative shortening of the

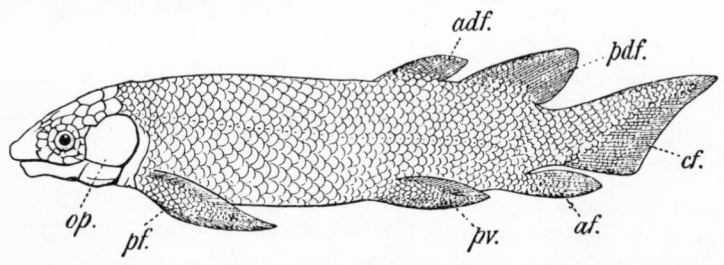

FIG. 111.

*Dipterus Valenciennesii*, Sedgw., restored. (After Traquair, slightly modified.)   *adf*, Anterior dorsal fin; *af*, anal fin; *cf*, caudal fin; *op*, operculum; *pf*, pectoral fin; *pv*, pelvic fin. (From Goodrich, *Vert. Craniata*, 1909.)

axis which is withdrawn to the base of the fin, the great development of the hypochordal fin (more especially its anterior lobe) which projects far beyond the axis, and the reduction of the epichordal fin to a mere vestige. An examination of the stages in the development of these tails shows that the original axial lobe or opisthure takes little or no share in the formation of the adult fin, the dermal rays of which are entirely derived from the hypochordal fin, and in the higher types from its anterior portion chiefly. Thus, in the ordinary forked homocercal caudal, the upper part is derived from the more posterior and the lower part from the more anterior region of the same hypochordal fin. A few of the dermal rays of the epichordal fin may persist dorsally near the base. Accompanying this reduction of the axis is the gradual establishment of the outward

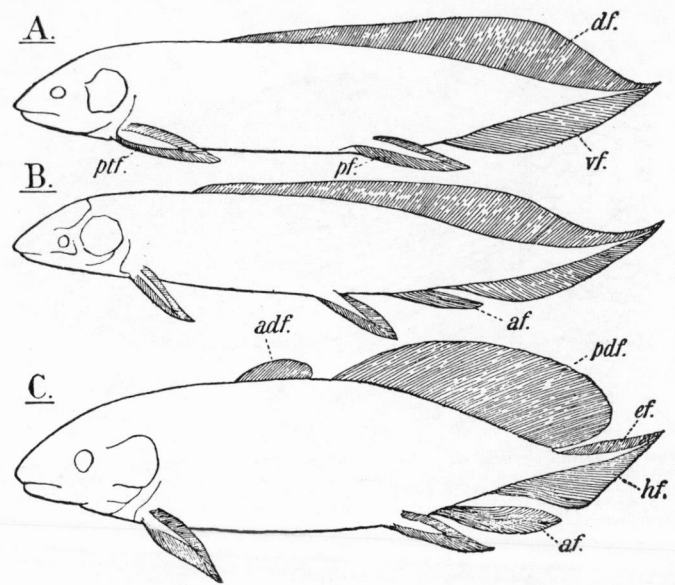

FIG. 112.

Restorations from Traquair of A, *Uronemus lobatus*, Ag., Lower Carboniferous; B, *Phaneropleuron Andersoni*, Huxley, Upper Devonian; C, *Scaumenacia curta*, Whiteaves, Upper Devonian. *adf*, Anterior dorsal fin; *af*, anal fin; *df*, dorsal fin; *ef*, epichordal lobe, and *hf*, hypochordal lobe, of caudal fin; *pdf*, posterior dorsal fin; *pf*, pelvic fin; *ptf*, pectoral fin; *vf*, ventral fin. (From Goodrich, *Vert. Craniata*, 1909.)

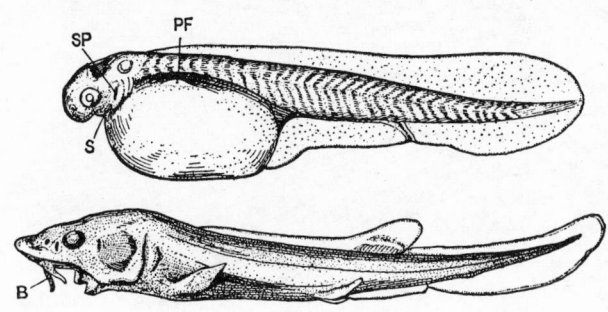

FIG. 113.

Larvae of *Acipenser* (from B. Dean, *Fishes Living and Fossil*, 1895). B, Barbel; PF, pectoral fin; S, mouth; SP, spiracle.

symmetry carried to a wonderful state of perfection in the higher Teleostei; it effects not only the scaling on the tail, but also the disposition of the lepidotrichia in the fin, Figs. 103, 116, 121-2.

The homocercal form is assumed in development not suddenly but gradually ; and tails belonging to the higher grades pass through lower

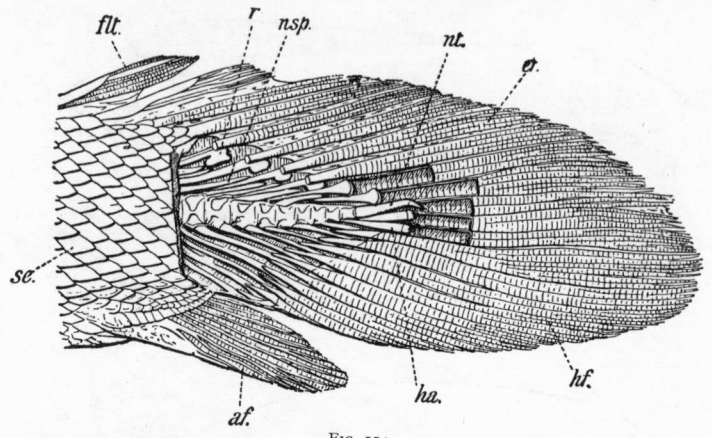

FIG. 114.

Dissected tail of *Polypterus bichir*, Geoffr. (After Kölliker.) *af*, Anal fin ; *ef*, epichordal fin ; *flt*, dorsal finlet ; *ha*, haemal arch ; *hf*, hypochordal fin ; *nsp*, neural spine ; *nt*, slightly upturned tip of the notochord ; *r*, endoskeletal radial ; *sc*, scales. The proximal ends of the dermal rays have been cut off to expose the radials and tip of the notochord. This tail is probably secondarily almost diphycercal. (From Goodrich, *Vert. Craniata*, 1909.)

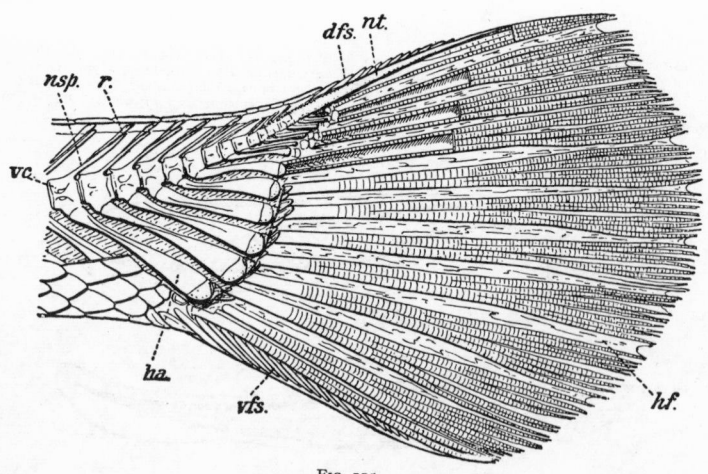

FIG. 115.

Dissected tail of *Lepidosteus*. (After Kölliker.) *dfs*, Dorsal fulcral scales ; *ha*, expanded haemal arch ; *hf*, hypochordal fin ; *nsp*, neural spine ; *nt*, upturned tip of the notochord ; *r*, dorsal radial ; *vc*, vertebral centrum ; *vfs*, ventral fulcral scales. The proximal ends of the dermal rays have been cut off to expose the endoskeleton. (From Goodrich, *Vert. Craniata*, 1909.)

grades in regular sequence. Moreover, intermediate forms occur, as for instance in *Lepidosteus* and *Amia*, between the heterocercal and homo-

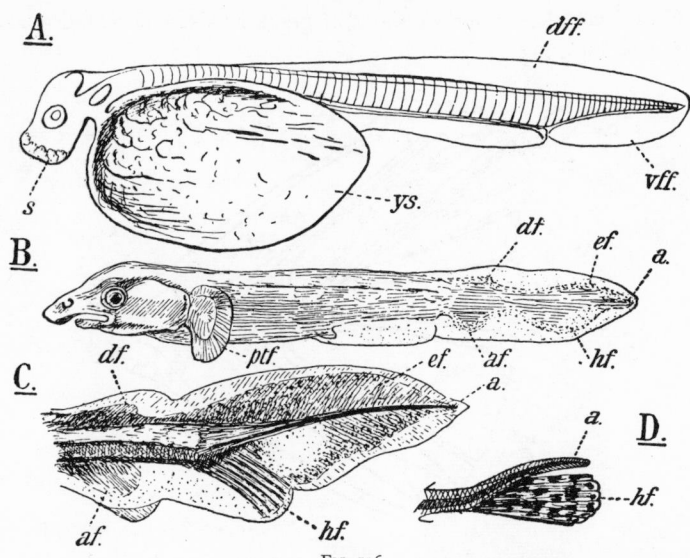

FIG. 116.

The development of the caudal fin of *Lepidosteus*. (After A. Agassiz.) A, Young larva with anterior sucker, *s* ; yolk-sac, *ys* ; continuous dorsal and ventral fin folds, *dff* and *vff* ; and straight notochord. The later stages, B, C, and D, show the upbending of the notochord, the dwindling of the axial lobe, *a*, which disappears in the adult (cp. Fig. 115), and the great development of the hypochordal fin, *hf*. *af*, Anal, *df*, dorsal, *ef*, epichordal, and *ptf*, pectoral fin. (From Goodrich, *Vert. Craniata*, 1909.)

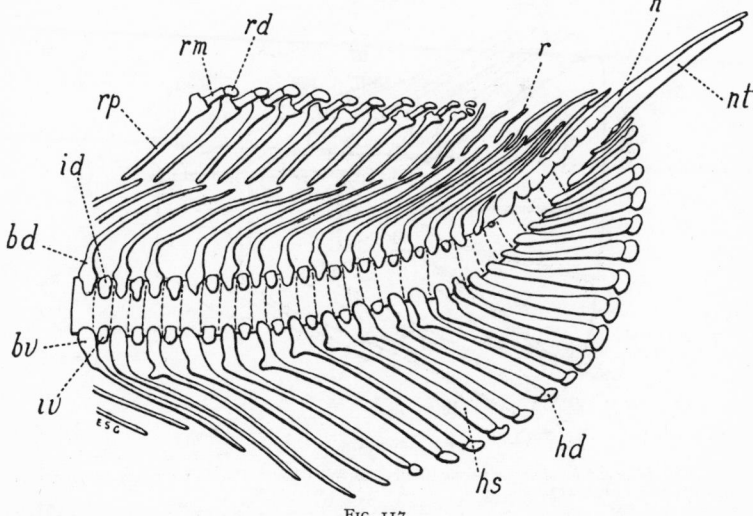

FIG. 117.

Left-side view of skeleton of tail of young *Amia calva*, about 45 mm. long. Endoskeleton cartilaginous ; limits of future bony centra just visible. *bd*, Basidorsal ; *bv*, basiventral ; *hd* and *hs*, distal and proximal elements of haemal spine ; *id*, interdorsal ; *iv*, interventral ; *n*, covering of neural canal composed of fused neural arches ; *nt*, tip of notochord ; *r*, radial ; *rd*, *rm*, and *rp*, distal, middle, and proximal elements of dorsal fin radial.

cercal, and an almost perfect series of gradations can be found among the fossils, Figs. 115-17, 35.

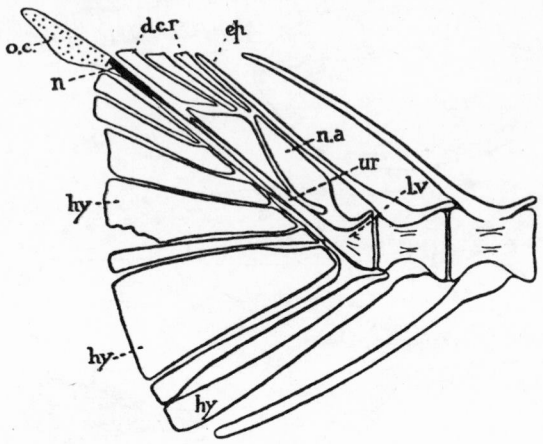

Fig. 118.

Skeleton of caudal fin of *Clupea pilchardus* (from R. H. Whitehouse, *P.R.S.*, 1910).    *d.c.r*, Dorsal radials ; *ep*, epural ; *hy*, hypural ; *l.v*, last vertebra ; *n*, notochord ; *n.a*, neural arch ; *o.c*, opisthural cartilage ; *ur*, urostyle.

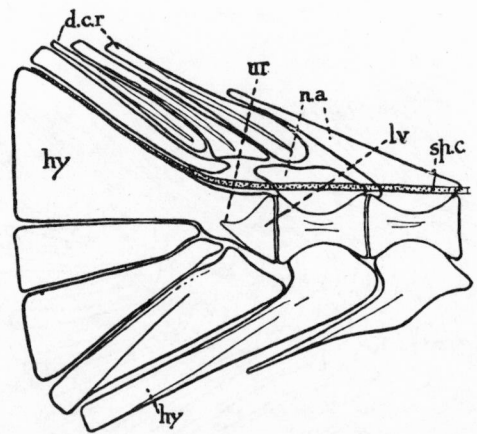

Fig. 119.

Skeleton of caudal fin of *Trigla lineata* (from R. H. Whitehouse, *P.R.S.*, 1910).    *sp.c*, Spinal cord, other letters as in Fig. 118.

In the most advanced or homocercal type, occurring only in the Teleostei, the notochord is much shortened and withdrawn ; though in some primitive forms (*Clupea*) it may still project surrounded by cartilage a little beyond the vertebral elements. The upturned region of the noto-chord is enclosed in a urostyle, a process of the last vertebral centrum which may represent the fused centra of this posterior region. This urostyle, at first independent (*Clupea*, Fig. 118), becomes in more specialised forms fused with the last hypural and reduced to a mere vestige. The neural arch of the penultimate centrum may become modified into a

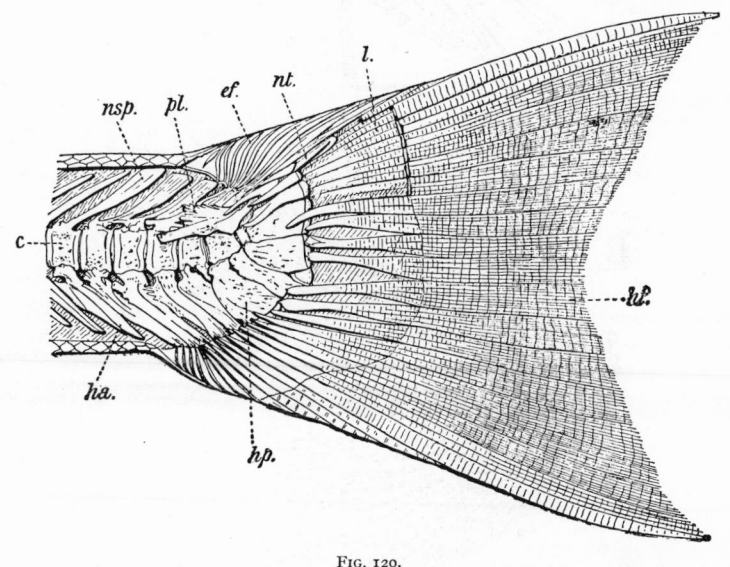

FIG. 120.

Dissected tail of *Salmo*. (After Kölliker.) *c*, Centrum of caudal vertebra; *ef*, epichordal dermal ray; *ha*, haemal arch; *hf*, hypochordal fin; *hp*, expanded haemal arch or hypural; *l*, dermal ray of opposite (right) side; *nsp*, neural spine; *nt*, upturned extremity of the notochord; *pl*, covering bony plate (modified neural arch ?). (From Goodrich, *Vert. Craniata*, 1909.)

pair of bones embracing the urostylar region. A few dorsal radials may remain free bearing dermal rays in this region, but tend to disappear in the more specialised tails. One of these radials may fuse with a dorsal arch to form a true 'epural'. But the most characteristic modification is the great development of the hypurals. More numerous and free along the urostyle in primitive forms (Clupeiformes) they tend to become reduced in number, increased in size, and the hindmost fuses with the last centrum. Finally, in the most specialised tails the hypurals are two in number, fused to the last centrum, and symmetrically disposed above and below the longitudinal axis, Figs. 119-23, 125.

With regard to the morphology of the hypurals it may be pointed out that there is good reason to believe that, as in the Selachians so in the Holostei, they are typically formed by the fusion of a radial with the spine of a haemal arch. Their structure in *Amia*, for instance, with a

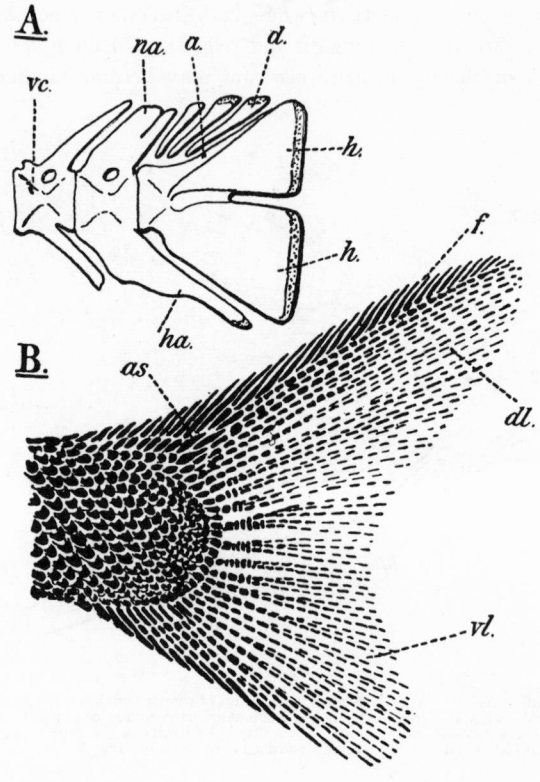

FIG. 121.

A, Endoskeleton of the tail of *Cottus gobio*, L. (After Lotz.) B, Tail of *Pachycormus heterurus*, Ag., showing the last external trace of the heterocercal structure. *a*, Bony sheath of tip of notochord; *as*, scales covering the upturned tip of notochord; *d*, dorsal radials (?); *dl*, dorsal lobe of hypochordal fin; *f*, fulcra; *h*, hypural bone; *ha*, haemal arch; *na*, neural arch and spine; *vc*, vertebral centrum; *vl*, ventral lobe of hypochordal fin. (From Goodrich, *Vert. Craniata*, 1909.)

distal or terminal cartilage resembling that of the radial, strongly suggests this origin, Fig. 117. In Teleosts, also, separate terminal cartilages may appear; but in the higher forms they no longer occur, and possibly the hypurals are there formed entirely from the haemal spine.

Although many Teleostei have more or less tapering and apparently

symmetrical tails, they are never truly protocercal.[1]   The assumption of
a tapering form is an adaptation to sluggish habits either in bottom living
or deep sea fishes, which leads to the reduction in size of the hypochordal
fin, and the elongation of the dorsal and anal fins until finally a con-

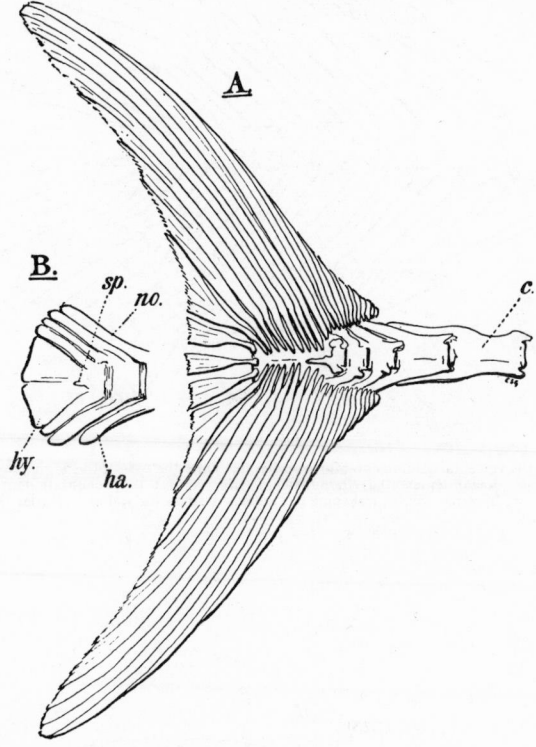

FIG. 122.

A, Skeleton of the tail of *Thynnus vulgaris*, Cuv. and Val., Tunny fish ; B, terminal caudal vertebrae
of *Scomber scomber*, L., Mackerel. *c*, Centrum ; *ha*, haemal arch ; *hy*, hypural compound bone,
partially concealed in A by the dermal rays ; *no*, neural arch ; *sp*, spine. (From Goodrich, *Vert.
Craniata*, 1909.)

tinuous fin-fold is re-established (Dollo, **120**).   Such isocercal tails, as they
may be called, have been repeatedly acquired in various Teleostean
families though with differences of detail (Anguilliformes, Notopteridae,
Gymnarchidae, Macruridae, Zoarcidae, etc.) ; but their true nature is

[1] The Gadidae have a peculiar tail-fin in which either the true caudal has
extended forwards, or it has combined with the posterior part of the median
dorsal and ventral fins (Figs. 123-4).

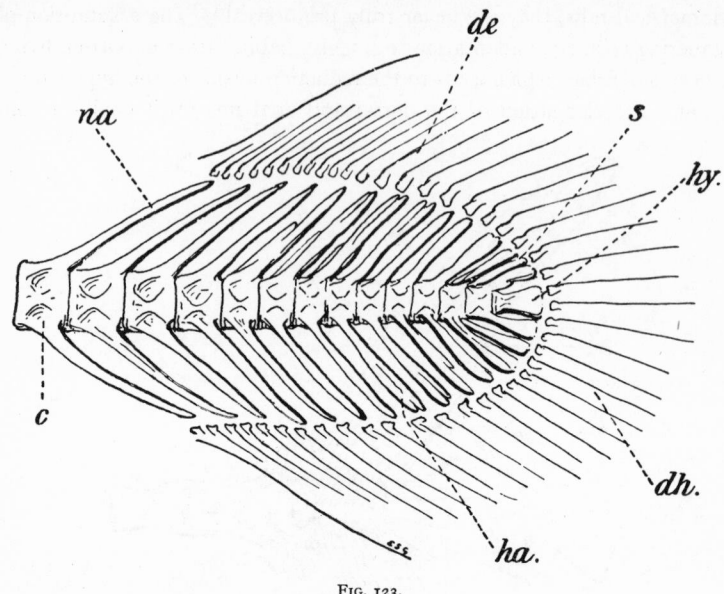

Fig. 123.

Tail end of the vertebral column of *Gadus morrhua*, L. Only the base of the dermal rays is indicated. *c*, Centrum ; *de*, dorsal (epichordal) dermotrichia ; *dh*, ventral (hypochordal) dermotrichia ; *ha*, haemal spine ; *hy*, hypural ; *na*, neural spine ; *s*, detached spine (or radial). (From Goodrich, *Vert. Craniata*, 1909.)

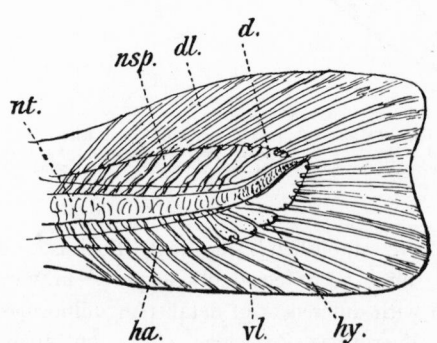

Fig. 124.

Tail of a young cod. (After A. Agassiz.) *d*, Dorsal cartilage (neural arch ?) ; *dl*, lepidotrichia of dorsal lobe of caudal fin ; *ha*, haemal arch ; *hy*, hypural ; *nsp*, neural spine ; *nt*, notochord. (From Goodrich, *Vert. Craniata*, 1909.)

always betrayed by their internal asymmetry, at all events in young stages, the extremity of the notochord being sharply bent upwards, and hypurals

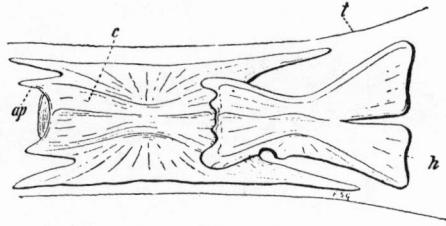

FIG. 125.

*Callionymus lyra*, L. Left-side view of the two last caudal vertebrae, enlarged. *ap*, Anterior articulating process ; *c*, centrum ; *h*, hypural expansion ; *t*, outline of tail incomplete. (From Goodrich, *Vert. Craniata*, 1909.)

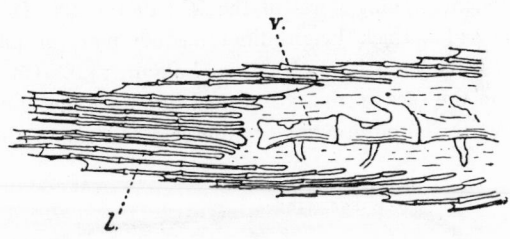

FIG. 126.

Skeleton of the extremity of the tail of *Fierasfer dentatus*, Cuv. (After Emery.) *l*, Lepidotrich ; *v*, last vertebra. (From Goodrich, *Vert. Craniata*, 1909.)

being present. They are cases of disguised homocercy. More complete disappearance of the caudal fin with truncation of the axis leads to yet another type of fin, called gephyrocercal, seen in *Fierasfer*, Fig. 126, and *Orthagoriscus* (Ryder, **130** ; Emery, **121**).

### DEVELOPMENT OF THE MEDIAN FINS OF FISHES

The development of the median fins is best known in the Selachians where it has been studied by Balfour (**142**), Dohrn (**159**), Mayer (**128**), Goodrich (**172**), and Schmalhausen (**133**). They are first indicated by a narrow ridge or fold of epidermis, the precursor of a wider longitudinal fold into which penetrates mesoblastic mesenchyme, Fig. 12. A continuous fold is thus formed running dorsally along the trunk to the tip of the tail, where it meets a similar ventral fold running forwards to just behind the cloaca, Figs. 104, 110. At an early stage the first indications of the definitive fins appear as local thickenings of the mesoblastic tissue. Meanwhile the whole median fold continues to grow and usually forms a provisional embryonic fin of considerable size. Soon, however, the local thickenings become enlarged, these regions alone developing into the adult

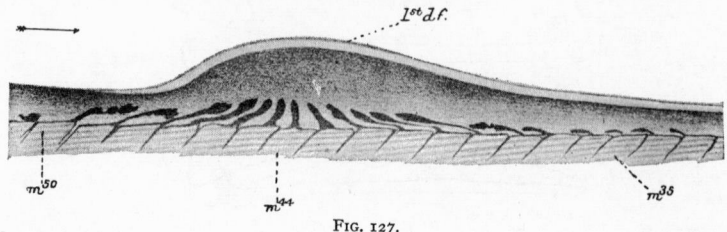

FIG. 127.

*Scyllium canicula.* Embryo 24 mm. long; right-side view of reconstruction of first dorsal fin. A single muscle-bud is shown derived from each myotome, *m*. (E. S. Goodrich, *Quart. Jour. Micr. Sci.*, 1906.)

fins while the intervening parts of the fold disappear. In each fin rudiment is formed a thick longitudinal median plate of mesenchyme in which the fin-skeleton later develops (Balfour, **142**). On either side of this plate, in the case of the dorsal fins, the myotomes give off into the fold small epithelial outgrowths or 'muscle-buds', the rudiments of the

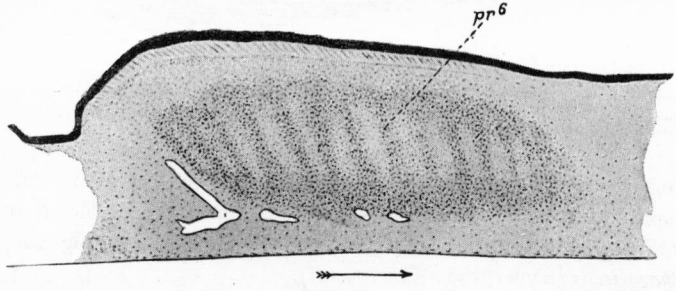

FIG. 128.

*Scyllium canicula.* Longitudinal section of first dorsal fin of embryo 33 mm. long, showing originally separate mesenchymatous rudiments of radials spreading and joining above and below. (E. S. Goodrich, *Quart. Jour. Micr. Sci.*, 1906.)

radial muscles (Dohrn, **159**; Mayer, **128**). Each myotome gives off one muscle-bud from its dorsal edge (Goodrich, **172**); but since, as will be explained later, the dorsal fins of Selachians are considerably shortened or 'concentrated' (the body growing faster in length than the base of the fin), the more anterior and posterior buds appear to move away from their myotomes to reach the base of the fin; they also decrease in size at the two ends. The buds become detached and give rise to the radial muscles, Figs. 127-9. Thus each adult radial muscle corresponds to and is (in the main) derived from one bud and therefore one segment. This primary strict segmentation is, however, to some extent

disturbed in later development, partly owing to increasing concentration
at both ends of the fin where the buds may be crowded and fuse
to form compound
muscles. Moreover,

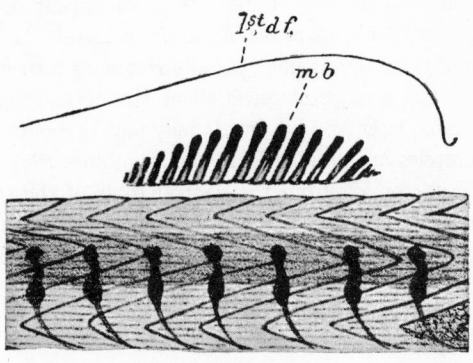

throughout the length
of the fin the buds
may be joined by ana-
stomosing bridges
allowing some tissue to
pass from a segment to
its neighbours, Fig. 129.
The right and left buds
are regularly disposed
in pairs, and between
each pair develops a
skeletal radial, Figs.
130-31. The first indi-
cation of the radials is

FIG. 129.

*Scyllium canicula.* Embryo 28 mm. long ; left-side view of reconstruction of region of first dorsal fin. *mb*, Muscle-buds, becoming
converted proximally into muscle fibres, and united by bridges at
their base. (E. S. Goodrich, *Quart. Jour. Micr. Sci.*, 1906.)

seen as a series of separate streaks of denser mesenchyme in the median
plate. These become defined as procartilaginous rods merging into each
other above and below, Figs. 128, 130-31. The whole skeleton of the
fin is so preformed and the various pieces of the adult structure

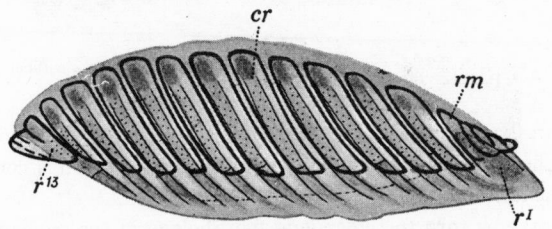

FIG. 130.

Reconstruction of first dorsal fin of embryo *Scyllium canicula*, 37 mm. long. Right-side view ;
blastema and procartilage grey, cartilage dotted, radial muscles in black outline. *cr*, Radial ; *rm*,
radial muscle ; $r^1$-$r^{13}$, radials. (E. S. Goodrich, *Quart. Jour. Micr. Sci.*, 1905.)

chondrify separately in it. The anal fin of Selachians develops in
essentially the same way ; but here (as also in the caudal fin) distinct
muscle-buds do not occur, the radial muscles being derived from proliferations of cells from the ventral border of the myotomes.

In all important points the development of the median fins of the
Osteichthyes resembles that of the Selachii. Segmental muscle-buds
appear to be absent in the Dipnoi but have been described in *Acipenser*,
*Amia*, and *Lepidosteus* (Salensky, **131** ; Schmalhausen, **133**), and in *Salmo*

(Harrison, **179**), where they occur not only in the dorsal but also in the anal fin. In the median fins of the Osteichthyes, which are usually little concentrated, the radials tend to appear as more distinctly separate procartilaginous rods than in the Selachii ; later they become chondrified and generally ossified, usually retaining their independence.

The important question of the nerve-supply of the fins will be discussed later (p. 133), but it may now be pointed out that since the radial muscles are derived from the myotomes they are innervated by efferent fibres coming from the ventral roots of the spinal nerves. Each radial muscle primarily is supplied from the nerve of that segment which gave rise to the bud from which it developed. This occurs in regular order

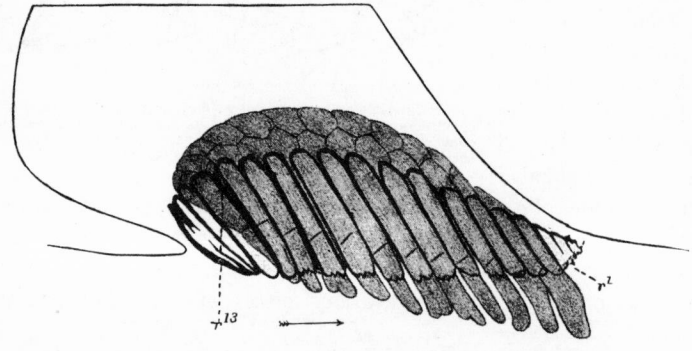

FIG. 131.

*Scyllium canicula.* Right-side view of skeleton and radial muscles (black outline) of first dorsal fin of adult. $r^{1-13}$, Radials. (E. S. Goodrich, *Quart. Jour. Micr. Sci.*, 1906.)

from before backwards. The number of spinal nerves supplying motor fibres to the fin, therefore, agrees with the number of buds contributing to its musculature, Figs. 143, 144.

We may now turn to the general morphology of the median fins. In many fish which in the adult state have discontinuous dorsal, caudal, and anal fins, these separate fins develop as differentiations in a continuous embryonic fin-fold, which becomes subdivided by the obliteration of certain regions. Moreover, traces of the fin-skeleton and musculature are found between the separate fins of many such fish, as for instance in *Squalus, Rhina, Pristis* (Thacher, **219** ; Mivart, **196**), and Teleosts, Figs. 26, 141. In Cephalochorda and in Myxinoidea the folds remain continuous. It is natural, then, to suppose that such has been the phylogenetic history of median fins, and that discontinuity is secondary. In support of this view it may be pointed out that in the Pleuracanthodii, an extinct group of Chondrichthyes, Carboniferous forms occur with a complete or almost complete dorsal fin-fold. Nevertheless, it is a notable fact that in most groups of fishes the most ancient known representatives are already provided with separate short dorsal or anal fins. This is the case not only with the Ostracodermi, which date from the Silurian, the Clado-selachii, and the Acanthodii, but also with the early Teleostomes such as the Osteolepidoti, Chondrostei, Amioidei, and Teleostei. Indeed greatly

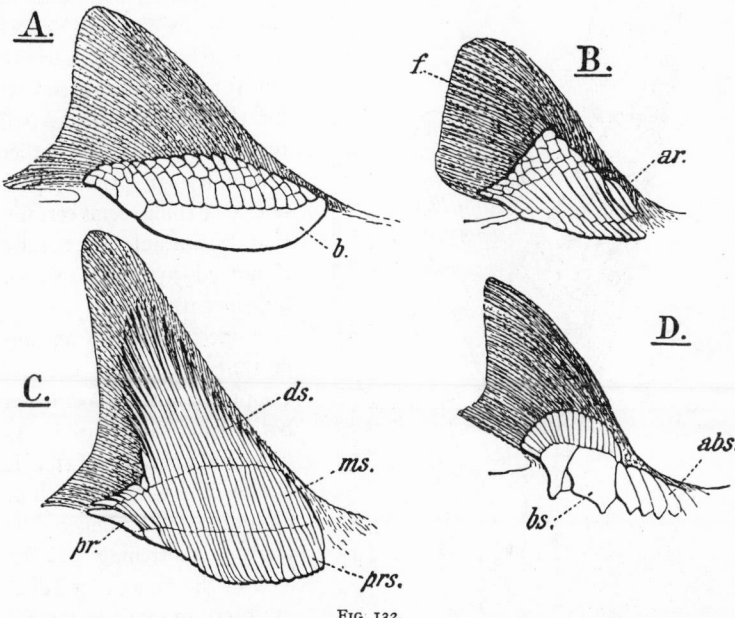

FIG. 132.

Dorsal fins, with the endoskeleton exposed, of: A, *Notidanus* (*Heptanchus*) *cinereus*, Gm.; B, *Ginglymostoma cirratum*, Gm.; C, *Zygaena malleus*, Risso; D, *Rhynchobatus djeddensis*, Forsk. (After Mivart.) *abs*, Anterior radials lying on vertebral column; *ar*, anterior radial; *b*, longitudinal basal; *bs*, basal; *ds*, distal segment of radial; *f*, fin web supported by ceratotrichia; *ms*, median segment of radial; *pr*, posterior radial; *prs*, proximal segment of radial. These figures illustrate the formation of basals by the concrescence of radials. (From Goodrich, *Vert. Craniata*, 1909.)

extended dorsal and anal fins are characteristic of the more specialised forms, such as the Platysomidae among Chondrostei, Amiidae and Pycnodontidae among Amioidei. The primitive extinct Leptolepidae among Teleostei possess short dorsal and anal fins; but these are greatly extended or even continuous folds in many modern families such as the Gymnotidae among Cypriniformes, the Lampridiformes, Mastacembelli-formes, the Zeorhombiformes, and the Anguilliformes. It also seems to hold good for the Dipnoi, where two dorsal and an anal occur in the Devonian *Dipterus*, but continuous fin-folds are present in the modern genera (p. 102).

The ontogenic history of the median fins, however, clearly shows that they are of fundamentally segmental structure as regards their nervous, muscular, and skeletal elements even if this primary segmentation agreeing with that of the body is obscured or lost owing to later specialisations. But it must be admitted that for the present the question remains open as to whether continuity is primitive or not. One thing seems certain, that discontinuity is generally if not always accompanied by concentration.

Concentration is an important process in the development of the fins of fishes both median and paired. As indicated above (p. 114), it is due to differential growth of fin and body, leading to the relative shortening of the base of the fin and crowding together of its segmental elements, especially at its anterior and posterior ends. Thus a dorsal fin, which in an embryo *Scyllium* is developed from some fourteen segments, comes to occupy only about six segments in the adult (Goodrich, **172**). As a rule more muscle-buds arise in the embryo than come to full development in the adult, some being suppressed at each end, Figs. 127, 143. It is owing

to concentration that, increasingly towards each end of the fin, the radial

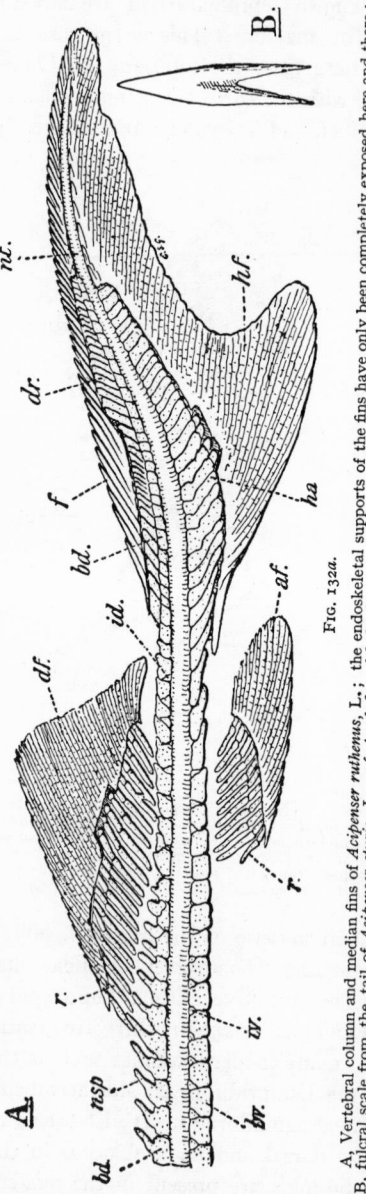

FIG. 132a.

A, Vertebral column and median fins of *Acipenser ruthenus*, L.; the endoskeletal supports of the fins have only been completely exposed here and there; B, fulcral scale from the tail of *Acipenser sturio*, L. *af*, Anal fin; *bd*, basidorsal; *bv*, basiventral; *df*, dorsal fin; *dr*, dorsal radials? of caudal region; *f*, fulcrum; *ha*, haemal arch; *hf*, hypochordal fin; *id*, interdorsal; *iv*, interventral; *nsp*, neural spine; *nt*, notochord; *r*, radial. (From Goodrich, *Vert. Craniata*, 1909.)

muscles become separated from the myotomes which gave rise to them, and the nerves are made to converge towards the narrowed base of the fin to supply them. Thus are formed longitudinal ' collector ' nerves, especially in front of the fin ; for here concentration is usually more pronounced.

The skeletal elements are likewise affected, and concrescence of the radials is the second important factor in the modification of the skeleton of fins [1] (Thacher, Mivart). It plays but a small part in the median fins of Actinopterygii, but may be seen in such Crossopterygii (Osteolepidoti) as *Eusthenopteron,* or *Glyptolepis,* where the numerous radials of the dorsal fin fuse at their base to form a longitudinal axis of several elements, Figs. 92, 155 A. A bony plate at the base of the very short median fins of Coelacanthini seems to represent the base of fused radials, Fig. 95. Concrescence is clearly shown in *Pleuracanthus* (Fritsch, **23**), where two short anals are formed containing a number of radials more or less completely com-bining proximally into jointed axis and basal pieces, Fig. 133. But it is in the Elasmobranchii that the

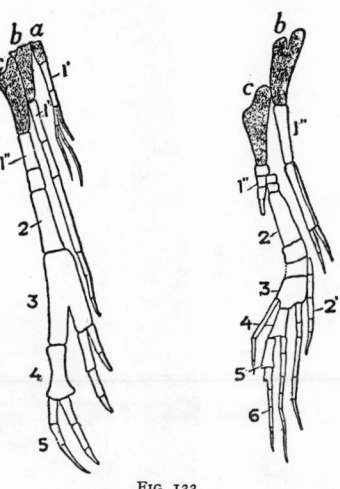

FIG. 133.

Skeleton of anal fins of *Pleuracanthus (Xena-canthus) Decheni,* Goldf. *a, b, c,* Haemal arches ; 1-6, segments of fin-radials. Right border pre-axial, and left postaxial. (After Fritsch, from A. S. Woodward.)

effects of concrescence are best seen. In the Holocephalan *Chimaera* the posterior dorsal fin is scarcely if at all concentrated, and here the parallel radials are separate and regularly distributed, Fig. 134. But in Holocephali generally the anterior dorsal becomes much concen-trated behind the anterior spine ; in *Myriacanthus* of the L. Lias, the radials are here represented by two or three pieces, while in the modern genera they fuse to a single cartilage, the whole fin-spine and all being erectile.

Many of the modern sharks still preserve separate segmental radials in the dorsal and anal fins, as in *Scyllium* and *Sphyrna* ; even in these, how-ever, a few of the radials may be fused, especially at their base. In others concrescence is very pronounced, as in the Notidanidae, where nearly all

[1] As noted above, it may also affect the muscles. A detailed study of the anatomy and development of unconcentrated fins is greatly needed.

the radials contribute to the formation of a continuous basal piece, Fig. 132.

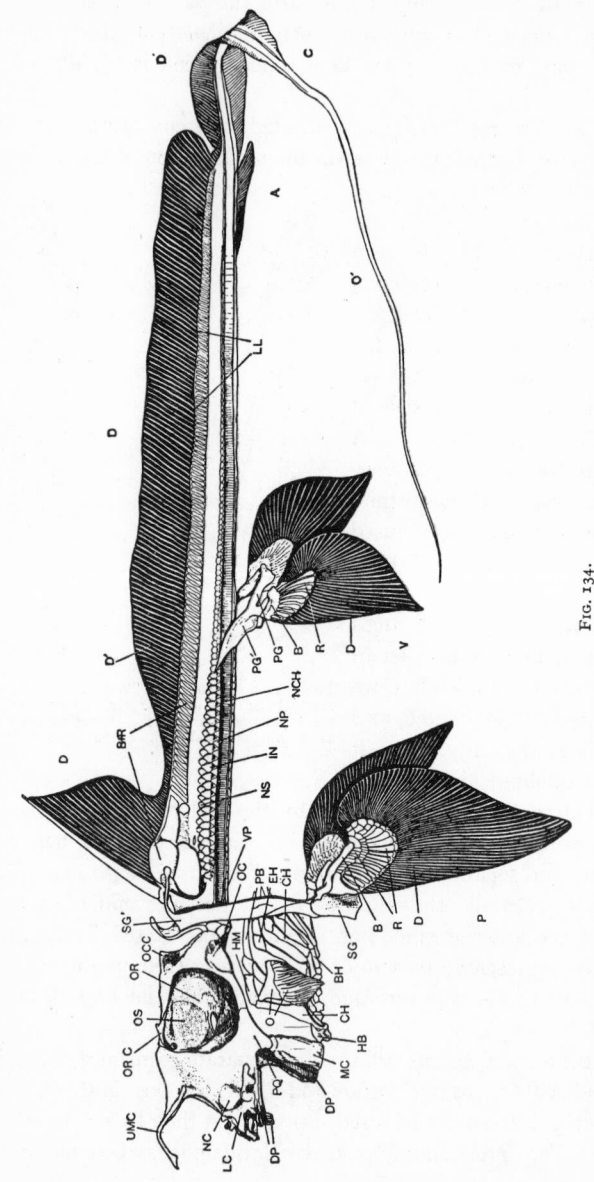

FIG. 134.

Skeleton of *Chimaera monstrosa* (after A. Graf, from B. Dean, *Fishes Living and Fossil*, 1895). A, Anal fin; B, basals; B and R, median basal and radials; BH, hypobranchials; C, caudal fin; CH, ceratohyal and ceratobranchial; D, dorsal fin; D′, dorsal fin; D′, ceratotrichia; DP, dental plate; EH, epibranchial; HB, basibyal; HM, epihyal=hyomandibula (?); IN, interdorsal; LC, labio-nasal; MC, Meckel's cartilage; NC, nasal capsule; OCC, occipital crest; OR, orbit; ORC, orbital crest; OS, interorbital septum; P, pectoral fin; PB, pharyngobranchial; PG, pelvic girdle; PG′, iliac process; PQ, palato-quadrate; R, radial; SG, pectoral girdle; SG′, scapular process; UMC, rostral; V, pelvic fin; VP, fused vertebrae.

Those forms in which the fin is armed with an anterior spine tend to have the radials much fused sometimes on both sides of it (Hetero-

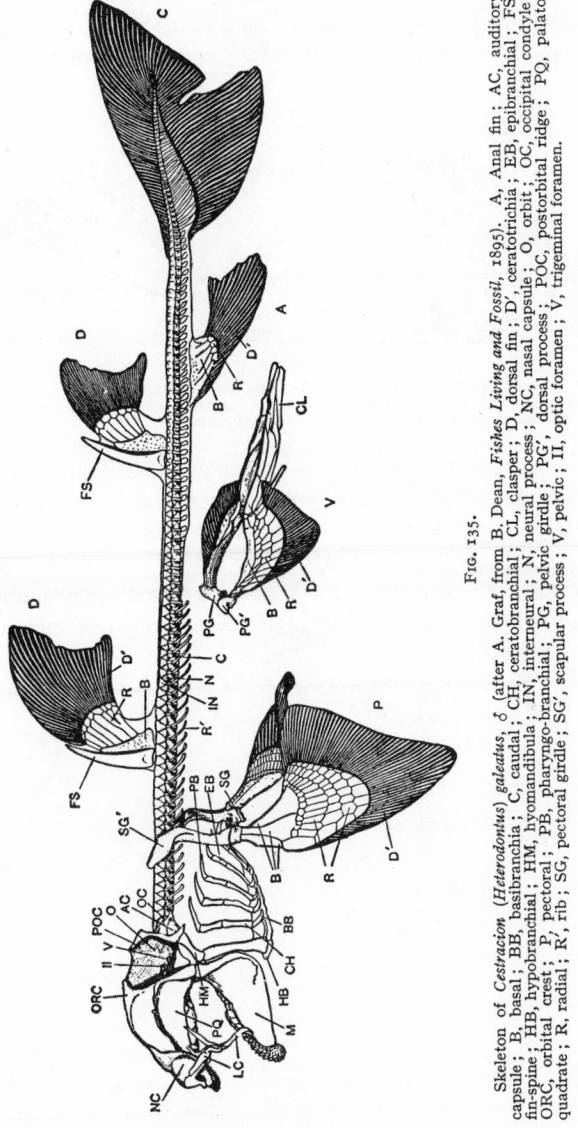

FIG. 135.

Skeleton of *Cestracion (Heterodontus) galeatus*, ♂ (after A. Graf, from B. Dean, *Fishes Living and Fossil*, 1895). A, Anal fin; AC, auditory capsule; B, basal; BB, basibranchial; C, caudal; CH, ceratobranchial; CL, clasper; D, dorsal fin; D', dorsal fin; D', ceratotrichia; EB, epibranchial; FS, fin-spine; HB, hypobranchial; HM, hyomandibula; IN, interneural; N, neural process; NC, nasal capsule; O, orbit; OC, occipital condyle; ORC, orbital crest; P, pectoral; PB, pharyngo-branchial; PG, pelvic girdle; PG', dorsal process; POC, postorbital ridge; PQ, palato-quadrate; R, radial; R', rib; SG, pectoral girdle; SG', scapular process; V, pelvic; II, optic foramen; V, trigeminal foramen.

donti, Spinacidae); and in the Rajiformes the radials may combine to form an oblique basal jointed axis, bearing separate distal radials, Fig. 136. In such fins the fin-skeleton usually rests on the vertebral column and the primitive metamery is almost completely lost (*Acanthias, Squatina, Rhinobatus, Raja*).

Finally it may be pointed out in favour of the theory that the median fins were probably primitively continuous ; and that, if we trace the origin

FIG. 136.

Left-side view of a portion of the tail of *Raja*. The vertebral column has been exposed in front, also the endoskeleton of the two dorsal fins, showing the concrescence of the radials at their base to form a posterior axis. (From Goodrich, *Vert. Craniata*, 1909.)

of the muscular and nervous elements which go to build up the dorsal fins of such a form as *Scyllium*, and spread them out as if concentration had not taken place, we find that whereas in the adult they occupy quite a short space, when ' deconcentrated ' they extend over some thirty segments forming a continuous fin-fold along a considerable length of the trunk and tail (see diagrams, Fig. 143). Discontinuity in such a case is due to concentration.

# CHAPTER III

## PAIRED LIMBS

## THE ORIGIN OF THE PAIRED LIMBS

**Theories of the Origin of the Paired Fins.**—The consideration of concentration and concrescence in median fins brings us to the problem of the origin of the paired limbs. Few questions concerning the general morphology of Vertebrates have aroused greater interest. Since it is generally recognised that the pectoral and pelvic limbs of Tetrapods must have been derived phylogenetically from the paired fins of their fish-like ancestors, the discussion of the general problem may be confined to the origin of the paired fins or ' ichthyopterygia ' of fishes of which there are typically two pairs, each strengthened by an endoskeleton composed of radials projecting into the outstanding fin-lobe, and supported by an endoskeletal girdle in the body-wall. The pectoral fins are placed immediately behind the gill-arches, and the pelvic fins (often called the ventrals), typically, just in front of the anus.

Two main rival and incompatible theories have been held of the origin of paired fins. According to that put forth by Gegenbaur (168-9) the paired fins are modified gill structures, the girdles representing gill-arches, and the fin-folds with their contained fin-skeleton representing gill-flaps or septa with their branchial rays. The position of the pelvic fins far back is explained as due to the shifting backwards or migration of these posterior arches which have lost their branchial function. This may be called the 'gill-arch theory', Fig. 137.

The modern version of the second theory, put forth almost simultaneously by Balfour (142) and Thacher (219), and later by Mivart (196), holds that the paired fins are of essentially the same nature as the unpaired fins, and have been derived from paired longitudinal fin-folds. The endoskeletal radials (somactidia, pterygiophores) would in both kinds

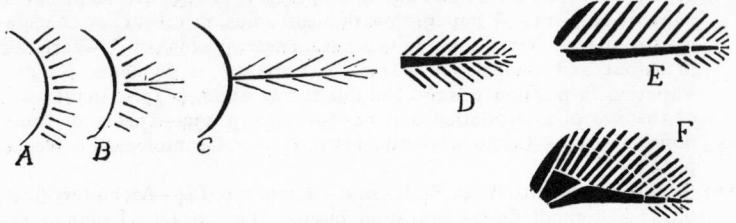

FIG. 137.

Diagram illustrating Gegenbaur's theory of origin of fin-skeleton from gill-arch and gill rays A-D; D, biserial archipterygium; D, E, F, origin of Selachian pectoral fin-skeleton from archipterygium. (From J. S. Kingsley, *Comp. Anat. Vertebrates*, 1926.)

have arisen for the stiffening of the fin-folds; and the girdles would have been developed by the extension inwards of the base of the radials so as to afford firm support for the outstanding fin. This, the now most generally accepted view, is known as the 'lateral-fold theory'.

Each of these theories may claim to have had among its supporters some of the most eminent exponents of vertebrate morphology. V. Davidoff, Fürbringer, Braus (144-8), and others have followed Gegenbaur; while Dohrn (159), Mayer (128), Wiedersheim (230), Haswell (180), Rabl (206), Mollier (197), Dean (154-6), A. S. Woodward (231), Harrison (179), Regan (208), Sewertzoff (215-17), and others have written in favour of the lateral-fold theory; Osburn (202) and Goodrich (172) have recently discussed these theories in detail, and brought forward much evidence in favour of the view that the paired fins were developed from lateral folds, and against the rival theory.

An examination of the development of the paired fins shows that in every important particular it resembles that of the median fins. First usually indicated by a narrow ridge of folded epidermis, they subsequently grow out as longitudinal folds of the body-wall into which penetrates mesenchymatous mesoblast. Epithelial muscle-buds soon push their way into the fin-fold; they spring from the ventral ends of the neighbouring myotomes and give rise to the radial muscles, Figs. 138, 143. The distribution and development of these buds is of great interest, all the phenomena characteristic of concentration in median fins being clearly shown in the less specialised forms, and more especially in Elasmobranchs. To begin with, the lateral fin-folds extend longitudinally over many more segments in the embryo than they do in the adult; the shortening of the base of the fin as it becomes more clearly marked off from the body leads to the formation of a distinct notch at its hinder end, Figs. 113, 139.

Muscle-buds may develop from the segments along the whole of the embryonic fold, and even beyond. They gradually become vestigial and disappear beyond the fin areas. Two such buds arise from each myotome in Selachians, except near the extreme ends of the series where they may be reduced to one. A large number reach the base of the fin, separate from their myotomes, divide into upper (dorsal) and lower (ventral) halves, and spreading outwards develop into the radial muscles of the adult fin, Figs. 139, 620. In Osteichthyes only one primary bud, which divides, or two buds are given off from each myotome (Teleostei:

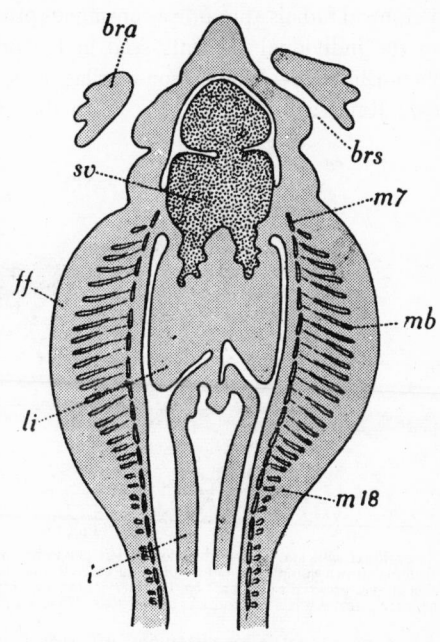

FIG. 138.

*Scyllium canicula*, embryo stage *N*. Reconstructed horizontal section. *bra*, Branchial bar; *brs*, branchial slit; *ff*, pectoral fin-fold; *i*, intestine; *li*, liver; $m^{7-18}$, ventral ends of metatic myotomes; *mb*, muscle-buds; those from myotomes 7 to 18 contribute to pectoral-fin musculature, behind them are vestigial buds.

Harrison, 179; Guitel, 175; Derjugin, 157. Chondrostei: Sewertzoff, 216-17; Ducret, 160; Kryžanovsky, 193. Dipnoi: Salensky, 213; Semon, 214; Agar, 141). Typically in all fishes a radial is differentiated between each pair of upper and lower muscle-buds (Rabl, Mollier, Derjugin). The radial muscles of the paired fins being thus derived from the myotomes naturally receive their motor nerve-supply from the ventral roots of the corresponding spinal nerves. Owing to concentration the nerves converge towards the base of the fins. In front and behind they may be gathered together so as to form a compound or 'collector' nerve, Fig. 143.

As in median so in paired fins the endoskeleton is differentiated in the continuous plate of dense mesenchyme situated in the fin-fold between the dorsal and ventral muscle rudiments. In Selachians the radials first appear as denser streaks, separate distally, but more or less combined proximally into a plate which extends inwards in the body-wall as the rudiment of the girdle, Fig. 620. Thus the separate limb girdle, basals, and peripheral radials appear in a continuous procartilaginous rudiment. Later on the individual elements seen in the adult arise *in situ* as separate chondrifications, leaving non-cartilaginous joints (Balfour, **142**; Mollier, **197**; Ruge, **211**, and others). Since the girdle is primarily outside the

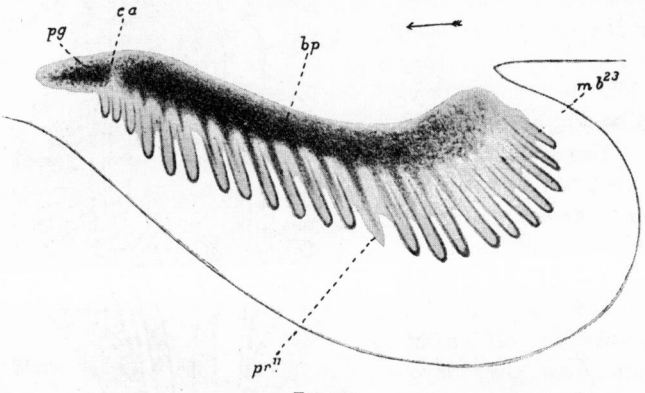

FIG. 139.

*Scyllium canicula.* Reconstruction of left pelvic fin of embryo 28 mm. long. Procartilaginous skeleton drawn complete; outer epithelial ends of muscle-buds overlying radials shown in outline except over preaxial radial 11. *bp*, Basipterygium; *ca*, nerve canal; *mb²³* twenty-third muscle-bud; *pg*, pelvic girdle. (E. S. Goodrich, *Quart. Jour. Micr. Sci.*, 1906.)

myotomes, and is an extension inwards from the base of the fin-skeleton, it is natural that some of the nerves should become surrounded by it as they pass from the inner surface of the myotomes round their ventral ends and outwards to supply the fin. Thus certain nerves, called diazonal, may be found in the adult to perforate the girdles, while other nerves pass before or behind them, Fig. 142.

These essential facts in the ontogeny of the paired fins have been well established in Selachians which are in many respects primitive; but most of them have been confirmed by observations on other fish such as the Chondrostei and higher Teleostomes, including the Teleostei.

On the other hand, it is difficult to find any facts which actually support the gill-arch theory, and much evidence may be brought against it. Indeed the theory could hardly have been conceived except at a time when the ontogeny of fins was scarcely known at all. If developed from gill-septa situated transversely to the long axis of the body, paired fin-folds would rather hinder than favour progression ; moreover, the two pairs would presumably be at first close together behind the other gills and in a position mechanically very disadvantageous. Now, in ontogeny, a paired fin never makes its appearance as a dorso-ventral fold ; but on the contrary always as a more or less extended longitudinal ridge.

The position of the pelvic fins was attributed by Gegenbaur to their backward migration. But neither in primitive fishes generally nor in their early fossil representatives are the pelvic fins more anterior. When, as in some of the specialised Teleostei, the pelvic fins are far forwards, there is good evidence that this position is secondary, Figs. 140-41 (p. 138).

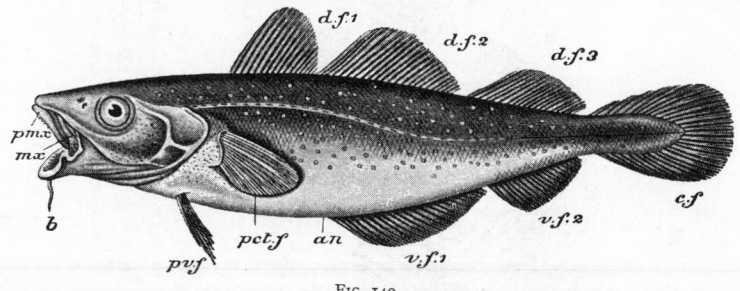

FIG. 140.

*Gadus morrhua* (Cod). *an*, Anus ; *c.f*, caudal fin ; *d.f* 1-3, dorsal fins ; *mx*, maxilla ; *pct.f*, pectoral fin ; *pmx*, premaxilla ; *pv.f*, pelvic fin ; *v.f* 1 and 2, anal fins. (After Cuvier.) (From Parker and Haswell, *Zoology*.)

The presence in ontogeny of vestigial muscle-buds in front of the pelvic fin-folds has been supposed to indicate backward migration. This, however, can hardly be so, since such buds are also found behind these same fins, and on both sides of the pectoral fins also. It has been urged that the presence of a ' nerve-plexus ' or compound collector nerve at and in front of the base of the pelvic fins (v. Davidoff, 153), and that the greater extension of the collector in the young than in the adult (Punnett, 1900), are evidence of backward migration. But, again, such a collector and greater extension are found at the posterior end of these same fins, and are similarly developed on both sides of the pectoral fins. The attempt to explain the posterior position of the pelvics on the supposition that ancestral Gnathostomes had very numerous gill-arches extending farther back than in any known forms (Fürbringer, Braus) has no evidence to support it. That the paired limbs occupy very different relative positions on the trunk in various forms is an obvious and striking fact which will be dealt with below (p. 136).

The gill-arch theory gives no intelligible explanation of the participation of a large number of segments in the formation of the musculature and nerve-supply of the paired fins. Yet a considerable and sometimes a very large number of spinal nerves and myotomes always contribute

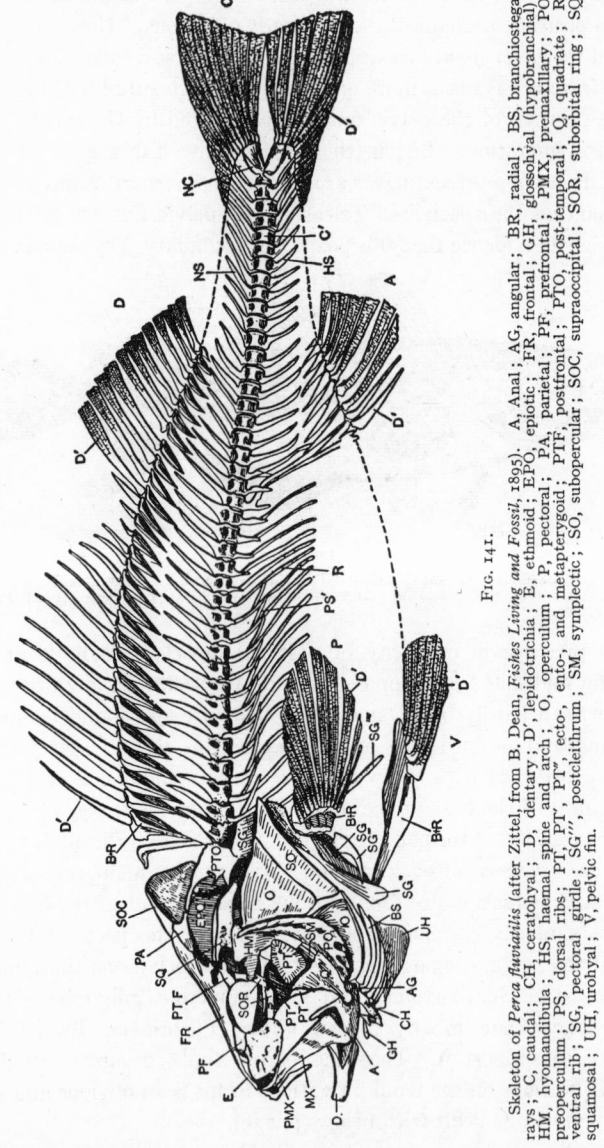

Fig. 141.

Skeleton of *Perca fluviatilis* (after Zittel, from B. Dean, *Fishes Living and Fossil*, 1895). A, Anal; AG, angular; BR, radial; BS, branchiostegal rays; C, caudal; CH, ceratohyal; D, dentary; D', lepidotrichia; E, ethmoid; EPO, epiotic; FR, frontal; GH, glossohyal (hypobranchial); HM, hyomandibula; HS, haemal spine and arch; O, operculum; P, pectoral; PA, parietal; PF, prefrontal; PMX, premaxillary; PO, preoperculum; PS, dorsal ribs; PT, PT', PT'', PT''', ecto-, ento-, and metapterygoid; PTF, postfrontal; PTO, post-temporal; Q, quadrate; R, ventral rib; SG, pectoral girdle; SG''', postcleithrum; SM, symplectic; SO, subopercular; SOC, supraoccipital; SOR, suborbital ring; SQ, squamosal; UH, urohyal; V, pelvic fin.

towards them; the area from which they are derived is wider than the actual base of the fin. This also applies to the paired limbs of Tetrapods, and, speaking quite generally, the lower the class of vertebrate concerned, the more segments take part in the formation of its paired limbs.

If the radials of the paired fins were derived from gill-rays and the girdles from gill-arches, we should expect their muscle-supply to be drawn, not from the myotomes, but from the unsegmental lateral-plate musculature innervated from the dorsal roots (p. 218). In the head region, although epi- and hypobranchial muscles of myotome origin may be associated with the visceral arches, yet the great bulk of the musculature of these arches is developed from the lateral-plate mesoblast and innervated

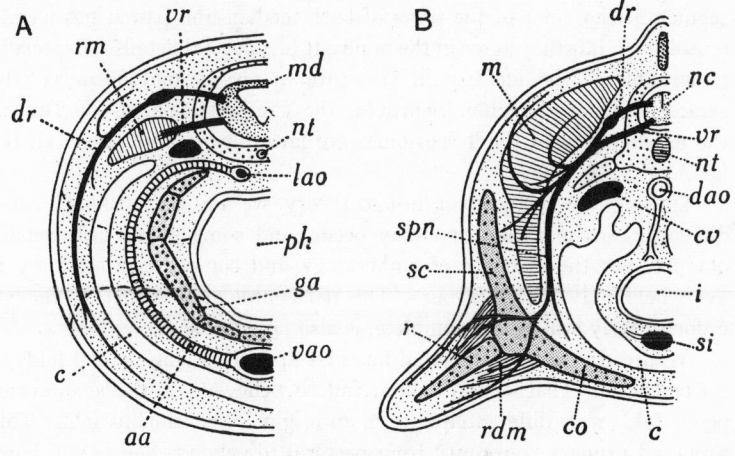

Fig. 142.

Diagrams to illustrate different morphological relations of *skeletal gill-arch* and *limb-girdle*. A, Transverse section of pharyngeal region; B, of anterior trunk region. *aa*, Arterial arch; *c*, coelom; *co*, coracoid region; *cv*, cardinal vein; *dao*, dorsal aorta; *dr*, dorsal root nerve; *ga*, skeletal gill-arch; *i*, gut; *lao*, lateral dorsal aorta; *md*, medulla; *m*, myomere; *nc*, nerve cord; *nt*, notochord; *ph*, pharynx; *r*, radial; *rdm*, radial muscle; *rm*, reduced myomere; *sc*, scapular region; *spn*, mixed spinal nerve; *si*, subintestinal vein; *vr*, ventral root nerve; *vao*, ventral aorta.

by cranial dorsal root nerves. It is true that in many forms there is a lateral-plate trapezius muscle attached to the dorsal end of the scapula and supplied from the vagus; but it may be pointed out that it only becomes so attached at a late stage in development, that it does not penetrate into the fin-fold, and that in any case there is no trace of such a muscle in the pelvic region.

But perhaps the most fatal of all objections to Gegenbaur's theory is the fact that gill-arches and limb-girdles differ radically from each other as regards their position relative to the coelom, nerves, blood-vessels, etc.; for whereas the gill-arches are morphologically internal, the girdles are external to these various structures. In fact, the girdles lie in the outer body-wall, while the visceral arches lie in the wall of the alimentary canal. Hence the paired fins and their girdles are supplied with blood-vessels from the segmental somatic system, with muscles from the myotomes, and with motor nerve-fibres from the ventral spinal roots. These various relations are illustrated in diagrams, Fig. 142.

Finally, the gill-arch theory offers no explanation whatever of the striking resemblance borne by the paired fins to the median fins, even in specialised forms, and in spite of their many necessary divergencies due to adaptation to different functions. The resemblance in development and structure is so close that we are forced to the conclusion that they are organs of essentially the same nature. Not only is the fundamentally segmental character of the parts of both median and paired fins clearly established, but they agree in the minutest histological details. Especially remarkable is the identity in structure of the dermal fin-rays : the ceratotrichia of the Chondrichthyes, the camptotrichia of the Dipnoi, the lepidotrichia of the Teleostomes are faithfully reproduced in all the fins.[1]

Turning now to the rival fin-fold theory, we find that although some difficulties in its application may occur, and some points still remain obscure, yet the evidence of embryology and comparative anatomy is overwhelmingly in its favour. The palaeontological evidence, though unfortunately still very incomplete, is also favourable.

As already mentioned, paired fins first appear as longitudinal folds of the body-wall. Thacher and Balfour, indeed, believed that the pectoral and pelvic folds were differentiated from an originally continuous fold. This supposed primary continuity from pectoral to pelvic region is not, however, an essential part of the theory.[2] Possibly from the first the paired fins, and indeed the unpaired fins also, were discontinuous. In modern forms the paired folds vary much in extent, and are not known to be truly continuous except in the case of Rajiformes, where the pectoral fins

---

[1] A variant of the gill-arch theory has been put forward by Kerr, 840, according to whom paired fins have been derived from external gills. This theory is open to all the objections urged against Gegenbaur's theory and to others besides. Prominent true external gills occur but rarely, and in rather advanced forms, among Osteichthyes and Amphibia. It is true that the pelvic fin (not the pectoral) of *Lepidosiren* may be provided with vascular filaments ; but these are only known to occur at a certain time and for a special purpose in the male of that one genus. Except for a very superficial resemblance to the highly specialised and reduced limbs of modern Dipneumones, external gills differ from paired limbs in every important respect.

[2] The palaeozoic Ostracodermi possessed lateral folds which in Cephalaspidae grew into outstanding lobes resembling the pectoral fins of higher fish (see Goodrich, 35, Fig. 173). It is possible that the paired pectoral folds developed first, and the pelvic folds only later in the Gnathostomata.

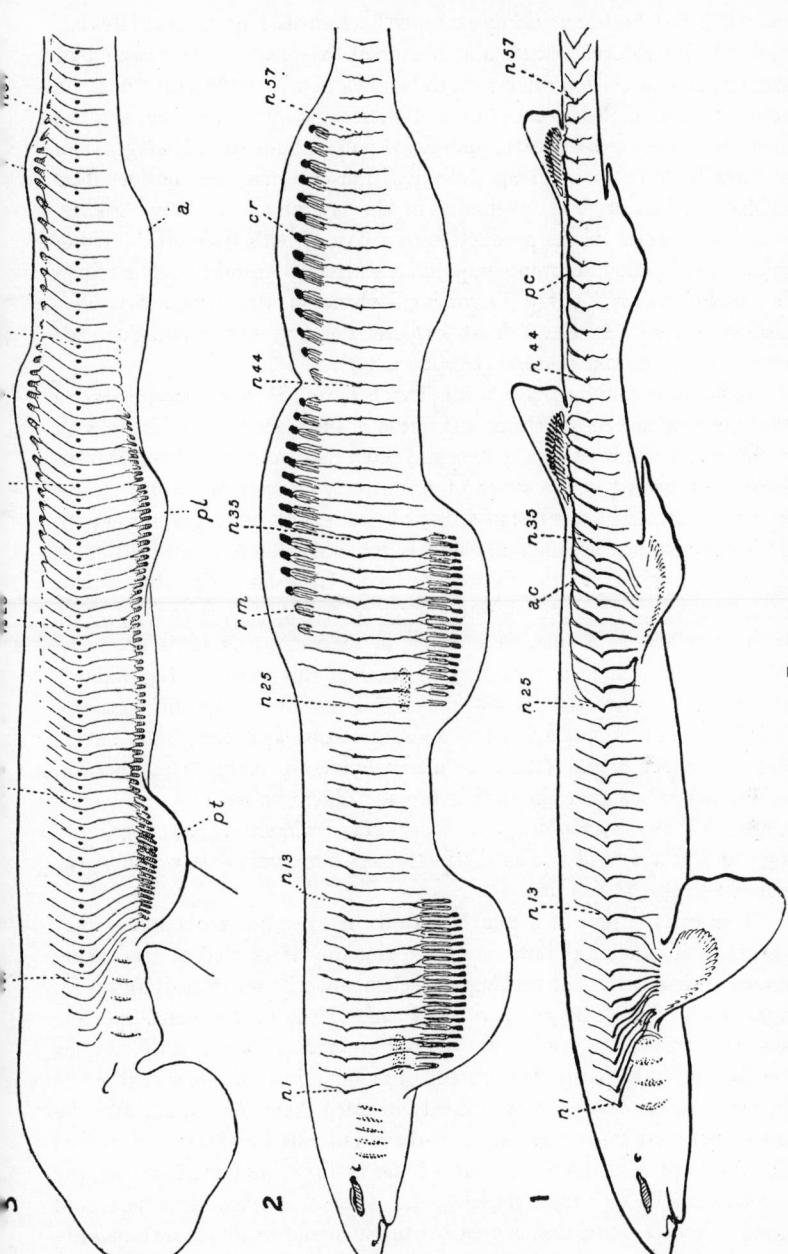

FIG. 143.

1, Diagram of an adult *Scyllium canicula*; the fins are expanded, and their nervous, muscular, and skeletal segmental elements are indicated by shaded oval areas; the girdles themselves are not shown. 2, Diagram of an adult *Scyllium canicula*, showing the nerve-supply of the fins. The nerve foramina in the girdles are indicated by shaded oval areas; the girdles themselves are not shown. 3, Diagram of an embryo *Scyllium canicula* about 19 mm. long, in which are shown the ganglia, the myotomes, and the muscle-buds. *a*, Anal fin; *ac*, anterior collector of first dorsal fin; *cr*, cartilaginous radial projecting beyond the radial muscles; *n* 1-57, spinal nerves and ganglia; *pc*, collector nerve of second dorsal fin; *pl*, pelvic fin; *pt*, pectoral fin; *rm*, radial muscle; *1d* and *2d*, first and second dorsal fins. (From E. S. Goodrich, *Quart. Jour. Micr. Sci.*, v. 50, 1906.)

have doubtless been secondarily extended backwards, Figs. 145, 146 (Mollier, 197). Nevertheless, such facts as the great extension of the muscle-bud areas and of the collector nerves both before and behind the paired fins, the concentration of the fin-elements and shortening of the fin-base, and the frequent presence of a greater number of muscle-buds in early stages than eventually come to build up the radial muscles, may be considered as evidence of an original continuity of the lateral folds. Very striking, in this connexion, is the production of a pair of buds from all the trunk myotomes forming an uninterrupted series from pectoral to pelvic region in some Selachians, Fig. 143 (*Pristiurus*; Dohrn, 159; Braus, 145. *Scyllium*; Goodrich, 172). In the Teleost *Lophius* the first pelvic bud succeeds immediately the last pectoral (Derjugin, 157).

It has been convincingly shown (Thacher, 219 ; Mivart, 196, and others) that the various types of the endoskeleton of the median fins of fishes, with more or less extensive basal plates and often rays branching from an axis, have been formed from a series of primitively discrete segmental radials by the concrescence and fusion of their basal regions, Figs. 132, 133, 135-6. This concrescence accompanies and is probably due to concentration or gathering together at the shortening base of the fin. That the similar manifold types of the endoskeleton of the paired fins, where concentration is even greater as a rule, have arisen in the same way can scarcely be doubted. Indeed it is necessary to assume this even on Gegenbaur's theory, since there the fin-skeleton is derived from originally separate gill-rays. The radials arise, not as outgrowths from the girdle, but as differentiations *in situ* within the mesenchymatous plate. The objection sometimes raised that the radials become differentiated in a continuous plate (as shown by Balfour, 142 ; Ruge, 211 ; Swinnerton, 300 ; Derjugin, 157, and others) and not as distinctly separate rudiments would apply equally to the median fins.

This early fusion of mesenchymatous or even procartilaginous rudiments with indefinite limits may be reasonably attributed to their being crowded together. The cartilaginous elements arise separately, Figs. 128, 130-31. In Selachians the peripheral ends of the radials first appear as separate streaks (Goodrich, 172). Supporters of the gill-arch theory, anxious to show that the paired fins are not of metameric structure and that the myotome-buds have only secondarily invaded them (Braus, 144-8), have also urged that the segmentation of the radial muscles of the adult paired fin does not correspond to that of the embryo, and further that the 'concordance' of radial muscles and skeletal radials does not hold good. Now it is true that in greatly concentrated fins, and more especially at the narrow base of such fins, fusion may take place between neighbouring muscle-buds and also between the rudiments of radials, that the metamerism may be greatly obscured, and that discrepancies may occur. But peripherally these disturbances occur chiefly at the two ends of the fin-fold. Usually in the middle region the concordance between muscle and radial is perfect ; and usually, even in highly concentrated fins, it is manifest in the peripheral parts, Figs. 131, 139.

Although adjacent muscle-buds anastomose at their base (Mollier, 197 ; E. Müller, 199-200), and the substance of an adult radial muscle may not be derived entirely from one bud, yet it has been shown to be derived mainly from that bud the position of which it continues to occupy throughout development, and the radial muscles, as in median fins, correspond in number and relative position to the buds from which they were formed, Fig. 144. This holds good, excepting for the above-mentioned discrepancies, in the paired fins of Selachians (Mollier, 197 ; Goodrich, 172). Since in these fish two primary buds are given off from each myotome, the number of adult radials and radial muscles is double that of the contributing segments (excepting always for reductions and disturbances at the anterior and posterior ends).

**Nerve Plexus.**—The consideration of the partial loss of the primary metamerism of radial muscles brings us to the question of the nature of the nervous plexus. That in a series of segments the motor component of each spinal nerve remains faithful to its myotome throughout the changes which may take place in ontogeny, if not actually proved, is in the highest degree probable from the evidence of comparative anatomy and embryology. That a motor nerve does not forsake the muscle in connexion with which it was originally developed to supply the muscle of some other segment is a conclusion in harmony with our knowledge of the nerve-supply of muscles in general, and in particular of those of the fins. We have seen above that the fin-muscles are primarily innervated from the segments from which they arose in ontogeny, the dorsal fins from branches of the dorsal rami, and the ventral and paired fins from branches of the ventral rami of spinal nerves. Now dissection reveals that these rami divide near the base of the fin and branch repeatedly, mingling to form a basal plexus whence arises a network of extraordinary complexity which spreads throughout the fin. Such a plexus of connected nerves is related not only to the median and paired fins of fishes, but also to the paired limbs of all Tetrapods (Mayer, 128, Harrison, 179, Goodrich, 172, in median fins; Mollier, 197, Braus, 144, 147, Hammarsten, 178, E. Müller, 199-200, in paired fins ; Fürbringer, 162-3, Sewertzoff, 215, and others in Tetrapods).

The number of spinal nerves sending motor fibres to the plexus

indicates the number of segments which have contributed to the musculature of the fin. But in the peripheral network the nerves would seem to
be inextricably mixed, and the original segmental order would seem to
be entirely lost. However, the branches of the spinal nerves are of mixed
character (sensory and motor), and the unsegmental appearance of the
network is chiefly due to the intermingling of sensory fibres ; the motor
fibres pass through it to their destination, where they may be distributed

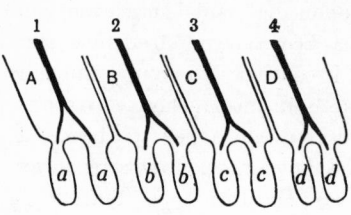

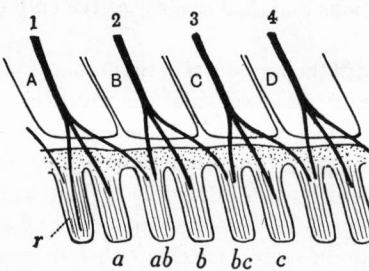

FIG. 144.

Diagram illustrating formation of adult *radial
muscles* from embryonic muscle-buds, and their motor
nerve-supply. Above, embryonic stage with a pair of
buds to each segment ; below, adult with radial muscles
compounded of material from adjacent buds. 1-4, Four
spinal nerves ; A-D, four myomeres ; *a-d*, muscle buds ;
*r*, radial muscle.

to the muscles with little overlapping (E. Müller, 200-1) or
none at all (as in the ventral
lobe of the caudal fin of *Scyllium*, Goodrich, 172). It has
been shown by experimental
stimulation that in the median
fins of Selachians the radial
muscles are supplied by the
spinal nerves in regular sequence
from before backwards (Goodrich, 172), and the same is the
case in the paired fins (Goodrich, 173; Braus, 148a; E.
Müller, 200-1). In the main,
then, segmental order is preserved. Even in the limbs of
Tetrapods, where all obvious
signs of segmentation are lost
in the adult muscles, this rule
has been shown to hold good
by dissection and experiment.
Here also plexus formation does
not entirely destroy segmental

order (Herringham, 182; Patterson, 203-4, and others). How then are
we to explain the fact that muscles of median fins and paired limbs may
be innervated by more than one spinal nerve ? The answer is, in all
probability, that this is due to the combination of the muscular tissue
of two or more segments. We have already mentioned above that the
muscle-buds of fins do not as a rule retain their original independence
but become connected by anastomosing bridges with their neighbours,
Figs. 129, 144. By such means myoblasts of adjacent segments may
combine to form compound radial muscles, whose segmental purity is
to that extent lost—to what extent varies, no doubt, in different fishes

and in different regions of the same fin. Experiments on paired fins in Selachians have yielded somewhat discordant results. While Braus concluded the overlap to be extensive, and that a single spinal nerve could supply some six or seven radial muscles, others have found that throughout the greater length of the fin each nerve supplies, as a rule, only one complete and two adjacent half-muscles (see diagram, Fig. 144).[1] In Tetrapods the combination and mixing of muscle substance derived from several segments is even more pronounced. But, strictly speaking, even here the nerves probably remain faithful to the muscle-fibres derived from their own segments; for it has been proved that each motor root supplies

[1] It would be interesting to determine the nerve-supply in median unconcentrated fins such as occur in Teleostei and Dipnoi.

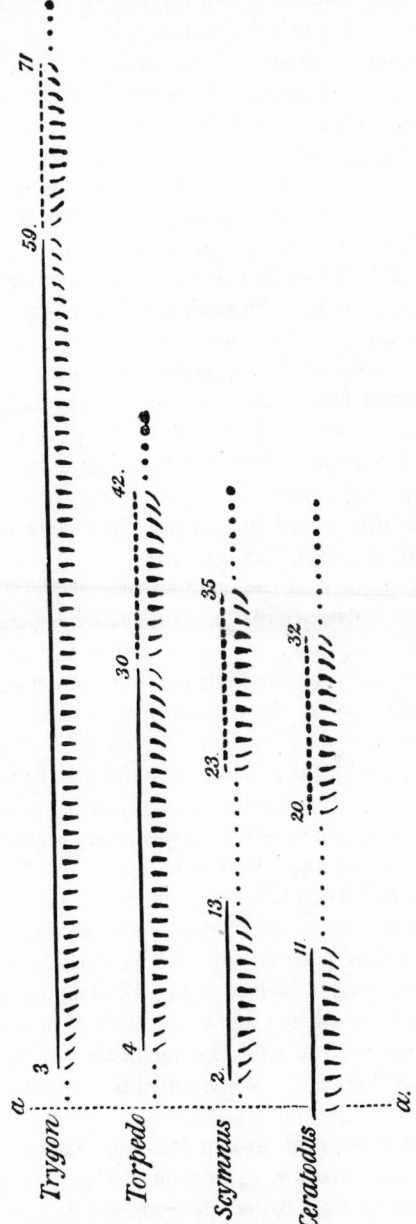

Fig. 145.

Diagrams, drawn to the same scale, indicating the nerve-supply of the paired fins in four fish. The spinal nerves are represented by the series of dots and strokes, the latter being those nerves which share in the formation of the 'limb plexus'. The thick horizontal line extends over the region supplying the pectoral fin, and the broken line over that supplying the pelvic fin. The line a–a shows the limit between the head and the trunk, and the numbers indicate the order of the true spinal nerves (from the results of H. Braus). (E. S. Goodrich, *Vert. Craniata*, 1909.)

its own special fibres, which are merely assembled and bound together in the same adult muscle (Sherrington).

**Variation in Extent.**—From the above it will be gathered that the number of spinal nerves which supply motor fibres to the muscles of median fin or paired limb is a sure guide to the number of segments which have contributed to its musculature; and, since the size of a motor nerve is proportional to the amount of muscle it supplies, the size of the various nerves entering a plexus may be taken as proportional to the share the various segments have taken in the composition of the musculature. So we find that the nerve components are usually stouter in the middle than at the two ends of a plexus, in agreement with the usual development of the muscle-buds, Fig. 143.

Very remarkable is the great variation in the extent of the paired and unpaired fins. This variation is not merely due to differences in concentration, but also to the fact that more or fewer segments contribute to their formation. Even if ' deconcentrated ' the median fins would not in most cases meet and stretch along the whole length of the body, nor would the paired fins spread completely from pectoral to pelvic region (see diagrams, Figs. 143, 145).

Every segment of the body seems capable of producing median fin-elements (compare *Amphioxus*; in Craniates perhaps the head segments should be excepted); and every segment of at least the trunk seems capable of producing paired fin-elements, muscular, nervous, and skeletal. This potentiality of the segments is, as a rule, actually expressed or called into force along restricted regions only. For instance, with regard to paired fin-elements in Selachians, the spinal nerves entering the plexus belong to pectoral segments 2-13 and pelvic segments 25-35 in *Scyllium*, segments 2-19 and 29-50 in *Heptanchus*, segments 4-30 and 31-42 in *Torpedo* (Braus, **144**; Goodrich, **172**). In the embryo of *Scyllium*, *Pristiurus*, and *Torpedo* every segment of the trunk from the pectoral to the pelvic region produces paired muscle-buds; but while in the sharks the intermediate buds are abortive, in *Torpedo* they form radial muscles to which correspond skeletal radials all along the trunk.

It may be concluded that every segment of the trunk is equipotential in this respect. The same equipotentiality with regard to paired limb-elements may no doubt be attributed to the trunk segments of Tetrapods (see below).

**On the Shifting of Median Fins and Paired Limbs in Phylogeny.**— We must now attempt to explain the very striking fact that median fins and paired limbs frequently change their position on the body in the course of phylogeny. Indeed, just as the limbs rarely are derived from exactly the same number of segments, so also they rarely occupy exactly the same place in the series of segments. This remarkable variation is seen not only in comparing closely related species, but even individuals of the same species, and occasionally the two sides of the same individual. Moreover, the variation affects both their position with regard to each other and to the body as a whole, and the shifting may take place in either direction.

First of all it may be noticed that, even if the ancestral Gnathostomes had possessed continuous fin-folds, the position of the median fins and

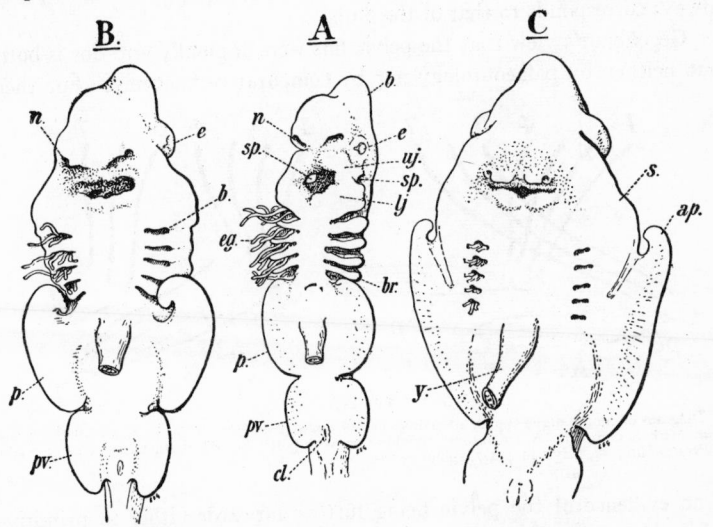

FIG. 146.

A, B, and C, Three successive stages in the development of *Torpedo ocellata*, Raf. The external gill-filaments have been removed on the left side. *ap,* Anterior region of pectoral fin growing forward; *b,* region of fore-brain; *br,* fourth branchial arch; *cl,* cloacal aperture; *e,* eye; *eg,* external gills; *lj,* lower jaw; *n,* opening of nasal sac; *p,* pectoral fin; *pv,* pelvic fin; *s,* ridge along which the pectoral fin will grow; *sp,* spiracle; *uj,* upper jaw; *y,* stalk of yolk-sac. (From Goodrich, *Vert. Craniata,* 1909).

paired limbs cannot be accounted for merely by their persistence in some regions and suppression in others. For in all classes there has been a perpetual alteration of position in the course of phylogeny both up and down the body.

The supporters of the gill-arch theory (Gegenbaur, **169**; Braus, **145**) held that these changes of position are due to the actual migration of the limb rudiment from one place to another. This view, put forward more especially to explain the posterior position of pelvic fins, is not borne out by embryology. There is little or no migration of the whole fin in onto-geny. A fin is not first formed in one place and then moved to another later. Considerable apparent motion may be brought about by processes of concentration, growth, and reduction. But the fin as a whole retains its position throughout ontogeny (with the single exception noted below of certain Teleosts, which does not affect the argument). This will be readily understood on comparing the diagrams, Fig. 143.

That there is no motion of the whole fin-rudiment is proved by the examination of the nerve-plexus. As already explained, the nerve-supply of an adult limb is a sure guide to the identification of the segments from which its elements have been derived, and the position of the plexus always corresponds to that of the limb.

Gegenbaur's view that the pelvic fins were originally anterior is borne out neither by palaeontology nor by comparative anatomy. For there

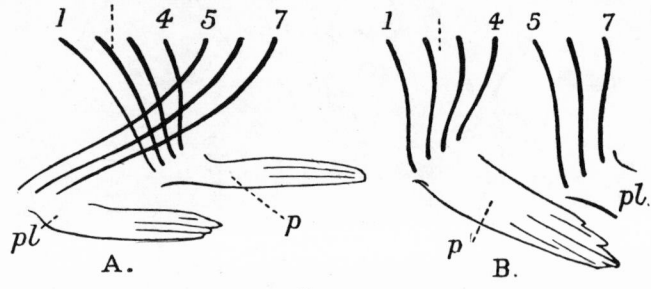

FIG. 147.

Diagram of motor nerve-supply of paired fins of *Gadus merlangus* (from E. S. Goodrich, *Quart. Jour. Micr. Sci.*, 1913). A, In natural position ; B, with pelvic brought back to its place of origin. *p*, Pectoral fin ; *pl*, pelvic fin ; 1-7, spinal nerves.

is no evidence of the pelvic being further forwards either in primitive fishes generally or in their early fossil representatives. When, as in some Teleostei, the pelvic fins are placed far forwards, their position is on good evidence considered to be secondary. In the Acanthopterygii they tend to shift from an abdominal to a 'thoracic' and finally to a 'jugular' position, and in such cases their nerve-plexus and the muscle-buds which give rise to their radial muscles are transposed with them as far as they can go (see Fig. 147, and footnote p. 140).

But if the shifting of limbs is not due to the actual migration of ready-formed embryonic rudiments, nevertheless such migration may occur to a very limited extent. For instance, in the frog the straining backwards of the pelvic plexus shows that the base of the hind-limb has moved backwards with the elongation of the pelvic girdle. In such fish as the Gadidae, where the pelvic fins have attained a jugular position actually in front of the pectorals, their real place of origin is betrayed by the nerves which are derived from the spinal cord from segments behind the origin of the pectoral plexus, crossing those which supply the pectoral fins, Fig. 147. Certain variations in the attachment of the pelvic girdle to the sacral vertebrae in Tetrapods may also be explained in the same way. For instance, the pelvic girdle of *Salamandra*, supplied by the 16th, 17th, and 18th spinal nerves, is occasionally attached to the 17th instead of to the 16th vertebra (v. Jhering, **187**). Only such small variations are due to migration, and the course of the nerves always indicates the real place of origin of the limb.

Three other explanations have been offered of the shifting of a limb together with its plexus : the theory of intercalation and excalation, the theory of redivision, and the theory of progressive modification or transposition.

According to the theory of intercalation (v. Jhering, **187**) the relative shifting of parts along a series of segments is due to segments having been dropped out or new segments having been added. To account for the extension of a limb or plexus over more or fewer segments, as well as for its shifting up or down the series, it is necessary to suppose that segments may be intercalated or excalated at any point in front of, within, or behind the limb and its plexus. At first sight this theory seems to afford a plausible explanation of simple cases of segmental variation, but it fails when applied to more complicated cases.[1] To account for the vast changes in the extent and position of the limbs which occur in most classes of Gnathostomes in the course of phylogeny, it would be necessary to assume that large numbers of segments have repeatedly been added to or dropped out of the series.[2] If such were the case we should expect to find zones of growth or zones of reduction where

---

[1] Taking the pelvic plexus of Mammals as an example, we find that v. Jhering first deals with such simple cases as *Sorex*, where a whole segment seems to have been added in front of it, some individuals having 13 and others 14 thoracic vertebrae, and the whole plexus and sacrum in the latter being situated further back. More difficult is it to explain variation in the Rabbit, where the lumbo-sacral plexus may include either nerves 25-30 or 24-30, the first sacral vertebra being the 27th in both cases. Here a nerve seems to have been intercalated in the middle of the plexus, since the crural moves one segment forward, while the more posterior ischiadic retains its position; yet the vertebrae are not changed. It has then to be further assumed that nervous and mesoblastic series of elements can move independently and fit on in new places, an assumption for which there is no evidence.

[2] A few examples of the variation in extent and of the shifting in position of the limb-plexus in Tetrapods may here be given (Fürbringer, **162-3**; Gadow, **165**, and others) :

The pectoral or brachial plexus of Anura usually is formed by spinal nerves 2, 3, 4 ; of *Proteus* by nerves 3, 4, 5 ; of *Megalobatrachus* by nerves 2, 3, 4, 5, 6. In Reptilia by nerves 4, 5, 6 in *Pseudopus* ; 6, 7, 8 in *Trionyx* ; 6, 7, 8, 9 in

new segments appear or old ones vanish. But no such zones occur, and segments grow only at the posterior end of the series. Moreover, the theory leads to absurd conclusions when applied to the paired fins of fishes.[1] These and other objections have been successfully urged against the theory of intercalation by Fürbringer and others. But if it is difficult on this theory to explain such ordinary cases, it becomes impossible to do so in the case of the relative shifting of median and paired fins in Elasmobranchs. The interesting and quite conclusive fact is that the two sets of fins shift independently. Thus the first dorsal is opposite the pectoral in *Lamna*, between the pectoral and pelvic in *Alopecias*, opposite the pelvic in *Scyllium*, and behind the pelvic in *Raja*. If it is granted that the fins are homologous in these four genera, no addition or suppression of segments can possibly account for their disposition (Goodrich, 173a).

The evidence against the theory of intercalation being overwhelming, we may examine the theory of redivision (Welcker, 228; Bateson, 143), which may be stated as follows : if one individual or organ is composed of, say, twenty segments and another of twenty-one or nineteen, the difference is due not to the addition or subtraction of a segment, but to the subdivision of the several individuals or organs into twenty, twenty-one, or nineteen segments respectively. Therefore, no segment of one case strictly corresponds to any one segment in the other two. If the number of segments were sufficiently increased or diminished by renewed subdivision, the number of segments between parts or organs might thus be altered. But their relative position to each other could only be altered if the redivision was unequal along the series. Clearly, such a statement would be no explanation at all, but merely a restatement in different words of the problem we set out to solve. No better than the theory of intercalation can it be applied to such cases as the apparent suppression

---

*Phrynosoma* ; 7, 8, 9, 10, 11 in *Crocodilus* ; 3, 4, 5, 6, 7 in *Chamaeleo*. In Aves by nerves 10-15 in *Columba*; 15-19 in *Anser*; 22-26 in *Cygnus atratus*.

The pelvic (lumbo-sacral) plexus includes nerves 8, 9, 10 in *Rana* ; 19-24 in *Phrynosoma* ; 22-26 in *Crocodilus*. In Man the brachial plexus is formed chiefly from nerves 5-9, and the lumbar plexus chiefly from nerves 21-25.

[1] For instance, in the smelt, *Osmerus eperlanus*, the pectoral fin is supplied by spinal nerves 1-4 and the pelvic by nerves 18-29 (Hammarsten, 178) ; while in the whiting, *Gadus merlangus*, nerves 1-4 supply the pectoral and nerves 5-6 the pelvic. Again, in *Scymnus* nerves 2-13 supply the pectoral and 23-45 the pelvic ; while in *Torpedo* the pectoral receives nerves 4-30 and the pelvic nerves 31-42. If the approximation of pectoral to pelvic fin were due to excalation, we should have to assume that the whole mid-trunk region had been suppressed in *Gadus* and *Torpedo*, and a new trunk region intercalated behind the pelvic, for instance, in *Gadus*.

of the mid-trunk in *Gadus* and *Torpedo*, or the independent shifting of the fins mentioned above.

There remains only the theory of transposition based on the 'Umformungstheorie' of Rosenberg (**209-10**), and first used to explain the varying extension of the different regions of the vertebral column. In his important works on anatomy, Fürbringer has shown how a limb-plexus may shift backwards or forwards like the limb it supplies. Obviously the nerves cannot actually move through the vertebral segments; it is, therefore, by progressive growth in one direction and by corresponding reduction in the other direction that change of position takes place. There is no transference of the limb-elements from one segment to another, no actual translocation or duplication of nerves, no intercalation or excalation, but a gradual assimilation of

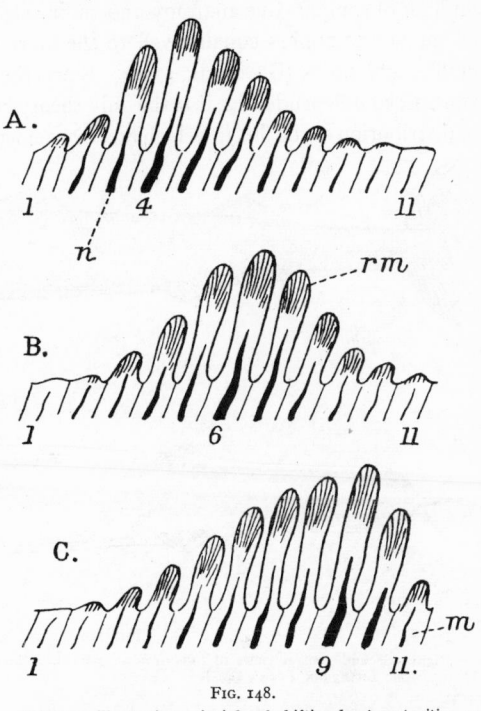

FIG. 148.

Diagram illustrating principle of shifting by *transposition* as seen in development of median fins. 1-11, Motor branches of spinal nerves; *rm*, muscle-buds forming radial muscles. In A, segment 4 contributes most; in B, segment 6; in C, segment 9.

neighbouring segments. Nerves at the anterior or posterior end may increase in size, and new nerves from adjoining segments may enter into the plexus. This, of course, accompanies the participation of new segments in the supply of muscle. So by gradual growth a limb supplied by, say, nerves 4, 5, and 6 may come to be supplied by nerves 3-7 or 1-8, and so on. Or, on the contrary, by a similar but reverse process of reduction, a limb supplied by nerves 1-8 may come to be supplied by nerves 3-7, or 4-6, Fig. 148.

Further, a limb-plexus may shift its position, without necessarily altering its structure from one region to another, by such a process of growth at one end accompanied by reduction at the other end. New segments being assimilated at one end, others may drop out, ceasing to contribute to the plexus, at the other. So we find in a plexus the more important and stouter nerves towards the middle, and the slenderer nerves towards either end. This explanation is in complete harmony with all the findings of comparative anatomy and embryology, and what has been said of the nerves applies equally well to the muscular and skeletal elements of fins and limbs (Goodrich, 173a). Since the various fins can thus be transposed independently, it is the only theory consistent with the changes of distribution of the fins in Selachians mentioned above (p. 140). The con-

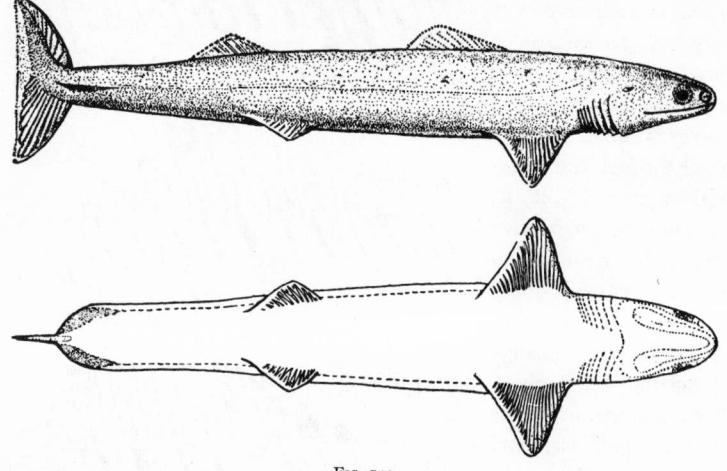

FIG. 149.

Right side and ventral views of *Cladoselache fyleri*, Cleveland Shales, Ohio; restored (from B. Dean, *Fishes Living and Fossil*, 1895).

clusion is that when structures appear to move up or down a segmental series, the shifting is due to a change in the incidence of the formative stimuli which determine the development of and differentiate the equipotential segments (Ruge, 212; Goodrich, 173a; Lebedinsky, 195).

**Conclusion.**—In conclusion it may be said that the lateral-fold theory alone agrees with the facts revealed by comparative anatomy and embryology. It was pointed out above (p. 130) that, although a primitive continuity of the lateral folds from pectoral to pelvic region is not an essential part of this theory, yet there is considerable embryological evidence in favour of this assumption. Whether much weight should be attached to Thacher's comparison with the metapleural folds of *Amphioxus*, and whether it may further be supposed that the two folds originally joined the median ventral fold behind the anus, is very doubtful. But it may be pointed out that in two genera of the Cephalochorda the right metapleural fold is continued into the preanal fold, and that the latter bears signs of a paired structure.[1]

Palaeontology affords some evidence of the existence of paired fin-folds. The primitive shark-like Palaeozoic Cladoselachii have paired fins in the form of longitudinal folds passing gradually without notch at either end into the body-wall, Figs. 149-50. The Acanthodii also possess paired fins of similar shape, but with the anterior border armed with a powerful spine probably formed of modified scales. As A. S. Woodward pointed out, the presence of a series of smaller spines and finlets between the pectoral

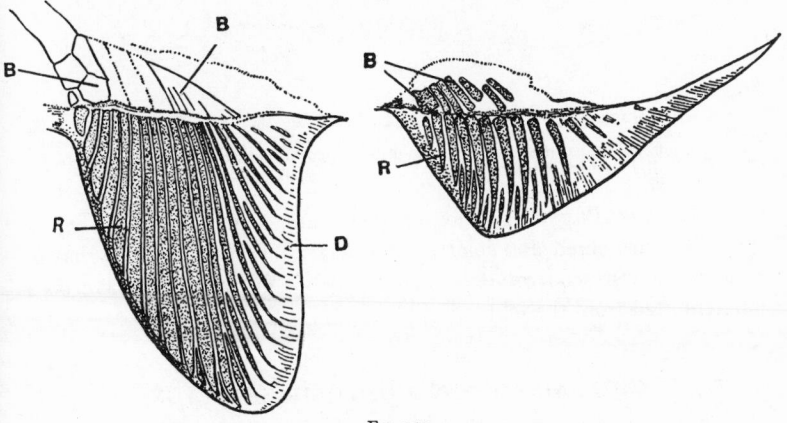

FIG. 150.

Paired fins of *Cladoselache fyleri* (from B. Dean, *Fishes Living and Fossil*, 1895). B, Basal cartilages; D, dermal fin-rays of pectoral; R, distal radials of fins. Pectoral fin on left, pelvic on right.

and pelvic in *Climatius* suggests that these were originally joined by a continuous fold.

The absence of any paired fins in Cyclostomes has always been a difficulty in adopting the view that the ancestral Craniates were provided with paired folds. But, if the conclusion be adopted that the modern Cyclostomes are the degenerate descendants of ancient Ostracoderms (Cope; A. S. Woodward; Stensiö, 135; Kiaer, 190), it appears not improbable that Lampreys and Hagfishes have lost the paired fin-folds, for indications of such folds have been found in most Ostracoderms (Lankester, 194; Traquair, 223-5; A. S. Woodward, 231; Kiaer, 190).

They appear to have been little developed in Anaspida, being chiefly represented by rows of spine-like scales specially developed in the pectoral

---

[1] It is uncertain what significance should be attached to the preanal fold of Teleostomes (*Amia, Lepidosteus*, and many Teleosts). Probably it is a true continuation of the median fin-fold, since it usually contains actinotrichia; but it may be a secondary extension of it, Figs. 113, 116.

region. In Pteraspidomorphi they form flattened pectoral ridges as in *Drepanaspis,* or more outstanding flaps as in Coelolepidae. The lateral folds become well marked in the pectoral region of Cephalaspidomorphi, and may be developed into prominent fin-like paddles, Fig. 151 ;

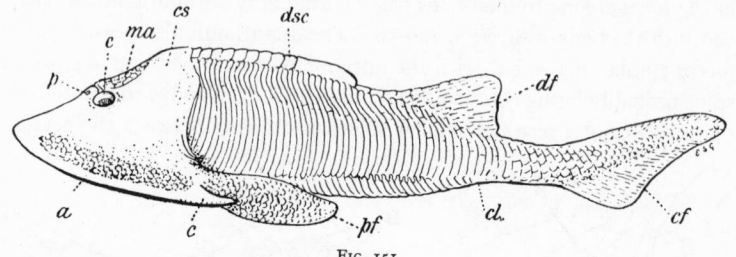

FIG. 151.

Restoration of *Cephalaspis Lyelli.* *a*, Lateral area with polygonal plates ; *c*, cornu of cephalic shield ; *cf*, caudal fin ; *cl*, position of cloaca ; *cs*, cephalic shield ; *df*, dorsal fin ; *dsc*, dorsal ridge scales ; *e*, orbit ; *ma*, median area with polygonal plates ; *p*, position of median pore ; *pf*, pectoral fin. (From Goodrich, *Vert. Craniata*, 1909.)

while in the Pterychthyomorphi these are represented by highly specialised armoured and jointed appendages. It is to be noted that in none of the Ostracodermi does a special pelvic fin appear to have been differentiated from the fold.

## THE PAIRED FINS AND THEIR SKELETON

The endoskeleton of the paired fins of fishes varies greatly in the different groups ; but, from what has been said above, it will be gathered that the various types of fin-skeleton, together with the girdles, have probably been derived phylogenetically from originally separate segmentally arranged radials with the help of concentration and concrescence. These radials appear to have been jointed in the ancestral Pisces. Very generally the radials of the median fins are subdivided into three pieces : a proximal deeply embedded (axonost), a middle, and a distal marginal piece (p. 91). Those of the paired fins were probably originally similarly jointed (pelvics of Chondrostei) ; but often they become further subdivided (Elasmobranchii, Fig. 159), or on the contrary simplified and reduced to one piece (Teleostei, etc., Figs. 173, 176, 205).

Although we shall not attempt to describe the different types of the endoskeleton of the paired fins in detail, we may discuss their possible phylogenetic origin, though neither anatomy nor embryology enables us to determine this for certain, and the evidence of palaeontology is still inconclusive.

According to Gegenbaur (**167-9**) the original type resembled the skeleton of the pectoral and pelvic fins of *Ceratodus*. This 'archipterygium' had a median jointed tapering axis articulating with the girdle, and was provided with an anterior preaxial and a posterior postaxial series of rather fewer radials, Figs. 152, 154. The radials were arranged in pairs on the segments of the axis, and diminished in size towards the distal extremity of the leaf-like fin (Günther, 1871; Huxley, 535; Howes, 183; Braus, 147). Such a 'biserial archipterygium' may be described as 'mesorachic' and 'rachiostichous' (Lankester). That it is a very ancient type can hardly be doubted. For, though at the present day it occurs only in the archaic *Ceratodus*,[1] it seems, judging from the outward appearance of the fins, to have been present in the pectoral and pelvic fins of primitive Dipnoi down to their earliest known representatives in the Devonian. It was also possessed by the Devonian Crossopterygii, but here the axis is usually shorter with fewer segments and more reduced postaxial radials in the pectoral fin (*Eusthenopteron*, Fig. 155; Whiteaves, 229; Traquair, 220; A. S. Woodward, 231; Goodrich, 171; Petronievics, 205); while in the only pelvic fin-skeleton known there are no separate postaxial radials at all (*Eusthenopteron*, Fig. 204; Goodrich, 171). Moreover, an almost perfect archipterygial type of endoskeleton is present in the pectoral fin of the Carboniferous Pleuracanthodii (Brongniart, 149; Fritsch, 23; Döderlein, 158; Jaekel, 186), though the pelvic fin shows only preaxial

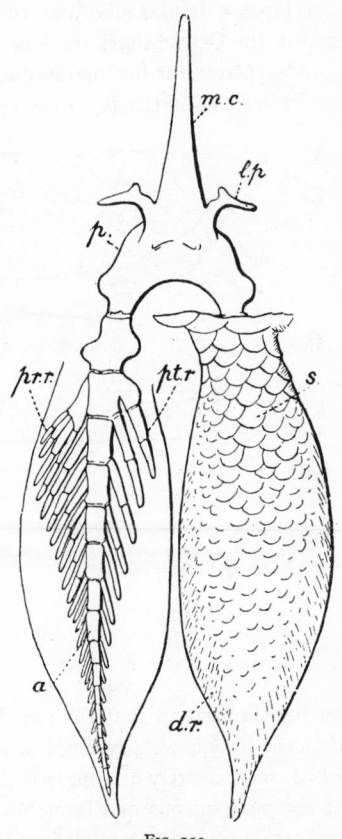

FIG. 152.

Ventral view of the pelvic girdle and fins of *Ceratodus Forsteri*, Kr. (Partly from Davidoff.) *a*, Jointed axis; *d.r*, dermal rays; *l.p*, lateral prepubic process; *m.c*, median epipubic process; *p*, pelvic girdle; *pr.r*, postaxial radial; *pt.r*, preaxial radial; *s*, scale covering axial region. (From E. S. Goodrich, *Quart. Jour. Micr. Sci.*, v. 45, 1901.)

---

[1] The fin-skeleton is entirely cartilaginous in all living Dipnoi (but in the extinct *Ceratodus sturi* its basal segment is ossified). The postaxial radials are not only more slender but also more numerous than the preaxial; consequently more than one may be attached to an axial element. They tend

radials attached to the axis. The biserial or archipterygial type is associated with a projecting ' acutely lobate ' shape of fin, with a well-developed muscular lobe, a narrow base and dermal fin-rays set all round; and in the Osteichthyes the lobe is covered with scales.

Gegenbaur further maintained that the various types of paired fin-skeleton found in the Teleostomi may be derived from the archipterygium

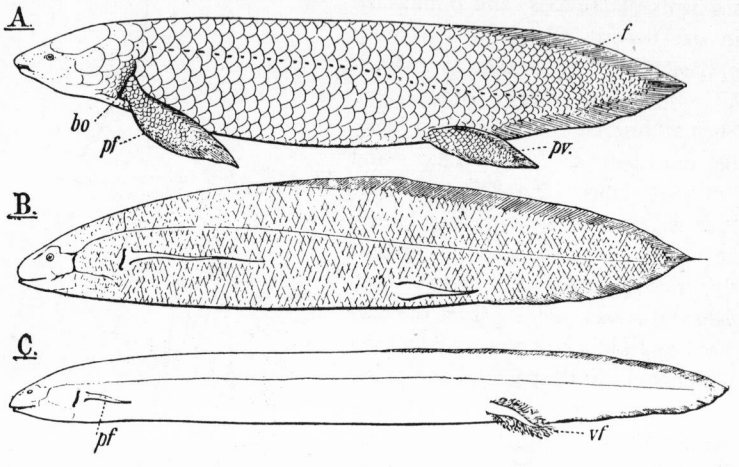

FIG. 152a.

A, *Ceratodus Forsteri*, Krefft ; B, *Protopterus annectens*, Owen (after Lankester) ; C, *Lepidosiren paradoxa*, Fitz. (after Lankester, modified). *bo*, Branchial opening ; *f*, median fin ; *pf*, pectoral fin ; *pv*, pelvic fin ; *vf*, vascular villi present on the male. (From E. S. Goodrich, *Vert. Craniata*, 1909.)

on the supposition that the axis became shortened and finally lost, and that the radials were reduced in number, especially the postaxial radials which soon entirely disappeared. The ' rhipidostichous ' type of skeleton of the pectoral fins of Elasmobranchs, in which the radials have a fan-like arrangement, he also deduced from the archipterygium on the supposition that the axis has been reduced and is represented chiefly by the posterior basal metapterygium, there being a large number of preaxial radials and at most only few vestigial postaxial radials, Fig. 156.

But on this theory the origin of the archipterygium itself still remains to be explained. We have already seen that Gegenbaur's view that it was derived from the branchial skeleton is untenable (p. 130). It may, however,

---

also to fuse at their base. A true joint occurs between the single basal and girdle.

In *Protopterus* and *Lepidosiren* the paired fins are much reduced and filamentous, with a slender jointed axis. The latter genus has lost all trace of lateral radials, and only vestigial preaxial radials remain in *Protopterus*, Figs. 91 and 152a.

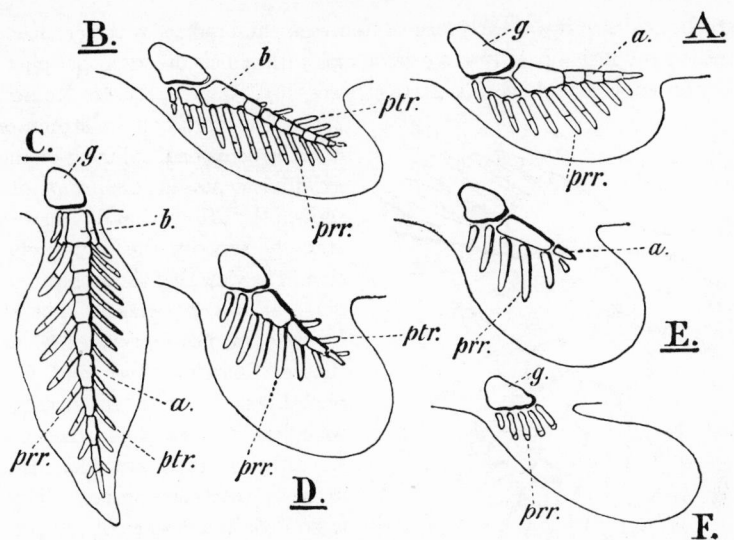

Fig. 153.

Diagrams showing the possible derivation from each other of the various types of pectoral fin skeleton in the Osteichthyes. A, Pleurorachic type (*Cladodus*) ; B, hypothetical stage leading to the mesorachic type C (*Ceratodus*) ; D, hypothetical type leading to E (*Acipenser, Amia*) ; F, teleostean type, reached either from A through E, or from C through D and E. *a*, Segment of axis ; *b*, basal of axis ; *g*, pectoral girdle ; *prr*, preaxial radial ; *ptr*, postaxial radial. (After Goodrich, *Vert. Craniata*, 1909.)

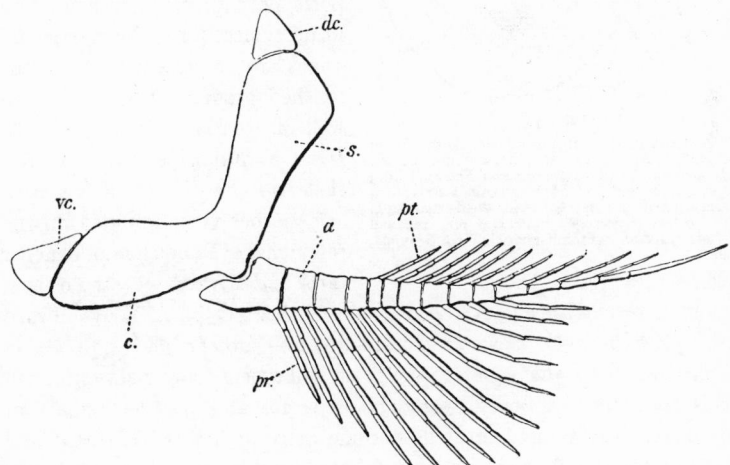

Fig. 154.

Left pectoral girdle and fin-skeleton of *Pleuracanthus Gaudryi*, Fr. *a*, Segmented axis of fin ; *c*, coracoid region ; *dc*, dorsal cartilage ; *pr*, preaxial radial ; *pt*, postaxial radial ; *s*, scapular region ; *vc*, ventral cartilage. (From E. S. Goodrich, *Vert. Craniata*, 1909.)

still be held that it was early formed from segmental radials by their concentration and fusion basally to a central axis with radials diverging peripherally on either side, Figs. 153-4, 156 (Howes, **183**; Haswell, **180-81**; Mollier, **197**). The variation in structure and the occasional splitting of the axial elements in *Ceratodus* described by Howes and Haswell strongly support this interpretation. The view that the archipterygium is a very ancient type of fin-skeleton, possibly ancestral to that of Chondrichthyes and Osteichthyes, is quite reconcilable with the 'lateral-fold theory'. Nevertheless, there are difficulties in the way of its acceptance. There is no definite evidence of the presence of distinctly postaxial rays in the pelvic fin of any Elasmobranch or Teleostome; even in the Pleuracanthodii and Crossopterygii (Osteolepidoti) the jointed axis supports only preaxial radials, and in its typical form the biserial fin seems to represent rather the finished product of specialisation well differentiated from the girdle than a primitive type of fin-skeleton.

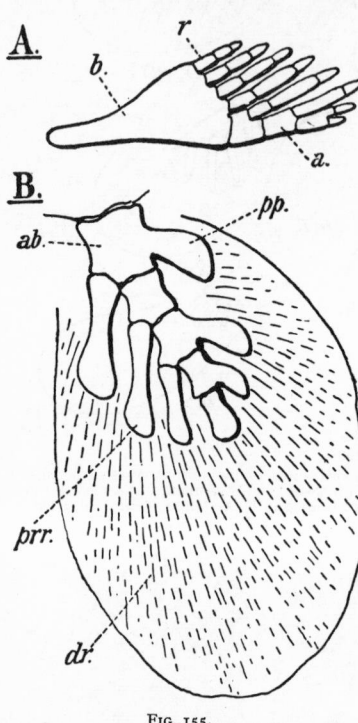

Fig. 155.

A, Endoskeleton of the second dorsal fin of *Glyptolepis leptopterus*, Ag.; B, skeleton of the left pectoral fin of *Eusthenopteron Foordi*, Wht.; restored. *a*, Segment of longitudinal axis; *ab*, basal segment of axis; *b*, basal; *dr*, dermal rays; *pp*, postaxial process (radial?); *prr*, preaxial radial; *r*, radial. (From Goodrich, *Vert. Craniata*, 1909.)

Another view, founded on the researches of Balfour(**142**), Thacher (**219**) and Mivart (**196**), and others, has more recently been developed by Wiedersheim (**230**), A. S. Woodward (**231**), Regan (**208**), Sewertzoff (**216-17**), and others, and is more in accordance with the general results of embryology and palaeontology. It is that the originally segmental separate and parallel radials of the paired longitudinal fin-folds become more or less concentrated and fused at their base, giving rise to a 'pleurorachic' and 'monostichous' or uniserial type of skeleton. In such a type the concrescence was greater at the anterior than at the posterior end of the fin, the longitudinal axis lay in the body-wall, and bore a single row of radials along its outer edge. The basal elements of the radials fused, especially anteriorly, to larger pieces of which the most anterior extended inwards and gave rise to the limb girdle, Figs. 153, 157. If this view is correct we should expect to find in primitive forms traces of a segmented longitudinal axis posteriorly, of progressive fusion of the basal elements anteriorly, of peripheral radials still attached to the girdle in front of the axial element,

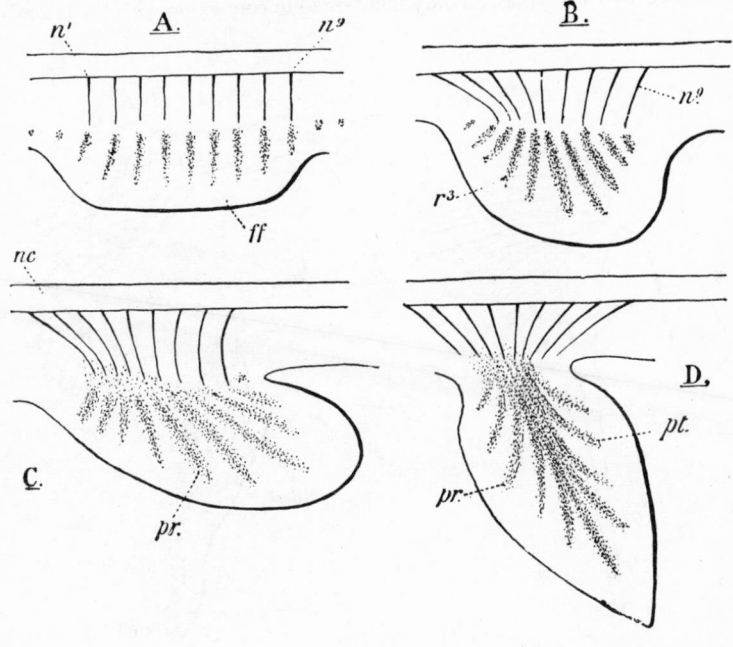

FIG. 156.

Diagrams to show the result of concentration on the skeleton and nerve-supply of a paired fin. A, B, C lead towards the Selachian type of fin; A, B, D towards the Dipnoan type. $n^{1-9}$, Nine spinal nerves supplying the fin; *nc*, nerve-cord; *r*, radials represented as seen in an early embryonic stage; *pr*, preaxial, and *pt*, postaxial radials; *ff*, fin-fold. (From Goodrich, *Vert. Craniata*, 1909.)

and of the segmental origin of the girdle itself. And this is just what we find in most early or primitive fishes, especially in the pelvic fin, for it is a remarkable fact that in many respects the pelvic limb lags behind the pectoral in development, except perhaps in Dipnoi and Tetrapods. From the primitive form, with the axis running parallel with the body-wall, the other types in which it projects outwards at an angle are supposed to have been derived by the freeing of its posterior end, and extension of the lobe at a greater and greater angle to the body. This is due, perhaps, not so much to the motion of the axis, as to its being formed more and more towards the centre of the fin-lobe. This change of position of the axis of concrescence would be accompanied by the shifting of an increasing number of the free ends of the radials to a postaxial position. The typical biserial mesorachic fin would represent, then, the final product of this phylogenetic process. This second theory is more completely in agreement with embryology and palaeontology than is that of Gegenbaur.

Most striking of all are the fins of the ancient Cladoselachii first described by Dean (154), already mentioned in connexion with the lateral-

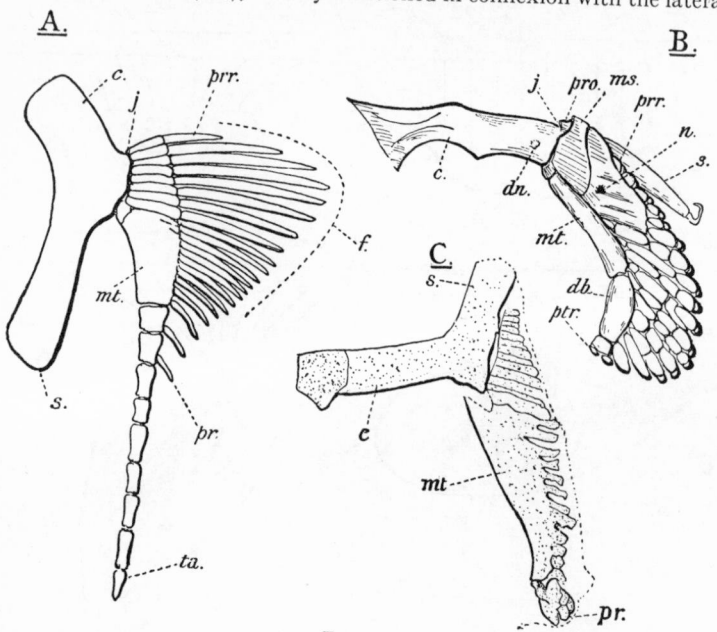

FIG. 157.

Skeleton of the pectoral arch and fin of A, *Cladodus Neilsoni*, Traq.; B, *Chlamydoselachus anguineus*, Garman; and C, *Symmorium reniforme*, Cope. (A restored from Traquair's figure, B and C after Braus.) *c*, Coracoid region; *db*, distal basal or 3rd segment of metapterygial axis; *dn*, diazonal nerve foramen; *f*, problematical fin outline; *j*, joint between girdle and fin; *ms*, mesopterygium; *mt*, metapterygium; *n*, nerve foramen; *pr*, posterior preaxial radial; *pro*, propterygium; *prr*, anterior preaxial radial; *ptr*, possibly postaxial radial; *s*, scapular region; *ta*, distal segment of metapterygial axis. (From E. S. Goodrich, *Vert. Craniata*, 1909.)

fold theory (p. 143). In *Cladoselache* not only are the peripheral radials almost parallel and unfused, but their basal segments are combined to form a longitudinal axial region in which the elements, especially in the pelvic fin, are still for the most part separate and but imperfectly differentiated from the girdle, Fig. 150.

The pectoral fins of the Devonian and Carboniferous genera *Cladodus* and *Symmorium* have a somewhat similar skeleton, but with the axis more definitely formed, especially in *Cladodus* where it is long, tapering, and many-jointed (Traquair, 222; Cope, 152). From a somewhat similar

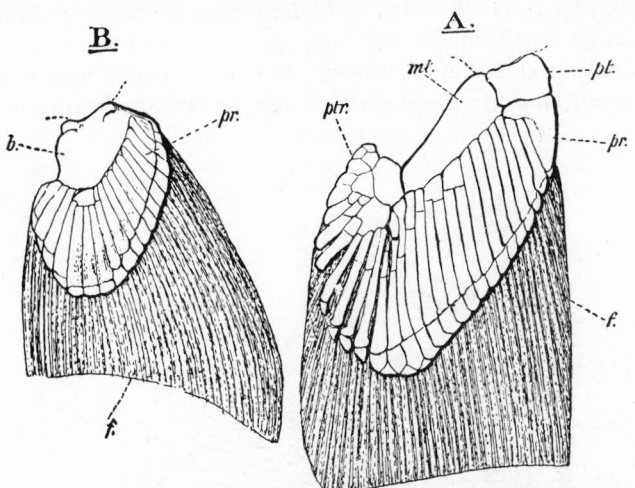

FIG. 158.

*Callorhynchus antarcticus*, Lac. The web of the fin, and the ceratotrichia, have been cut across. (After Mivart.) *b*, Basipterygium; *f*, fin-web; *mt*, metapterygium; *pr*, preaxial radials; *pt*, propterygium; *ptr*, cartilages representing postaxial radials. (From Goodrich, *Vert. Craniata*, 1909.)

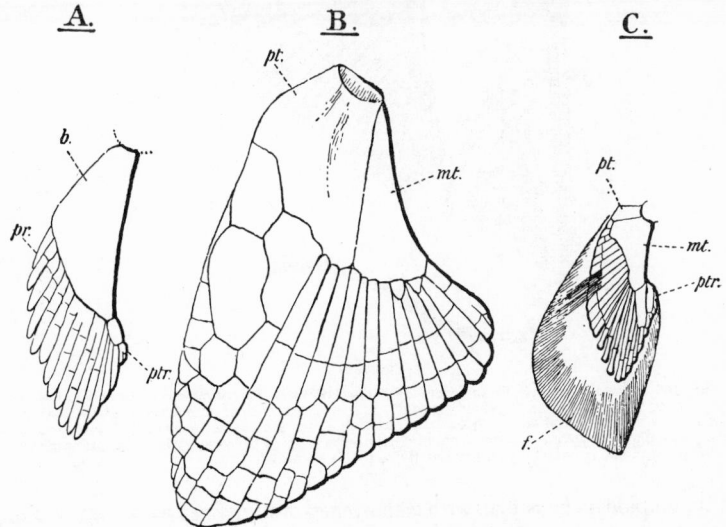

FIG. 159.

Skeleton of the pectoral fin of A, *Scymnus lichia*, Cuv. (after Gegenbaur); B, *Heterodontus* (*Cestracion*) *Philippi*, Lac. (after Gegenbaur); C, *Centrophorus calceus*, Gthr. (after Woodland). In the latter the web of the fin is represented. *b*, Basipterygium; *f*, fin-web; *mt*, metapterygium; *pr*, preaxial radials; *pt*, propterygium; *ptr*, postaxial radials. (From E. S. Goodrich, *Vert. Craniata*, 1909.)

type may have developed that of *Pleuracanthus*, where the pectoral axis has many postaxial radials, Figs. 154, 157.

The pectoral fins of the Selachii have a prominent muscular lobe into which projects an endoskeleton very variable in detail, but built

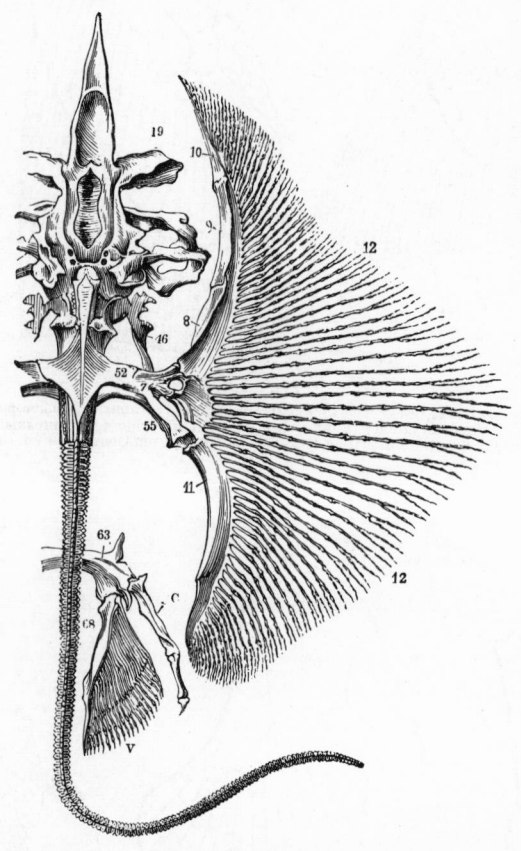

FIG. 160.

Skeleton of *Raja batis*, L. (From Owen, *Anat. of Vertebrates*, by permission of Messrs. Longmans and Co.) 7, Scapular region of pectoral girdle; 8, 9, 10, segments of anterior axis of pectoral fin; 11, posterior axis; 12, radials of expanded pectoral fin; 19, preorbital process; 52, cartilage plate joining scapula to vertebral column; 55, posterior outgrowth of pectoral girdle; 63, pelvic girdle; 68, basipterygium; *c*, anterior enlarged radial; *v*, pelvic fin radials.

on the rhipidostichous plan with a shortened or ill-defined axis, Figs. 158-9. Gegenbaur attempted to show that the ground plan consisted of three basal pieces, the pro-, meso-, and metapterygium articulated to the girdle, and each bearing radials. The pro- and mesopterygium were considered to be formed by the fusion of the basal joints of preaxial radials, while the metapterygium, with sometimes some posterior terminal elements, was supposed to represent the original axis not formed by concrescence. Some few small radials occasionally found on the posterior border were taken to represent remains of the postaxial series, and the whole was compared to a reduced and modified archipterygium. However, the distinction drawn between the posterior and largest basal (metapterygium) and the others is not justified by comparative anatomy or embryology (p. 144). Indeed, Huxley (535) identified the original axis in the meso-

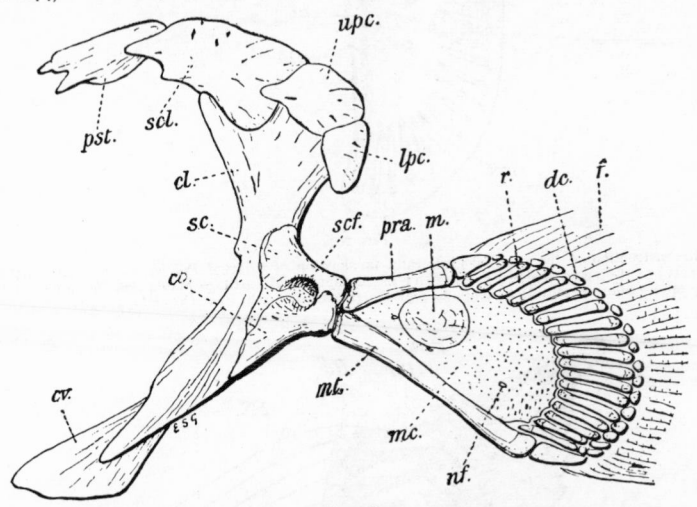

FIG. 161.

Skeleton of the right half of the pectoral girdle and of the right fin of *Polypterus bichir*, Geoffr. Inner view. *cl*, Cleithrum ; *co*, coracoid ; *cv*, clavicle ; *dc*, distal radial cartilage ; *f*, dermal rays ; *lpc*, lower postcleithrum ; *m*, mesopterygial bony plate ; *mc*, mesopterygial cartilage ; *mt*, metapterygium, or postaxial radial ; *nf*, nerve foramen ; *pra*, preaxial radial ; *pst*, post-temporal ; *r*, radial ; *sc*, scapula ; *scf*, scapular foramen ; *scl*, supracleithrum ; *upc*, upper postcleithrum. (From Goodrich, *Vert. Craniata*, 1909.)

pterygium. All the basals are doubtless formed by concrescence, traces of which can still be seen even in the adult fin, and an endless variety of detail in the shape and composition of the elements is presented by the various families and genera. There may be a single basal, as in *Scymnus* ; two basals as in *Heterodontus* and *Chimaera* ; three, as in *Scyllium* and *Squalus* ; or five, as in *Myliobatis*. It is also important to note that, in Rajidae, an anterior axis is formed by concrescence, similar to the original posterior metapterygial axis, Figs. 146, 160 (Bunge, 151 ; Howes, 184).

The endoskeleton of the pectoral fin of the Teleostomi has already been dealt with in the preceding discussions, and it need here only be pointed out with regard to the Crossopterygii (Osteolepidoti) that while in the Osteolepidae it may have been typically mesorachic and biserial,

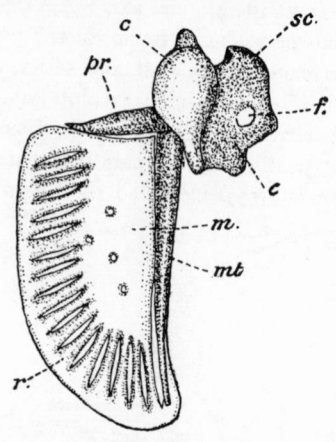

FIG. 162.

Reconstruction of the pectoral girdle and fin-skeleton of a larval *Polypterus*, enlarged. (After Budgett.) *c*, Coracoid region; *f*, foramen; *m*, mesopterygial cartilage plate; *mt*, metapterygium; *pr*, propterygium; *r*, radial; *sc*, scapular region. (From Goodrich, *Vert. Craniata*, 1909.)

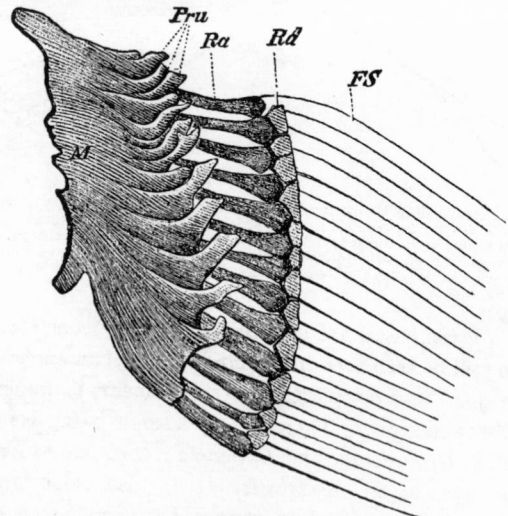

FIG. 163.

Right pelvic fin of a young *Polyodon folium*. From the dorsal side. *FS*, Bony dermal rays; *M*, metapterygium; *Pru*, uncinate ('iliac') processes; *Ra, Ra¹*, radii of the first and second orders. (From Wiedersheim, *Comp. Anatomy*.)

in the Rhizodontidae the jointed axis is relatively short and the postaxial radials much reduced, Fig. 155 (Whiteaves, **229**; A. S. Woodward, **231**;

Goodrich, **171** ; Broom, **150**). On the other hand, the fin-skeleton of the Actinopterygii shows no definite signs of a mesorachic and biserial structure. It resembles rather that of the Selachii. In the modern Chondrostei the pectoral fin-skeleton has a posterior axis and a consider-

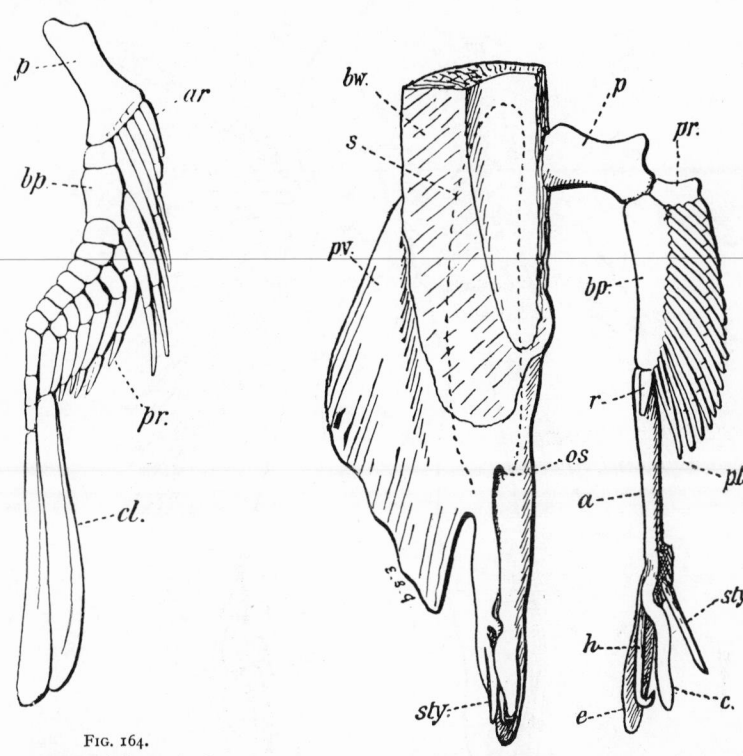

FIG. 164.

Pelvic girdle and fin-skeleton of a male *Pleuracanthus Oelbergensis*, Fr. (After Fritsch.) *ar*, Anterior preaxial radial resting on girdle; *bp*, segmented basipterygial axis; *cl*, modified radials of clasper ; *p*, pelvic girdle (left half) ; *pr*, preaxial radials. (From Goodrich, *Vert. Craniata*, 1909.)

FIG. 165.

Dorsal view of the pelvic girdle and fins of a male *Squalus acanthias* ; the skeleton has been exposed on the right side. *a*, Axial cartilage of clasper ; *bp*, basipterygium ; *bw*, cut body-wall ; *c*, dorsal covering plate ; *e*, ventral plate ; *h*, hook; *os*, opening of glandular sac ; *p*, pelvic girdle ; *pr*, propterygial, or anterior basal ; *pt*, posterior radial ; *pv*, pelvic fin ; *r*, modified radial ; *s*, outline of glandular sac embedded in body-wall dorsal to girdle ; *sty*, hard style. (From Goodrich, *Vert. Craniata*, 1909.)

able number of preaxial radials, several of which are articulated in front to the girdle (Gegenbaur, **166** ; Wiedersheim, **230** ; Hamburger, **177** ; Rautenfeld, **207** ; Regan, **208** ; Sewertzoff, **217**). That of *Polypterus*, though highly specialised in the adult (Gegenbaur, **166** and **168** ; Klaatsch, **192**), with two basal pieces reaching the girdle, an expanded central piece, and numerous peripheral free radials, has been shown by

Budgett (10) to develop in the young much as in the Selachii, with a posterior axis and preaxial radials only, Figs. 161-2.

In *Amia* the pectoral fin-skeleton more closely resembles that of *Acipenser*, but the axis is shorter and the radii ossified ; while in *Lepi-*

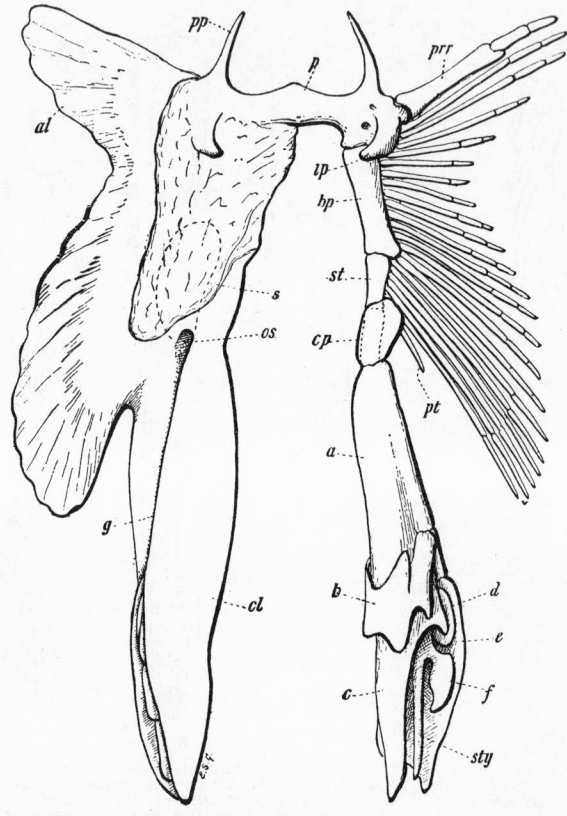

FIG. 166.

*Raja blanda*, Holt. Dorsal view ; the cartilaginous skeleton has been completely exposed on the right side. *a, b, c, d, f,* Cartilages of clasper ; *al,* anterior lobe of pelvic fin ; *bp,* basipterygium ; *cl,* clasper ; *cp,* covering-plate ; *ip,* iliac process ; *os,* opening of sac ; *p,* pelvic girdle ; *pp,* prepubic process ; *prr,* enlarged preaxial radial ; *pt,* posterior preaxial radial ; *s,* dotted line indicating ventral glandular sac ; *st,* second segment of basipterygial axis ; *sty,* styliform cartilage. (From Goodrich, *Vert. Craniata,* 1909.)

*dosteus* reduction has gone still further, Fig. 173. Finally, in the Teleostei the axis has disappeared and all the radii come to articulate on the girdle. Usually there are not more than five, of which the first is small and closely bound to the enlarged anterior dermal ray. Occasionally there are more, as in *Malapterurus, Muraenolepis,* and Anguilliformes (eight in *Anguilla*),

Fig. 176, a peculiarity which may be due to the retention of a more primitive and larger number (Sagemehl, 378 ; Derjugin, 157). In connexion

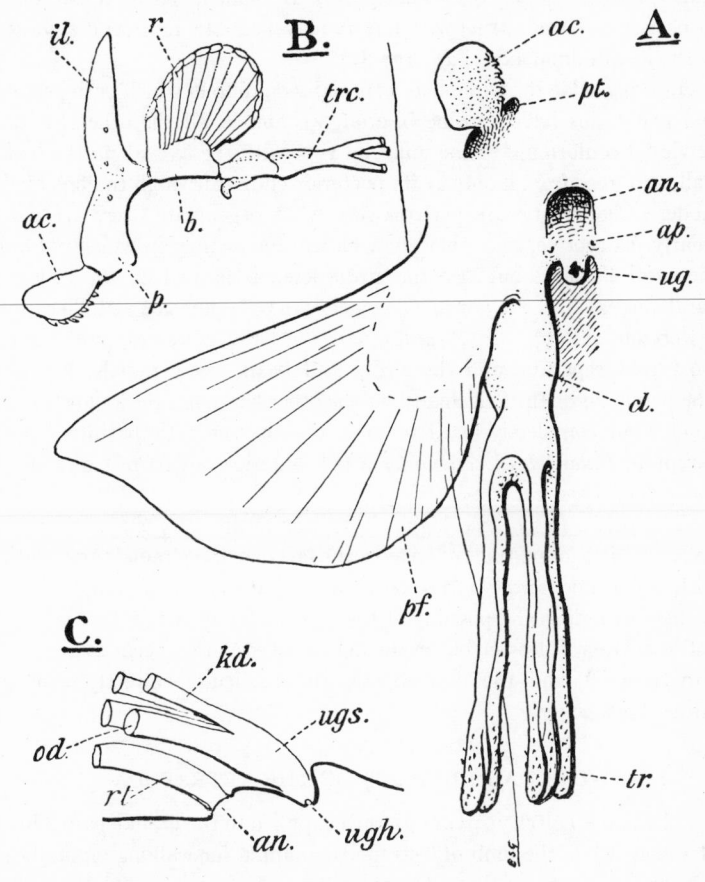

FIG. 167.

*Chimaera monstrosa*, L. A, Ventral view of the right pelvic fin of a male ; B, ventral view of the left half of the pelvic girdle and pelvic fin of a male (after Davidoff) ; C, diagram showing the opening of rectum and urinogenital sinus in the female. *ac*, Anterior clasper armed with denticles ; *an*, anus ; *ap*, abdominal pore ; *b*, basipterygium ; *cl*, posterior clasper ; *il*, iliac process ; *kd*, kidney duct ; *od*, oviduct ; *p*, pelvic cartilage ; *pf*, pelvic fin ; *pt*, pocket into which the anterior clasper can be withdrawn ; *r*, radial ; *rt*, rectum ; *tr*, trifid extremity of clasper ; *trc*, its cartilage cut short ; *ug*, urinogenital papilla ; *ugh*, its opening ; *ugs*, urinogenital sinus. (From Goodrich, *Vert. Craniata*, 1909.)

with the pectoral skeleton of the Teleostei it should be mentioned that there is generally developed in the young from the hinder margin of the plate of mesenchyme from which arise the girdle and the radials (p. 132) a long process passing backwards along the body-wall ; later it remains attached as a cartilaginous process to the girdle, but always disappears more or less completely in the adult (Emery, 121 ; Swinnerton, 300 ; Haller, 176 ; Derjugin, 157 ; Vogel, 226). By some it has been considered to be a new larval structure ; but it may possibly represent a vestige of the longitudinal axis, Figs. 177-8.

Leaving aside the Dipnoi, as a specialised group in which both pectoral and pelvic fins have become biserial, we find in all the other Pisces a pelvic fin conforming to the uniserial type with the axis along the body-wall, and freed from it only at its posterior end. Although the fins of the modern Chondrostei are perhaps somewhat degenerate, they are particularly instructive, since they show clearly the manner in which not only the axial elements but also the girdle itself is formed by the fusion of basal pieces, Figs. 163, 209 (Thacher, 219 ; Regan, 208 ; Mollier, 198 ; Sewertzoff, 216-17). In *Pleuracanthus* the basal pieces are still for the most part separate, and the girdle still bears many radials, Fig. 164. The pelvic fin of the Selachians, on the other hand, has the axial elements much more completely fused to form the characteristic basipterygium ; except in *Chlamydoselachus*, only a few anterior radials rest directly on the girdle,[1] Figs. 27, 165-6.

The pelvic fins of the higher Teleostomes are very much shortened and show little or no trace of an axis, the few remaining radials articulating with the pelvic girdle. *Polypterus* has only four such radials ; small vestiges of radials and possibly of the axis are found in *Lepidosteus*, *Amia*, and the lower Teleostei, but in the higher Teleosts they seem to disappear altogether (?), and the dermal rays then articulate directly with the girdle, Figs. 205-7.

### THE PAIRED LIMBS OF THE TETRAPODA

The name Ichthyopterygium is applied to the fin-like paired limbs of Pisces, while the limb of Tetrapods, adapted for walking on land, has been given the name Cheiropterygium. It is also called the penta-dactyle limb, because both the fore and the hind limb are primitively provided with five well-developed functional digits.[2]

---

[1] In the male Pleuracanthodii and Selachii (but apparently not in Clado-selachii) the posterior end of the pelvic fin, with its contained endoskeleton consisting of the apex of the axis and about three radials, is converted into a specialised intromittent organ, the so-called clasper or myxopterygium (Gegenbaur, 167 ; Jungersen, 188-9 ; Huber, 185 ; Leigh-Sharpe, 195a). The Holocephali have in addition a smaller anterior clasper developed from the front end of the fin (Davidoff, 153). See Figs. 164-7.

[2] The number of digits may be reduced in specialised forms, but the number five was doubtless established in the ancestral Tetrapod. The majority of

It is important to notice that, although the fore and hind limbs may in the course of evolution and in adaptation to various modes of life come to differ greatly from each other, yet there is good evidence that they are built on essentially the same plan and were primitively alike. The pentadactyle limb is differentiated into three regions (stylopodium, zeugopodium, autopodium), bent at an angle to each other. The first or proximal region (upper-arm or brachium of fore-limb ; thigh or femur of hind-limb) projects outwards from the body ; the second region (fore-arm or antebrachium ; shank or crus) extends downwards ; the third region (hand or manus ; foot or pes) rests on the ground and bears the five separate digits. The endoskeleton consists of a single element in the proximal region (humerus ; femur), two elements in the middle region (preaxial radius in fore-limb, and tibia in hind-limb ; postaxial ulna in fore-limb, and fibula in hind-limb), and several elements in the distal region. The elements of these three regions articulate with each other by well-defined joints. The endoskeletal elements of the autopodium or distal region are further differentiated into proximal, middle, and distal sections (carpus, metacarpus, and phalanges of digits in the fore-limb ; tarsus, metatarsus, and phalanges in the hind-limb). Well-defined joints may also become differentiated between these various elements, Fig. 168.

In spite of the great variety in the number and disposition of the elements of the carpus and tarsus in the different groups, a generalised primitive plan may be made out consisting of a row of three proximal elements (proximal carpalia or tarsalia), five distal elements (distal carpalia or tarsalia), and about three central elements between them (centralia). The metacarpus and metatarsus consist of five elements each (meta-carpalia, metatarsalia), and the free digits have a varying number of phalanges of which the primitive formula may have been 2, 3, 4, 5, 3.

In general structure and development the cheiropterygium resembles the ichthyopterygium ; there is the same contribution from many spinal nerves, the same sort of nerve-plexus at the base of the limb, the same contribution from many myotomes to form the musculature.

In the Amphibia and many of the higher Amniota the latter arises from the ventral ends of the myotomes as proliferations which combine to a continuous mass ; but in others (Lacertilia) each myotome of the limb region produces one epithelial muscle - bud, and the segmental

---

extinct and all living Amphibia have no more than four digits in the manus, yet some of the earliest and most primitive known representatives of the class have the usual number five (*Diplovertebron*, Watson, **644** ; *Eryops*, Cope, **12**). Traces of a preaxial digit in front of the first (pollex) and of a postaxial digit behind the fifth (minimus) have been described.

structure is at first well defined (Mollier, **197** ; Sewertzoff, **215**).  As in fishes the muscle-buds may dwindle at each end of the series, and some may disappear in the course of development.   For instance, in *Ascalobotes* (Sewertzoff, **215**) spinal nerves 6-10 enter the pectoral plexus, while in the embryo the plexus includes nerves 4 and 5 ; muscle-buds arise from

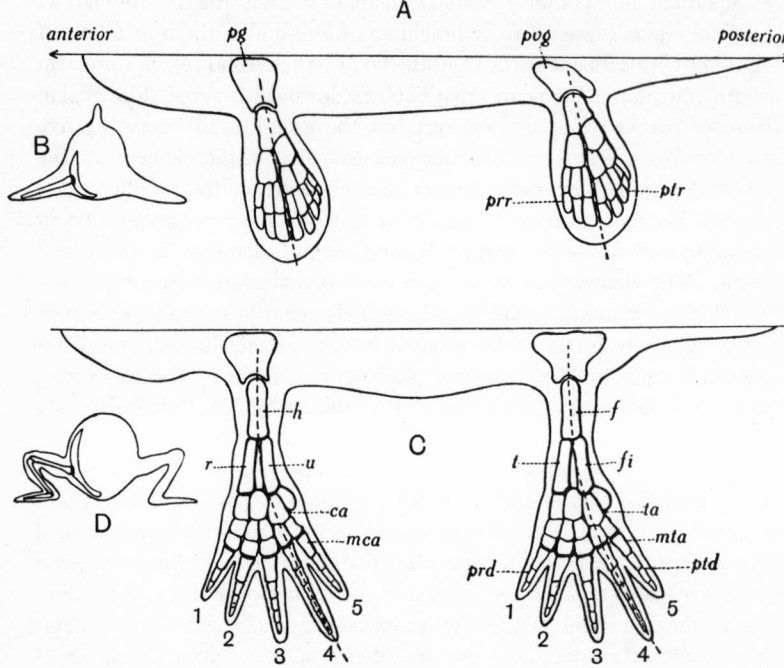

FIG. 168.

Diagrams illustrating comparison between *ichthyopterygium* and *cheiropterygium*, and possible derivation of latter from former.   A, Primitive aquatic fish-like form with similar pectoral and pelvic fins provided with a skeleton approximating that described in Sauripterus ;  B, transverse section of same in pectoral region ;  C, primitive Tetrapod with similar pectoral and pelvic walking limbs ;  main axis of limb taken through 4th digit ;  D, transverse section of same in pectoral region.  *ca*, Carpus ; *f*, proximal element, femur ; *fi*, fibula ;  *h*, proximal element, humerus ;  *mca*, metacarpus ;  *mta*, meta-tarsus ;  *pg*, pectoral, and *pvg*, pelvic girdle ;  *prd*, *prr*, preaxial digit and radial ;  *ptd*, *ptr*, postaxial digit and radial ;  *r*, radius ;  *t*, tibia ;  *ta*, tarsus ;  *u*, ulna.

the myotomes supplied by spinal nerves 2-10 ;  but the first four do not contribute to the adult limb muscles.   The buds grow into the limb-fold, become mesenchymatous, and fuse to a continuous mass from which develops a dorsal and a ventral plate.   Between these two the mesenchyme gives rise to the endoskeleton, spreading inwards to form the girdle.   The original segmentation of the muscles and nerves is obscured.   Later the two plates form not only the muscles of the outstanding limb, but grow inwards to give rise to those muscles passing from limb to girdle which

are supplied by branches of the plexus.  New muscles to the girdle may be
added later from the myotomes, and are innervated from the thoracic
spinal nerves.  The development of the cheiropterygium is in full agreement with the lateral-fold theory.

The limbs first appear as longitudinal folds.  In some Amniotes the
pectoral and pelvic folds are local enlargements of a continuous lateral
ridge (Wolffian ridge) which later disappears.  It is improbable, however,
that this represents an ancestral continuous fin-fold.  The limb rudiment
grows into an outstanding lobe with pre- and postaxial edges and a
narrowing base.  Soon the distal region becomes expanded, and from it
grow out the free digits.  Meanwhile the limb rudiment has become
twisted so that its main axis is bent backwards, its original dorsal surface
turned outwards, its original ventral surface turned inwards.  Its preaxial edge thus becomes ventral and its postaxial edge dorsal.  Later
the manus and pes are so disposed that the preaxial digit is turned
forwards and inwards and the postaxial digit backwards and outwards.

Many attempts have been made to derive the cheiropterygium from the
ichthyopterygium, but none has proved convincing.  Gegenbaur (169-170)
believed it to have arisen from an ' archipterygium ' like that of *Ceratodus*,
the base of which articulates with the girdle by a single element comparable to the humerus or femur.  However, the comparison of the more
distal elements of the two types is not easy, and his view that the axis is
represented in the anterior pentadactyle limb by the humerus, radius,
and first digit (and the corresponding elements in the hind-limb), and
that the other four digits are postaxial, has not been generally accepted.
Huxley (535), on the other hand (who identified the main axis of the
Selachian fin in the mesopterygium), drew the main axis through the
humerus, intermedium centrale, third distal carpal, and third digit
(digits 1 and 2 being preaxial, 4 and 5 postaxial, and the radius and ulna
being compared to the pro- and metapterygium respectively).  The
attempt of Klaatsch (192) to derive the cheiropterygium from such a fin
as the pectoral of *Polypterus* is still less satisfactory, since this fin appears
to be highly specialised.  Moreover, the pelvic fin of *Polypterus* is
obviously far too much reduced and specialised to have given origin to
the pentadactyle limb.  More promising is the comparison with the
pectoral fin of the Rhizodont *Eusthenopteron* made by Watson (227),
who considers the main axis to pass through the humerus, ulna, and fourth
digit.  But here again the fin (especially the pelvic fin) is too specialised
towards the Teleostome type, with short endoskeleton, large fin-web,
and powerful dermal rays, to be truly primitive.  Lately Broom has
drawn attention to the pectoral fin of the related Upper Devonian *Sauri-*

*pterus,* which seems to have possessed a better developed and more primitive endoskeleton. It has a single proximal segment (humerus), two more distal elements (radius and ulna), and about a dozen marginal radials (Broom, 150; Gregory, Miner and Noble, 174). From such a fin-skeleton that of a pentadactyle limb might conceivably have been developed, Fig. 168; but nothing is known of the pelvic fin of this fish.

We may conclude that as yet nothing for certain is known of the origin of the cheiropterygium. It may have been derived from a fin not unlike that of the Devonian Dipnoi or Crossopterygii. At all events it is clear that we should expect the fish-like ancestor of the Tetrapoda to have possessed pectoral and pelvic fins alike in structure, with outstanding muscular lobe, extensive endoskeleton with at least five radials, small web, and few if any dermal rays.

# CHAPTER IV

## LIMB GIRDLES

## THE PECTORAL GIRDLE

THE pectoral limb is supported by an endoskeletal girdle [1] consisting of
right and left halves extending in the body-wall above and below the
articulation of the limb ; the scapular region is dorsal and the coracoid
region ventral.    Primitively the girdle lies not only outside the vertebral
column and ribs, but also outside the longitudinal muscles of the body
(myomeres) and spinal nerves, which latter pass before, behind, or through
the girdle to reach the limb (see p. 129 and Fig. 142).    As the girdle sinks
below the surface close behind the last gill-arch the myomeres are disturbed
and interrupted ventrally and to a less extent dorsally.    The dorsal
portions of the muscle segments are continued to the skull, only superficial
fibres becoming specialised and inserted on the scapula as anterior pro-
tractors, levators, and posterior retractors.    To this scapular region is
also attached the superficial trapezius, a lateral plate muscle supplied by

---

[1] The first origin and development of the limb girdles are discussed in
Chapter III.

a branch of the vagus (p. 129). The coracoid region interrupts the ventral portions of the lateral muscle segments, separating the ' hypoglossal musculature ' inserted on its anterior border from the muscles of the ventral body-wall inserted on its posterior border. Primitively (in Elasmobranchii) the limb-muscles are only inserted on the girdle near the limb articulation, but they gradually extend more and more on the girdle in higher forms.

To the original endoskeletal girdle is added in Osteichthyes and Tetrapoda a set of protective and strengthening dermal bones to which many of the muscles become attached.

**Pisces.**—The endoskeletal pectoral girdle is well developed in the Chon-

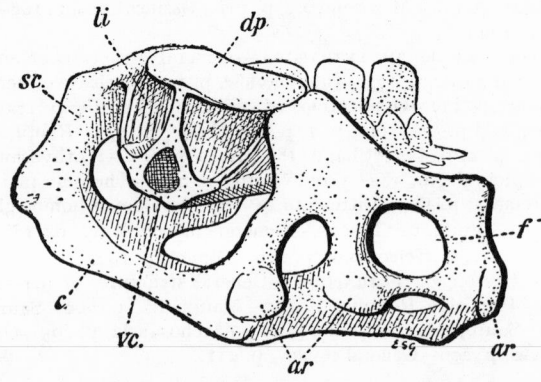

FIG. 169.

Pectoral girdle and portion of the vertebral column of *Raja blanda*, Holt; oblique left-side view. *ar*, Articular facets for pectoral fin; *c*, coracoid region; *dp*, dorsal plate; *f*, foramen; *li*, ligament; *sc*, scapular region; *vc*, vertebral column. (From Goodrich, *Vert. Craniata*, 1909.)

drichthyes. The two scapulocoracoids remain separate in the Pleuracanthodii, where each is provided with a separate ventral infra-coracoidal and dorsal suprascapular element, Fig. 154 (Fritsch, **23**; Döderlein, **158**; Jaekel, **186**). In the Elasmobranchii the two halves are firmly united by ligament (Notidani) or more usually fused in the middle line ventrally, Fig. 169. A small median ventral element has been described in *Heptanchus* and *Hexanchus* (Haswell, **181**; T. J. Parker, **113**; Hanson, **257**). It is probably a derivative of the coracoids, and its comparison to the sternum of the Tetrapoda is of doubtful value (see above, p. 84). The scapular region tapers dorsally, and sometimes ends in a separate suprascapula (*Squalus*). The coracoid region expands immediately below the pericardium. Diazonal nerves usually pierce the girdle and divide into dorsal and ventral branches supplying dorsal and ventral fin-muscles. These nerves enter usually by a single internal foramen leading to a canal which divides and opens by external supraglenoid and coracoid foramina above and be-low the glenoid articula-tion of the fin. In the Rajiformes, where the girdle has to support the enormously devel-oped pectoral fins, it becomes much enlarged, strengthened, fenes-trated, and firmly con-nected to the vertebral column by a cartilagin-ous plate probably of suprascapular origin, Fig. 169. The Acan-thodii are remarkable in

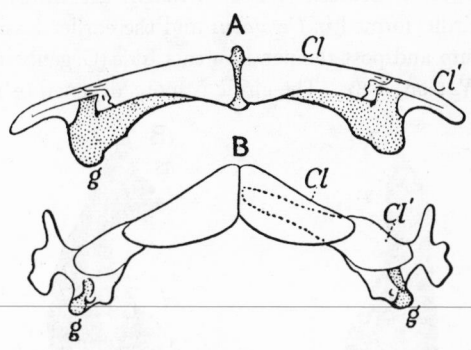

FIG. 170.

Pectoral girdle of A, *Ceratodus*; B, *Polypterus*. Ventral view. (After Gegenbaur, *Vergl. Anat.*, from Goodrich, *Vert. Craniata*, 1909.) *Cl*, Clavicle; *Cl'*, cleithrum; *g*, articular facet for fin-skeleton.

often having calcified dermal plates strengthening the endoskeletal girdle and simulating the clavicle and cleithrum of Osteichthyes (A. S. Woodward, 231).

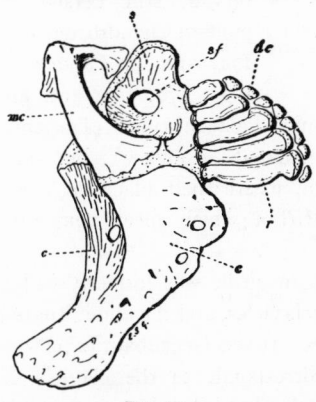

FIG. 171.

Inner view of the right half of the endo-skeletal pectoral girdle and fin of *Salmo salar*, L. *c*, Coracoid; *dc*, distal cartilages of radials; *mc*, mesocoracoid arch; *r*, fifth radial; *s*, scapula; *sf*, scapular foramen. (From Goodrich, *Vert. Craniata*, 1909.)

The girdle of the Osteichthyes is provided with dermal bones forming the posterior boundary of the branchial chambers, and on to which fit the opercular folds (p. 498). This dermal 'secondary' girdle consists of paired bones: ventral clavicles, lateral cleithra overlying the articular region, supra-cleithra, and dorsal post-temporals or suprascapulars, Fig. 161. It is important to notice that the dermal girdle in all Osteichthyes (except a few specialised forms in this respect degenerate, such as the Anguilliformes, Fig. 176) is con-nected to the posterior region of the skull by means of the post-temporal, which generally forks, and is attached to the tabular and epiotic regions in Teleostei, Figs. 141, 175.

The endoskeletal 'primary' girdle of Dipnoi, though unossified, is still well developed, especially in *Ceratodus*, Fig. 170, where it consists of two large scapulocoracoids bearing the articular knobs, and a separate ventral cartilage probably derived from the coracoids. There are no diazonal nerves. These cartilages are firmly connected to the dermal girdle, formed in *Ceratodus* and the earlier fossil forms of clavicle, cleithrum and post-temporal on each side (Gegenbaur, 170, 251; Gregory, 123; Watson, 648). The girdle is more degenerate in the modern *Protopterus*

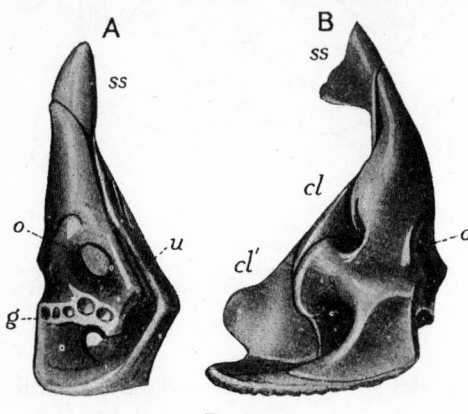

FIG. 172.

Left pectoral girdle of *Acipenser sturio*. A, Oblique view from behind; B, inner view. (After Gegenbaur, *Vergl. Anat.*, from Goodrich, *Vert. Craniata*, 1909.) *cl*, Cleithrum; *cl'*, clavicle; *g*, articular facets for pectoral fin-skeleton; *o, u*, open channel; *ss*, suprascapula.

and *Lepidosiren* where the post-temporal is vestigial (Bridge, 433; Wiedersheim, 230).

The general tendency in Teleostomes has been for the endoskeletal girdle to become reduced, and for the dermal bones to serve more and more for the support of the fin and the attachment of the muscles. The primitive clavicles, seen in Crossopterygii, still persist in modern Chondrostei, Fig. 174, and in *Polypterus*, Figs. 170, 161, and are known to have been present in the extinct Palaeoniscoidei (Traquair, 616; Stensiö, 218) and in the Belenorhynchidae (Stensiö, 134); but they have been lost in all other Actinopterygii, where their place has been taken by forward extensions of the cleithra which meet ventrally, Fig. 174.[1]

This large dermal bone in the Teleostean girdle was formerly called the clavicle, the bones dorsal to it the supraclavicles, and the bone situated ventral to it in lower fishes the infraclavicle. It was Gegenbaur (251) who showed that this ventral bone really corresponds to the clavicle of Stegocephalia and higher Tetrapods, and that the large so-called 'clavicle' of the Teleost is a more dorsal element to which he gave the name cleithrum. The nomenclature of all the bones has, therefore, been altered.

While the Actinopterygian dermal girdle is thus typically much developed, the endoskeletal girdle is usually reduced to shortened scapulo-

[1] Postcleithra are present in *Polypterus* and the Holostei. In Teleostei a postcleithrum is often characteristically lengthened, Fig. 141.

coracoids at the base of the fin, not meeting in the middle line, and firmly attached to the cleithra alone, Figs. 173-7. Modern Chondrostei, however, still preserve a large cartilaginous scapulocoracoid with a suprascapula, Fig. 172. In these and the lower Holostei (Amioidei, Lepidosteoidei, Cypriniformes, Clupeiformes) the scapulocoracoid has a middle region projecting obliquely, bearing an outer horizontal glenoid articular surface, a scapular region (shortened in Holostei), and a ventral coracoid region bifurcated in front. The scapular region is hollowed out by a muscle canal

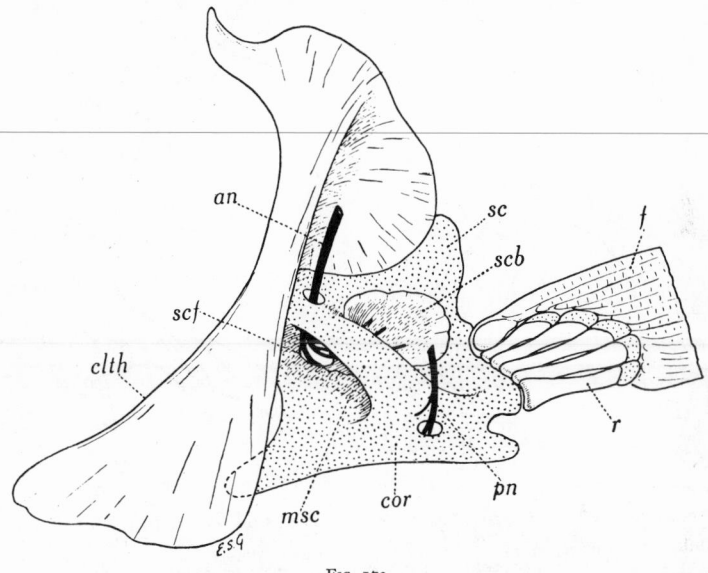

FIG. 173.

*Lepidosteus osseus.* Inner view of right cleithrum, with endoskeleton of pectoral girdle, and of fin. Nerves black, cartilages dotted. *an,* Anterior compound nerve ; *clth,* cleithrum ; *cor,* coracoid region ; *msc,* mesocoracoid arch ; *pn,* posterior compound nerve ; *r,* sixth radial ; *sc,* scapular region ; *scb,* scapular bone ; *scf,* scapular foramen.

through which pass dorso-medial muscles of the fin and which is closed medially by a mesocoracoid arch, Figs. 171-3 (Spange of Mettenheimer, Spangenstück of Gegenbaur, mesocoracoid of Gill). This arch is a structure of some importance (Parker, 288 ; Gegenbaur, 166 ; Romer, 294). It is present in all the lower Actinopterygii (Chondrostei and Holostei mentioned above), and though absent in Polypterini, is probably primitive and derived from the boundary of the pit for the insertion of fin-muscles and the diazonal nerve canal of Elasmobranchs. In Chondrostei the anterior diazonal nerves enter the canal from in front, and their dorsal branches issue through the posterior opening above the glenoid region, while their ventral branches pass through a foramen in its floor to the ventro-lateral muscles below the glenoid region (Swinnerton, 300).[1]

While the muscle pits and nerve canal are thus confluent in Chondrostei and the Teleostei, in *Amia* and *Lepidosteus*, Fig. 173, the anterior diazonal nerves enter the canal through the mesocoracoid arch. Probably a secondary condition, since in young stages of *Amia* the nerves enter

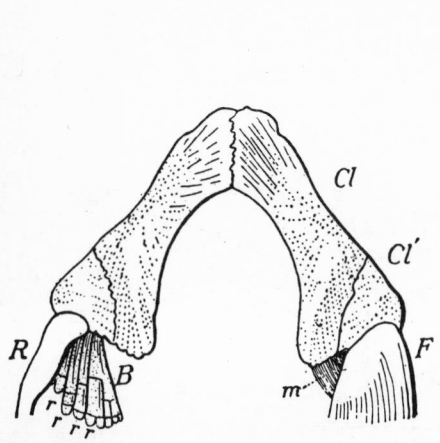

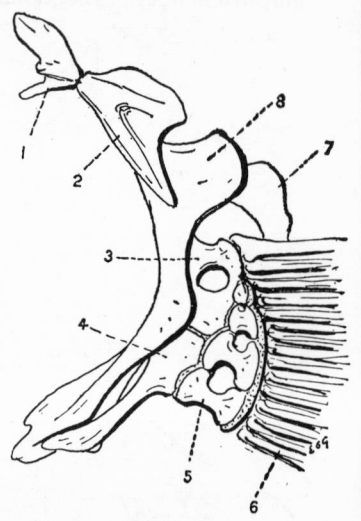

FIG. 174.

Pectoral girdle and fins of *Acipenser sturio*. Ventral view. (After Gegenbaur, *Vergl. Anat.*, from Goodrich, *Vert. Craniata*, 1909.) *B*, Postaxial edge of fin-skeleton; *Cl*, clavicle; *Cl'*, cleithrum; *F*, base of left fin; *m*, muscle; *R*, enlarged preaxial dermal ray; *r*, endoskeletal radials.

FIG. 175.

Skeleton of left half of pectoral girdle and fin of *Pterois volitans*. 1, Post-temporal; 2, supracleithrum; 3, scapular; 4, coracoid; 5, radial; 6, lepidotrich; 7, postcleithrum; 8, cleithrum. (From Goodrich, *Vert. Craniata*, 1909.)

from in front as usual (E.S.G.). The posterior diazonal nerves pierce the coracoid behind. The mesocoracoid arch, already very narrow in many of the Teleostei where it exists, is absent in the higher Teleostei (Boulenger, 426). In these it appears to have been lost owing to the confluence of the openings of the muscle canal now opened up, accompanying the tendency of the base of fin to become more and more vertical (Swinnerton, 300 ; Wasnetzoff, 305).

The endoskeletal girdle remains cartilaginous in *Amia*, develops a dorsal scapular bone in *Lepidosteus*, and a ventral coracoid bone in addition in the Teleostei. These bones share in the formation of the

[1] This foramen enlarges and becomes the scapular foramen present in the scapula of all Holostei.

glenoid articulation, the preaxial radials resting on the scapula and on the coracoid.

Little is known of the phylogenetic history of these bones, nor is it at all certain that they are strictly homologous with the scapula and coracoid of the Tetrapoda (p. 174). Bryant (465) has figured a small scapulocoracoid bone in *Eusthenopteron*, and Stensiö (218) has described the primary girdle of the Palaeoniscid *Acrorhabdus* as formed of a single scapulocoracoid bone, smaller but somewhat like the cartilage in *Acipenser*,

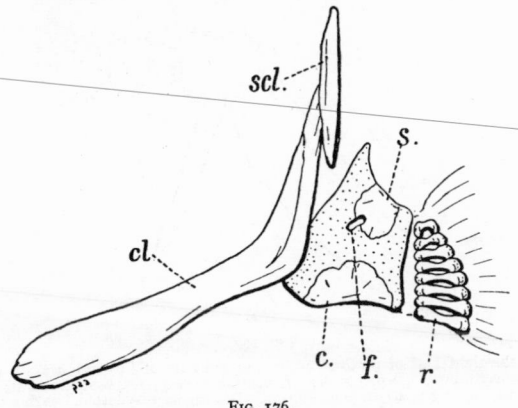

FIG. 176.

Skeleton of the left half of the pectoral girdle and of the fin of *Anguilla vulgaris*, L. *c*, Coracoid ; *cl*, cleithrum ; *f*, foramen ; *r*, eighth radial ; *s*, scapula; *scl*, supracleithrum. The cartilage is dotted. (From Goodrich, *Vert. Craniata*, 1909.)

and apparently with an excavated mesocoracoid arch. Our knowledge of the endoskeletal girdle in the fossil Teleostomes is still very incomplete.

The development of the primary pectoral girdle in Pisces has been studied by many observers, among whom one may mention Balfour (142), Mollier (197), and Braus (145, 148) in Selachii ; Mollier (198), Wiedersheim (230), and Sewertzoff (217) in Chondrostei ; Swirski (301), Vogel (226), Derjugin (157), and especially Swinnerton (300) in Teleostei.

The blastematous or procartilaginous rudiment of the girdle in the body-wall is at first continuous with that of the fin-skeleton (p. 126). Later the scapulocoracoid is separately differentiated as a cartilage which spreads so as to enclose the diazonal nerves. In Teleosts the mesocoracoid arch develops late as an outgrowth from the middle region which grows upwards to join a smaller process from the tip of the scapula. The coracoid plate develops a large anterior so-called precoracoid process, representing the main limb of the coracoid, and a slenderer postcoracoid process. The former may meet its fellow in the middle line, and may even fuse with it to a transverse bar in larval Clupeoids (Derjugin, **157**;

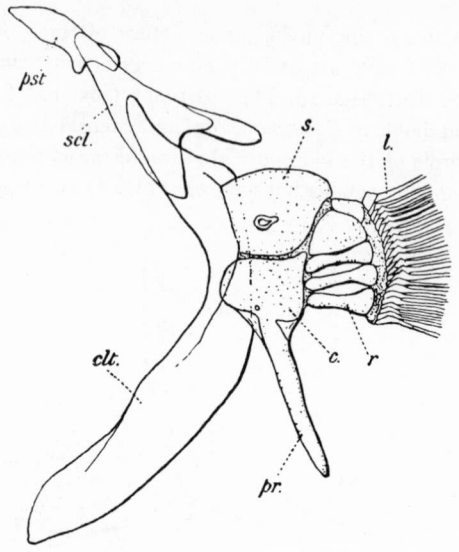

FIG. 177.

Skeleton of the right half of pectoral girdle and right fin of *Fierasfer acus*, L (after Emery). *c*, Coracoid; *clt*, cleithrum; *l*, lepidotrich; *pr*, ventral process; *pst*, post-temporal; *r*, 5th radial; *s*, scapula with small foramen; *scl*, supracleithrum. The cartilage is dotted. (From Goodrich, *Vert. Craniata*, 1909.)

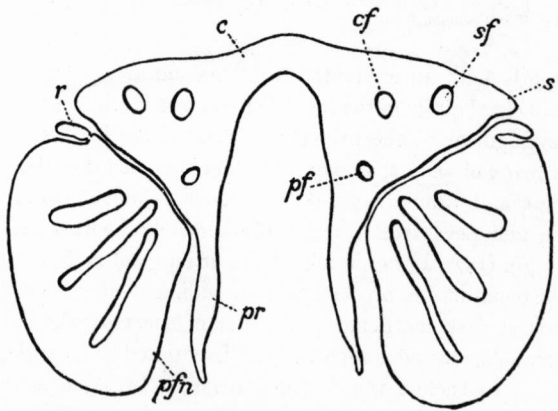

FIG. 178.

*Clupea pilchardus*, young. Cartilaginous skeleton of pectoral fins and girdle. (Goodrich, *Linn. Soc. J. Zool.*, 1919.) *c*, Coracoid region; *cf*, coracoid foramen; *pf*, postcoracoid foramen; *pfn*, pectoral fin skeleton; *pr*, posterior process; *r*, anterior radial; *s*, scapular process; *sf*, scapular foramen.

Goodrich, **255**); but it is later much reduced and usually shortened, often, however, leaving a small anterior ventral cartilage (Parker, **288**). The postcoracoid process may reach a remarkable length, and run backwards in the body-wall far behind the articulation of the fin, Figs. 177-8; but it also is later reduced and disappears more or less completely. Swinnerton suggests that it represents the original 'metapterygial' axis of the fin-skeleton (p. 157). But this view is difficult to reconcile with the structure of these parts in the lower Teleostomes, and the fact that the postcoracoid process arises from the girdle itself proximally to the glenoid articulation. More probably it is a secondary development of larval Teleosts.

## THE PECTORAL GIRDLE IN TETRAPODA

The pectoral girdle of Tetrapods, like that of Osteichthyes, consists of a primary endoskeletal girdle strengthened by dermal bones (Gegenbaur, **166, 170**; Parker, **288**; Fürbringer, **250**). The primary girdle is of two halves, each developed from a continuous scapulocoracoid cartilage in the embryo, which becomes variously modified, fenestrated, and even subdivided in the different groups. A glenoid facet for the humerus is situated on its outer posterior border; dorsally extends the scapular region and ventrally the coracoid region. The coracoid plates meet and even overlap ventrally, and abut against the front edge of the sternum. The secondary dermal

FIG. 179.

Clavicles and interclavicle of *Ophiacodon* (from Williston, *Osteology of Reptiles*, 1925).

girdle in such primitive Tetrapods as the Stegocephalia consists of paired ventral clavicles, and dorsal cleithra applied to the anterior edge of the scapulocoracoid. In addition there is a median interclavicle (episternum), usually lozenge or T-shaped and underlying ventrally the coracoids and sternum, Figs. 179, 180, 182. In Stegocephalia these dermal bones often preserve the external sculpturing characteristic of the covering bones on the head. Thus, excepting for the interclavicle, which is probably an enlarged scale of the median ventral series, the dermal girdle in these early Tetrapods closely resembles that of primitive Osteichthyes, with this important difference, that it is not connected to the skull. This character is, however, probably secondary, since there is evidence that in some of the earliest and most primitive Stegocephalia, such as the Carboniferous genera *Eogyrinus* and *Batrachiderpeton*, a

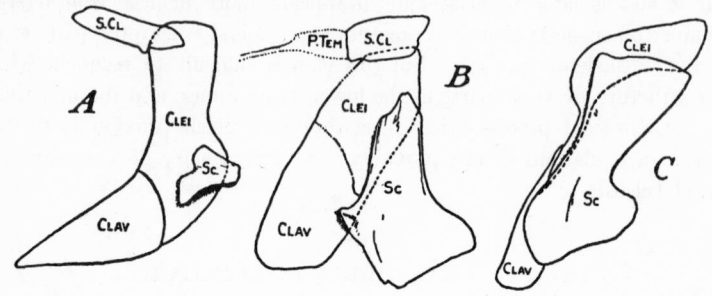

FIG. 179a.

Inner view of right half of pectoral girdle (interclavicle omitted) of : A, *Eusthenopteron* ; B, *Eogyrinus* ; C, *Cacops* (from D. M. S. Watson, *Tr. Roy. Soc.*, 1926). *Clav*, Clavicle ; *Clei*, cleithrum ; *P.Tem*, post-temporal ; *Sc*, scapulocoracoid ; *S.Cl*, supracleithrum.

post-temporal joined the cleithrum to the tabular, Fig. 179a (Watson, 306 ; Romer, 294).

The cleithrum tends to disappear in later forms. It has vanished in the modern Urodela, together with the other dermal bones, but appears

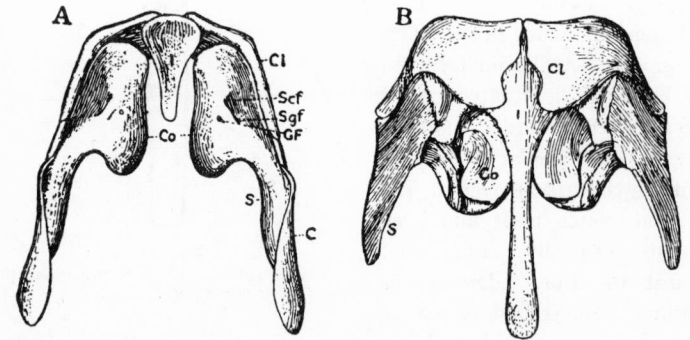

FIG. 180.

Pectoral girdle of A, *Cacops*, dorsal view, and B, *Conodectes* (Seymouria), ventral view. *C*, Cleithrum ; *Cl*, clavicle ; *Co*, coracoid region ; *GF*, glenoid foramen ; *I*, interclavicle ; *S*, scapular region ; *Scf*, supracoracoid foramen ; *Sgf*, supraglenoid foramen. (From Williston, *Osteology of Reptiles*, 1925.)

to persist in the Anura as the ossification which overlies the suprascapula (Schmalhausen, 296). In a reduced condition it still occurs in many Cotylosauria (*Diadectes*, *Pareiasaurus*, etc.), in some Theromorpha (*Dicynodon*, *Clepsydrops*, *Edaphosaurus*, *Moschops*, Williston (95), Gregory and Camp (256a), Romer (294), Watson (307), Seeley, and others), and, according to Jaekel (536), in the primitive Chelonian,

*Triassochelys*; otherwise it is unknown in Reptiles, Birds, and Mammals, unless it is represented as a vestige by an early ossification of the scapular spine described by Broom in Marsupials (**239**).

The clavicle remains in all Tetrapods, excepting highly specialised forms such as the Urodela among Amphibia, certain Lacertilia (Chamele-

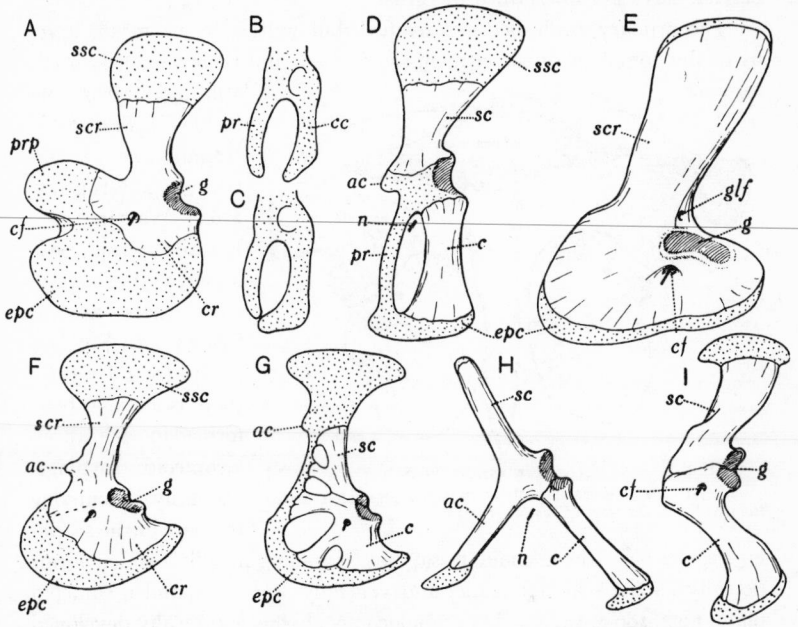

FIG. 181.

Diagrammatic figures of left half of pectoral girdle, outer view. A, *Megalobatrachus*; B, very young, and C, older stage in development of *Rana* (from A. Goette, but mesenchyme should join lower ends of cartilaginous processes); D, later stage, *Rana*; E, *Eryops*; F, *Sphenodon*; G, *Iguana*; H, *Chelone*; I, *Crocodilus*. Cartilage dotted. *ac*, Acromial process; *c*, coracoid bone; *cc*, coracoid cartilage; *cf*, coracoid foramen; *cr*, coracoid region; *epc*, epicoracoid cartilage; *g*, glenoid cavity; *glf*, supraglenoid foramen; *n*, diazonal nerve; *pr*, 'procoracoid' process and bar (part of coracoid plate?); *prp*, 'procoracoid' process; *sc*, scapular bone; *scr*, scapular region; *ssc*, suprascapula.

ontes, etc.), the Ophidia, the higher Crocodilia and Dinosauria among Reptilia. Except in flightless forms in which the clavicles may be reduced or lost (*Struthio, Apteryx*) they are fused in Aves to form the characteristic furcula, already present in *Archaeopteryx*, Fig. 194. Clavicles are also lost or vestigial in several groups of the Mammalia (Marsupialia, Ungulata, Cetacea, Carnivora, Rodentia, etc.).

An interclavicle occurs in no modern Amphibian, but persists in modern Reptilia with a well-developed pectoral girdle (Rhynchocephalia, Crocodilia, Chelonia, Lacertilia), and was present in the primitive extinct forms. Alone among Mammalia the Monotremes possess a well-developed interclavicle, an important feature indicating their primitive structure, Fig. 197. A vestige of the interclavicle is probably represented by the so-called omosternum or presternum of Mammalia, which is not really preformed in true cartilage, and sometimes ossifies from two centres (Gegenbaur, 170; Broom, 239; Watson, 307). Vestiges of the interclavicle have been described in Birds.

The primary girdle becomes ossified, but writers by no means agree as to the homology of the elements so formed, and their nomenclature is still in a state of con-

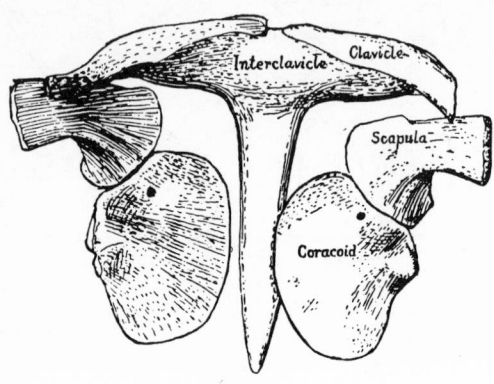

fusion (Howes, 263-4; Broom, 241; Williston, 95; Gregory, 256a; Watson, 207; Romer, 290, 294; Miner, 285). The principal facts are as follows: In Stegocephalia (and Urodela) there is a single bone formed in each scapulocoracoid cartilage, primarily occupying the base of the scapular region near the glenoid fossa, but spreading in fully ossified forms dorsally as the scapular blade, and ventrally as the expanded coracoid plate, Figs. 180 A, 181 E. The scapulocoracoid bone is typically developed in such a primitive form as *Eryops* (Cope, 243; Romer, 292, 294; Miner, 285). Its internal supraglenoid buttress represents the mesocoracoid region of the Teleostome scapulocoracoid, and is pierced as in the fish by a supraglenoid foramen, doubtless for the diazonal nerves to the dorsal limb-muscles, and a more ventral supracoracoid or coracoid foramen for nerves to the ventral limb-muscles (supracoracoid or suprascapular nerve).

FIG. 182.

Ventral view of pectoral girdle of *Champsosaurus* (after Brown, from Williston, *Osteology of Reptiles*, 1925).

In primitive Reptilia (*Seymouria, Diadectes,* etc.), on the other hand, two centres of ossification appear—a dorsal scapula and a ventral coracoid, Figs. 180 B, 183 A, separated by a suture which crosses the glenoid cavity. In other Cotylosauria (Captorhinidae, Pareiasauria, Procolophonia) and in Theromorpha three centres of ossification occur; there being, in addition to the scapula, a posterior coracoid and an anterior procoracoid (epicoracoid), Figs. 183 B, C, 184 A, 185 A. The latter bone more or less completely surrounds the coracoid foramen from in front and below, and may penetrate to the glenoid cavity as a wedge between the scapula and the coracoid. The other extinct and all modern Reptilia, and Aves, have only

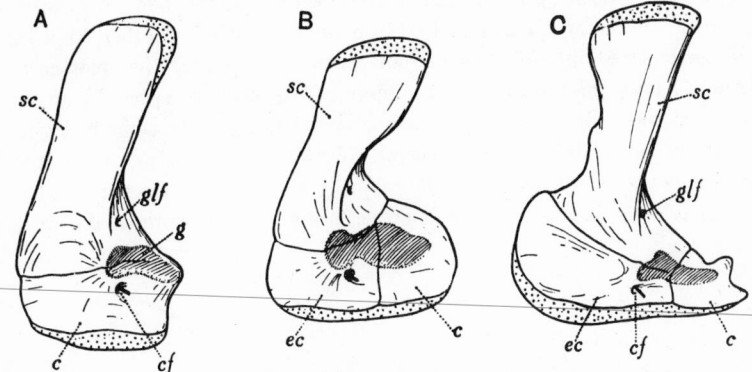

FIG. 183.

Outer view of left half of endoskeletal pectoral girdle with cartilaginous parts restored (dotted). A, *Diadectes*; B, *Labidosaurus*; C, *Dimetrodon*. Lettering as in Fig. 184.

a single coracoid element, sharing as usual in the formation of the glenoid cavity and enclosing as a rule the coracoid foramen, Figs. 181 F-I, 186, 86. The Mammalia, on the other hand, belong to the group with two ventral

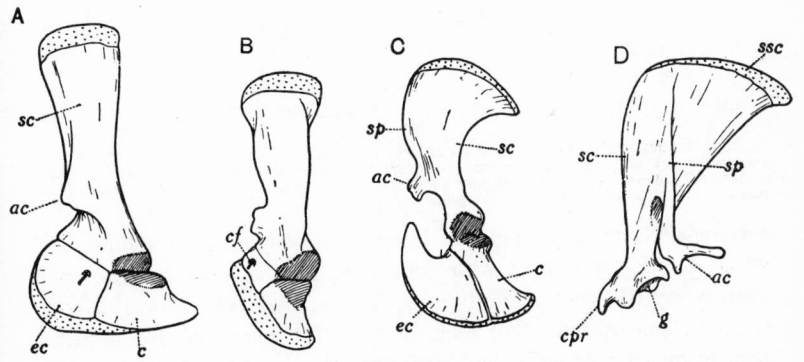

FIG. 184.

Outer view of left half of endoskeletal pectoral girdle of: A, *Dicynodon*; B, *Cynognathus*; C, *Ornithorhynchus*; D, *Lepus*; cartilage restored (dotted). *ac*, Acromion; *c*, coracoid; *cf*, coracoid foramen; *cpr*, coracoid process; *ec*, procoracoid; *g*, glenoid cavity; *glf*, glenoid foramen; *sc*, scapula; *sp*, spine.

elements in addition to the scapula, as is clearly seen in the Monotremata (Seeley; Cope; Williston, 95; Watson, 207; Romer, 294; Miner, 285; Gregory, 523). Now Williston has shown that in early Pelycosauria there are two ventral elements (as in other Theromorpha), but that of these the posterior bone (his metacoracoid) may be much the smaller, Fig. 183 c, and he believed it to be ossified late in *Ophiacodon* and not at all in the primitive *Varanosauras* and *Varanoops* (Case, 469 ; Williston, 95) ; Broili (436) and Watson (307) have since described a posterior bone in *Varano-saurus*. Williston concluded that the single coracoid of other Reptiles is the enlarged anterior element (our procoracoid, p. 174), the 'metacora-coid' having disappeared. This opinion has been accepted by many (Broom, 241 ; Gregory, 523 ; Watson, 207 ; Hanson, 258), some believing that the posterior coracoid (metacoracoid) has been lost and others that it has never been acquired in the majority of Reptiles. On very insuffi-cient evidence it must on either view be assumed that the principal ventral

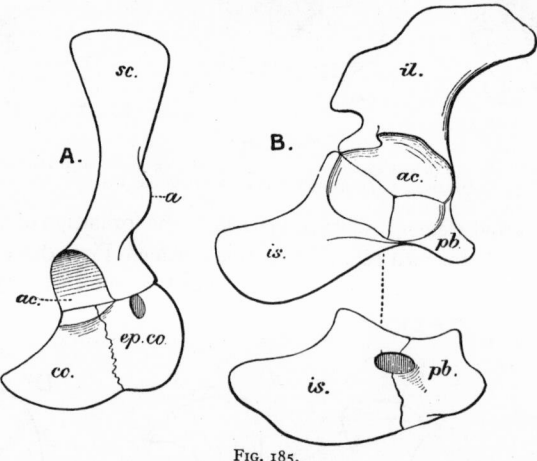

FIG. 185.

Right pectoral arch, outer aspect (A), and right pelvic arch, outer and inferior aspects (B), of a *Dicynodont*. Karoo Formation, Cape Colony. (From A. S. Woodward, *Vertebrate Palaeontology*, 1898.) *a*, Acromial process ; *ac*, glenoid cavity for humerus, and acetabulum for femur ; *co*, coracoid ; *ep.co*, procoracoid ; *il*, ilium ; *is*, ischium ; *pb*, pubis ; *sc*, scapular.

coracoidal elements are not homologous throughout the Tetrapoda. The whole question is fraught with difficulties, and has given rise to much controversy (Gegenbaur, Fürbringer, Goette, Lydekker, Howes, Broom, Gregory, and others). The older and simpler view, that the posterior bone (coracoid) sharing in the formation of the glenoid cavity and forming the posterior edge of the coracoid plate is homologous throughout, would seem to be nearer the truth than the complicated interpretations later authors have tried to substitute for it.

Examining the evidence more in detail we may begin with the Amphibia. Known stages in the development of *Archegosaurus* seem to show that in Stegocephalia the scapulocoracoid arises from one centre of ossification which spreads dorsally and ventrally. Its ventral coracoid plate comes to embrace the coracoid foramen. In modern Urodela also one centre is usually present, and its coracoid region may enclose the foramen. In *Amphiuma* and *Siren*, however, Parker describes separate coracoid and scapular bones. In these and other Amphibia (including doubtless the Stegocephalia) unossified cartilage may remain at the dorsal extremity of the scapula, as a suprascapula, and at the ventral end of the coracoid region, as infracoracoid cartilage (epicoracoid). There is also in Urodela a forwardly directed cartilaginous 'procoracoid process', membrane closing the notch between it and the coracoid, Figs. 87 B, 181 A.

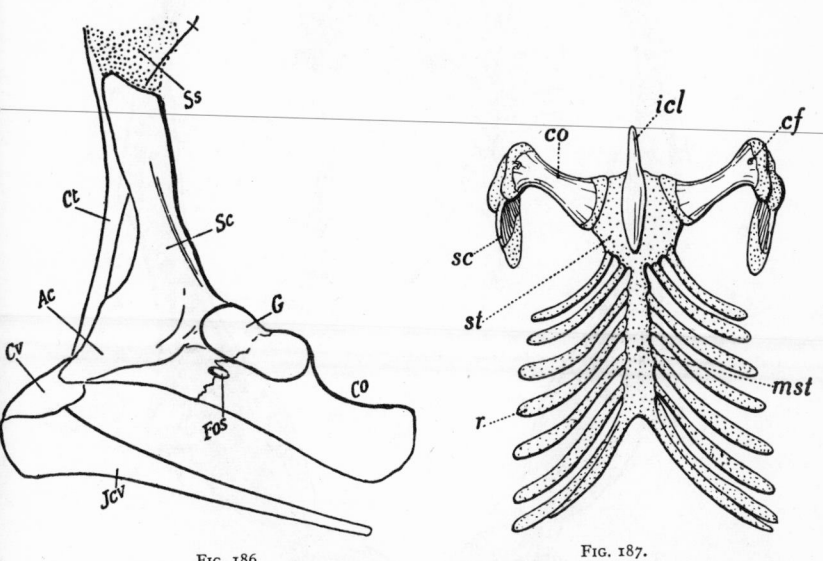

FIG. 186.

Pectoral girdle of *Triassochelys* (after Jaekel, from Williston, *Osteology of Reptiles*, 1925). *Ac*, Acromion; *Co*, coracoid; *Ct*, cleithrum; *Cv*, clavicle; *Fos*, coracoid foramen; *G*, glenoid cavity; *Jcv*, interclavicle; *Sc*, scapula; *Ss*, suprascapula.

FIG. 187.

Ventral view of pectoral girdle, sternum, and sternal ribs of late embryo *Crocodilus acutus* (after W. K. Parker, 1868). *mst*, Median prolongation of sternum. Other letters as in Fig. 190.

The primary girdle of the Anura consists of two halves which overlap ventrally (as in Urodela) in the Arcifera; but meet in the middle line in the Firmisternia, Fig. 87. Each half consists of a scapulocoracoid cartilage with an ossified scapula (with a supraglenoid foramen) and a coracoid. The latter bone forms the hinder limit of a large fenestra in the coracoid plate closed below by the epicoracoid cartilage, and in front by the procoracoid cartilage to which is closely adherent the clavicle (Gegenbaur).[1] Where

[1] Goette (254) maintained that this bone is a true ossification of the cartilage; but Gegenbaur (166, 170) showed that it is really a membrane bone, separated by a thin layer of tissue from the underlying cartilage. If so, this clavicle must have sunk below the muscles to cling to the procoracoid cartilage.

the clavicle abuts on the scapula an 'acromial process' is present, Figs. 87 C, D, 181 B, D.

The 'fenestra' appears to include the coracoid foramen,[1] since it lets through the suprascapular nerve; but it is not closed by membrane.

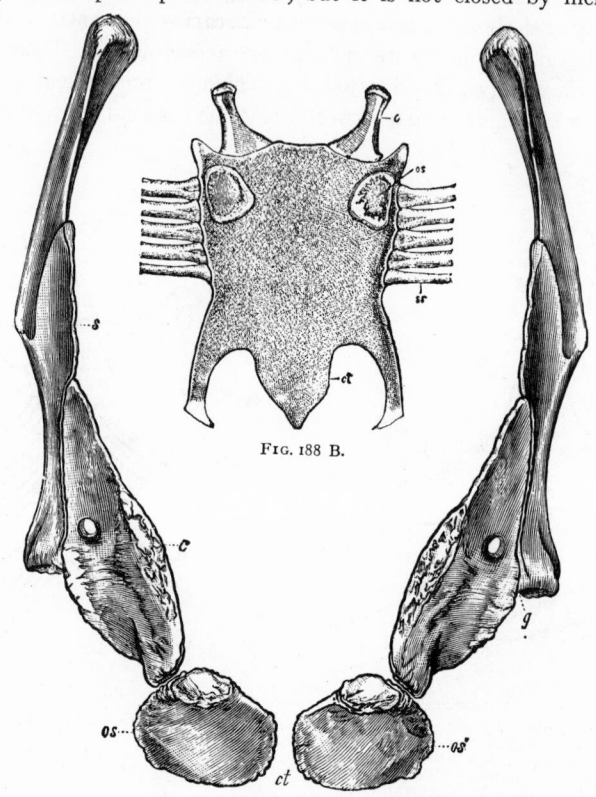

FIG. 188 B.

FIG. 188 A.

A, *Brontosaurus excelsus.* Jurassic: Wyoming. Pectoral arch, anterior aspect, with sternum of young ostrich *Struthio camelus* for comparison (Fig. B). (After A. S. Woodward, *Vertebrate Palae- ontology,* 1898.)  *c,* Coracoid; *ct,* sternal cartilage; *g,* glenoid cavity for humerus; *os,* sternal bone; *s,* scapula; *sr,* sternal ribs.

This fact renders it difficult to adopt Gegenbaur's view that the anterior process of Urodela is derived from the procoracoid bar of Anura by the breaking through of a fenestra. The Urodelan process may possibly be

[1] According to Goette (254) the fenestra in Rana becomes surrounded in ontogeny by two cartilaginous processes starting from the acetabular region, an observation confirmed by Fuchs (249). But it has recently been shown that in other Anura it is a true fenestra originating in a procartilaginous plate, and may be considered as formed by the enlargement of the coracoid foramen (de Villiers, 303).

derived from the acromial process (Eissler, **246**; Anthony and Vallois, **235**), or more probably is a new development of the ventral plate.

We have already seen that in the most primitive extinct Reptilia there are present separate scapula and coracoid bones. The former bears a small acromial process where the clavicle is attached, and the latter encloses the coracoid foramen. From such a primitive girdle can be derived that of the Sauropsidan Reptiles (including Chelonia and Lacertilia, and all modern Reptiles) and of the Birds. It is typically developed in *Sphenodon* and other Rhynchocephalia, Fig. 181 F (Howes and Swinnerton, **49**; Schauinsland, **583**). The primary girdle is very similar in the Dinosauria; but they lose the dermal clavicles and interclavicle, Fig. 188. While the Parasuchia still possess a primitive

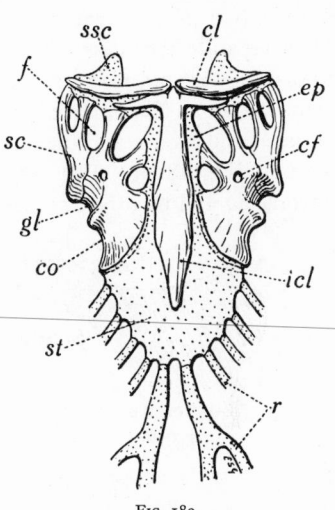

FIG. 189.

Ventral view of pectoral girdle, sternum, and sternal ribs of *Iguana tuberculata*.

pectoral girdle, in the Crocodilia the clavicle is lost and the coracoid much elongated, Fig. 187. There is no evidence in any of these Reptiles

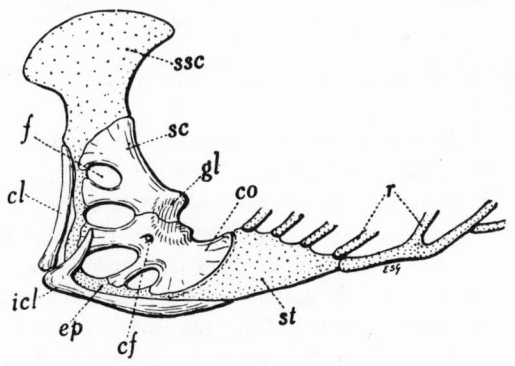

FIG. 190.

Left-side view of pectoral girdle, sternum, and sternal ribs of *Iguana tuberculata*. Cartilage dotted. *cf*, Supracoracoid foramen; *cl*, clavicle; *co*, coracoid; *ep*, epicoracoid cartilage; *f*, fenestra; *gl*, glenoid cavity; *icl*, interclavicle; *r*, ventral ends of ribs; *sc*, scapula; *ssc*, suprascapula; *st*, sternum.

of the occurrence of a fenestra or of more than one coracoidal bone in the ventral plate.

A highly specialised girdle occurs in the Chelonia. Here the dermal

clavicles and interclavicle are closely associated with more posterior
dermal plates (apparently derived from gastralia) to form a ventral
plastron (Gegenbaur, 170), while the endoskeletal girdle forms on each
side a separate triradiate support for the limbs, movably connected to
carapace above and plastron below so as to allow for respiratory movements (p. 600). The coracoid (usually without foramen) and the scapula
become slender rods, and the latter bears a long process directed antero-
ventrally, Fig. 181 H. This process has been compared by some to the
procoracoid and by others to the acromion, and the earlier stages of the

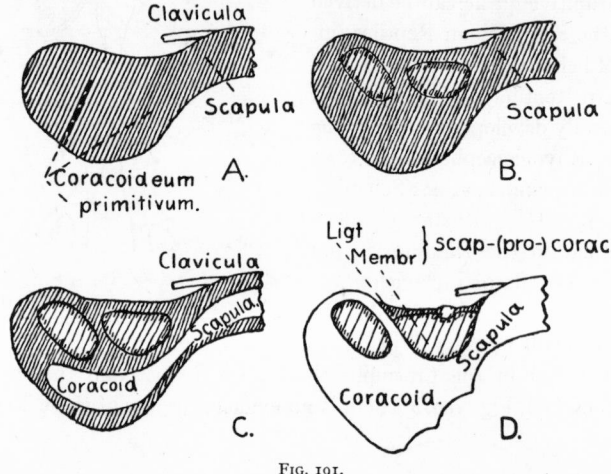

FIG. 191.

Diagrams showing development of coracoid region of pectoral girdle in *Lacerta* ; procartilage darkly
shaded. Fenestrae are formed in procartilaginous ventral plate. (From C. van Gelderen, *Anat. Anz.*,
1925.)

development of the scapulocoracoid cartilage have not been sufficiently
described (Goette, 254 ; Fuchs, 249) to determine for certain whether
there has been fenestration of a ventral plate.[1] However, since in the
primitive Chelonian, *Triassochelys* (Jaekel, 536), the process is much
shorter, it is probably merely an exaggerated acromial process, Fig. 186.

The coracoid and even the scapular regions of the Lacertilia become
pierced by membranous fenestrae, Figs. 189, 190, 191, 181 G, and it has
been shown (Goette, 254 ; van Gelderen, 252-3 ; Bogoljubsky, 237) that this
is due to the fenestration during development of an originally continuous
procartilaginous plate (like that which persists in *Sphenodon* as cartilage
and finally as bone). In it appears the coracoid bone with its foramen,
and the fenestra or fenestrae leave behind the clavicle an anterior band of

---

[1] No cartilage can be seen in the embryo joining the ventral ends of the
coracoid and ventral scapular process, nor does a membrane stretch across.

cartilage running from the ventral infracoracoid cartilage to the acromial
region. Later this band may be more or less completely replaced by
ligaments, Fig. 191.

The Ophidia have lost all trace of a pectoral girdle, and it is very
reduced and degenerate in many of the legless Lacertilia (Cope, **244** ;
Boulenger).

The primary girdle of Birds is considerably modified for flight. The
scapula in Carinatae is sword-shaped, and lies almost parallel to the
vertebral column; it is movably articulated to the elongated coracoid (with

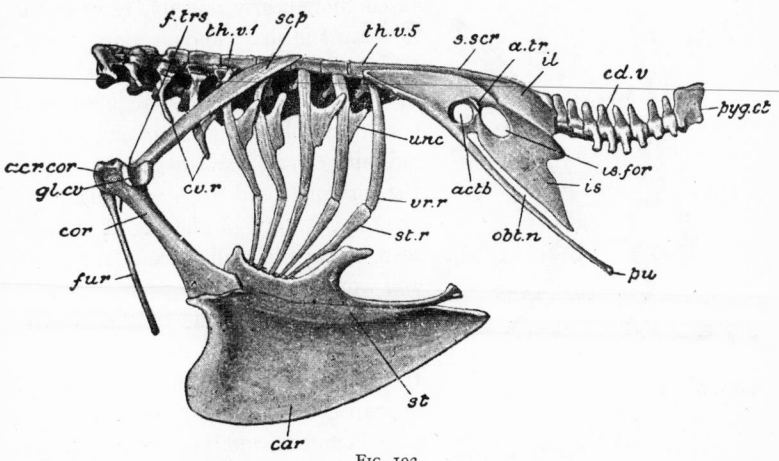

Fig. 192.

*Columba livia.* The bones of the trunk. *acr.cor*, Acrocoracoid ; *a.tr*, anti-trochanter ; *actb*,
acetabulum ; *car*, carina sterni ; *cd.v*, caudal vertebrae ; *cor*, coracoid ; *cv.r*, cervical ribs ; *f.trs*,
probe passed into foramen triosseum ; *fur*, furcula ; *gl.cv*, glenoid cavity ; *il*, ilium ; *is*, ischium ;
*is.for*, ischiadic foramen ; *obt.n*, obturator notch ; *pu*, pubis ; *pyg.st*, pygostyle ; *scp*, scapula ;
*s.scr*, syn-sacrum ; *st*, sternum ; *st.r*, sternal ribs ; *th.v.1*, first, and *th.v.5*, last thoracic vertebra ;
*unc*, uncinates ; *vr.r*, vertebral ribs. (From Parker and Haswell, *Zoology*.)

a supracoracoid foramen or notch), Fig. 192. The very primitive Jurassic
*Archaeopteryx* (Petronievics and Woodward, **289**), however, has a scapula
and a short coracoid (pierced by the supracoracoid foramen) more closely
resembling those of Archosaurian reptiles, Fig. 194 A. The Ratitae have a
short broad coracoid, and from the base of the scapular region there arises
an anterior process (called ' precoracoid ' process), the homology of which is
difficult to interpret. The precoracoid process when present in Carinatae
is on the coracoid itself, and in *Apteryx* it is known to arise by fenestration of the cartilage (T. J. Parker, **66**). An opening is formed, separate in
some species from the supracoracoid foramen ; later the cartilaginous bar
in front becomes ligamentous and may finally be ossified, Figs. 86, 193, 194.
The ' precoracoid ' or ' prescapular ' process of the Struthiones appears to

correspond to that of *Apteryx*, but develops as an outgrowth (Broom, **240**), which, in *Struthio* itself, grows down to join the coracoid and enclose a fenestra. The supracoracoid foramen persists in *Casuarius* ; in other genera it appears to be confluent with the ' precoracoid ' notch or fenestra. The precoracoid process described above recalls that of the Chelonian scapula, is present in *Archaeopteryx* on the scapula (Petronievics and Woodward, **289**), and is possibly to be regarded as an acromion.

In good fliers the scapula is articulated to the coracoid at an acute angle of less than 90°. In *Archaeopteryx*, however, the two bones, though

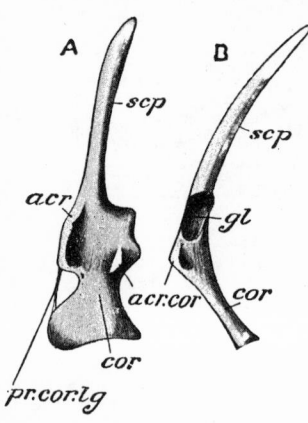

FIG. 193.

*Apteryx mantelli.* The left shoulder girdle. A, anterior; B, lateral (outer) surface. *acr*, Acromion; *acr.cor*, acro-coracoid; *cor*, coracoid; *gl*, glenoid cavity; *pr.cor.lg*, procoracoid, reduced to a ligament; *scp*, scapula. (After T. J. Parker; from Parker and Haswell, *Zoology*.)

fused, more nearly resemble those of the Dinosaurs in shape and position ; and in those birds which have lost the power of flight the girdle is reduced, the coraco-scapular angle enlarged (Dodo, Solitaire, *Ocydromus, Notornis*, etc.), and the coracoid fused to the scapula, Figs. 193, 194. Some of the flightless Moas seem to have lost all trace of the girdle and wing.

The pectoral girdle of the aquatic Ichthyosauria is but little specialised. It preserves, in addition to the dermal T-shaped interclavicle and clavicles, a scapula and expanded coracoid, Fig. 195. The Sauropterygia, although less completely adapted to aquatic life, acquire a much more modified girdle (Owen, 1865 ; Conybeare ; Hulke, 1892 ; Seeley, **298** ; Boulenger, 1896). Clavicles and interclavicle are still normally developed in Mesosauria (Seeley, **297a** ; Broom, **239a** ; McGregor, **279a**), and the primary girdle has a scapula with fairly large dorsal blade and an expanded coracoid pierced by a foramen. But in the Nothosauria the dermal bones form a strong arch widely separated from the more posterior coracoid (von Meyer, 1847 ; Boulenger, 1896). The tendency for the dorsal blade of the scapula to become reduced, and for its ventral extension to enlarge, already seen in this suborder, is carried to an extreme in Plesiosauria (Seeley, **298** ; Andrews, **232** ; Watson, **308**). Here the coracoid becomes very large ; and sends forward a ventral process which in more specialised and later forms (*Microcleidus, Cryptocleidus*, Fig. 196) meets a posterior process of the ventral plate of the scapula, thus surrounding a fenestra. Meanwhile the dermal bones are much reduced (in *Muraenosaurus* the clavicles disappear, and in *Microcleidus* the interclavicle) and come to lie on the inner dorsal side of the scapular plate.   These modifications lead to the formation of a very solid ventral endoskeletal girdle which can afford a firm basis of insertion for pectoral muscles and resist the thrust of the powerful swimming paddles.   The exact nature of the ventral scapular

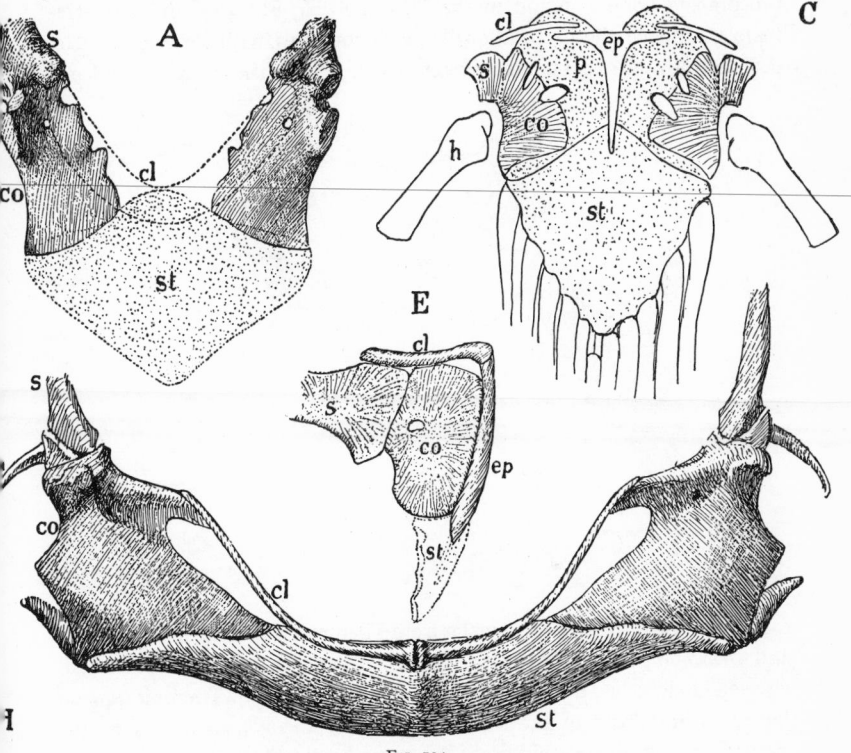

Fig. 194.

Pectoral girdle and sternum of : A, *Archaeopteryx*, Jurassic ; C, *Carsosaurus*, Cretaceous (after Nopsca) ; E, *Euparkeria* (after Broom) ; H, *Hesperornis*, Cretaceous (after Marsh).   *cl*, Clavicle ; *co*, coracoid ; *ep*, interclavicle ; *h*, humerus ; *p*, epicoracoid cartilage ; *s*, scapula ; *st*, sternum. (From G. Heilmann, *Origin of Birds*, 1926.)

extension is not quite clear, but it appears to be formed by the growth of the acromial or prescapular bony process ; on the other hand, it may be an ossification of a procoracoid bar due to the fenestration of the ventral plate.   It is probable that even in Nothosauria there was an extensive fenestrated cartilaginous plate, ossified only posteriorly, Fig. 196.

It has already been mentioned (p. 174) that in many Cotylosauria there is in addition to the scapula and coracoid a third bone developed in the primary girdle, the epicoracoid of Cuvier (precoracoid or procoracoid), situated in front of the coracoid and more or less completely enclosing the coracoid foramen, Fig. 183. This procoracoid, as it is now generally called, is seen typically developed in *Pareiasaurus* and *Procolophon*, and doubtless together with the coracoid occupied the greater part of a wide originally cartilaginous plate. A similar and quite obviously homologous procoracoid bone is found in the Theromorpha, Fig. 184, and Monotremata.[1] Indeed the pectoral girdle of Monotremes, with its interclavicle, procoracoid, and other points of resemblance, affords the strongest evidence

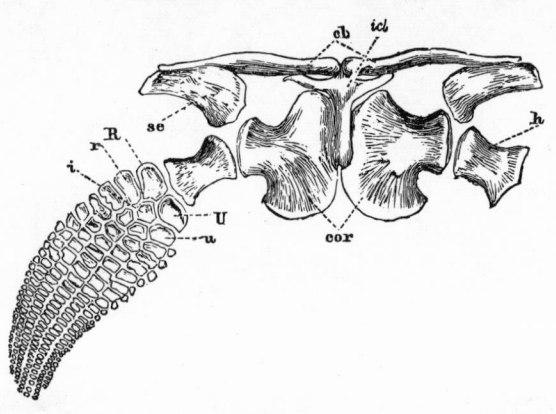

FIG. 195.

*Ichthyosaurus communis*, Conyb. Lower Lias: England. Pectoral arch and right fore-limb; ventral aspect, ⅓. *cl*, Clavicle; *cor*, coracoid; *h*, humerus; *i*, intermedium; *icl*, interclavicle (partly covered by clavicles); *R*, radius; *r*, radiale; *sc*, scapula; *U*, Ulna; *u*, ulnare. (From K. Zittel, *Palaeontology*.)

for the derivation of the Mammalia from Theromorph ancestors. *Echidna* and *Ornithorhynchus* preserve a T-shaped expanded interclavicle, well-developed clavicles, a strong acromial process still as in Theromorphs on the anterior border of the scapula, a large coracoid articulated to the sternum, and a procoracoid excluded from the glenoid cavity, Fig. 197.

The scapula of Cynodont Theromorphs already shows in its everted anterior edge the beginning of the formation of the acromial spine and prespinous fossa so characteristic of the Mammalia. The procoracoid may take a share in the formation of the glenoid cavity in Theromorphs.

There is a marked difference between the girdle of Monotrematous and Ditrematous Mammals. In all Ditremata, while the ventral elements have been much reduced and the interclavicle has disappeared, the

[1] The presence of the procoracoid in these forms may be taken as evidence that the order Cotylosauria is polyphyletic, some families being related to the ancestors of the Theromorphs, and others to the Sauropsidan stem.

scapula forms a wide blade expanding in front, so that the acromion and its ridge or spine come to lie on its outer surface separating an anterior from a posterior fossa, Figs. 184 D, 200 (McKay and Wilson). In the

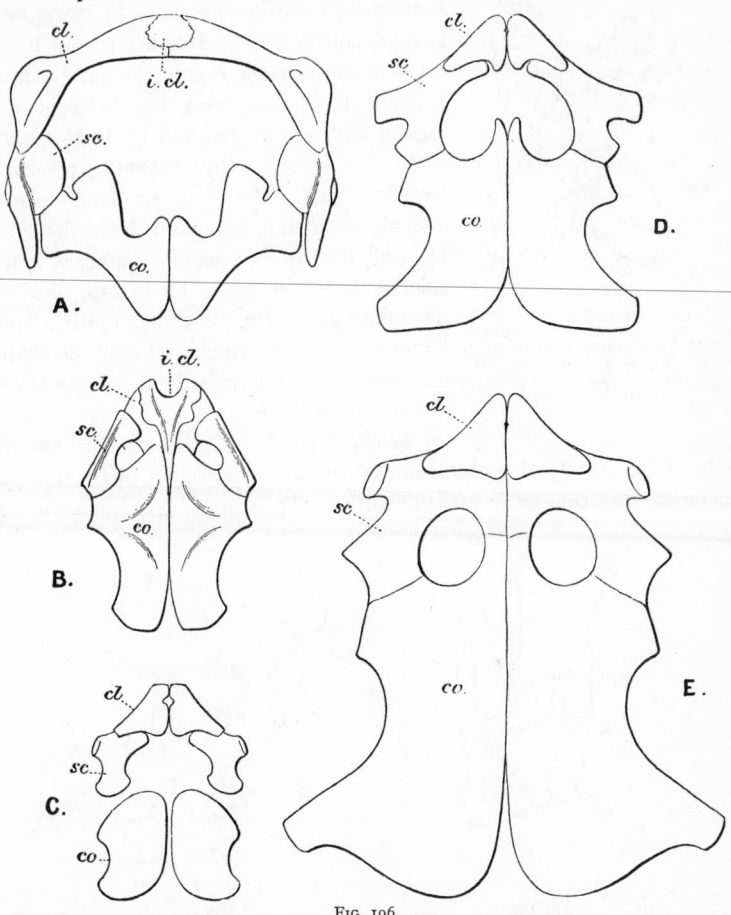

FIG. 196.

Diagram of pectoral arch of Sauropterygia, showing gradual atrophy of clavicular elements. A, *Nothosaurus mirabilis*; dorsal aspect. M. Triassic, Würtemberg. B, *Plesiosaurus*; ventral aspect. L. Jurassic, Lyme Regis. C, D, E, *Cryptocleidus oxoniensis*; dorsal aspect of three successive stages of growth. U. Jurassic, Peterborough. (After A. S. Woodward, *Vertebrate Palaeontology*, 1898.) *cl*, Clavicle; *co*, coracoid; *i.cl*, interclavicle; *sc*, scapula.

adult Marsupial the coracoid region is reduced to merely a ventral bony process of the scapula. But Broom (**239**) has shown that in such genera as *Trichosurus* and *Dasyurus* the coracoid cartilage in the embryo reaches the sternum, and the acromial process is near the anterior edge of the scapula, Figs. 198-9 (in *Trichosurus* the procoracoid region is still represented in embryonic mesenchyme). These important observations have been confirmed (Watson, **307**), and extended to *Didelphys* (Romer).

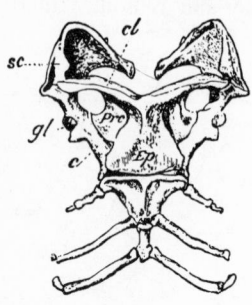

FIG. 197.

Ventral view of pectoral girdle and anterior portion of sternum and sternal ribs of *Ornithorhynchus* (from Flower, *Osteol. of Mammalia*, 1885). *c*, Coracoid; *cl*, clavicle; *Ep*, inter-clavicle; *gl*, glenoid cavity; *prc*, pro-coracoid.

As shown by Howes (**263-4**) the coracoid process may ossify separately in Placentals (*Lepus*) and be retained as a separate bone often of considerable size in the adult (some Edentata). This process has been homo-logised with the procoracoid by Howes, and with the coracoid by Broom (**241**) and Gregory (**523**). Moreover, in some forms a small ossification occurs on the hinder sur-face of the glenoid cavity which is con-sidered as the coracoid by Howes, and as an epiphysis by Broom and Gregory. The homology of these two ventral bony elements can hardly be determined on the evidence at present available.

**Conclusion.**—In conclusion, it may be said of the Tetrapod pectoral girdle that the homologies of the dermal elements present no great difficulties. They may be compared to

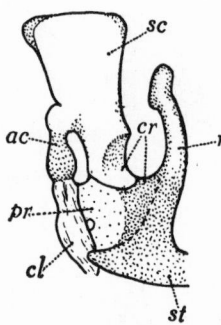

FIG. 198.

*Trichosurus vulpecula.* Embryo 8·5 mm. long. Reconstruction of shoulder girdle and part of sternum; cartilage white, procartilage dotted; left-side view (from Broom, 1900). *ac*, Acromial process; *cl*, clavicle; *cr*, coracoid region; *pr*, pro-coracoid region, mesenchymatous; *r*, first sternal rib; *sc*, scapular region; *st*, sternum.

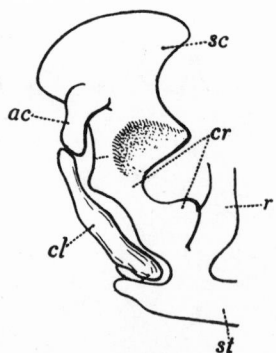

FIG. 199.

*Trichosurus vulpecula.* Embryo 14·8 mm. long. Left-side view of reconstruc-tion of shoulder girdle (from Broom, 1900). Lettering as in previous figure.

those of a primitive Teleostome, the post-temporal connexion being lost in all but the most primitive Stegocephalia, and a median interclavicle being added ventrally. On the other hand, the history of the endoskeletal elements in the specialised groups is by no means clear.

While in Stegocephalia there is a simple girdle with an expanded ventral plate and a single scapulocoracoid bone, in modern Anura a fenestra develops in the ventral plate (apparently from the coracoid foramen), and a posterior coracoid bone appears separate from the scapula. The Amniota seem to have independently acquired a similar coracoid bone sharing in the formation of the glenoid cavity and strength-

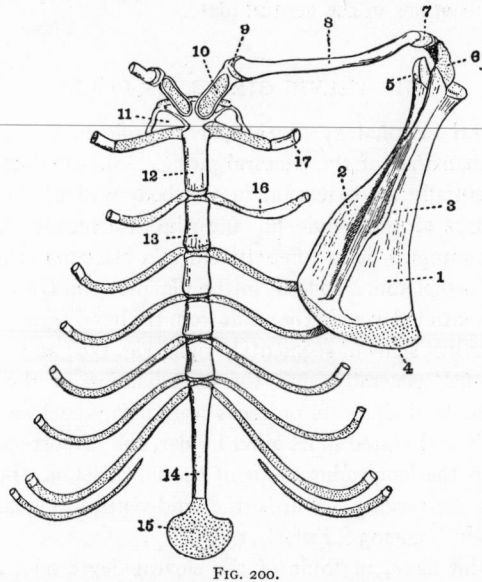

FIG. 200.

Dorsal view of sternum and right half of shoulder girdle of *Mus sylvaticus*. (From S. H. Reynolds, *Vertebrate Skeleton*, 1913.) 1, Postscapular fossa; 2, prescapular fossa; 3, spine; 4, suprascapular border unossified; 5, coracoid process; 6, acromion; 7, secondary cartilage; 8, clavicle; 9, secondary cartilage; 10, ' omosternum '; 11 and 12, presternums (manubrium or first sternebra); 13, sternebra, first segment of mesosternum; 14, xiphisternum; 15, cartilaginous termination of xiphisternum; 16, second sternal rib; 17, first vertebral rib.

ening the posterior edge of the ventral plate. Fenestration of this plate occurs in Lacertilia, and probably in Sauropterygia; but in most Reptiles and in Birds the coracoid bone apparently occupies the whole extent of the ventral plate. In those forms which possess only this coracoid, it typically encloses the nerve foramen. The acromial process of the scapula, already incipient in Amphibia, appears to be secondarily extended ventrally in Chelonia and possibly in Sauropterygia. In some Cotylosauria, the Theromorpha, and the Mammalia, a new ossification, the procoracoid, appears in the ventral plate usually enclosing the coracoid foramen and situated in front of the coracoid. Thus, as far as two bones can ever be said to be homologous with one, the single coracoid of the Diaptosaurian or Sauropsidan Reptiles which lead towards the Birds may be considered homologous with the coracoid and procoracoid of those Synaptosaurian or Theropsidan (and Cotylosaurian) Reptiles which lead towards the Mammals. The pectoral girdle offers evidence of the early divergence of the Reptilia into these two main branches.[1]

Thus, outside the Cotylosauria, Theromorpha, and Mammalia, there is never more than one ventral bone ; and in no Tetrapod are there more than two ossifications in the ventral plate.

## THE PELVIC GIRDLE OF PISCES

The general morphology of the pelvic girdle in Pisces is less well understood than that of the pectoral girdle. Like the latter the pelvic girdle is essentially an extension in the body-wall of the fin-skeleton for the support of the pelvic fin and the attachment of its muscles (p. 149). In ontogeny it is differentiated in a blastema continuous with that of the fin-skeleton. Indeed, in the Cladoselachii (Dean, 154-5) it is scarcely differentiated even in the adult from the basal region of the radials and shows distinct signs of segmental origin, Fig. 150 ; and it may be said of primitive fish generally that the consolidation of the girdle from originally segmental elements proceeds from before backwards. Radials are primitively articulated to its outer border, and its posterior end passes gradually into the longitudinal axis of the fin-skeleton. Better defined pelvic plates converging towards the mid-ventral line are found in Pleuracanthodii, Fig. 203 ; Fritsch, 23.

The Selachii have, in front of the cloacal depression, a transverse plate formed by the fusion of paired pelvic cartilages. To its outer border is

[1] It may be added that it is not impossible that a fenestration has occurred in the majority of, if not in all, the Amniota, leaving a cartilaginous acromial (or precoracoid) bar extending from the scapula to the infracoracoid cartilage (Gegenbaur, Fürbringer). The excavated anterior edge of the coracoid in such forms as Phytosauria and Sauropterygia suggests this interpretation. If the fenestra grew large and the anterior bar was reduced to an acromion and even finally lost, the coracoid would remain as the only ventral element, as seen in most diving Reptiles and Birds. Likewise the procoracoid and coracoid, in those forms where both these bones occur, may be ossifications in the plate posterior to a fenestra which has broken through in front. The various anterior cartilaginous or bony bars and processes (' precoracoid ', ' acromion ', scapular process, etc.) seen in Plesiosauria, Chelonia, Aves, and perhaps in Lacertilia, would then all be derived from the bar originally closing the fenestration in front. Nevertheless, since there is no convincing evidence of the existence of such a complete acromial bar in primitive Amniotes, this view has not been generally adopted.

attached the fin-skeleton, Fig. 201. The pelvic plate interrupts the ventral body-wall muscles inserted on its anterior and posterior edges. Diazonal nerves usually pierce it, and in *Chlamydoselachus*, where the pelvic plate is very long, there are two series of nerve foramina indicating that it is derived from many segments, Fig. 27. Generally a slight elevation occurs above the articulation of the fin, and in Batoidei this may develop into a considerable dorsal process comparable to the ilium of Tetrapods,

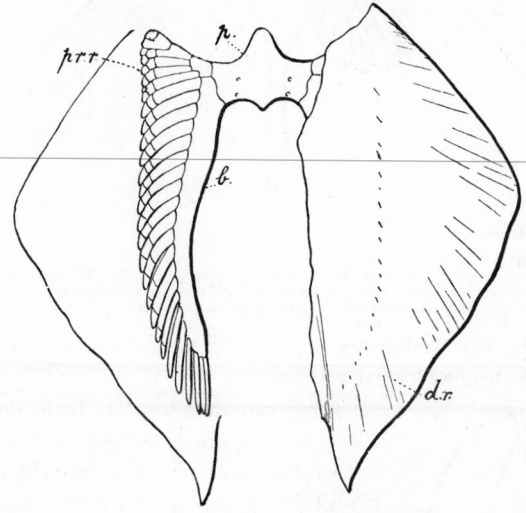

FIG. 201.

Ventral view of the pelvic girdle and fins of *Heptanchus cinereus*, Gm. ; in this and the succeeding figures the complete skeleton is exposed on one side only. *a*, Jointed axis; *b*, basipterygium; *c*, anterior cartilage; *dr*, dermal rays; *p*, pelvic girdle; *prr*, preaxial radial; *s*, scale covering lobe. Lettering for Figs. 204-8. (From E. S. Goodrich, *Quart. Jour. Micr. Sci.*, v. 45, 1901.)

Fig. 166. The Holocephali, in which the two halves of the girdle remain separate, also have a large dorso-lateral ' iliac ' process.

The two halves of the originally cartilaginous girdle of Teleostomes ossify, except in modern Acipenseroidei, in the form of two separate bones lying horizontally in the body-wall, meeting in front of the anus and bearing the fin-skeleton at their divergent posterior ends (Polypterini, Amioidei, Lepidosteoidei, and Teleostei, Figs. 35, 205-7). Small cartilages may be detached at their anterior ends (*Polypterus*, Fig. 205), and rarely the two pelvic plates may meet in a median cartilage as in *Gadus*.

Various observers have considered these pelvic plates to be parts of the fin-skeleton which has shifted inwards, and have hence called them basipterygia or metapterygia (Davidoff, **153** ; Gegenbaur, **170** ; Wiedersheim, **230**), believing the true girdle to be represented by the small anterior cartilages mentioned above. But, while Wiedersheim held that these

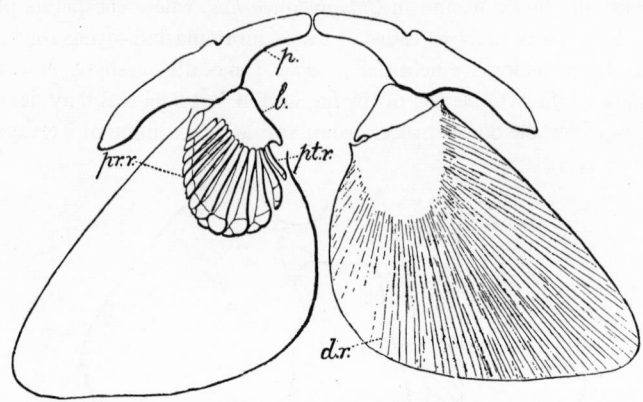

FIG. 202.

Ventral view of the pelvic girdle and fins of *Chimaera monstrosa*, L., ♀. The skeleton is completely exposed on the left side. *b*, Basipterygium ; *d.r*, web of right fin with ceratotrichia ; *p*, pelvic cartilage ; *pr.r*, preaxial radials ; *pt.r*, postaxial radials. (From *Quart. Jour. Micr. Sci.*, v. 45, 1901.)

represent the first rudiments of a girdle, Gegenbaur on the contrary looked upon them as its last vestiges.

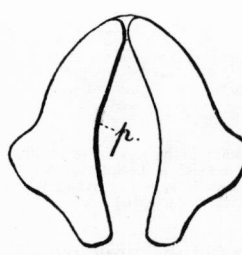

FIG. 203.

Ventral view of the pelvic girdle of *Pleuracanthus Gaudryi*, Brogn. (From E. S. Goodrich, *Quart. Jour. Micr. Sci.*, v. 45, 1901.)

There can, however, be little doubt that these theories are erroneous (Goodrich, **171**). Since pelvic bones are found normally developed in all Teleostomes from the Devonian Osteolepidoti (*Eusthenopteron*, Fig. 204) to the present day, there is no reason for rejecting the older view that they are the halves of a true girdle, comparable to that, for instance, of the Pleuracanthodii. Moreover, their position in the body-wall and relation to the nerves and musculature clearly show that they do not belong to the fin. The limit and joint between fin-skeleton and girdle remains always near the base of the fin-fold in fishes, and there is no evidence that it has shifted inwards and been carried to the anterior tip of the pelvic bone or cartilage.[1]

It is probably the structure of the girdle in modern Chondrostei which has led to this unlikely interpretation. For, especially in the somewhat degenerate living representatives of the group, the limit between the

---

[1] Stensiö adopts an intermediate view : that, during the course of phylogeny, to the original pelvic plate of Teleostomes has been added a region belonging to the base of the fin-radials (**134**).

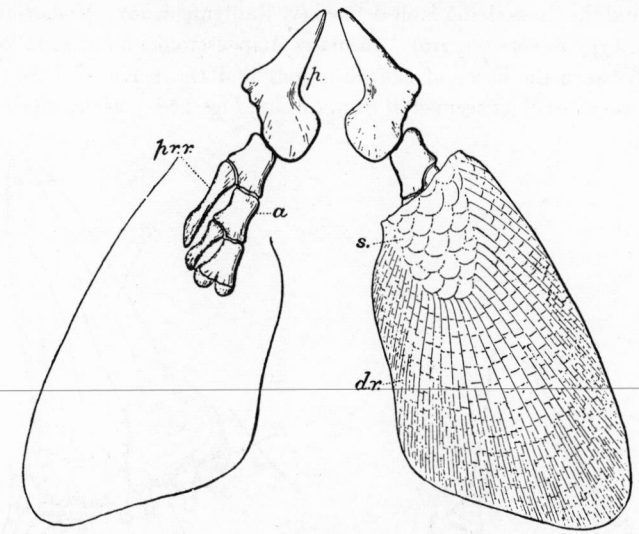

FIG. 204.

Ventral view of the pelvic girdle and fins of *Eusthenopteron Foordi*, Whit., restored.   For lettering see Fig. 201.   (From E. S. Goodrich, *Quart. Jour. Micr. Sci.*, v. 45, 1901.)

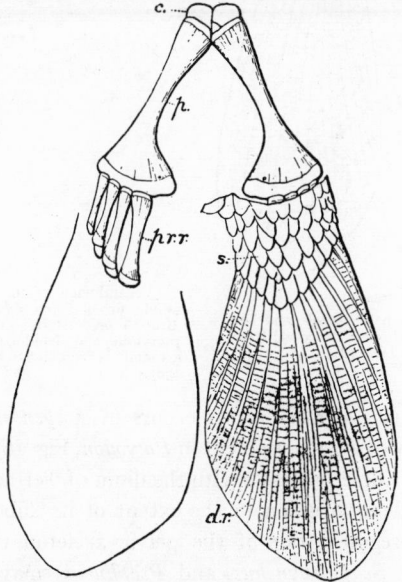

FIG. 205.

Ventral view of the pelvic girdle and fins of *Polypterus bichir*, Geoffr.   For lettering see Fig. 201.
(From E. S. Goodrich, *Quart. Jour. Micr. Sci.*, v. 45, 1901.)

girdle and the fin-skeleton is ill-defined (v. Rautenfeld, **207**; Mollier, **198**; Stensiö, **134**; Sewertzoff, **216**). In many Acipenseroidei no definite joint exists between the bases of the fin-radials and the pelvic plate, which preserves traces of its segmental composition, Figs. 208-9, as described by

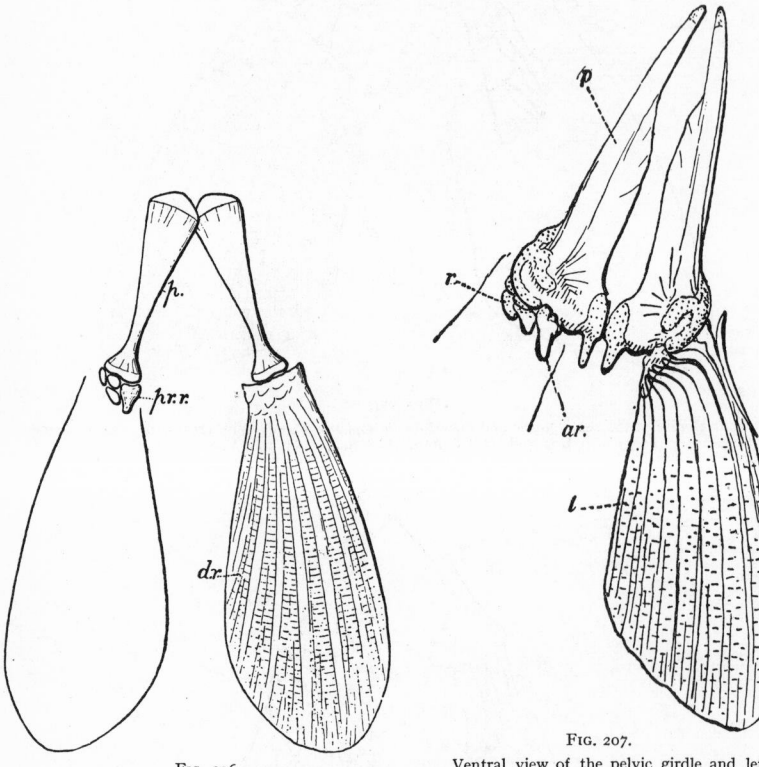

FIG. 206.

Ventral view of the pelvic girdle and fins of *Amia clava*, Bon. (Partly from Davidoff; from E. S. Goodrich, *Quart. Jour. Micr. Sci.*, v. 45, 1901.)

FIG. 207.

Ventral view of the pelvic girdle and left pelvic fin of *Salmo salar*, L. (Modified from Bruch.) *ar*, Posterior radia or remains of basipterygium; *l*, lepidotrich; *p*, pelvic bone; *r*, radial. (From E. S. Goodrich, *Vert. Craniata*, 1909.)

Thacher. An 'iliac' dorsal process occurs in *Acipenser*, and a similar process is developed on each segment in *Polyodon*, Fig. 163 (Thacher, **219**). The homology of these processes with the ilium of Tetrapods is doubtful. The great individual variation in the extent of its subdivision and the almost complete segmentation of the pelvic skeleton in some modern forms (*Acipenser, Scaphirhynchus,* and *Psephurus*) may be due to the more or less complete retention of an embryonic condition, and not to truly primitive structure. Nevertheless, their pelvic girdle seems to be at about the same stage of differentiation as that of the more primitive

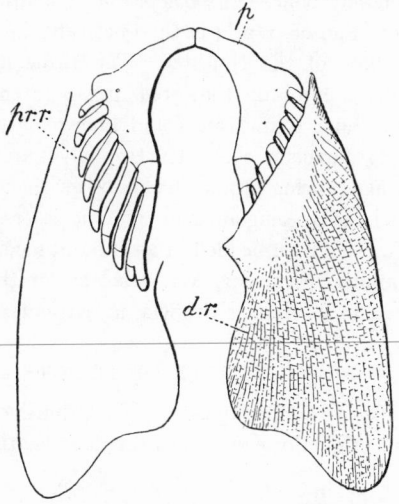

FIG. 208.

Ventral view of pelvic girdle and fins of *Acipenser sturio*, L.   (From E. S. Goodrich, *Quart. Jour. Micr. Sci.*, v. 45, 1901.)

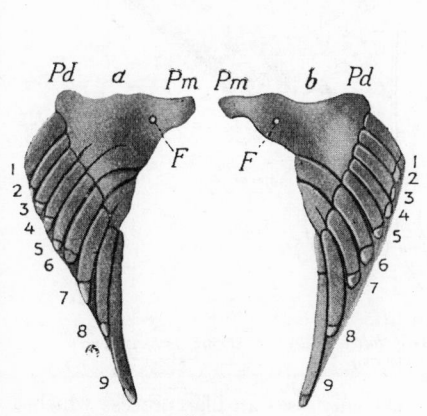

FIG. 209.

Ventral view of the cartilaginous skeleton of the pelvic girdle and fin of *Scaphirhynchus* (after Rautenfeld). *Pm*, median, and *Pd*, dorsal process of girdle; *F*, nerve foramen; 1-9, radials.   (From Goodrich, *Vert. Craniata*, 1909.)

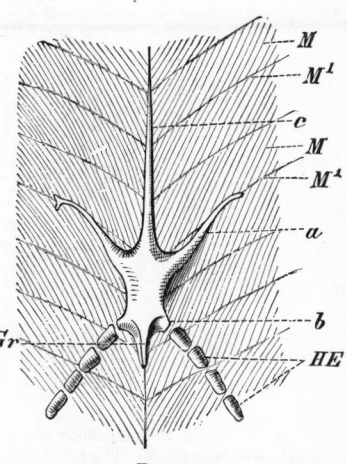

FIG. 210.

Pelvis of *Protopterus*. From the ventral side. *a*, Prepubic process, which may become forked at its distal end ; *b*, process to which the pelvic fin (*HE*) is attached; *c*, epipubic process ; *Gr*, ridge for attachment of muscles ; *M*, myotomes ; *M¹*, intermuscular septa. (From Wiedersheim, *Comp. Anat.*)

Chondrichthyes.   The presence of foramina for diazonal nerves is also good evidence that the plate is part of a true girdle.

A well-defined ossified girdle has been found in Crossopterygii in the form of two triangular bones (*Eusthenopteron*; Goodrich, 171) supporting the fin-skeleton, Fig. 204; and in the Coelacanthini the pelvic plates clearly resemble those of the Holostei. The girdle in Palaeoniscoidei and Saurichthyoidei is more like that of *Acipenser* (Stensiö, 134).

The girdle in Dipnoi is unossified and known only in living forms (Günther, 1871; Wiedersheim, 230). The two halves are completely fused to a median cartilage bearing prominent knobs for the articulation of the fin-skeleton, and a long tapering anterior epipubic process. At each side is a slender prepubic process embedded in an intermuscular septum. There are no nerve foramina, Figs. 152, 210. Except for the absence of an ilium the girdle resembles that of Urodela, in particular of *Necturus*.

## THE PELVIC GIRDLE OF TETRAPODA

The pelvic girdle of the Tetrapoda consists primitively of two halves, each formed of an originally continuous cartilage bearing an acetabular

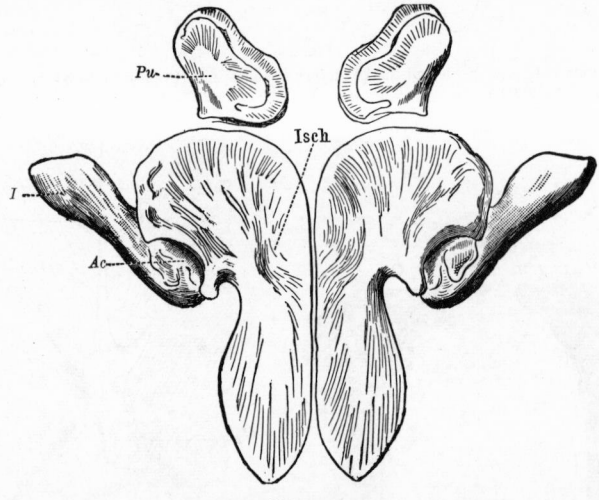

FIG. 211.

Pelvic arch of *Mastodonsaurus giganteus*, Jaeg. (after Fraas). *I*, Ilium; *Isch*, ischium; *Pu*, pubis; *Ac*, acetabulum. (From K. Zittel, *Palaeontology*.)

cavity for the head of the femur. Dorsally rises an iliac process which is typically firmly attached to the distal end of one or more sacral ribs. Ventrally the cartilage expands into a wide pubo-ischiadic plate, which meets that of the opposite side in a long ventral symphysis. The girdle encircles the abdominal cavity in front of the anus, and being more or less rigidly fixed to the vertebral column affords a firm basis for the articulation of the hind-limb, and for the insertion of its muscles. In typical well-ossified terrestrial forms three bones occur, the ilium, pubis, and ischium, all meeting in the acetabulum. The ventral plate interrupts the ventral body-wall muscles, separating the abdominal muscles partially

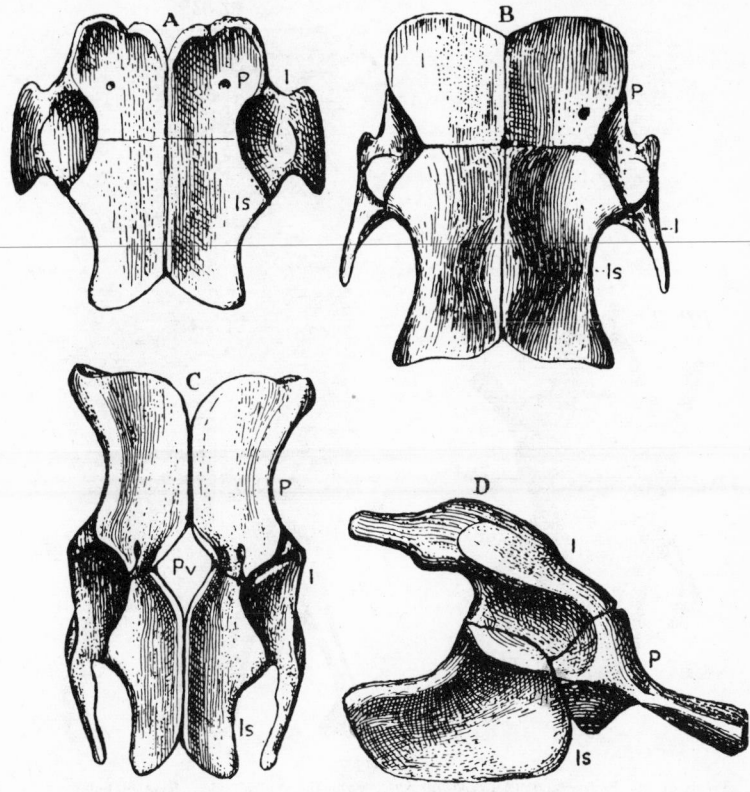

FIG. 212.

Pelvic girdle of A, *Cacops*, ventral view; B, *Conodectes* (*Seymouria*), ventral view; C, D, Varanops, ventral and side view. *I*, ilium; *Is*, ischium; *P*, pubis. (From Williston, *Osteology of Reptiles*, 1925.)

attached to its anterior border from the caudal muscles partially attached to its posterior border, while the outer surface of the plate serves chiefly for the insertion of limb-muscles (Vialleton, 302; Gregory and Camp, 256a; Romer, 391-2, 394-5). To a less extent the ilium interrupts the lateral myomeres more dorsally. In such primitive forms as the Amphibia, muscles derived from them are inserted over the ilium; but in higher Tetrapods these are shifted to the inner surface of the dorsal

extremity of the ilium as the insertions of the limb-muscles spread
over it.

**Amphibia.**—The primitive type of girdle is seen in Stegocephalia
typically developed (Cope ; Williston, **95** ; Romer).   The ilium is almost

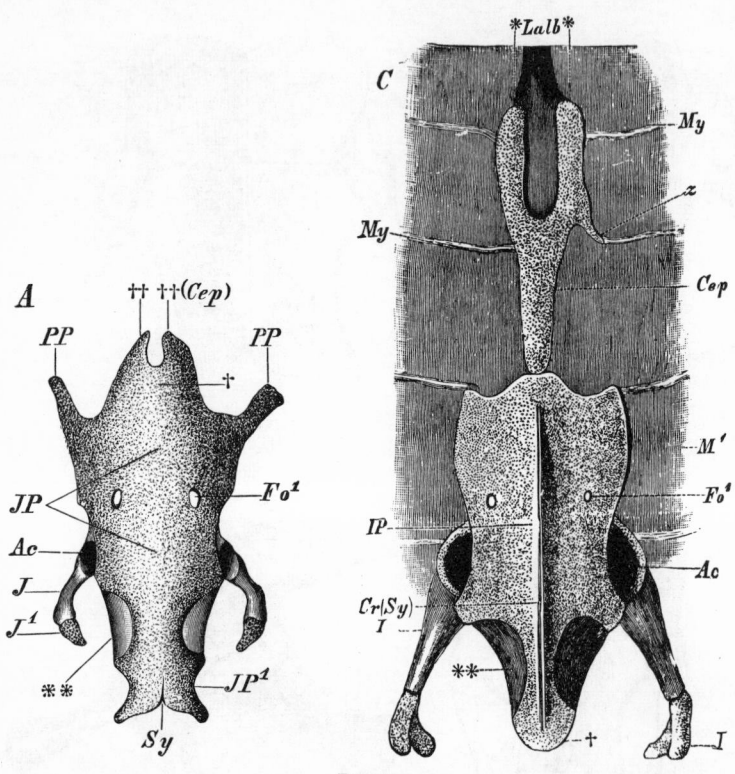

FIG. 213.

Pelvis of (A) *Proteus* and (C) *Cryptobranchus*. From the ventral side.  *Ac*, Acetabulum ; *Cep*,
ypsiloid cartilage ; *Cr (Sy)*, muscular ridge on the ventral side of the ischiopubis ;  *Fo*, *Fo¹*, obturator
foramen ;  *J*, *J¹*, ilium ;  *JP*, *JP¹*, ventral pelvic plate (ischiopubis) ;  *Lalb*, linea alba ;  *My*, intermuscular septa ;  *PP*, prepubis ;  *Sy*, symphysis ;  ** (in A), ossified region of the ischium ;  *z*, outgrowth from this bifurcation ;  † (in C), hypoischiatic process, present in the Derotremata and
Necturus ;  †† (*Cep*), epipubis.  (From Wiedersheim, *Comp. Anatomy of Vertebrates*.)

vertical, and the ventral plate is broad with a large ischium and usually
smaller pubis (not ossified in Branchiosauria), both no doubt embedded
in a continuous cartilaginous plate in the living.   The pubis comes to surround the diazonal obturator nerve in an obturator or pubic foramen, Figs.
**211**, **212 A**.   In Amphibia generally the ilium tapers dorsally and meets
only one sacral rib, while in Amniota it is expanded as a rule to cover
two or more sacral ribs and transverse processes.   The Embolomerous

Stegocephalia, however, have an ilium expanded backwards as in *Cricotus* (12) and *Eogyrinus* (Watson, 644), which seems to have been but loosely attached to the long, scarcely modified sacral ribs. The Urodela have a girdle built on the primitive plan, but the ossifications are less developed, and the pubis is not as a rule ossified at all, though rudiments appear in *Salamandra* (Wiedersheim, 230). In *Amphiuma* and *Proteus* with degenerate hind-limbs the ilium does not reach the vertebral column. The cartilaginous ventral plate is in *Necturus* prolonged into a long

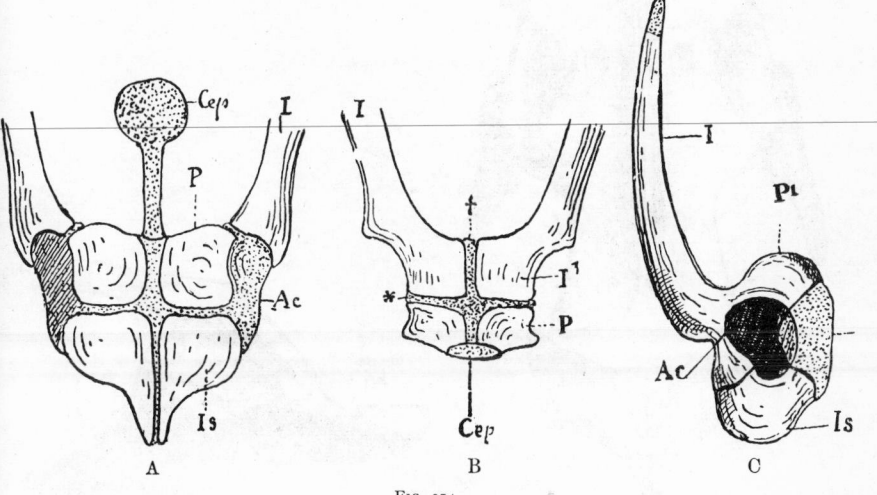

FIG. 214.

Pelvis of Anura. A, *Xenopus*, from below; B, the same from the front; C, *Rana esculenta*, from the right side. *Ac*, Acetabulum; *Cep*, ypsiloid cartilage; *I*, ilium; *I¹* (in *Xenopus*), the proximal end of the ilium, which is separated from its fellow and from the pubis by a +-shaped zone of cartilage, †, *; *Is*, ischium; *P*, pubis (*P¹* in *Rana*, pubic end of ilium). (From Wiedersheim, *Comp. Anat. of Vertebrates*.)

epipubic process recalling that of Dipnoi (p. 194). In other genera there may be a separate Y-shaped ypsiloid cartilage (*Salamandra, Cryptobranchus*, Fig. 213). Smaller paired lateral prepubic processes are also generally present. The Anura have a much reduced ventral plate, while the ilium is greatly extended forwards, an adaptation to their leaping mode of progression by means of enlarged hind-limbs. Only in *Xenopus* is the pubis ossified, Fig. 214 A. A median ypsiloid cartilage similar in origin to that of Urodela occurs in this genus.

Believed to be of paired origin, like the plate itself, and to be formed from the pubic cartilage by forward growths, which may fuse more or less completely in the middle line, and may also become secondarily detached from the plate (Wiedersheim, 310), the ypsiloid cartilage has been held to be homologous with the epipubic median process of

Amniotes. But others maintain that it is of separate origin, and primarily a chondrification in the linea alba between the posterior myomeres sometimes extending into the myocommata (Baur, 236; Whipple, 311). It may perhaps be compared to the sternal cartilage further forwards.

**Primitive Reptilia.**—The pelvic girdle of primitive Reptilia closely re-

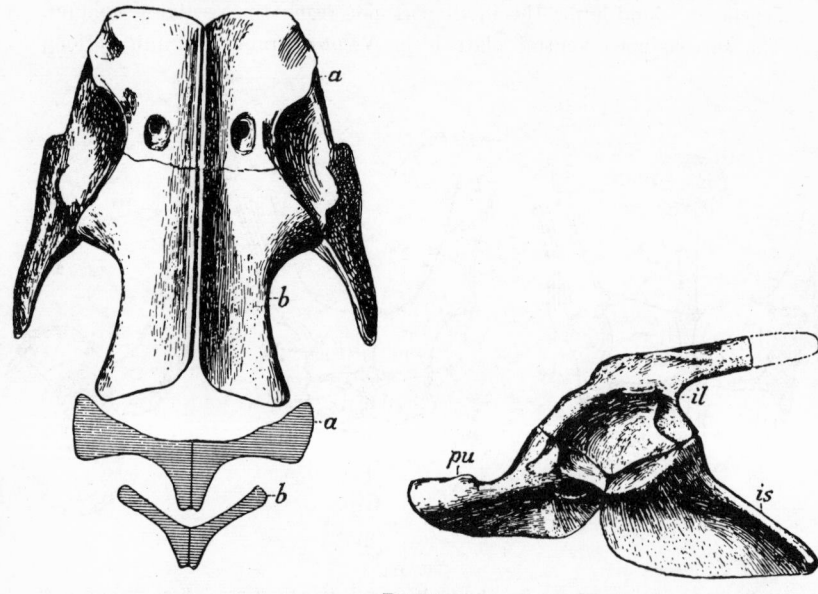

FIG. 215.

Ventral view of pelvic girdle of *Limno-scelis paludis*. Cross-section through pubes at *a*, and through ischia at *b*. (From Williston, *Osteology of Reptiles*, 1925.)

Left-side view of pelvic girdle of *Ophiacodon*. *il*, Ilium; *is*, ischium; *pu*, pubis. (From Williston, *Osteology of Reptiles*, 1925.)

sembles that of the Stegocephalia, with a stout vertical ilium and complete ventral plate composed of an ischium and a pubis pierced by an obturator foramen, Figs. 212, 215. But in some of the Cotylosauria the dorsal region of the ilium is considerably extended both forwards and backwards. The backward extension in these and other reptiles seems to be correlated with the development of a powerful tail. It is often pronounced in Theromorpha such as Dromosauria and Pelycosauria. The obturator foramen tends to become enlarged, and gives rise to a fenestra separating the pubis from the ischium in Dicynodontia and Theriodontia.[1]

[1] The central opening in the mid ventral line between the bony pubes and ischia (pubo-ischiadic of Williston, 95) probably was filled with cartilage, and does not seem to correspond to the true lateral fenestra of either the Synapsidan or Diapsidan pelvic girdles.

The expansion forwards of the ilium with an everted crest, and the

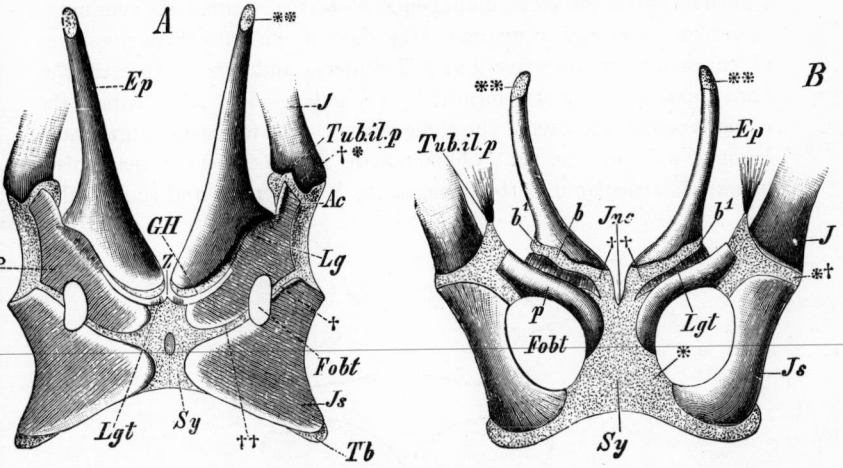

FIG. 216.

Pelvis of (A) *Echidna hystrix* (adult), and (B) *Didelphys azarae* (foetus, 5·5 cm. in length). From the ventral side. *Ep*, Epipubis or prepubis (marsupial bone); *Fobt*, obturator foramen; *J*, ilium; *Js*, ischium; *Lg* and *Lgt*, ligament between the pubis and epipubis; *P*, pubis; *Sy*, ischiopubic symphysis; *Tub.il.p*, iliopectineal tubercle; **, cartilaginous apophysis at the anterior end of the epipubis. In Fig. A, *GH*, articulation between the pubis and epipubis; *Tb*, cartilaginous tuber ischii; *Z*, process on the anterior border of the pubis; †*, †, ††, ilio- and ischio-pubic sutures. In Fig. B, *b*, *b¹*, cartilaginous base of the epipubis, continuous with the interpubic cartilage at †; *, *†, ischio-pubic and ischio-iliac sutures. (From Wiedersheim, *Comp. Anat. of Vertebrates.*)

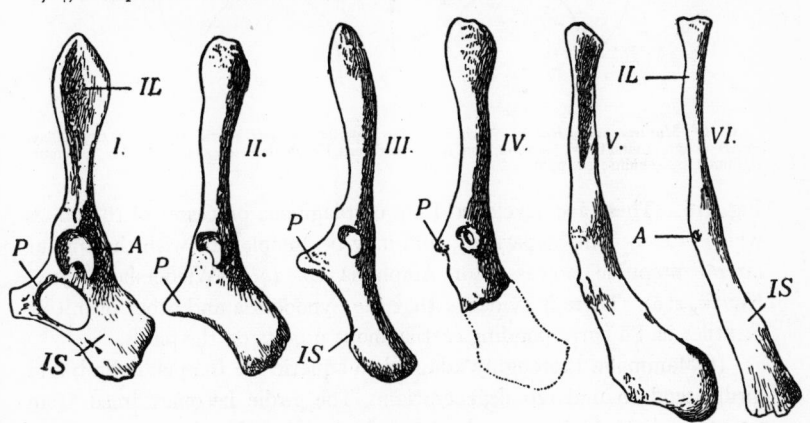

FIG. 217.

Outer view of left pelvic bone of: I. *Eotherium*, Middle Eocene, Egypt; II. *Eosiren*, Upper Eocene, Egypt; III. *Halitherium*, Oligocene, Europe; IV. *Metaxytherium*, Miocene and Pliocene, Europe; V. *Halicore dugong*, recent, Indo-Pacific Ocean; VI. *Halicore tabernaculi*, recent, Red Sea. *A*, Acetabulum; *IL*, ilium; *IS*, ischium; *P*, pubis. (From O. Abel, *Stämme der Wirbeltiere*, 1919.)

growth of the ventral plate backwards in Cynodontia, leads to the mammalian type of girdle.

**Mammalia.**—The mammalian girdle has the ilium usually greatly extended forwards, the acetabulum being behind the sacrum; the symphysis somewhat shortened (sometimes very short as in many Insectivora, or absent as in some Insectivora and Chiroptera), and in some Insectivores, Carnivores, and Primates formed by the pubes only. In Edentata the ischia may join the caudal vertebrae behind. The foramen obturatorium becomes a large fenestra. Characteristic epipubic bones ('marsupial' bones) are articulated to the pubes of the Monotremata and Marsupialia,

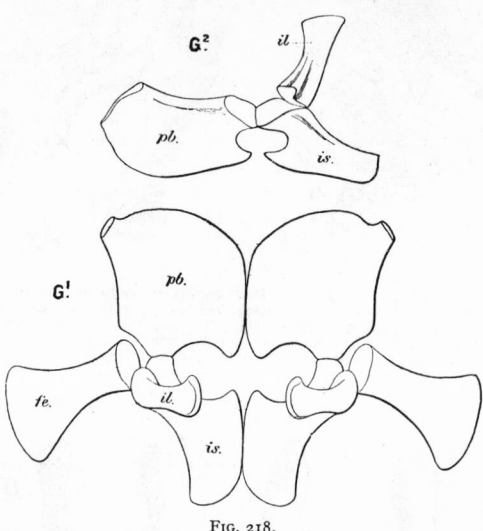

Fig. 218.

G¹, G², *Muraenosaurus leedsi.* Pelvis from the superior and left lateral aspect. Oxford Clay, Peterborough. (After C. W. Andrews, from A. S. Woodward, *Vertebrate Palaeontology*, 1898.) *fe*, Femur; *il*, ilium; *is*, ischium; *pb*, pubis.

Fig. 216. These are developed from cartilaginous processes of the pubes which later become separated, and may be homologous with the similar lateral prepubic processes of Amphibia (p. 196) (Wiedersheim, 310; Nauck, 286). There is evidence that the Cynodontia and other primitive Reptiles had a corresponding cartilaginous process on the pubis.

In Mammalia thoroughly adapted to aquatic life the pelvic limb and girdle tend to undergo degeneration. The girdle becomes freed from its attachment to the sacral ribs and may be reduced in Cetacea to a small and simple bony rod 'floating' in the body-wall. A similar reduction takes place in Sirenia, Fig. 217.

**Sauropterygia and Ichthyosauria.**—The Sauropterygia preserve a primitive type of girdle, but the wide ventral plate is pierced by an obturator fenestra between pubis and ischium, Fig. 218. A separate obturator

foramen occurs, however, in *Nothosaurus* (Andrews). While in the more
primitive Triassic Ichthyosauria (*Cymbospondylus*, *Toretocnemus* (Merriam,

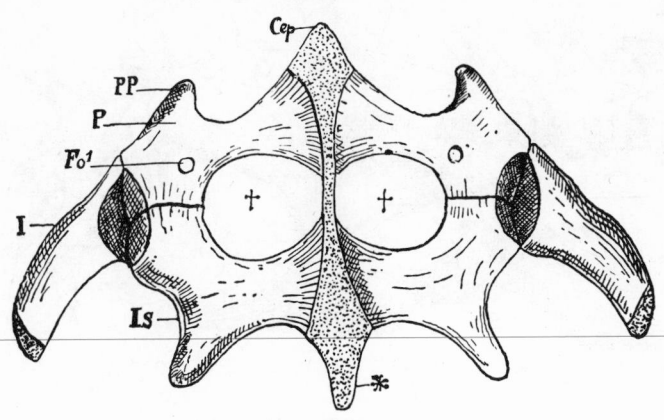

FIG. 219.

Pelvic arch of *Sphenodon*. (After Credner.) From the ventral side. *Cep*, Epipubic cartilage ;
*Fo¹*, obturator foramen ; *I*, ilium ; *Is*, ischium ; *P*, pubis ; *PP*, prepubis ; *, hypoischiatic process ;
†, †, ischiopubic foramina. (From Wiedersheim, *Comp. Anatomy.*)

283)) the pelvic girdle is provided with a well-developed ilium connected
to a sacral rib, and large expanded pubis and ischium, in later forms,

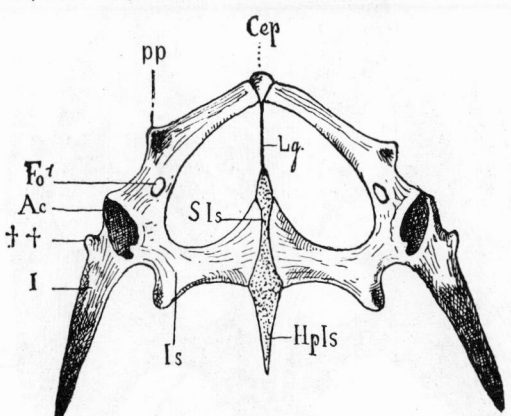

FIG. 220.

Pelvis of *Lacerta vivipara*. From the ventral side. *Ac*, Acetabulum, in which the three pelvic
bones come together ; *Cep*, epipubis, composed of calcified cartilage ; *Fo¹*, obturator foramen ;
*HpIs*, hypoischium, which becomes segmented off from the hinder ends of the ischia in the embryo
as a paired structure ; *I*, ilium, with its small preacetabular process ††, much more strongly developed
in crocodiles, dinosaurians, and birds ; *Is*, ischium, forming a symphysis at *SIs* ; *Lg*, fibrous ligament ;
*P*, pubis ; *pp*, prepubic process. (From Wiedersheim, *Comp. Anatomy.*)

where the hind-limbs are reduced and propulsion was mainly performed
by the caudal fin, the girdle becomes more and more degenerate. The

ilium pubis and ischium are small rod-like bones in a 'floating' girdle

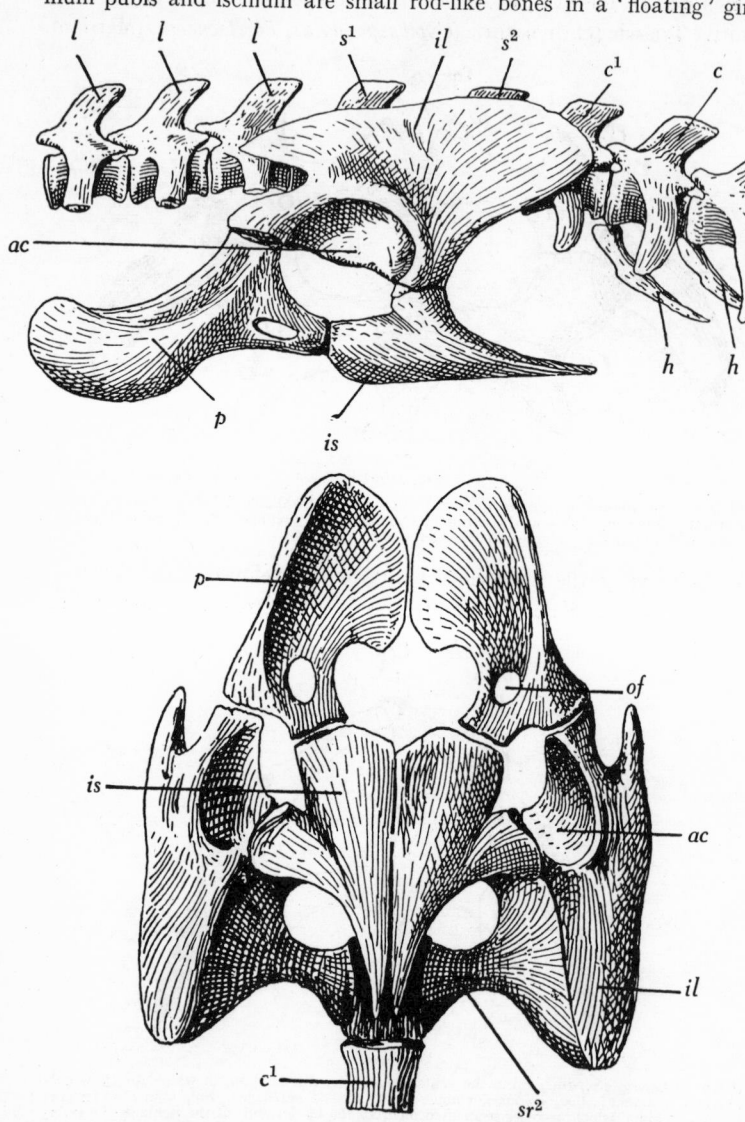

FIG. 221.

Left-side view of pelvic girdle and part of vertebral column of *Aëtosaurus crassicauda* (after C. Fraas, '07, from O. Abel, *Stämme der Wirbeltiere*, 1919). *ac*, Acetabulum; $c^{1-2}$, caudal vertebrae; *h*, chevron bones, haemal arches; *il*, ilium; *is*, ischium; *l*, lumbar vertebrae; *p*, pubis; $s^{1-2}$, sacral vertebrae.

in the Jurassic *Ichthyosaurus*. *Ophthalmosaurus*, which died out in the

Cretaceous, had a vestigial girdle, the small pubis and ischium being fused (Andrews, 232-3).

**Reptilia Sauropsida and Aves.**—The pelvic girdle of the Sauropsidan Reptiles is no doubt derived from the Stegocephalian type. Typically the ilium is inclined and lengthened backwards, and except for this the

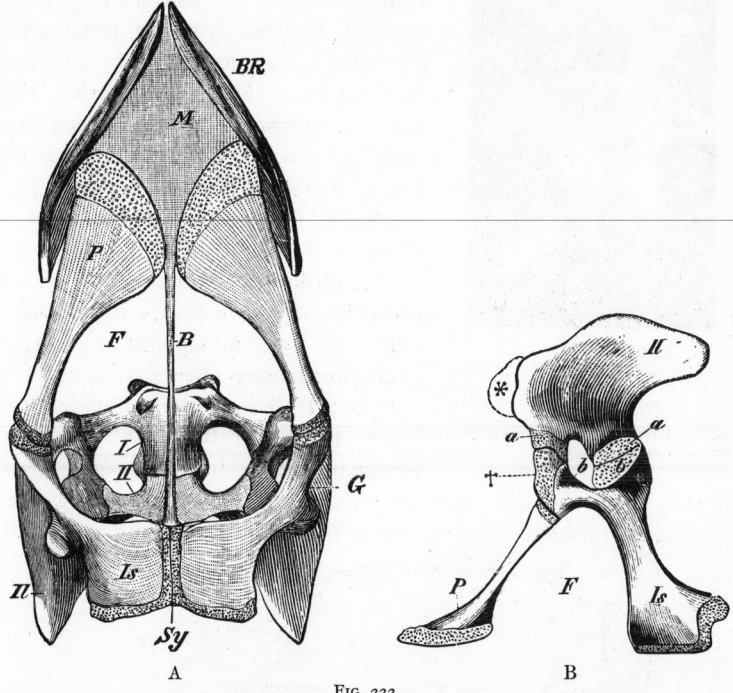

FIG. 222.

Pelvis of a young *Alligator lucius*. A, ventral, and B, lateral view. *B*, Fibrous band between the pubis and symphysis ischii ; *b*, foramen in the acetabulum, bounded posteriorly by the two processes, *a* and *b*, of the ilium and ischium respectively ; *F*, ischiopubic foramen ; *G*, acetabulum ; *Il*, ilium ; *Is*, ischium ; *M*, fibrous membrane extending between the anterior margin of the pubis and the last pair of ' abdominal ribs ' (*BR*) ; *P*, pubis ; *Sy*, symphysis of ischium ; *, indication of a forward growth of the ilium, such as is met with in dinosaurians and birds ; †, pars acetabularis, which is interposed between the process *a* of the ilium and the pubis ; *I, II*, first and second sacral vertebrae. (From Wiedersheim, *Comp. Anatomy.*)

girdle is little changed in such primitive forms as the Champsosauria and Phytosauria, where the ventral plate is formed of expanded pubes and ischia, meeting no doubt in a long cartilaginous symphysis. But in others a fenestra closed by membrane develops in the ventral plate between the pubis and the ischium, Fig. 219. It is not the enlarged obturator foramen, as it appears to be in the Theropsida (Synapsida), since the obturator nerve passes independently through the pubis (except in those forms where the nerve foramen and the fenestra become secondarily confluent), and it may be called the pubo-ischiadic or ischiopubic fenestra.

The Rhynchocephalia, Lacertilia, and Chelonia usually develop strong

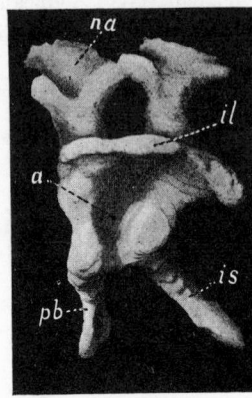

FIG. 223.

Outer view of left half of pelvic girdle and two sacral vertebrae of embryo *Crocodilus.* From wax reconstruction of cartilage made by G. R. de Beer. *a,* Acetabulum; *il,* ilium; *is,* ischium; *na,* neural arch; *pb,* pubis.

prepubic and postischial processes. The ventral plate may be much reduced ventrally owing to the enlargement of the fenestra, the two fenestrae being often separated in the adult merely by a median ligament (some Chelonia, Lacertilia, Fig. 220). A prominent median cartilaginous prepubic process may remain in front, and a similar posterior hypoischial process behind (separate in some adult Lacertilia).

The girdle may be reduced in legless Lacertilia to a mere vestige in the body-wall; but even in Ophidia a vestigial girdle often remains (Meckel, 1824; Mayer, 1825–29; J. Müller, 1838; Duerden and Essex, 1923), sometimes with a clawed vestige of the hind-limb (Boidae).

It is among the Archosauria that the pelvic girdle undergoes the most remarkable specialisations, for some of which it is very difficult to account.

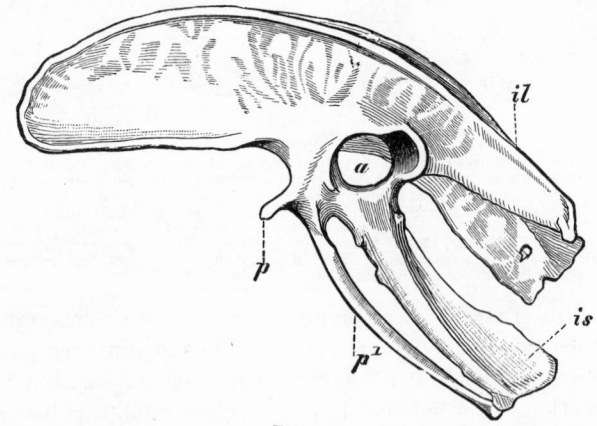

FIG. 224.

Pelvis of *Apteryx australis.* Lateral view. (After Marsh.) *a,* Acetabulum; *il,* ilium; *is,* ischium; *p,* pectineal process from the pars acetabularis; *p¹,* pubis. (From Wiedersheim, *Comp. Anatomy.*)

The Phytosauria (Parasuchia), as already mentioned, still preserve a primitive form of girdle with the ilium expanded chiefly backwards, and

large plate-like pubis and ischium (v. Meyer, 1847 ; McGregor, 279). The
ilium extends forwards as well as backwards, especially in Dinosaurs, and
the pubo-ischiadic fenestra becomes large between the divergent lengthened
pubis and ischium in Pseudosuchia, Fig. 221, and Saurischia. The
Theropodous Saurischia have the ventral ends of the pubis and ischium
enlarged and flattened at the symphysis, forming apparently surfaces on
which the body could be supported at rest.   In Saurischia the acetabulum
also becomes pierced—the lower border of the ilium being excavated.   A
similar piercing of the acetabulum occurs in Crocodilia,[1] Pterosauria, Ornithischia, and Aves.   Doubtless it was always closed by membrane as it is
seen to be in living Crocodiles and Birds.   But, whereas in Pseudosuchia

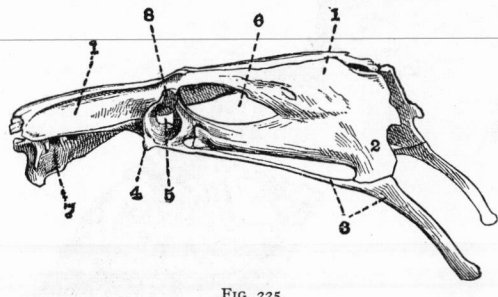

FIG. 225.

Lateral view of pelvis and sacrum of *Anas boschas* (from S. H. Reynolds, *Vertebrate Skeleton*, 1913).
1, Ilium ;  2, ischium ;  3, pubis ;  4, pectineal process ;  5, acetabulum ;  6, ilio-sciatic foramen ;  7,
fused vertebrae ;  8, antitrochanter.

and Saurischia the pubis and ischium are normally disposed and form
ventral symphyses, in Crocodilia the ilium and ischium surround the acetabulum excluding the pubis ; while the pubis is movably articulated to the
ischium, directed forwards and downwards, and forms no true symphysis,
Fig. 222.   The ischium of Pterosauria is a short broad plate (sometimes
pierced by the obturator foramen ?), the pubis being excluded from the
acetabulum and articulated to its front edge (the pubes are fused across
the mid line in *Rhamphorhynchus*, *Pteranodon*, and *Nyctosaurus*). These
facts led Fraas (1878) and Seeley (297) to believe that the true pubis
has in these reptiles been fused to the ischium, and Seeley maintained
that the detached so-called pubis is an epipubis comparable to the marsupial bones of Mammalia.   Considering how nearly related the Crocodilia
are to other Archosauria with a well-developed normal pubis (Eosuchia,
Parasuchia, Pseudosuchia, Saurischia), it is hard to believe that the pubis
has been so completely reduced ; yet it must be admitted that a thorough

[1] In the embryo Crocodile the iliac, pubic, and ischiadic cartilages are in
continuity and the acetabulum is closed.   The piercing of the acetabulum and
separation of the pubis take place late, Fig. 223.

investigation of the development of the Crocodilian pubis is urgently needed before its homology can be determined. Lately v. Huene (**266**) has held that the so-called pubis of Crocodiles and Pterosaurs is a 'prepubis' com-

FIG. 226.

*Hesperornis regalis*, Marsh. Upper Cretaceous: Kansas. Restoration of skeleton, $\frac{1}{8}$. (After Marsh, from K. Zittel, *Palaeontology*.)

parable to the 'prepubic' process of Ornithischia, the structure of whose pelvic girdle we must now consider.

Ever since Huxley insisted on the near relationship of Birds to Dinosaurs, attention has been centred on the interpretation of the homologies of the pelvic bones in these groups. The general resemblance between the girdle of such forms as *Iguanodon* or *Camptosaurus* on the one hand, and the Cassowary, Apteryx, or Tinamou on the other, is striking, Figs. 224, 226, 229; for not only is the ilium greatly expanded in both cases, but the

ischium is much lengthened, and extending backward parallel to it is a slender pubic bone provided, in the reptile, with a large anterior 'prepubic' process. Corresponding to it in the bird is a ' pectineal ' process of much smaller size. Moreover, the resemblance is completed by the presence, in many birds, of a process of the ischium similar to the obturator process overlapping the ' postpubis ' in

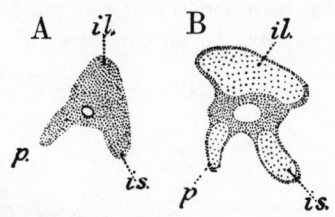

FIG. 227.

Side view of pelvis of bird embryos (after Mehnert, 1888). A, *Podicipes*; B, *Larus*. *il*, Iliac region; *is*, ischium; *p*, pubis.

Ornithischia and incompletely cutting off an obturator space, Figs. 225, 227. Now the older anatomists held that the slender backwardly directed bone is a true pubis, and Huxley compared it to the postpubic process of Ornithischia, believing the pectineal process to be the reduced remnant of their prepubic process. According to this view the main

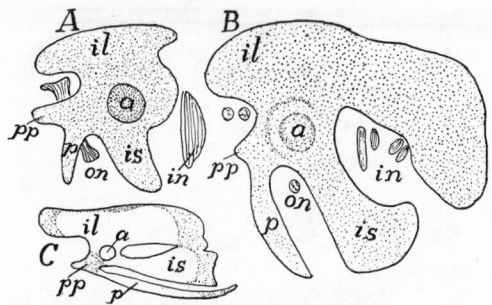

FIG. 228.

Development of pelvic girdle of chick, left-side view (after Johnson, '83, from J. S. Kingsley, *Vertebrate Skeleton*, 1925). A, 6-day chick; B, older stage; C, 20-day chick. Cartilage stippled, bone white. *a*, Acetabulum; *il*, ilium; *in*, ischiadic nerve; *is*, ischium; *on*, obturator nerve; *p*, pubis; *pp*, pectineal or prepubic process.

shaft of the pubis must have been rotated backwards in both Ornithischia and Aves. Evidence that rotation has occurred in birds is obtained from their development, since, as shown by Bunge (242) and Mehnert (280) and corroborated by Johnson (270), Parker (66), Broom (240), Lebedinsky (274), and Levin (276), the procartilaginous rudiment of the pubis is at first nearly vertical, and later shifts backwards, Figs. 227-8. That the true pubis has been rightly identified in Birds may be considered as established, since in *Archaeopteryx* the pubes, which still

are joined in a symphysis, are elongated slender bones projecting backwards parallel to the ischia, Fig. 233; but the homology of the pectineal
process, to which the ambiens muscle is attached, is far less certain. It
has been shown that this process ossifies, not as Huxley imagined from
the pubis, but in Carinates from the ilium. Marsh and others concluded

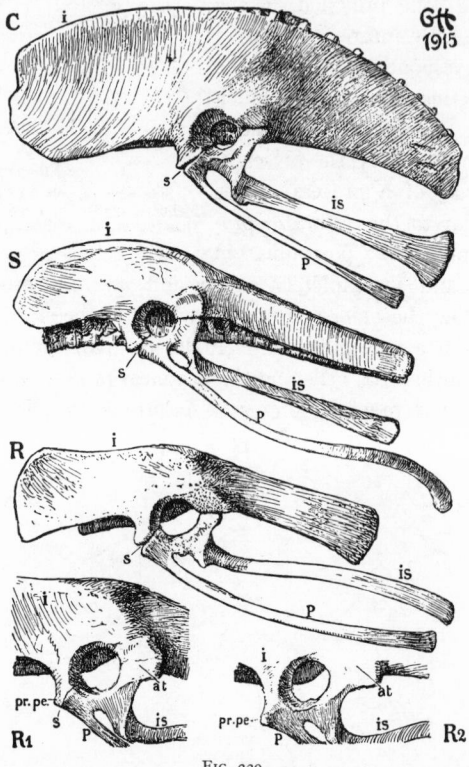

FIG. 229.

Left-side views of pelvic girdles of young : C, *Casuarius* ; S, *Struthio* ; and R, *Rhea* ; R₁, acetabular region of full-grown Rhea ; R₂, of old Rhea. *pr.pe*, Processus pectinealis ; *s*, suture between
ilium and pubis. (From G. Heilmann, *Origin of Birds*, 1926.)

that it is not the homologue of the prepubis but a new formation
(supported since by Lebedinsky and Heilmann). The large prepubic
bone of Ornithischia was then held to be the true pubis from which a
secondary postpubic process developed, absent in Ceratopsia, still small
in *Allosaurus*, fully developed in *Iguanodon*, Figs. 230-31, 232. The
resemblance to Birds on this view is deceptive and due to convergence.
The question, however, was not thus settled, for it was found that the
pectineal process in *Apteryx* and the Ratitae (Baur, 236; T. J. Parker,

66) is ossified as much from the pubis as from the ischium ; it could still be interpreted as a stage in the reduction of the prepubic process, Fig. 229. Lebedinsky maintains that in early stages the cartilaginous rudiments of ilium, pubis, and ischium appear separately and that the pectineal process arises from the ilium ; but even this observation is not conclusive, since the separate origin of the cartilages can have no phylogenetic significance. Of more consequence is the fact that the

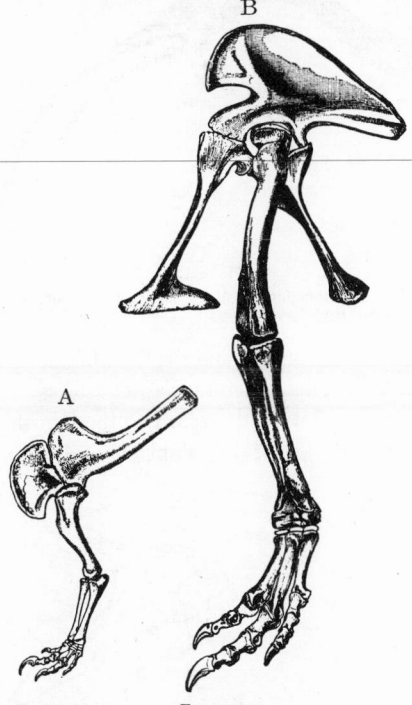

FIG. 230.

*Allosaurus agilis*, Marsh. Upper Jura : Colorado. Restoration of anterior (A) and posterior (B) limbs, ⅒. (After Marsh, from K. Zittel, *Palaeontology*.)

pectineal process in *Archaeopteryx* is quite small. Finally, v. Huene (266) and others maintain that the pubis has rotated not only in Birds, but also in Ornithischia, Crocodilia, and Pterosauria (Romer, 291, 293, 295). According to this view the pectineal process and the prepubic process are new formations, and the latter supplants the true pubis. The postpubis of Ornithischia would then represent the dwindling true pubis, small in *Allosaurus*, altogether gone in advanced Ceratopsia (also Crocodilia and Pterosauria), where the prepubic process has taken its place (in somewhat the same position as the original pubis in primitive reptiles). This interpretation entails the conclusion that the old Order Dinosauria is composed of two distinct groups : the Saurischia allied to the Phytosauria and

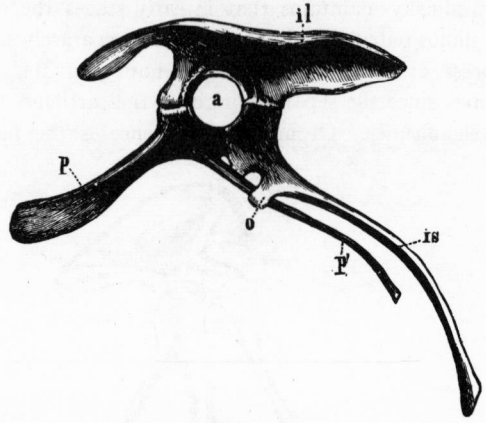

FIG. 231.

Pelvis of *Iguanodon*, $\frac{1}{20}$. *a*, Acetabulum ; *il*, ilium ; *is*, ischium ; *o*, obturator process ; *p*, prepubic process ; *p'*, pubis. (From K. Zittel, *Palaeontology*.)

Pseudosuchia (with normal pubis), and the Ornithischia having a common ancestry with the Crocodilia, Pterosauria, and Aves. The evidence is still far from complete ; but with regard to the Ornithischia it may be pointed out that a rotation of the pubis has already begun in such

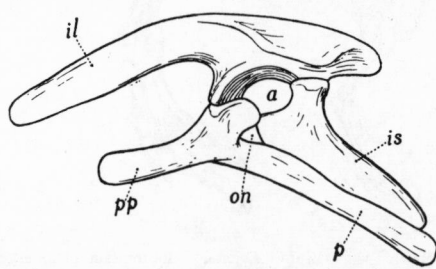

FIG. 232.

*Stegosaurus undulatus.* Outer view of left half of pelvic girdle (from Marsh). *a*, Acetabulum ; *il*, ilium ; *is*, ischium ; *on*, obturator notch ; *p*, pubis ; *pp*, prepubic process.

primitive Archosauria as *Euparkeria* and *Ornithosuchus*, Fig. 233 (Broom, 442 ; Gregory and Camp, 256a), and that the enlargement of the prepubis and dwindling of the pubis can on this view be traced through the newly discovered *Protiguanodon*, and *Protoceratops*, to *Triceratops*, where it appears as a mere vestige.

In Ornithischia the ischia may unite in a symphysis, but not the postpubes, while the prepubes are widely divergent. The Neornithes lose the symphysis altogether (except in *Struthio*), the right and left pubes and ischia being widely divergent. The ilium is also very much enlarged before and behind as thin plates excavated internally for the kidneys, and embracing a large number of lumbar and caudal vertebrae in the sacrum. Usually the ischium is likewise expanded and fuses behind with the ilium enclosing an ischiadic fenestra, Fig. 225.

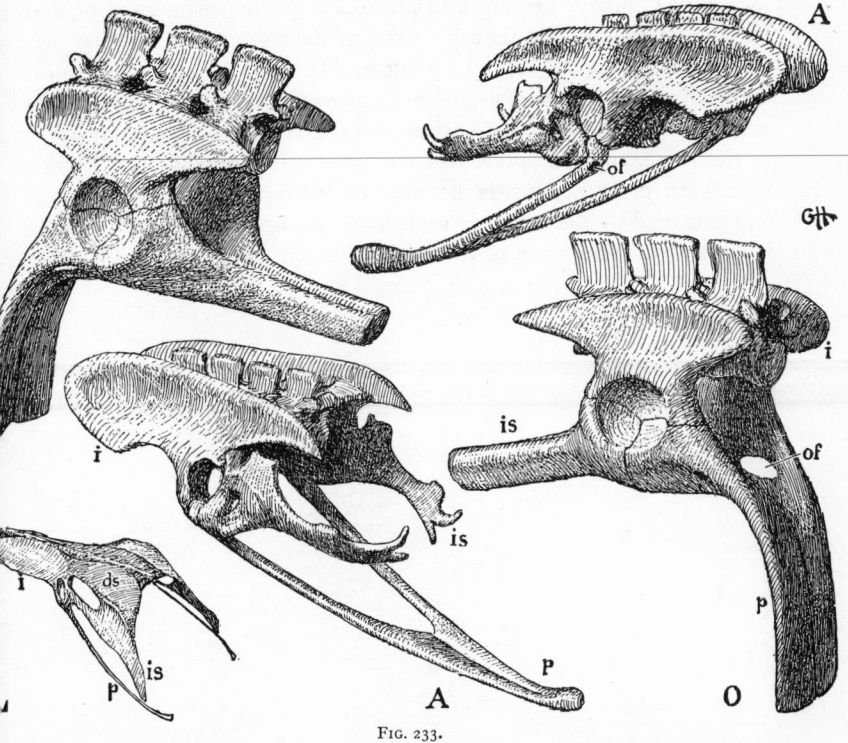

FIG. 233.

Pelvic girdle and sacrum of: A, *Archaeopteryx*, restored; O, *Ornithosuchus woodwardi*, restored (after E. T. Newton and R. Broom); L, young gull. *ds*, Dorsal expansion of ilium; *i*, ilium; *is*, ischium; *of*, obturator foramen; *p*, pubis. (From G. Heilmann, *Origin of Birds*, 1926.)

**Conclusion.**—Of the pelvic girdle in general it may be concluded that it appears to have been developed at the base of the pelvic limbs from paired plates in the body-wall, which tend to meet and fuse in the mid-ventral line in front of the cloacal aperture. In Pisces the girdle may become ossified as a single bone on each side ; but in Tetrapods the ventral plate develops a dorsal iliac process which articulates with the outer end of one or more sacral ribs. Whether the 'iliac' processes sometimes found in fish are the forerunners of the true ilia is doubtful.  Of the three typical ossifications in each half of the girdle of Tetrapoda, the pubis (pierced by an obturator foramen) and ischium combine in primitive forms to make a complete ventral plate (Amphibia and lowest Reptilia).  But in higher forms a fenestra appears in the plate more or less completely separating the pubis from the ischium.  In Mammalia and Theromorpha (and the majority of other Synapsidan Reptiles) this fenestra appears to be formed and to have developed in phylogeny by the enlargement of the obturator foramen.  On the other hand, in the Sauropsidan Reptiles the two openings are at first independent.  The pelvic girdle undergoes many changes in the various groups in divergent adaptation to different modes of progression ; the most remarkable of these changes are seen in the Archosaurian Reptiles and the Birds.  In Crocodilia and Pterosauria the pubis apparently becomes excluded from the acetabulum, and is carried by the ischium ; while in Ornithischia and Aves the pubis is rotated backwards to a position parallel to the ischium.

## CHAPTER V

## MORPHOLOGY OF HEAD REGION

## GENERAL MORPHOLOGY OF THE HEAD AND SKULL

THE structure of the trunk segments having been described (Chapter I.), that of the head may now be considered. The first question which arises is whether the head is segmented like the rest of the body or represents a primitively unsegmented anterior region. The anatomy of the Craniata would at first sight seem to suggest that the head region differs fundamentally from the trunk; that the skull is not segmented like the vertebral column; or that, if segmentation there exists, it is restricted to the gills and their arches. The muscles show no obvious sign of segmentation; the cranial nerves are some with and others without ganglia, and seem to be distributed in an irregular manner very different from the orderly disposition of the spinal nerves. Closer study of its structure and development, however, soon brings the conviction that the head region of the Craniate is truly segmented, that it is composed of a number of segments essentially similar to those of the trunk, and that segmentation originally extended to the anterior end of the body as it still does in *Amphioxus*. It would appear that owing to the Vertebrates being elongated bilaterally-symmetrical animals the anterior end became progressively differentiated in relation to the presence of the chief organs of sense, the brain, the mouth, and the respiratory gill-slits. Thus head and trunk regions became more and more specialised in divergent directions, and the line of demarcation between them more and more definite. So we find this process of cephalisation more pronounced in higher than in lower forms, in older than in younger stages of development.

In the interpretation of the head region the skeleton has always played the chief part. So early as 1792 Frank compared the skull to a single vertebra, and a few years later Goethe and Oken put forth a celebrated vertebral theory of the skull according to which it is composed of from three to six vertebrae conforming to the same plan as those of the trunk. Rathke and Reichert upheld the theory on embryological grounds, and Owen further elaborated it. The 'vertebral theory' was generally adopted until Huxley shattered its foundations in a famous Croonian lecture (1858). Having traced a fundamental plan common to the skull in all classes of the Craniata, both in development and in adult structure, he showed that the 'skull' is first membranous, then cartilaginous, and that the ossifications which appear later in the higher forms have even less to do with any primary segmentation comparable to that of the vertebral column than had its cartilaginous predecessor. The skull, in fact, arose long before bony vertebrae appeared. Huxley's argument, based on the researches of Rathke and Reichert, led him to the conclusion that the skull is not a modified portion of the bony vertebral column, and that although both started from the same primitive elements they immediately began to diverge.

After the overthrow of the 'vertebral theory' a new interpretation was gradually built up; it may be called the 'segmental theory' of the

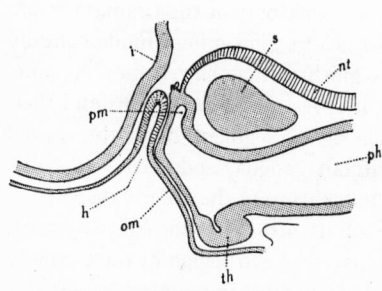

FIG. 234.

Diagram of median sagittal section of embryo *Torpedo* (from Dohrn's figures, 1904) showing region of mouth and hypophysis, *h. i*, Infundibular outgrowth of floor of brain; *nt*, notochord; *om*, oral membrane; *ph*, pharynx; *pm*, region of paired outgrowth of premandibular somites; *s*, median vascular sinus cephalicus; *th*, thyroid outgrowth.

head and skull. Huxley had insisted on the importance of the pituitary space as marking a point of comparison in the head of all Craniates. To this place reaches the anterior end of the notochord, above it arises the mesocephalic flexure of the brain, through it pass the internal carotids, and into it grows the hypophysis from below, Figs. 234-5. Behind it extends the basal plate of the cranium, and it is embraced by the divergent posterior ends of the trabeculae cranii. The basal plate behind, the trabeculae in front, and the auditory optic and olfactory capsules were considered to represent the fundamental elements of the skull which combined into a continuous cranium; to these were added the visceral arches completing the skeleton of the head (Huxley, 1858; Gaupp, 342-3).

The next important step is due to Gegenbaur (1872), who from a

study of the skeleton of the Elasmobranchs considered the post-pituitary
or vertebral region of the skull into which the notochord extends to be
composed of about nine segments, as evidenced by the cranial nerves and
visceral arches, comparable to spinal nerves and vertebrae farther back.
Specialisation and reduction of the muscles is supposed to have led to the
concrescence and solidification of this region of the skull from which the
prevertebral region, pierced only by the optic and olfactory nerves, may
have grown forwards.  Stöhr ('79, '81, '82) held that the hinder limit of
the skull extended farther and farther back in the ascending Vertebrate
series by the concrescence or assimilation of segments from behind : a con-

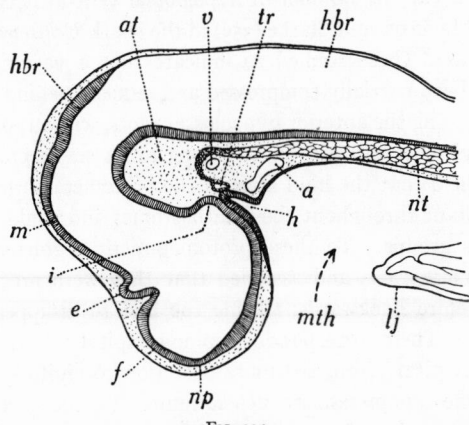

FIG. 235.

Median sagittal section of embryo *Scyllium canicula*, Stage J.  *at*, Acrochordal mesenchyme ; *e*,
epiphysis ; *f*, fore-brain ; *h*, hypophysis ; *hbr*, hind-brain ; *lj*, lower jaw ; *m*, mid-brain ; *mth*, mouth ; *np*,
recessus neuroporicus ; *tr*, transverse canal uniting premandibular somites.  Other letters as in Fig. 234.

clusion borne out in a general way by Gegenbaur (345-6), Rosenberg (377),
and many others since.  Sagemehl (378) drew a distinction between the
primary cranium, a ' protometameric ' region of fused segments, and the
' auximetameric ' region of true vertebral elements later added to it.
Froriep (339, 498), who analysed the occipital region in development and
discovered vestigial dorsal nerve-roots and ganglia corresponding to the
hypoglossal nerve compounded of ventral roots, distinguished between
that region of the skull without obvious segmentation in front of the
vagus group of nerves, which he called the prespinal region, and the
post-vagal or spinal region of assimilated vertebral elements.

    The next step in the theory of the head and skull is marked by
Fürbringer's monograph on the nerves of the occipital region (340).  Following Stöhr and Froriep, he maintained that the vagus marks a division
between two regions of different value.  Anterior to the vagus extends the

older ' Palaeocranium ', the only skull found in the Cyclostomes ; while behind the vagus lies a newer region to which segments have been added.[1] This ' Neocranium ' formed by the assimilation of originally free skeletal segments and including corresponding nerves (called spino-occipital by Fürbringer) is supposed to have been built in successive stages. First of all was added to the palaeocranium the protometameric neocranium of seven segments, represented in Elasmobranchs and Amphibia ; and later the auximetameric neocranium of three additional segments found in the Amniota, with even more segments added in certain of the higher Pisces such as *Acipenser*. Fürbringer's views were chiefly founded on the occurrence of a varying number of hypoglossal ventral nerve-roots (first discovered by Jackson and Clarke (356) in the shark *Echinorhinus*) underlying the vagus. These seemed to indicate that a varying number of segments had been partially compressed and reduced behind the auditory capsule. Believing the anterior hypoglossal roots, without obvious corresponding dorsal roots and ganglia, to belong to his seven protometameric segments, he held that the hind limit of the protometameric neocranium remained constant throughout the Gnathostomes and could be identified in the various groups. To these protometameric segments he applied the letters *t u v w x y z*, and assumed that they were progressively reduced from before backwards, *t* being the first to disappear and *z* the last to remain. Their corresponding spino-occipital nerves were distinguished as ' occipital ' from the more posterior ' occipito-spinal ' nerves included by the auximetameric neocranium. To these occipito-spinal nerves the letters *a*, *b*, and *c* were applied, the first free spinal nerve being in that case the 4th. Although Sewertzoff and others maintained that the chief distinction is between a ' spinal ' and a ' prespinal ' region, yet Fürbringer's conclusions have been far too generally accepted. The limit between occipital and occipito-spinal segments assumed by him to occur at a constant and recognisable point throughout the Gnathostomes as a matter of fact can only arbitrarily be determined ; nor is there any clear evidence of the postulated disappearance of a large number of protometameric segments. Only definite anatomical and embryological evidence can decide what serial number is to be assigned to the last occipital or the first free spinal nerve in any species (see footnote, p. 227).

**The Segmentation of the Head.**—Whereas in the higher Vertebrates the head shows no obvious signs of segmentation, as we pass to the lower fishes the distinction between the head and the trunk becomes less marked ;

---

[1] The question of the composition of the vagus nerve, which is of great importance in connexion with the views of Gegenbaur and Fürbringer on the phylogenetic development of the skull, is discussed on p. 767.

in Cyclostomes it is difficult to say where one begins and the other ends ; and finally in *Amphioxus* the body is clearly segmented from end to end. Moreover, a study of the development even of the higher forms makes the signs of segmentation increasingly plain. It has therefore been concluded that the head region is the result of a process of cephalisation of the anterior segments in an originally uniform series, leading to their modification and more or less complete fusion, so that finally almost all trace of the primitive segmentation disappears in the finished product. To unravel the constituent elements and determine their composition and number it is necessary to study their development and first origin. This applies not only to the skeleton, but also to the musculature, nervous elements, sense organs, branchial apparatus, and blood-vessels, all of which may supply corroborative information.

Now since segmentation in the Vertebrates is primarily expressed in the mesoblastic tissues, it is from the mesoblast that we must expect to derive the most convincing evidence. We have already seen (p. 6) that in the trunk of the Craniate the more dorsal part of the mesoblast forms segmental somites and sclerotomes from which are derived segmental myotomes (myomeres) and skeletal elements respectively, and to which correspond segmental nerves. A ventral motor root supplies each myotome and a dorsal root (chiefly sensory) passes behind it. In his epoch-making works on the development of the Elasmobranch Fishes (1874–78) Balfour showed that eight 'head-cavities' or hollow somites are formed whose walls give rise to the muscles of the head. The first is preoral and the seven others correspond to the mandibular, hyoid, and five branchial arches. His tabular statement is given below, and the best and most

TABLE OF THE CEPHALIC SEGMENTS FROM F. M. BALFOUR, 1877.

| Segments. | Nerves. | Visceral arches. | Head-cavities or cranial muscle-plates. |
|---|---|---|---|
| Preoral 1 | 3rd and 4th and ? 6th nerves (perhaps representing more than one segment) | ? | 1st head-cavity |
| Postoral 2 | 5th nerve | Mandibular | 2nd head-cavity |
| ,,     3 | 7th nerve | Hyoid | 3rd    ,, |
| ,,     4 | Glossopharyngeal nerve | 1st branchial arch | 4th    ,, |
| ,,     5 | 1st branch of vagus | 2nd    ,,    ,, | 5th    ,, |
| ,,     6 | 2nd    ,,    ,, | 3rd    ,,    ,, | 6th    ,, |
| ,,     7 | 3rd    ,,    ,, | 4th    ,,    ,, | 7th    ,, |
| ,,     8 | 4th    ,,    ,, | 5th    ,,    ,, | 8th    ,, |

recent work has fully confirmed his main conclusions (excepting position of 4th and 6th nerves). Of the many attempts since made by

Dohrn (333), Froriep (1905), and others to prove that there are more or fewer mesoblastic segments in this region of the head of Elasmobranchs, none has succeeded. Marshall, following Balfour, emphasised the comparison between the somites and lateral plate of the trunk and the dorsal head-cavities and more ventral mesoblast in the gill-arches of the head. The segmentation of the head-cavities he held to be independent of that of the gill-clefts ; he described the origin of the four eye-muscles supplied by the oculomotor nerve from the premandibular somite, and from the third somite the origin of the posterior rectus supplied by the abducens, which is the ventral root of the facial segment. Next came an important contribution from van Wijhe, in 1882, who described in detail the development and fate of the eight somites discovered by Balfour, and showed that a typical head segment contains on each side a somite (myotome and sclerotome) below which extends lateral-plate mesoblast with a cavity passing down a visceral arch. The dorsal and ventral nerve-roots related to each segment remain separate from each other, as they had been shown by Balfour to be in early stages in the trunk, and as they permanently remain in *Amphioxus* and *Petromyzon*. *The dorsal ganglionated root supplies the visceral muscles derived from the lateral plate, while the ventral root supplies those derived from the myotome.* The auditory sac marks off three pro-otic segments, of which the ophthalmicus profundus, trigeminal, and facial nerves are the dorsal roots ; while the oculomotor, trochlear, and abducens are the ventral roots. Further, van Wijhe distinguished more clearly between the true somites and the lateral plate, and definitely traced the development of the eye-muscles from the corresponding three myotomes, and the origin of the hypoglossal roots from the metaotic segments of which the glossopharyngeal and vagus represent the dorsal roots only. Van Wijhe, however, attributed nine segments to the head ; the tenth, with typical mixed spinal nerve, he called the first of the trunk (396).

Since the pioneer work of Balfour, Marshall, and van Wijhe, numerous investigators have studied the development of the head not only in Elasmobranchii (Dohrn, 333-4 ; Hoffmann, 354 ; Sewertzoff, 384 ; Neal, 368 ; Ziegler, 399 ; Goodrich, 349 ; de Beer, 320) but in other Gnathostomes, such as the Reptilia (Corning, 331 ; Filatoff, 337 ; Johnson, 358), Birds (Rex, 375 ; Matys, 367 ; Adelmann, 313), and Mammals (Fraser, 338). Although their results are not always in agreement, yet, leaving certain controversial points to be dealt with later, the general conclusions may be summarised as follows.

The head in the Gnathostomata is segmented up to a point just behind the hypophysis, where the notochord merges into the original roof of the

archenteron from the side walls of which the mesoblast develops. This
mesoblast becomes subdivided into dorsal segmented somites and ventral
unsegmented lateral plate. The
head somites are of the same
nature as and form a continuous
series with those of the trunk. In
so far as the wall of the head
somite develops into a myotome
with muscle persisting in the adult
it is found to be supplied by the
ventral motor root of its segment.
The corresponding dorsal ganglionated root passes behind each
somite.[1] The gill-slits pierce the
lateral plate intersegmentally.
Visceral arches are thus formed,

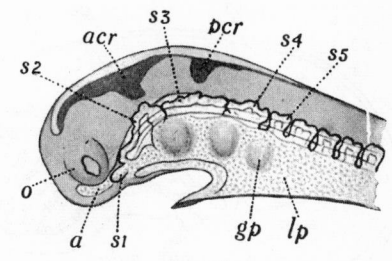

Fig. 236.

*Scyllium canicula*, left-side view of anterior region
of embryo, Stage F. *acr* and *pcr*, Anterior and posterior proliferations of neural crest ; *a*, anterior proliferation of mesoblast ; *gp*, hypoblastic gill-pouch
showing through ; *lp*, lateral plate mesoblast ; *o*,
optic cup ; *s* 1-5, first to fifth mesoblastic somites.

and down each passes the dorsal nerve-root supplying motor fibres to
the visceral muscles derived from the lateral plate (jaw and branchial

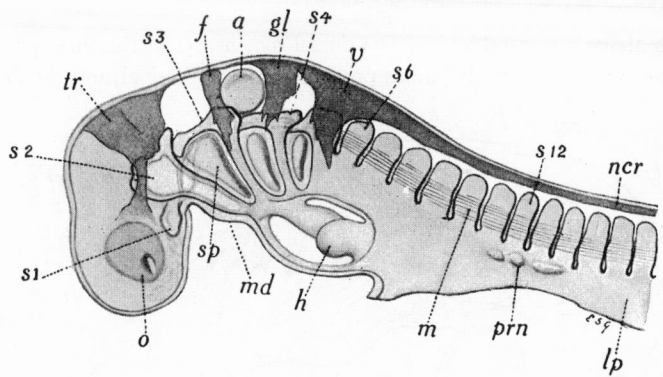

Fig. 237.

*Scyllium canicula*, embryo 5 mm. long, Stage G. Left-side view of anterior region. *a*, Auditory
placode ; *h*, heart in pericardial coelom ; *md*, mandibular arch ; *ncr*, neural crest ; *o*, optic cup ; *prn*,
pronephric rudiments ; *s* 1-12, somites ; *lp*, lateral plate of unsegmented mesoblast ; *sp*, first or spiracular gill-slit. Rudiments of profundus and trigeminal *tr*, facial *f*, glossopharyngeal *gl*, and vagus
ganglia *v*, derived from neural crest are shown darkly shaded.

arch musculature). The primitive uniform disposition of the somites
is disturbed by the development of the auditory sac and capsule
marking off three anterior pre-auditory or pro-otic somites from the

[1] The terminal, the olfactory, and the optic nerves are not counted as
segmental nerves ; and the auditory is considered to be derived from the facial
nerve (see Chapter XIV.).

post-auditory or metaotic somites. The first somite is the premandibular, the next the mandibular, and the more posterior somites lie

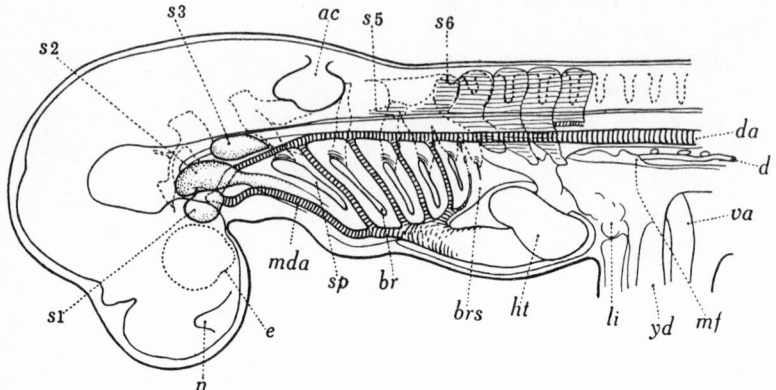

FIG. 238.

Diagrammatic left-side view of anterior region of embryo *Scyllium canicula*, Stage J. Compare Fig. 239.　Nerves represented in dotted lines.　*br*, First branchial slit ; *brs*, fifth branchial slit still closed ; *d*, Müllerian duct ; *da*, dorsal aorta ; *e*, eye ; *ht*, heart ; *li*, liver ; *mda*, mandibular aortic arch ; *mf*, Müllerian funnel ; *n*, nasal sac ; *s1*, premandibular somite ; *s2*, mandibular, and *s3*, hyoid somites ; *s5*, fifth somite with vestigial myomere ; *s6*, sixth somite with myomere passing behind vagus ; *sp*, spiracular slit ; *va*, vitelline artery ; *yd*, yolk duct.

each above a visceral arch. The dorsal-root nerves of the three pro-otic
segments are the ophthalmicus profundus, the trigeminal, and the facial ;

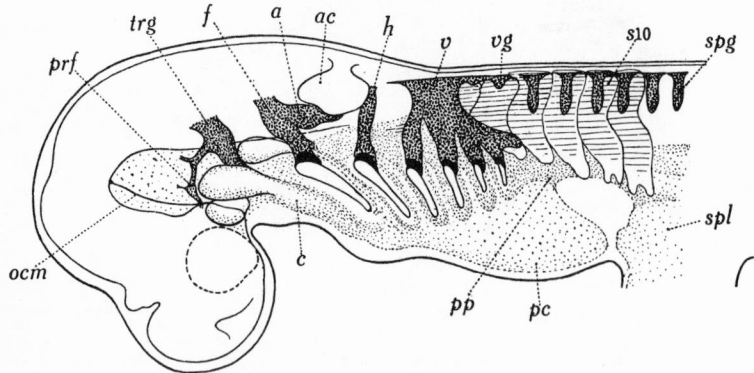

FIG. 239.

Diagram of anterior region of embryo *Scyllium canicula*, Stage J ; left-side view, showing developing cranial and spinal nerves darkly shaded, and epibranchial placodes black.　*a*, Auditory ; *f*, facial ; *h*, glossopharyngeal ; *prf*, profundus ; *spg*, spinal ; *trg*, trigeminal ; *v*, vagus ganglia ; *ac*, auditory sac ; *c*, coelomic canal in mandibular bar ; *ocm*, oculomotor nerve ; *pc*, pericardial coelom ; *pp*, position of pericardio-peritoneal canal passing above septum transversum ; *s10*, myotome of tenth segment ; *spl*, peritoneal or splanchnic coelom of trunk ; *vg*, vestigial ganglia of vagus region.

those of the metaotic segments are the glossopharyngeal and the compound vagus, one branch of which corresponds to each somite in this

region (see p. 767). The pro-otic somites are entirely subordinated to the use of the movable optic capsule enclosing the eye, and give rise to the extrinsic eye-muscles. The premandibular forms the rectus superior, rectus anterior and rectus inferior, and obliquus inferior, all supplied by the oculomotor nerve. The mandibular somite, supplied by the trochlear nerve, gives rise to the obliquus superior; while the third or hyoid somite forms the rectus posterior supplied by the abducens nerve (see p. 227). The first metaotic somite crushed by the growing auditory capsule never

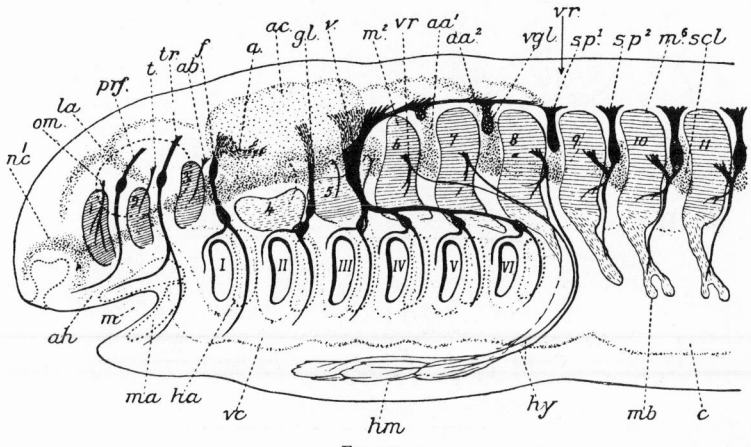

FIG. 240.

Diagram illustrating *segmentation of head* in a Selachian (E. S. Goodrich, *Q.J.M.S.*, 1918, modified). Skeletal visceral arches indicated by dotted outlines. *vr*, Posterior limit of head region; *I-VI*, gill-slits; 1-11, somites, pro-otic from 3 forwards, metaotic from 4 backwards; *a*, auditory nerve; *ab*, abducens n.; *ac*, auditory capsule; *ah*, anterior mesoblast (anterior ' head-cavity '); *c*, coelom in lateral plate mesoblast; *f*, facial n.; *gl*, glossopharyngeal n.; *ha*, hyoid arch; *hm*, hypoglossal muscles derived from somites 6, 7, 8; *hy*, hypoglossal nerve compounded from branches of ventral roots of those segments; *la*, orbital cartilage; *m*, mouth; *m²*, *m⁶*, second and sixth metaotic myomeres; *ma*, mandibular arch; *mb*, muscle-bud to pectoral fin; *nc*, nasal capsule; *aa¹*, *aa²*, first and second arches which with third make up occipital region; *om*, oculomotor n.; *prf*, profundus n.; *scl*, sclero-mere of segment 10; *sp¹*, vestigial dorsal root and ganglion of first spinal nerve; *sp²*, second spinal n. complete; *t*, trochlear n.; *tr*, trigeminal n.; *v*, complex root of vagus n.; *vgl*, vestigial dorsal root and ganglion of segment 7; *vc*, ventral coelom extending up each visceral bar; *vr*, ventral nerve-root of segment 6. Myomeres longitudinally striated, nerves black, scleromeres and cartilage dotted.

forms a myomere in the Gnathostomes, and soon breaks down into mesenchyme; it has no ventral root. The second metaotic somite (fifth of the series) forms a vestigial myomere of a few muscle fibres which may later degenerate together with the ventral root supplying them. The third and succeeding somites persist as more or less complete myomeres. As in the pro-otic so in the metaotic region the gill-slits interfere with the development of these myotomes which do not extend down the lateral body-wall, but contribute to the formation of the epibranchial and hypobranchial musculature, Fig. 241. The ventral roots of these metaotic segments contribute to the formation of the hypoglossal nerve

supplying the muscles just mentioned.   Although a sclerotome arises from
each somite, fusion between them takes place so early that no definite
trace of segmentation can be detected in the cranium, except in the
occipital region to which sclerotomes in varying number become assimilated and fused (see p. 226).   A skeletal visceral arch develops behind
the mouth and each gill-slit ; vascular arches correspond to them.   Such
in brief are the chief conclusions embodied in the ' Segmental theory of

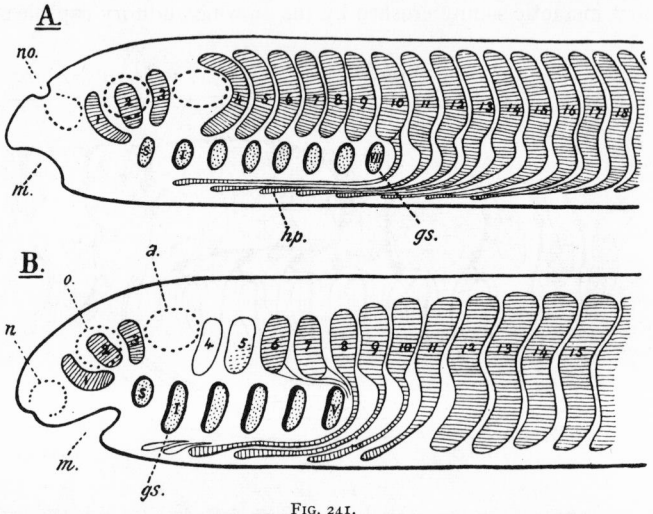

FIG. 241.

Diagrams of anterior region of *Cyclostome*, A, and of *Gnathostome*, B, showing position and development of somites 1-18 ; myomeres are shaded.   In A all somites form myomeres ; in B no myomere
appears in somite 4, and only a vestigial myomere in somite 5.   *n*, Nasal, *o*, optic, and *a*, auditory
capsules indicated by dotted lines ; *gs I-VII*, gill-slits ; *hp*, hypoglossal muscles derived from
myotomes ; *m*, mouth ; *na*, nasal opening ; *s*, spiracular slit.   (From *Vertebrata Craniata*, 1909,
modified.)

the Head '.   Certain special points must now be elaborated, and certain
difficult and controversial subjects discussed.

While the main conclusions mentioned above have been chiefly based
on work carried out on the Elasmobranchs, very favourable material for
the purpose, they have mostly been corroborated by observations on
other Gnathostomes, as already mentioned.   But it is important also to
notice that they have been strongly supported by the work of Koltzoff
on the development of *Petromyzon* (361).   He finds the same three pro-otic
somites giving rise to the eye-muscles as explained above, and the same
corresponding nerves.   But, possibly owing to the small size of the
auditory organ and the less development of the skull which has not yet
acquired an occipital region (p. 216), all the metaotic somites develop
myotomes which persist in the adult.   Thus in the Cyclostome every

somite from the premandibular backwards is represented in the adult, and there is an uninterrupted series of myotomes from the first metaotic or glossopharyngeal segment to the trunk. Such a condition represents an interesting transition between that of the Gnathostome, in which one or more myotomes are always suppressed behind the auditory sac, and that of the Cephalochorda, in which the myotomes pass evenly from end to end, Figs. 241, 738.

The first mesoblastic segment in *Amphioxus*, however, produces no myotomes, and it may now be asked whether the premandibular somites are really the first of the series in the Craniata. They arise near the extreme anterior end of the archenteron (Hatschek, 352 ; Koltzoff, 361 ; Dohrn, 334 ; Neal, 368-9), but J. B. Platt described in *Squalus* a pair of head-cavities developing still farther forward (373). These she believed to represent the most anterior somites, a view supported by Neal. Since, however, they soon disappear and form no permanent structure, are scarcely or not at all developed in other Elasmobranchs (Dohrn ; de Beer), have not been found at all in other Gnathostomes, and are absent in *Petromyzon*, it seems more probable that they are derivatives of the premandibular segment, as held by Dohrn and van Wijhe. Moreover, there is good reason to believe that the premandibular segment represents the first in *Amphioxus*.[1]

The next point concerns the number and disposition of the somites in the auditory region. While in the scheme outlined above (p. 218) somites, nerves, and gill-slits correspond and follow in regular order, according to van Wijhe the fourth somite, crushed below the auditory capsule, belongs to the facial nerve segment, which would be really double, formed by the combination of the third and fourth somites. In spite of the fact that it would disturb the orderly sequence of these parts of the head, van Wijhe's interpretation has been adopted by a number of authors (Neal, 368 ; Hoffmann, 354 ; Braus, 145 ; Sewertzoff, 384). Nevertheless, it cannot be considered as well founded. It involves the assumption that a gill-slit

---

[1] These first somites acquire an opening to the exterior, either into the oral hood cavity as in *Amphioxus* (on the left side only, Hatschek's pit) or into the hypophysis as in Gnathostomes, for instance Selachians (Ostroumoff ; Dohrn), Birds (Goodrich), and probably Reptiles (Salvi, 379). For this and other reasons they seem to correspond throughout the Vertebrata (Goodrich, 349). The first pair of somites is also remarkable for being joined together in early stages by a transverse connexion, which often becomes hollow (see Figs. 242-3) ; thus the right and left myocoeles may be for a time in communication. The connexion is not secondarily established, but is due to the retention of that portion of the extreme anterior wall of the archenteron from each side of which the first somites grow out. It is not retained in *Amphioxus*, nor apparently in *Petromyzon*.

arch and nerve have disappeared in the hyoid region, for which there is

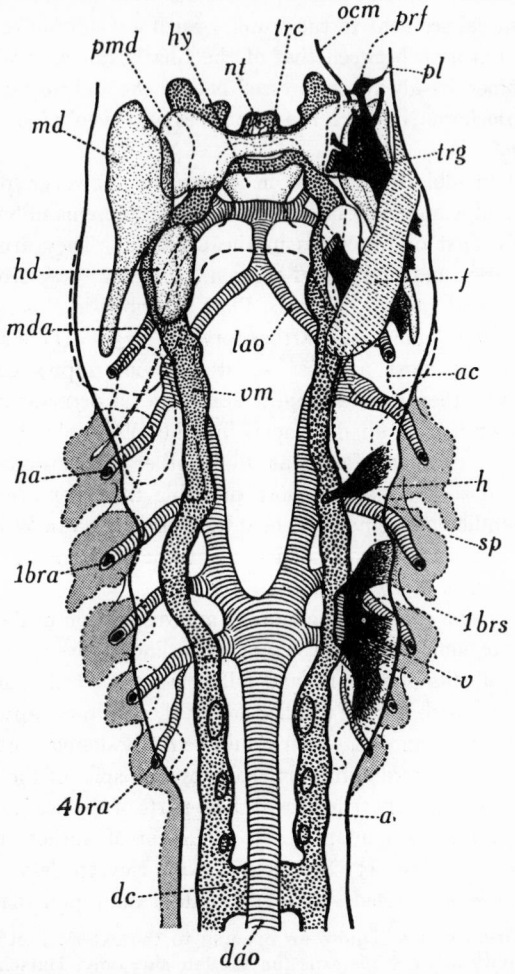

FIG. 242.

Diagrammatic reconstruction of thick frontal section of anterior region of embryo *Scyllium canicula*, Stage K. Arteries cross-lined, veins darkly stippled, nerves on right black. Dorsal outline drawn in continuous line, ventral outline in broken line. *a*, Anterior cardinal ; *ac*, broken line indicating ventral portion of auditory sac ; *bra*, branchial arterial arches ; *dao*, median dorsal aorta ; *dc*, ductus Cuvieri ; *f*, cut surface of acustico-facial ganglion and placode ; *h*, glossopharyngeal ; *ha*, hyoid aortic arch ; *hd*, third or hyoid somite ; *hy*, hypophysis ; *lao*, right lateral aorta ; *md*, second or mandibular somite ; *mda*, mandibular aortic arch ; *nt*, tip of notochord ; *ocm*, oculomotor ; *pl*, placode ; *pmd*, first or premandibular somite ; *prf*, profundus ganglion ; *sp*, spiracular slit ; *trc*, transverse premandibular canal ; *trg*, trigeminal ; *v*, vagus ; *vm*, vena capitis medialis.

no good evidence in any embryo or adult Craniate. A renewed and careful study of the development of several Selachians shows that the third somite belongs to the facial and the fourth to the glossopharyngeal segment, and that no segment has disappeared in this region (Ziegler, 399 ;

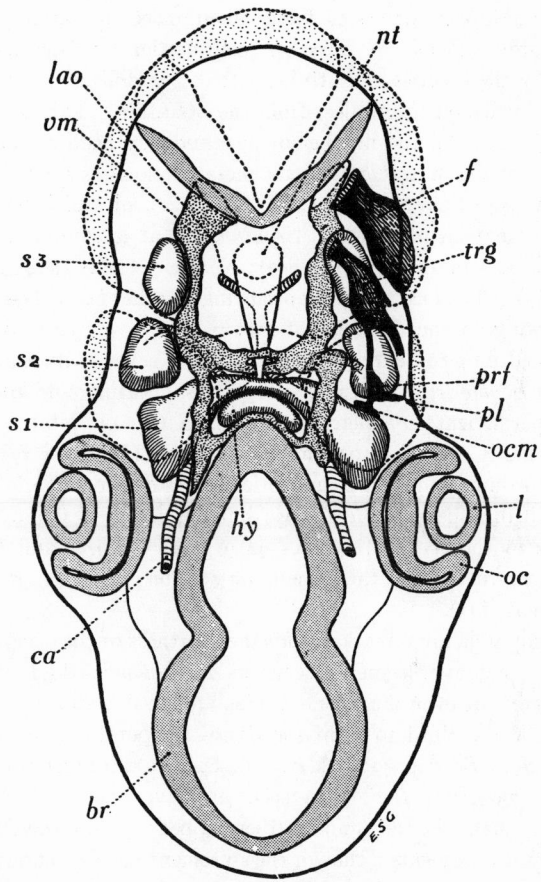

Fig. 243.

*Scyllium canicula*, embryo Stage K. Reconstructed thick transverse frontal section of head-cutting medulla above and fore-brain below. *br*, Fore-brain; *ca*, cerebral artery; *f*, facial nerve with placode ; *hy*, hypophysis ; *l*, lens ; *lao*, lateral aorta (internal carotid) ; *nt*, notochord ; *oc*, optic cup ; *ocm*, oculomotor nerve ; *pl*, placode attachment of profundus ganglion, *prf* ; *s1, s2, s3*, first, second, and third somites or head-cavities; note transverse connexion between first pair ; *trg*, trigeminal ganglion ; *vm*, vena capitis medialis. Upper anterior section outlined in black line, lower posterior in broken line.

Goodrich, 349 ; de Beer, 320). Moreover, these results agree with those of Koltzoff on *Petromyzon*, Figs. 236-40.

The important question as to the number of segments included in the occipital region of the head involves two separate but related problems:

the first concerns the number of segments suppressed by the auditory capsule overgrowing them from in front ; the second concerns the number of segments added by assimilation from behind.[1] It is clear that in the Gnathostomes both processes have taken place in varying degree in different groups ; but the work on this question has been so much influenced by the theories of Fürbringer that it is difficult to obtain trustworthy evidence on the subject from the literature. It is probable that even in the Selachii the number of post-auditory head segments varies slightly. *Squalus acanthias* has six metaotic somites (van Wijhe, 396 ; Hoffmann, 354; Sewertzoff, 383 ; de Beer, 320), of which the last four produce permanent myomeres. *Scyllium* has at least four, and at most five, metaotic somites (Goodrich, 349) ; *Spinax* possibly as many as seven (Braus, 145). The exact number occurring in other fish is less accurately known, owing to the difficulty of making out how many disappear in front. According to Schreiner there would be seven metaotic somites in *Amia* and *Lepidosteus*, the three anterior disappearing, and the last four forming permanent myomeres (381). In *Salmo* occipital somites are found, probably belonging to segments 4, 5, and 6 (Harrison, 179 ; Beccari, 319). According to Greil three metaotic somites develop muscle behind the first, which disappears in *Ceratodus* ; but Sewertzoff describes two more myomeres in the occipital region (592). In *Lepidosiren* and *Protopterus* there appear to be only three metaotic somites, of which the two last persist (Agar, 141).

The Amphibia are remarkable for the shortness of the occipital region. Only three metaotic segments occur in *Amblystoma* ; the first produces no myomere, but even the second is much reduced, its muscle combining with that of the third to form the dorsal temporal muscle (Platt, 374 ; Goodrich, 347 ; Froriep, 499). Marcus describes a third metaotic myomere in Apoda (752), but the Anura seem to have only two (Elliot, 336 ; van Seters, 382). In the Amniota there appear to be always more than three metaotic segments ; though the statement usually made that in the Amniote more segments have been added to the nine already present in the head of Selachians is quite misleading. Froriep (1883), one of the first to attempt the analysis of the occipital region, described four post-vagal myotomes in the chick, and apparently the same number in ruminants. Recently the question has been reinvestigated by Jager (357) in the chick, who finds four occipital myotomes behind the vagus, and one vestigial below it (probably belonging to metaotic somites 2-6 or segments 5-9 of the whole series). The last four have nerves ; but only the last two preserve

---

[1] The most posterior head segment is the last whose myomere is supplied by a ventral nerve-root passing through the skull wall.

their hypoglossal roots in the adult.   The researches of Hoffmann (354),
van Bemmelen (1889), Chiaruggi (329), and Beccari (319) show that the
three hypoglossal roots of adult Amniotes belong to myomeres derived
from metaotic segments 3-5 or possibly 4-6 (6-8, or 7-9 of the whole series).

   It may be concluded that in the Gnathostomes a varying number of
segments may enter into the composition of the head, and that consequently its hinder limit is inconstant in position.   The first metaotic
segment never produces permanent muscle or nerve.   The second and
sometimes even the third somite may also disappear.   In the Selachii from
four to seven metaotic segments share in the formation of the occipital
region ; there is a similar variation among the Teleostomes.   On the
other hand, the Dipnoi appear to possess only from three to possibly five
metaotic segments ; thus approaching the Amphibia in which there are
rarely if ever more than four.   The Amniota have a larger number, for in
them five, or possibly six, metaotic segments occur, of which only the
last two or three persist.   It is important to realise that the head region
can only arbitrarily be defined.   It may vary in extent according as we
take somites, scleromeres, nerves, or gill-slits and arches as our criterion,
since these structures do not necessarily involve the same number of
segments.   This point will be made clearer when we treat of the cranial
nerves (Chapter XIV.), and the occipital region of the skull itself (pp. 67,
242).[1]

## THE EYE-MUSCLES

   Throughout the Craniata the eye-muscles are extraordinarily constant in
number, disposition, and innervation.   There are six muscles, four musculi
recti and two musculi obliqui, adapted for moving the eye-ball in various
directions, Fig. 244.   The anterior or internal rectus, the superior rectus,
the ventral inferior rectus, and the inferior obliquus are supplied by the 3rd
nerve ; the posterior or external rectus by the 6th nerve.   The 4th nerve
supplies the superior obliquus.   While the mm. recti are generally attached
close together to the basal region of the wall of the orbit postero-ventrally
to the optic foramen, the oblique muscles usually spring from the planum
antorbitale.   Apart from the Cyclostomes, little change occurs except for
the addition of a retractor bulbi close to the optic stalk in Reptiles and
Mammals (Corning, 332 ; Matys, 367 ; Allis, 402), and two corresponding

---

[1] From the above account it will be gathered that no line can be drawn
between ' protometameric ' and ' auximetameric ' segments, between ' occipital '
and ' occipitospinal ' nerves ; that the series of somites and nerves is continuous behind the auditory sac ; and that, although the first few (not more
than three) may disappear more or less completely in development, none disappears in the middle of the series.   Fürbringer's attempt to identify nerve $z$
or nerve $a$ as fixed points is, therefore, not justified (see further, pp. 216, 242).

muscles in Birds (m. quadratus and m. pyramidalis) used for moving the nictitating membrane (Corning, 332 ; Slonaker, 1921).

The interesting developmental history of these muscles from the three pro-otic somites has already been described (p. 218). As shown by Balfour (317), Marshall (365-6), van Wijhe (396), Platt (373), Lamb (363a), Gast (341), Neal (369), and others, these somites acquire so-called head-cavities in the Selachii from whose walls the muscles develop ; the anterior, superior, and inferior recti, and the inferior obliquus, being derived from the first somite, the superior obliquus from the second somite, and the posterior rectus from the third. To the rudiment of the external rectus is added, in Selachians, some substance from the second somite (muscle E of Platt) ; but, while Dohrn and Neal maintain that this contributes to the adult muscle, others (Lamb, 363a ; Johnson, 358 ; de Beer, 320-22) hold that it does not do so. This conclusion is supported by the fact that the 6th nerve alone supplies the external rectus, and it does not appear to be a compound nerve.

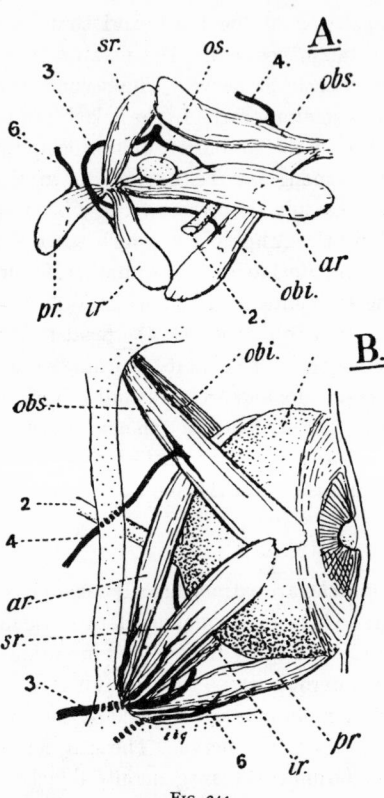

Fig. 244.

*Squalus acanthias.* A, Outer view of muscles and nerves of right orbit, from which the eye has been removed ; B, dorsal view of right eye. *ar*, Anterior, *ir*, inferior, *pr*, posterior, and *sr*, superior rectus muscle ; *obi*, inferior, and *obs*, superior oblique muscle ; *os*, cartilaginous optic stalk ; 2, optic, 3, oculomotor, 4, pathetic, and 6, abducens nerve. (After Goodrich, *Vert. Craniata*, 1909.)

A similar development, derivation of the eye-muscles, from the three pro-otic somites (in which ' head-cavities ' usually appear) has been described in Amphibia (Marcus, 752), in Reptilia (Corning, 331 ; Johnson, 358), in Aves (Rex, 375 ; Adelmann, 314), and in Mammalia (Fraser, 338). In spite of certain discrepancies in these accounts, it may be considered as firmly established that in all the Gnathostomes the history of the eye-muscles is like that given above for the Selachian. The retractor bulbi of Reptiles and Mammals and the quadratus and pyramidalis of Birds are derived from the third somite and hence are supplied by a branch of the abducens.

The disposition of the eye-muscles in the Petromyzontia differs somewhat from that found in the Gnathostomes (P. Fürbringer, 340a; Corning, 332; Koltzoff, 361; Ducker, 335; Tretjakoff, 1178; Cords, 330; Addens, 312). Koltzoff has described their development in *Petromyzon* from the three pro-otic somites. But, although the muscles conform in general to the Gnathostome plan, the rectus inferior seems to be innervated not only by the oculomotor but also by the abducens (Tretjakoff), or by the abducens alone in most species. According to Addens this is due neither to different development of muscles nor to change of peripheral innervation, but to a rootlet (r. inferior) of oculomotor fibres having shifted backwards and become associated with the abducens root. The two-branched apparent abducens of *Petromyzon* would, then, be a compound nerve; and the general disposition and innervation of the eye-muscles in Cyclostomes would differ in no essential from those of other Craniates. The eye is so degenerate in the Myxinoidea that no muscles are developed.

It is clear from the above account that already in the common ancestor of the Cyclostomes and Gnathostomes the paired eyes must have been well developed, the pro-otic somites specialised, and the chief muscles of the eye-ball differentiated.

# CHAPTER VI

## THE SKULL

## THE SKULL AND CHONDROCRANIUM

**General Composition.**—The skeleton of the head is made up in the Craniata of various elements of diverse origin which become more or less closely combined to form what we loosely call the 'skull' and visceral arches. Many of these constituent elements are more clearly distinguishable in lower than in higher forms, in earlier than in later stages of development. The membranous covering of the central nervous system, becoming strengthened by cartilages to protect the brain and afford attachment to muscles, gives rise to the brain-case or cranium proper. Cartilaginous capsules enclose the three chief paired organs of sense, and of these the olfactory in front and the auditory capsule behind become fused to the brain-case, while the optic capsule between them remains free, thus allowing the eye to move. Out of these parts is built up the primitive skull or chondrocranium (neurocranium of Gaupp), seen in adult Cyclostomes and Chondrichthyes, and the embryo of all the higher Craniates. There are also developed in the head cartilaginous visceral arches : a pair behind the mouth, and a pair behind each pair of gill-slits. They primarily served to bear the gills and to strengthen the wall of the pharynx, while allowing it to contract and expand. In Gnathostomes the first or mandibular arch bends over the corner of the mouth and forms two bars, the upper and lower primitive jaws bearing the lips and teeth and serving to seize the food. The upper bar is called the palato-pterygo-quadrate or palato-quadrate, and the lower the mandibular or Meckel's cartilage. The mandibular and the second or hyoid arch usually become intimately connected with the chondrocranium above, while the more posterior visceral arches, the true branchial arches in Pisces, remain free from the skull, and become much modified and reduced in air-breathing Vertebrates.

In the Osteichthyes and Tetrapoda these primitive cartilaginous elements of the skull may be more or less ossified, and further strengthened by various dermal bony plates added from the outside. A very complex structure is thus built up, the anatomy and development of which will be dealt with later. Our present purpose is to trace out the primary parts of which the skull is composed, to discover whether a fundamental plan can be made out common to all the Craniata, and to ascertain what evidence there may be of a segmental structure.

Setting aside the Cyclostomes in which the skull is in many respects highly specialised, we find in the more primitive Gnathostomes a continuous cartilaginous chondrocranium. For descriptive purposes it may be distinguished into a posterior occipital region connected with the vertebral column and surrounding the foramen magnum ; an otic region containing the auditory capsules ; an orbito-temporal region ; and an anterior ethmoid region with the nasal capsules separated by a median nasal septum. The brain cavity extends from this septum backwards through the three more posterior regions. Primitively the side walls are pierced for the passage of cranial nerves and blood-vessels, and the floor in the orbito-temporal region is pierced by the fenestra hypophyseos for the passage into the cranial cavity of the internal carotid arteries and the hypophysis (pp. 214, 240). The hypophysial ingrowth usually becomes completely nipped off, and lodges as the pituitary body in a special depression, known as the pituitary fossa, on the floor of the brain-case which grows below it. Up to this region extends the notochord in the floor of the embryonic cranium, Fig. 245 A. A posterior ' chordal ' region of the skull can therefore be distinguished from an anterior ' prechordal ' region (Kölliker). A host of observers have studied the structure and development of the chondrocranium, among whom may be mentioned Rathke; Huxley; W. K. Parker (556-74); Gegenbaur; Kölliker; Born, who introduced the method of solid reconstruction of sections ; Stöhr, one of the first to apply it ; van Wijhe, who invented the method of differential staining of whole specimens ; and Gaupp, who contributed much to our knowledge of the skull, and wrote a masterly account of the subject in 1905 (343).

**Elements of Chondrocranium of Gnathostome.**—Speaking generally, the cartilaginous cranium is better developed in lower than in higher forms, more complete in earlier than in later stages, when it becomes to a great extent replaced by endochondral or dermal bones, and even partially reduced to membrane. To discover the fundamental elements out of which this chondrocranium is built up we must appeal to embryology. Unfortunately, although the later stages are comparatively well known, its first origin has been little studied since the days of Parker. However, the work of later authors, more especially of Sewertzoff (384) and van Wijhe (397) on Selachii, Pehrson on *Amia* (372), Veit on *Lepidosteus* (393), Stöhr (388) on *Salmo*, Platt (374) and Stöhr (386-7) on Amphibia, Sonies on Birds (385), Noordenbos (370), Terry (390), Fawcett on Mammals (489-492), and de Beer (321, 324, 421-2), enables us to conclude that the following elements can be identified throughout the Gnathostomes : the base of the skull in the anterior or prechordal region appears as paired trabeculae cranii, while the side walls in the orbito-temporal region arise from paired orbital or sphenolateral cartilages ; paired parachordals in the chordal region give rise to the basal plate, to which are added in front an acrochordal cartilage and behind more or less distinctly segmental elements completing the occipital region. The nasal septum is formed by the union and upgrowth of the anterior ends of the trabeculae, of which the nasal capsules are also usually an extension, though separate cartilages often help to complete them. The auditory capsules generally appear first of

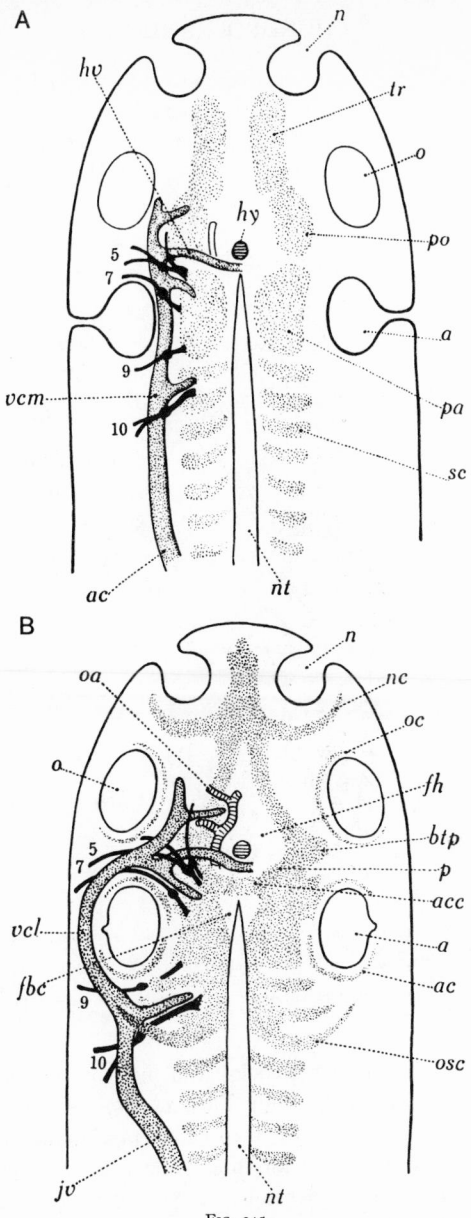

FIG. 245.

Diagrams illustrating development of *chondrocranium in Gnathostome* and relation of basal elements and sense capsules to certain cranial nerves and blood-vessels ; dorsally situated orbital cartilage omitted. A, Younger stage with procartilaginous elements separate ; B, older stage with cartilaginous elements partially fused. *a*, Auditory sac ; *ac*, auditory capsule ; *acc*, acrochordal cartilage ; *btp*, basitrabecular process ; *fbc*, basicranial fenestra ; *fh*, hypophysial foramen ; *hv*, hypophysial vein ; *hy*, hypophysis ; *jv*, jugular vein ; *n*, nasal sac ; *nc*, nasal capsule ; *nt*, notochord ; *o*, optic cup ; *oa*, optic artery from internal carotid ; *oc*, optic capsule ; *osc*, occipital arch = last occipital sclero- mere ; *p*, place of junction with base of pila antotica ; *pa*, parachordal ; *po*, polar cartilage ; *sc*, sclero mere ; *tr*, trabecula proper ; *vcl*, vena capitis lateralis ; *vcm*, vena capitis medialis.

all as one or two independent cartilaginous plates, which grow round the auditory sacs and soon fuse with the parachordals. The notochord is probably the only truly median element included in the skull. Its anterior end, projecting beyond the basal plate, always degenerates, and

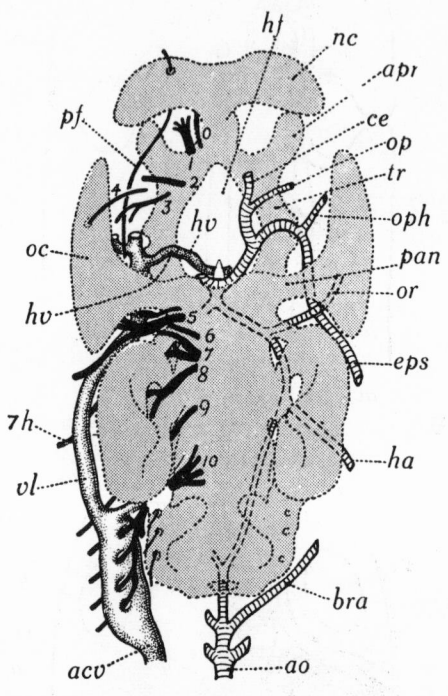

FIG. 246.

Diagram of skull of embryo Selachian; dorsal view. Cranial nerves on left-side black; arteries cross-lined; veins darkly shaded; cartilage grey. *acv*, Anterior cardinal; *ao*, dorsal aorta; *apr*, antorbital process; *bra*, first epibranchial; *ce*, cerebral; *eps*, efferent pseudobranchial; *ha*, efferent hyoid; *hf*, fenestra hypophyseos; *hv*, hypophysial; *nc*, nasal capsule; *oc*, orbital; *op*, optic; *oph*, ophthalmic; *or*, orbital; *pan*, pila antotica; *pf*, profundus; *vl*, vena capitis lateralis; 1-10, cranial nerves; *o*, nervus terminalis. Dotted lines indicate the course of arteries below cartilages.

even the portion which becomes enclosed in the plate usually disappears more or less completely in the adult, Figs. 245-6-7.

**Trabeculae.**—It is usual for the trabeculae cranii to develop independently as a pair of rods below the fore-brain, one on either side of the hypophysis (see, however, Mammalia, below, p. 262). They soon fuse in front and with the parachordals behind. A median hypophysial space (fenestra hypophyseos, or anterior basicranial fenestra) thus becomes enclosed between the trabeculae and the basal plate, letting through the hypophysis and internal carotids (p. 214). In Elasmobranchii, Dipnoi, Amphibia, and

Mammalia (p. 240) this fenestra is later closed by cartilage, leaving usually only two carotid foramina.[1]   In other Gnathostomes it generally remains open, being only closed ventrally by the dermal roofing bone of the palate, the parasphenoid,[2] Figs. 248, 250-54.

As Gaupp has shown, there are two types of skull : the platybasic and the tropybasic.   In the former the trabeculae remain wide apart in the orbito-temporal region, an intertrabecular plate unites them in front, and an extensive brain cavity is continued forward to the nasal capsules, Figs. 251, 259, 260.   This possibly more primitive type is found in the Chondrichthyes and lower Osteichthyes (*Acipenser, Amia, Polypterus*, and

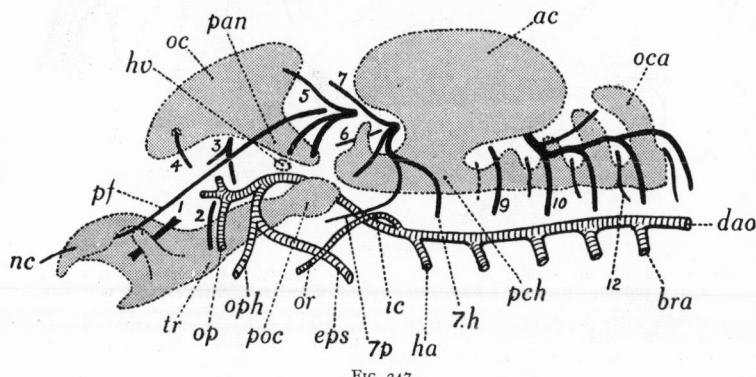

FIG. 247.

Diagram of skull of Selachian embryo before the fusion of main cartilaginous elements ; left-side view.   Cranial nerves black ;   arteries cross-lined ;   cartilage grey.   *ic*, Internal carotid ; *oca*, posterior scleromere of occipital arch ; *poc*, polar cartilage fused to trabecula but not yet to basal (parachordal) plate, *pch* ; *pan*, pila antotica not yet fused to basal plate ; facial foramen for *7p*, palatine, and *7.h*, hyomandibular branch of facial not yet closed by prefacial commissure ; *12*, posterior root of hypoglossal.   Compare with Fig. 246 for later development and lettering.

some Teleostei such as the Cypriniformes among living forms), Dipnoi, and Amphibia.   In the tropybasic type the trabeculae tend to fuse immediately in front of the hypophysis to form the base of a median interorbital septum continuous with the internasal septum farther forward, Figs. 254, 255.

This type occurs in a very pronounced form in the majority of Teleostei

[1] According to Gaupp (504), in the course of development in *Rana* the internal carotid shifts.   The carotid first becomes enclosed in a foramen, then this becomes confluent with the oculomotor foramen, cutting through the trabecula.   The internal carotid and ophthalmic arteries now lie outside the skull, and in the adult the cerebral artery enters the skull by the oculomotor foramen.   *Polypterus* and the Teleost *Amiurus* also show a similar anomalous condition (Allis, 803).

[2] A median hypophysial canal may persist through the parasphenoid region in certain fossil fish (*Pygopterus, Acanthodes* (Jaekel, 1903), and in *Polypterus*).

(p. 256), and also in the Birds and higher Reptiles (p. 392). The interorbital

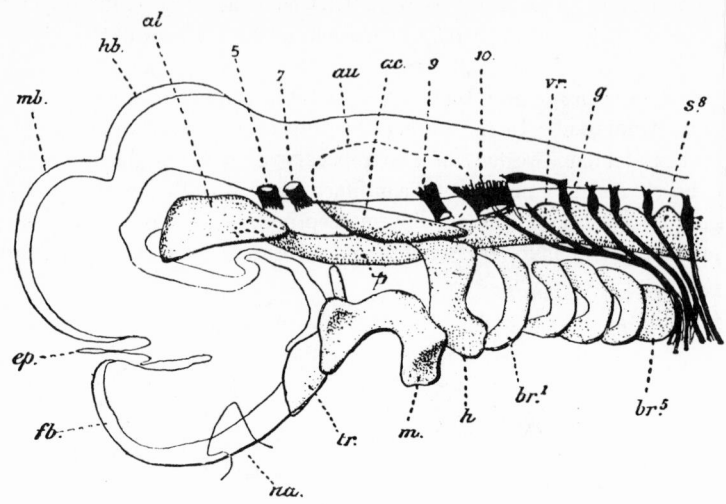

FIG. 248.

Reconstruction of the head of an embryo of *Squalus acanthias*, enlarged. (After Sewertzoff.) *ac*, Cartilage of auditory capsule ; *al*, orbital (alisphenoid) cartilage ; *au*, auditory capsule ; *br¹⁻⁵*, first to fifth branchial arches ; *ep*, epiphysis ; *fb*, fore-brain ; *g*, spinal ganglion ; *h*, hyoid arch ; *hb*, hind-brain ; *m*, mandibular arch ; *mb*, mid-brain ; *na*, nasal pit ; *p*, parachordal plate ; *s⁸*, eighth scleromere ; *tr*, trabecula ; *vr*, ventral spinal root ; 5, 7, 9, 10, roots of the trigeminal, facial, glossopharyngeal, and vagus nerves. (From Goodrich, *Vert. Craniata*, 1909.)

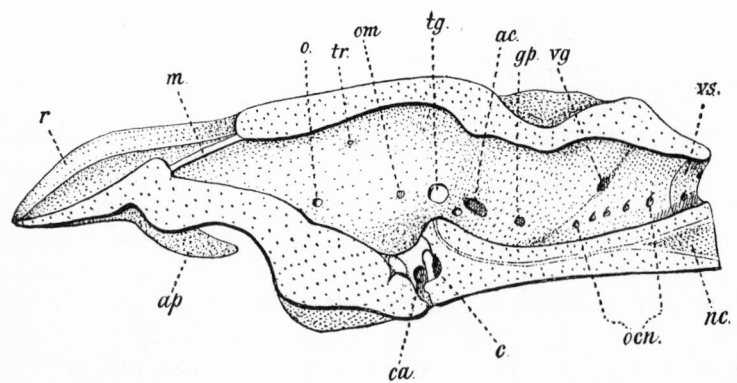

FIG. 249.

Inner view of the right half of the skull of *Hexanchus*. (After Gegenbaur.) *ac*, Foramen for auditory, *gp*, for glossopharyngeal, *o*, for optic, *ocn*, for spino-occipital, *om*, for oculomotor, *tg*, for trigeminal, *tr*, for trochlear, *vg*, for vagus, and *vs*, for occipito-spinal nerve ; *ap*, antorbital process ; *c*, carotid foramen ; *ca*, interorbital canal ; *m*, membrane over fontanelle ; *r*, rostrum. (From Goodrich, *Vert. Craniata*, 1909.)

septum is less extensive in Mammalia. It was probably slightly developed even in the most primitive Amphibia and Teleostomes (p. 390). In certain specialised reptiles, however, the interorbital septum is no longer formed ; and in the Ophidia the trabeculae remain separate throughout most of the orbito-temporal region (Parker, 563).

When they first develop the trabeculae may be bent downwards at a considerable angle to the basal plate, especially in the Selachii where the cephalic flexure is very pronounced, Fig. 248 (Sewertzoff, 384) ; but later they straighten out. The fusion of the trabecula to the parachordal may take place by means of an at first separate polar cartilage. First described

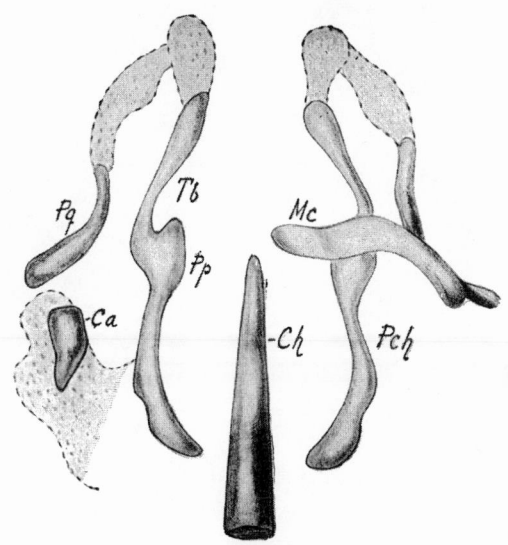

FIG. 250.

*Amia calva*, Stage 3 ; ventral view of skeleton of head. (From T. Pehrson, 1922.) *Ca*, Auditory capsule ; *Ch*, notochord ; *Mc*, Meckel's cartilage ; *Pch*, parachordal ; *Pp*, polar cartilage ; *Pq*, palatoquadrate ; *Tb*, trabecula.

by van Wijhe in Selachii (*Squalus*, 397), it has since been found in other forms (Veit in *Lepidosteus*, de Beer in *Scymnus*, Pehrson in *Amia*, Sonies in Birds) (' anterior parachordals ' of Stöhr). Whether this polar element has any important significance or merely is the hind end of the trabecula separately chondrified remains uncertain. It forms an infrapolar process in Crocodiles and Birds, which may come to surround the internal carotid artery in many Birds.

An outer antorbital process in front and a basitrabecular (' basipterygoid ' of authors) process farther back serve for the attachment of the palato-pterygo-quadrate bar in many of those Craniates in which this bar is complete (Chapter VII.).

Of the phylogenetic origin of the trabeculae little is known. That they are not visceral arches, as suggested by Huxley, there can be little doubt.[1] Their position in the cranial wall and relation to neighbouring parts points to the trabeculae belonging to the axial skeleton. They are said to be derived from the sclerotomes of the first or first and second

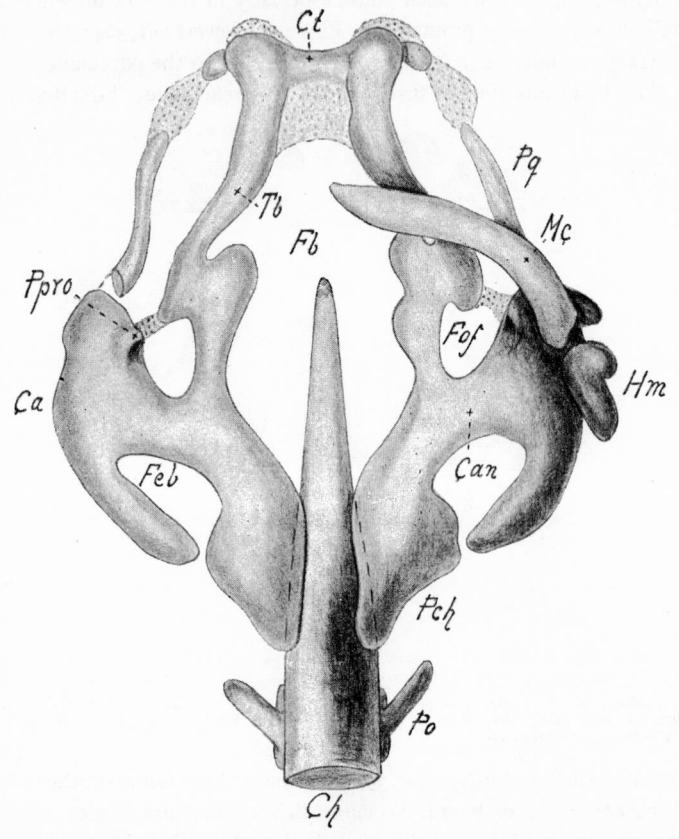

FIG. 251.

*Amia calva*, Stage 5; ventral view of skeleton of head. (From T. Pehrson, 1922.) *Can*, Commissura basicapsularis anterior; *Ct*, commissura trabecularis; *Fb*, fenestra basicranialis+fen. hypophyseos; *Feb*, fenestra basicapsularis; *Fof*, facial foramen; *Hm*, hyomandibula; *Po*, pila occipitalis; *Ppro*, pro-otic process. Other letters as in Figs. 250 and 258.

segments (Koltzoff, 361; Sewertzoff, 384), yet they show no sign of segmentation unless it be the subdivision already mentioned into anterior and polar regions. They can scarcely be compared to a pair of segmental neural

[1] Allis has revived Huxley's view, believing the trabeculae to represent premandibular arches which have swung upwards to fuse with the membranous brain-case, and the polar cartilages to be the dorsal elements of the mandibular arches (1923 and 1925).

arches farther back, since they project forwards beyond the truly segmented region of the head.  On the whole the trabeculae are best considered as structures *sui generis* developed to support and protect the
fore-brain and nasal sacs.

**Basal Plate.**—The notochord, surrounded by its sheaths, extends
primitively throughout the post-hypophysial basal plate region, beyond
which it projects in a hook-like curve bending down below the flexed
brain (p. 214) and just behind the hypophysis, Figs. 235, 245, 249.  The
tip of the notochord degenerates early, and the remainder of the free
portion piercing the thick 'acrochordal' connective tissue filling the
space formed by the cerebral flexure
disappears later.  Even the part embedded in the basal plate usually
degenerates in still later stages ; but
it may persist as a shrunken vestige
in Elasmobranchs, or more completely
in Dipnoi and certain lower Teleostomes (Acipenseridae).

Parachordal cartilages, essentially
paired (see, however, below), give rise
to the greater part of the basal plate,
Figs. 250, 252, 255.  They soon join
across, either below, or above, or enclosing the notochord; but often
leaving a membrane between their
diverging front ends.  The true relations of the skull elements and the
median fenestrae in the pituitary
region have been considerably mis-

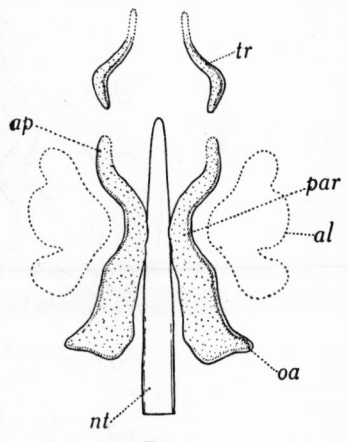

FIG. 252.

*Salmo fario*, embryo 9·5 mm. long.  Skeleton
of head from preparation by G. R. de Beer.  *al*,
Auditory labyrinth ;  *ap*, 'anterior parachordal'
=polar cartilage (?) ;  *nt*, notochord ;  *oa*, occipital arch ;  *par*, parachordal ;  *tr*, trabecula.

understood even by Gaupp (Allis, **406, 412, 413** ; de Beer, **421-2**).  As
shown in Fig. 256, the anterior end of the notochord is in typical forms
bent upwards following the cerebral flexure.  The floor of the cranium
is presumably likewise folded upwards, and here forms a pocket into
which pushes the pituitary body (combined hypophysis and infundibulum).  The pituitary vein runs across from left to right orbit in a
space (interorbital canal) below the notochord.  This space is either
intramural (excavated in the thickness of the cranial wall) or extra-
cranial, as held by Allis.

As already mentioned, dense mesenchymatous tissue lies in the transverse plica encephali ventralis ; it here surrounds the notochord, and
closes in front the membranous fenestra basicranialis posterior which

remains for a time in development between the divergent anterior ends
of the parachordals. The crista sellaris, a special cartilaginous formation in the acrochordal tissue, forms eventually the dorsum sellae
(Gaupp, 343; Sonies, 385; Noordenbos, 370; Voit, 394-5; Jager, 357;
de Beer, 421). The crista stretches across from the base of one pila antotica
to the other, and lies not at the level of the cranial floor formed by the

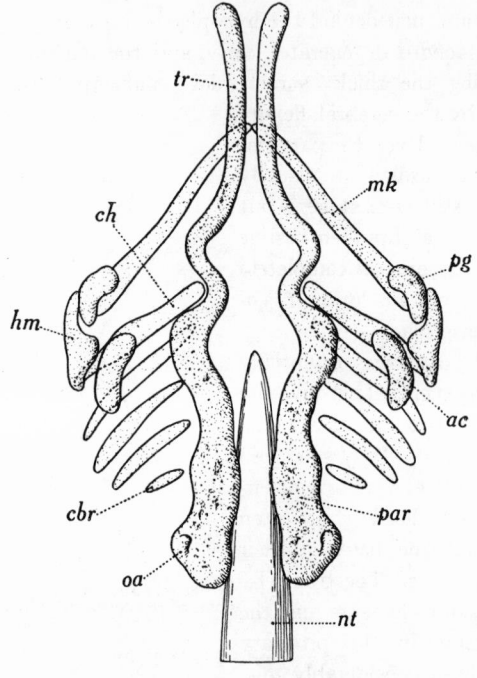

Fig. 253.

*Salmo fario*, embryo 10·5 mm. long. Skeleton of head from preparation by G. R. de Beer.
*ac*, Auditory capsule; *ch*, ceratohyal; *hm*, hyomandibula; *mk*, Meckel's cartilage; *pg*, palatoquadrate. Other letters as in Fig. 252.

trabeculae in front and the parachordals behind, but dorsal to these in
the plica, and overhanging the pituitary fossa from behind, Figs. 234-5,
256, 263, 274, etc. It is notched or pierced by the abducens nerve. In
later stages the parachordals join the acrochordal bridge and the fenestra
may be obliterated, Fig. 261.

When the posterior ends of the trabeculae (polar cartilages) come to
fuse somewhat ventrally with the anterior ends of the parachordals there
is enclosed a space, the primitive fenestra hypophyseos, through which
internal carotids and hypophysis reach the cranial cavity. The pituitary

vein runs across dorsally to this fenestra.  In later stages cartilage may
extend inwards from the trabeculae (or from special centres in Mammals,
p. 262) so as more or less completely to obliterate the fenestra, leaving,
however, carotid foramina.  Thus may be formed a cartilaginous floor
to the pituitary fossa or sella turcica, Fig. 256.  From the above
description it is clear that the fenestra hypophyseos and posterior
basicranial fenestra do not lie in the same plane, but that the latter to
some extent overlies the former from behind.

The basal plate is a compound structure, and the first origin of the
parachordals is somewhat complicated and variable.  In the Selachii van

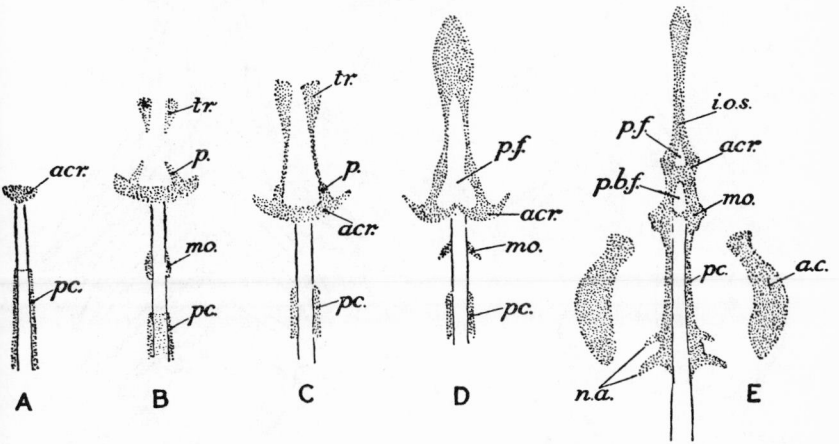

FIG. 254.

Diagrams illustrating the early development of the chondrocranium of birds.  (Based on figures
by Sonies, 1907.)  A, Chick, 11 mm.;  B, duck, 13 mm.;  C, duck, 15 mm.;  D, duck, 14 mm.;
E, chick, 12 mm.    a.c, Auditory capsule;  acr, acrochordal cartilage;  i.o.s, interorbital septum;
mo, mesotic cartilage;  n.a, neural arch;  p, polar cartilage;  p.f, pituitary foramen;  p.b.f, posterior
basicranial fontanelle;  pc, parachordal;  tr, trabecula.  (From J. G. Kerr, Embryology, 1919.)

Wijhe has shown that they appear as plates extending along each side of
and finally enclosing the notochord.  No certain signs of segmentation
are found in front ; but in the post-auditory region the myocommata
are attached to the plate, and here upgrowths, passing between and
joining above the roots of the glossopharyngeal and hypoglossal nerves,
may be considered as segmental elements forming the occipital arch or
pila occipitalis.  The so-called anterior parachordals and mesotic cartilages, described by Stöhr and others in Teleostomi and Amphibia as
arising separately but soon joining the more posterior true parachordals,
possibly represent the polar elements and really belong to the trabecular
region.  In Birds, however, a true anterior 'mesotic' parachordal is
present in early stages, Fig. 254 (Teleostei: Stöhr, 388 ; Swinnerton,

389; de Beer, 422. *Amia:* Pehrson, 372. Amphibia: Stöhr, 386-7; Platt, 374). In Birds (Parker, 556-7, 568, 572; Sonies, 385) and in Mammals (Noordenbos, 370; Fawcett, 489-92; Terry, 390) the basal plate appears first as a median bilobed cartilage and grows forwards to join the acrochordal cartilage and trabeculae.

The basal plate with its side wings forming occipital arches probably contains rudiments corresponding to the pleuro- and hypocentra

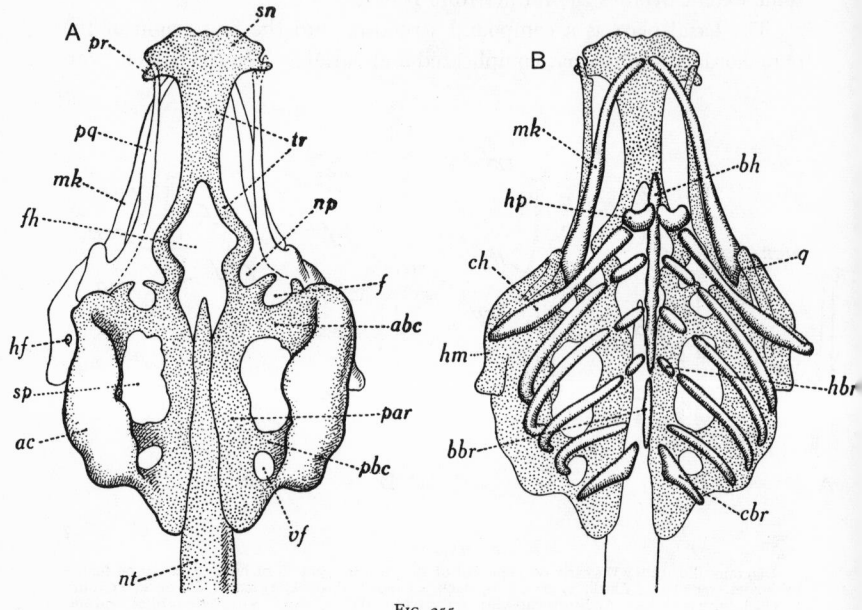

FIG. 255.

*Salmo fario*, embryo about 14 mm. long. A, Dorsal, and B, ventral view of cartilages of skull and visceral arches (from preparation by de Beer). *abc*, Anterior basicapsular commissure; *ac*, auditory capsule; *bbr*, basibranchial; *bh*, basihyal; *cbr*, ceratobranchial; *ch*, ceratohyal; *f*, facial foramen still open; *fh*, fenestra hypophyseos; *hbr*, hypobranchial; *hf*, foramen for hyomandibular nerve; *hm*, hyomandibular; *hp*, hypohyal; *mk*, mandibular; *np*, notch for palatine nerve; the lateral commissure is seen developing between it and *f*; *nt*, notochord; *par*, parachordal; *pbc*, posterior basicapsular commissure; *pq*, palatoquadrate; *pr*, antorbital process; *q*, quadrate; *sn*, solum nasi (ethmoid plate); *sp*, fissura basicapsularis; *tr*, trabecula; *vf*, foramen for vagus.

and neural arches seen in the vertebral column; segmental elements are usually very indistinct, though just recognisable in the plate of Birds (Froriep, 398; Sonies, 385) and Mammals (Terry, 390). Thus the basal plate is doubtless really formed of paired elements representing the scleromeres of several segments even in its front region.

**Side Walls.**—Considering now the side wall of the brain-case, we find, as already mentioned, that in the Selachii it shows in the occipital region signs of segmentation, being formed of a number of scleromeres

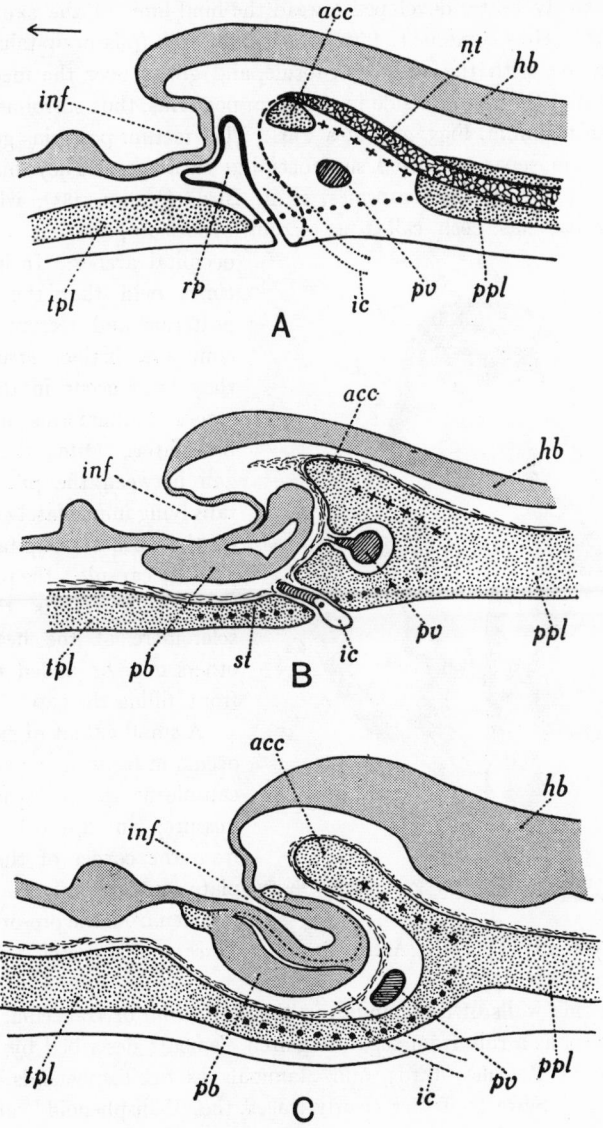

Fig. 256.

Diagrammatic longitudinal sections of *pituitary region* of head of: A, embryo Gnathostome; B, adult Selachian; C, late embryo Mammal. Showing relation to surrounding structures of *foramen hypophyseos* (marked by line of black dots) and *fenestra basicranialis posterior* (marked by line of crosses). *acc,* Acrochordal cartilage; *hb,* floor of hind-brain; *ic,* internal carotid; *inf,* infundibulum; *nt,* notochord; *pb,* pituitary body; *ppl,* parachordal basal plate; *pv,* pituitary vein; *rp,* hypophysis; *st,* floor of sella turcica; *tpl,* trabecular plate.

progressively better developed toward the hind limit of the skull, Figs.
247, 248. They combine to form an occipital arch (pila occipitalis) which
fuses above with the auditory capsule, and grows over the medulla to
join that of the opposite side in a tectum posterius, thus surrounding the
foramen magnum, Figs. 259, 263, 274. This tectum posterius generally
arises from separate paired supraoccipital cartilages. They may fuse
first with the auditory capsules, as in Birds (Sonies, 385), when the
roofing bar has been called a tectum synoticum, or first with the

occipital arches. It is sometimes held that the tectum
posterius and tectum synoticum are distinct structures;
they both occur in the early
stages of some forms, and combine. later. Often there is a
gap between the pila occipitalis lying immediately in front
of the future occipital joint
and the capsule; the pila then
at first represents the last
scleromere of the head, but
others may be added to it in
front, filling the gap.

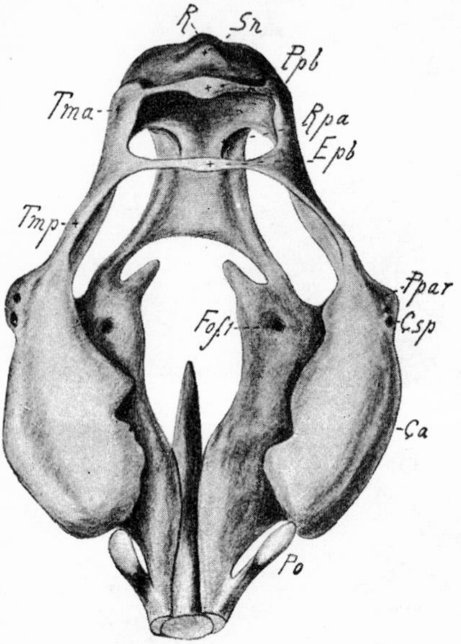

A small extent of side wall
occurs in front of the auditory
capsule as the prefacial commissure, an upward growth
from the corner of the basal
plate cutting off the facial
foramen from the pro-otic fora-

Fig. 257.

*Amia calva*, Stage 9, dorsal view of chondrocranium
(from T. Pehrson, 1922).

men, Figs. 263, 271. In Anura and *Acipenser* and Holostei it fails to
develop (see p. 259).

The side walls of the cranium in the prechordal or trabecular region
are formed as a rule from separate paired elements described by Parker
(556-70) in Reptiles, Birds, and Mammals as orbitosphenoids or alisphenoids. Sewertzoff first clearly traced these 'alisphenoid' cartilages
in Selachians (384), Figs. 246-7-8. They have since been called spheno-
laterals by Gaupp (343) and pleurosphenoids by van Wijhe (397),
according to whom they originate from two rudiments: a more anterior
dorsal and a more posterior ventral (lamina antotica). Each of these
orbital cartilages, as they may be called, soon produces a pila antotica,

which, joining the outer corner of the basal plate (or its acrochordal region) behind the hypophysial vein, separates an orbito-nasal fissure in front from a pro-otic fissure behind, Fig. 270.

Later the upper posterior edge of the orbital cartilage grows back as a commissura orbito-parietalis (taenia marginalis posterior) to join the capsule and close the incisura prootica above. Its upper anterior edge grows forward to meet the nasal capsule as a taenia marginalis anterior or commissura spheno-ethmoidalis, thus completing the margin

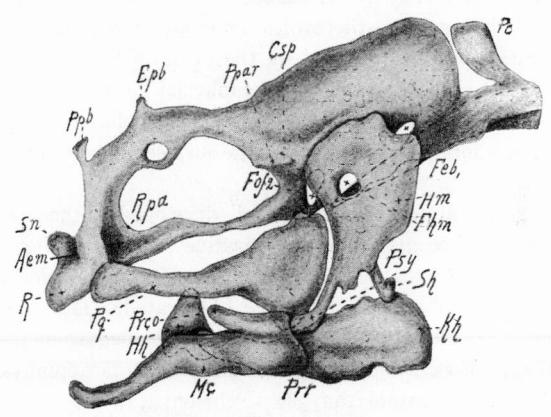

FIG. 258.

*Amia calva*, Stage 9, left lateral view of chondrocranium, mandibular and hyoid arches (from T. Pehrson, 1922). *Aem*, Anterior eye-muscle canal; *Csp*, spiracular canal; *Epb*, epiphyseal bar; *Feb*, foramen for glossopharyngeal; *Fhm*, foramen for hyomandibular branch of facial; *Fof₁*, palatine for.; *Fof₂*, facial for.; *Hh*, hypohyal; *Kh*, ceratohyal; *Po*, pila occipitalis; *Ppar*, parotic process; *Ppb*, paraphysial bar; *Prco*, coronoid process; *Prr*, retroarticular process; *Psy*, symplectic process; *R*, rostrum; *Rpa*, parethmoid ridge; *Sh*, stylohyal; *Sn*, nasal septum; *Tma, Tmp*, anterior and posterior taenia marginalis. (Lettering for Figs. 251, 257, and 258.)

of the orbit and delimiting an orbito-nasal foramen.[1] By the meeting of downgrowths from the orbital and upgrowths from the trabeculae the optic and other foramina are enclosed and the side wall is completed, Figs. 257-8, 263, 275.

Except in the Elasmobranchii and Amphibia, the side walls are usually very incomplete ; in the latter the orbital cartilages have been described as separate elements only in *Necturus* (Platt, 374), and the side walls appear to develop in continuity with the trabeculae. It is important to notice that the pila antotica fails to develop in Teleostomes, possibly on account of the formation of a posterior eye-muscle canal (p. 279), Fig. 258. It is absent, also, in Ditrematous Mammals, Fig. 282.

[1] This fissure is lengthened into an orbito-nasal canal in *Amia*, which is enlarged in Teleostei to form the anterior myodome for the oblique eye-muscles.

The orbital cartilages in the Reptiles and Birds spread above the interorbital septum to form the planum supraseptale (Gaupp, 343, 506). In the Mammalia they are represented by the well-known alae orbitales, which meet the trabecular bar here forming a short, narrow, interorbital septum, Fig. 275.

**Roof.**—The roof of the chondrocranium usually remains very incomplete except in the occipital region, where the foramen magnum becomes surrounded by cartilage, as explained above. Elsewhere the membranous roof is strengthened chiefly by dermal bones. But in the Elasmobranchii, where no such bones exist, the orbito-temporal as well as the occipital region becomes completely roofed by the overgrowth of cartilage from the sides, leaving only a large median epiphysial fontanelle in front and two small fenestrae behind, openings for the endolymphatic ducts, Fig. 249. Paired apertures for nerves supplying the surface of the head pierce the extensions over the orbits.

The chondrocranium is generally well developed in the lower Osteichthyes, and may become thick and massive with advancing age. In such forms as *Ceratodus, Acipenser, Amia,* and *Salmo,* the dorsal fontanelles may become almost if not quite obliterated. The roof is here formed from a transverse 'epiphysial bar' developed from the supraorbital cartilages, Figs. 257-8, which cuts off the anterior epiphysial from a posterior fontanelle (Swinnerton, 389; Pehrson, 372). By the extension of this bar and its junction with the tectum posterius the roof may be completed. In most of the higher Teleostei, however, the fontanelles remain large, or the bar may even disappear.

No median chondrocranial roof is usually found in the Amniota beyond the tectum synoticum and tectum posterius; but in the Anura, among Amphibia, cartilage extends over the anterior region of the braincavity as well, Figs. 450, 506.

**Sense Capsules.**—The ethmoid region of the chondrocranium of Gnathostomes is developed in relation to the snout, the nostrils, the mouth and upper jaw, and more especially the enclosure of the paired nasal sacs. As the latter sink inwards capsules envelop them, arising mostly on either side from the intertrabecular plate and median septum rising above it, and the posterior and lateral antorbital process of the trabecula.

The nomenclature of Gaupp, devised for the description of this region in Tetrapods, is now generally adopted. A median septum nasi separates the right from the left cavum nasi in which lie the olfactory sacs. The roof of the capsule is called the tectum, the side wall the paries, and the floor the solum nasi. The anterior wall is the cartilago cupularis from which small cartilagines alares may be separated off.   The posterior wall, separating the cavum nasi from the orbit, is the planum antorbitale or orbito-nasalis.   A fenestra narina, leading to the external nostril, becomes separated from a fenestra basalis serving for the internal nostril or choana by the lamina transversalis anterior of the solum nasi.   A foramen epiphaniale remains for the exit of the nervus lateralis nasi at the

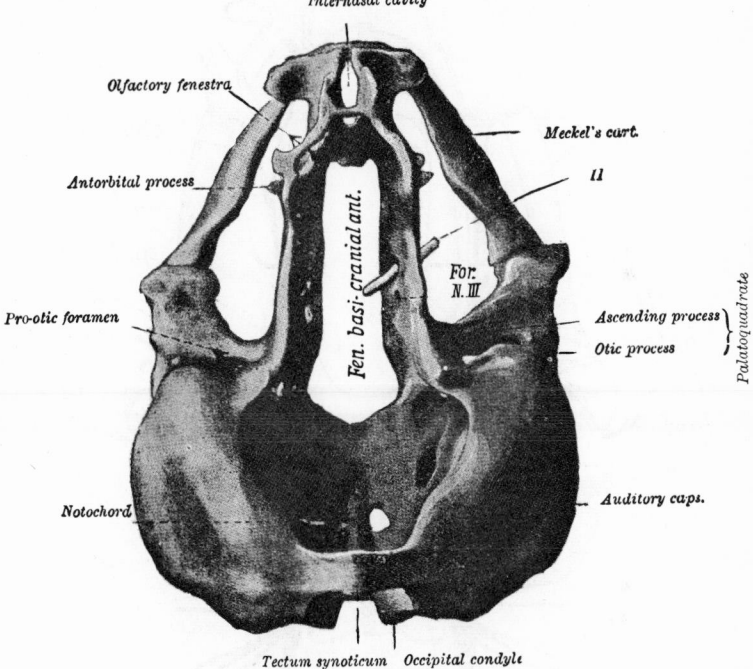

FIG. 259.

Neurocranium (platybasic type) and mandibular arch of larval newt (*Triton taeniatus*), 2 cm. in length, seen from above.  × 25.  (From a model by E. Gaupp.  Wiedersheim, *Comp. Anatomy.*) Fenestra basicranialis anterior = confluent f. basicr. post. and f. hypophyseos.

side, and a foramen apicale in front for the n. medialis nasi, two branches of the profundus nerve, Figs. 255, 257-8, 260, 274.

The nasal capsule in fishes develops in continuity with the front end of the trabeculae.   An antorbital process grows out from the trabecula, forms the posterior wall, or planum antorbitale, and joins above with the internasal septum to close off the olfactory foramen.   In the Teleostomes, where the original nasal opening becomes divided into two nostrils situated at the side of the head, the tectum is but little developed.

In the Tetrapoda, where the incurrent nostril serves not only to bring air to the nasal sac, but also to the lung, and where the nasal groove has closed over so as to form a canal leading to the buccal cavity by an

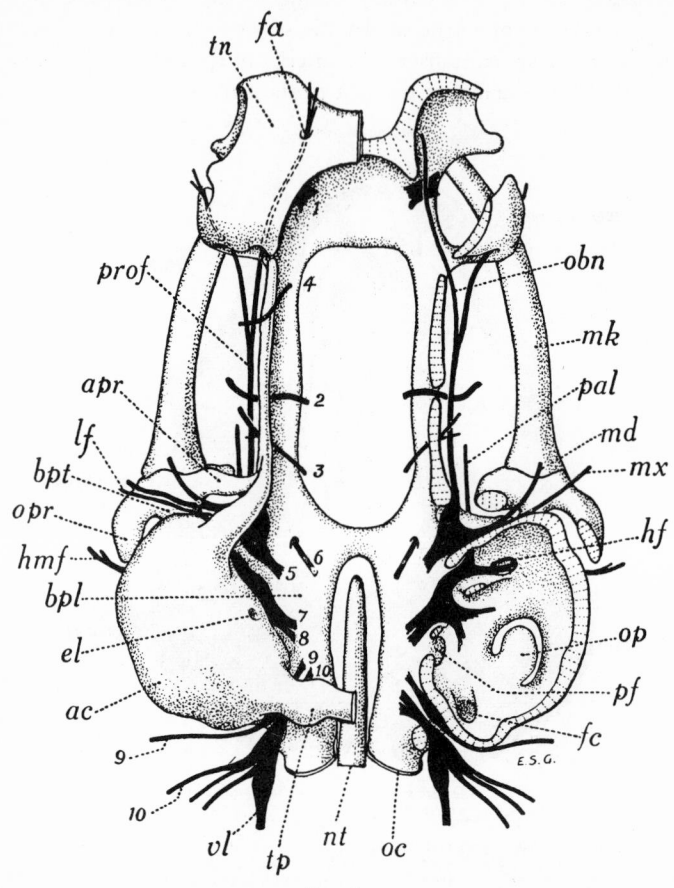

FIG. 260.

*Salamandra maculosa*, larva. Reconstruction of chondrocranium, etc.; dorsal view. *ac*, Auditory capsule ; *apr*, ascending process ; *bpl*, parachordal basal plate ; *bpt*, basal process ; *el*, foramen endolymphaticum ; *fa*, foramen apicale ; *fc*, fenestra cochleae ; *hf*, foramen faciale ; *hmf*, hyomandibular branch of facial nerve ; *lf*, buccal branch of facial (supraorbital branch removed to expose structures below) ; *md*, mandibular nerve ; *mk*, Meckel's cartilage ; *mx*, maxillary nerve ; *nt*, notochord in posterior basicranial fenestra, which is closed in front by acrochordal bridge delimiting posterior limit of hypophysial fenestra ; *obn*, orbito-nasal branch ; *oc*, occipital condyle ; *op*, operculum ; *opr*, otic process ; *pal*, palatine nerve ; *pf*, fenestra perilymphatica ; *prof*, profundus ; *tn*, tectum nasi ; *tp*, tectum posterius ; *vl*, lateralis branch of vagus ; 1-10, cranial nerves in black. On right dorsal parts of cartilages removed by horizontal cut.

internal nostril (a disposition already found in the Dipnoi), the nasal capsule becomes more elaborately developed.

The cavity of the sac tends to be subdivided into a more ventral air

passage and a more dorsal olfactory chamber, whose wall becomes folded
to offer more surface for the olfactory epithelium; moreover, the ventral
wall becomes strengthened by a transverse extension from the septum
forming a lamina transversalis anterior, separating a fenestra narina from
a fenestra choanalis or basalis for the internal nostril. As this lamina

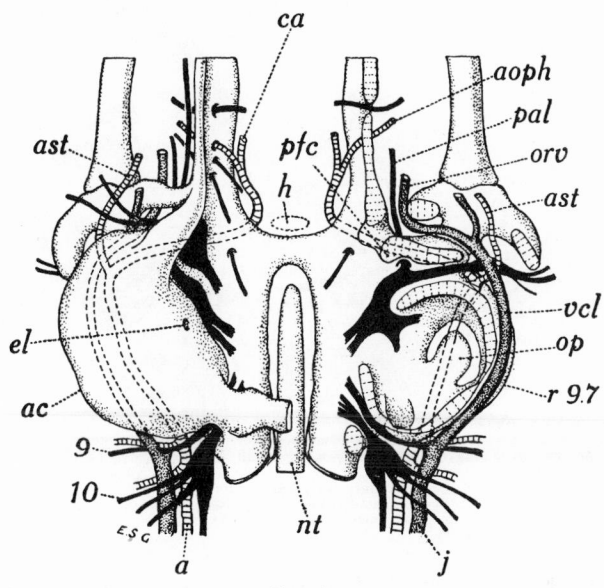

FIG. 261.

*Salamandra maculosa*, larva. Posterior region of reconstruction shown in Fig. 260, with arteries
(cross-lined) and veins (shaded). *a*, Lateral aorta; *aoph*, ophthalmic; *ast*, stapedial; *ca*, cerebral;
*h*, hypophysis; *j*, jugular; *orv*, orbital; *pfc*, prefacial commissure; *r* 97, ramus from glossopharyngeal to facial; *vcl*, vena capitis lateralis.

fuses with the outer paries the sac in this region is entirely surrounded
by cartilage.

The nasal capsule in Amphibia develops much as in the Teleostomes
from extensions of the front end of the trabecula and an antorbital
process, Figs. 259, 260. It becomes fully formed after metamorphosis,
though membranous gaps usually remain in the wall; and, owing to the
great development of large intermaxillary glands passing between the
capsules, the median septum becomes much reduced in the Urodela
(Parker, 558; Born, 325; Wiedersheim, 651; Gaupp, 504; Higgins, 353).

In the Amniota the capsules are usually more complicated, and tend
to grow back along the correspondingly elongated septum nasi to accommodate the enlarging nasal chamber (Reptiles: Parker, 564-5; Gaupp,
506; Rice, 376; Kunkel, 362. Aves: Sonies, 385. Mammalia: Noordenbos,

370). The anterior and posterior walls apparently originate as independent cartilages which spread and fuse with each other and the septum. Just behind the fenestra narina the nasal sac becomes surrounded, the lamina transversalis anterior being completed below ; but farther back the floor is usually very incomplete, and represented only medially by a longitudinal strip, the paraseptal cartilage, underlying Jacobson's organ and primitively

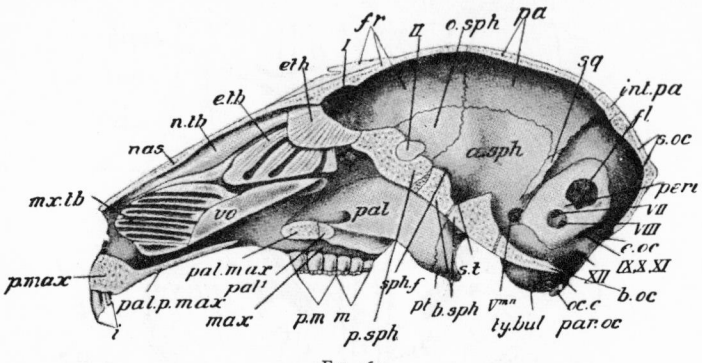

FIG. 262.

*Lepus cuniculus.* Skull in longitudinal vertical section. The cartilaginous nasal septum is removed. *a.sph*, Alisphenoid ; *e.oc*, exoccipital ; *e.tb*, ethmo-turbinal ; *eth*, ethmoid ; *fl*, fossa for flocculus of brain ; *i*, incisors ; *mx.tb*, maxillary turbinal ; *n.tb*, naso-turbinal ; *pal'*, palatine portion of the bony palate ; *peri*, periotic (petrous portion) ; *p.sph*, presphenoid ; *sph.f*, sphenoidal fissure ; *s.t*, sella turcica, or depression in which the pituitary body lies ; I, foramina for olfactory nerves ; II, optic foramen ; *Vmn*, foramen for mandibular division of trigeminal ; VII, for facial nerve ; VIII, for auditory nerve ; IX, X, XI, for glossopharyngeal, vagus, and spinal accessory ; XII, for hypoglossal. (From Parker's *Practical Zoology*.)

joining the lamina transversalis posterior or inturned edge of the planum antorbitale closing the fenestra basalis behind,[1] Figs. 263-4, 274-5.

Although the planum antorbitale appears to be homologous with the part derived from the antorbital process in lower forms, it chondrifies separately in the Amniotes.[2] The paraseptal and antorbital cartilages

[1] It is characteristic of the terrestrial Tetrapoda that an apparatus is developed to keep the surface of the eye moist. Epidermal glands secrete a watery fluid into the orbit which is carried away by a lacrymo-nasal duct from the anterior corner of the orbit to the nasal cavity. This duct develops as a longitudinal groove or thickening of the epidermis which sinks from the orbit to the external nostril, and becoming hollowed out comes to lead into the nasal cavity (Born, 325):

[2] Jacobson's organ is a specialised portion of the sensory region of the nasal sac which tends to become separated off from the main chamber in Tetrapods. Ill-defined and variable in living Amphibia, it is typically developed in Amniota as a sac blind posteriorly, but opening in front of or near the naso-palatine canal. It lies near the septum, supported by the paraseptal cartilage, and overlying the prevomer (Figs. 261, 264). It appears to be an organ of smell, in communication with the buccal cavity. (Broom, 1895-8; Seydel, 1885, 1891; Symington, 1891.) See page 367.

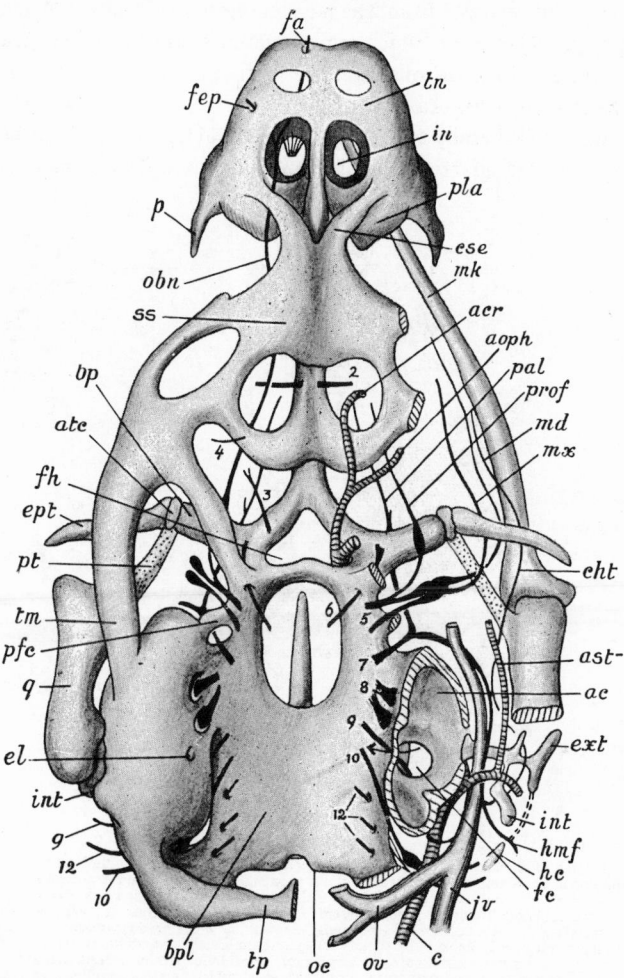

FIG. 263.

Diagram of cartilages, nerves, and blood-vessels of head of embryo *Lacerta*; dorsal view. Cartilages partly removed on right. Nerves black, arteries cross-lined, veins shaded. *ac*, Auditory capsule; *acr*, anterior cerebral; *aoph*, ophthalmic; *ast*, stapedial; *atc*, meniscus pterygoideus; *bp*, basitrabecular process; *bpl*, basal plate; *c*, internal carotid; *cht*, chorda tympani; *el*, endolymphatic foramen; *ept*, epipterygoid flattened out; *ext*, extrastapedial; *fa*, foramen apicale; *fc*, fenestra cochleae; *fep*, fenestra epiphaniale; *fh*, foramen hypophyseos; *hc*, top of hyoid cornu; *hmf*, hyoid branch of facial; *in*, fenestra for internal nostril; *int*, intercalary (dorsal process); *jv*, jugular vein; *md*, mandibular branch; *mk*, Meckel's cartilage on right side; *mx*, maxillary branch; *obn*, orbito-nasal branch of profundus; *oc*, occipital condyle; *ov*, occipito-vertebral; *p*, process (perhaps = part of pterygoquadrate); *pal*, palatine; *pfc*, prefacial commissure; *pla*, planum antorbitale; *prof*, profundus; *pt*, procartilage, vestigial part of palatoquadrate; *q*, quadrate; *ss*, septum supraseptale; *tm*, taenia marginalis posterior; *tn*, tectum nasi; *tp*, tectum posterius or synoticum. An arrow passes through foramen perilymphaticum internum (recessus scalae tympani). 2-12, cranial nerves.

run close to, but separate from, the median septum ventrally. According to Gaupp (343) the fusion which may sometimes take place between this posterior region of the capsules and the septum is secondary (Mammalia, and perhaps some other Amniota).

The Amniota generally tend to develop folds of the olfactory epithelium extending into the olfactory chamber and supported by turbinals, cartil-

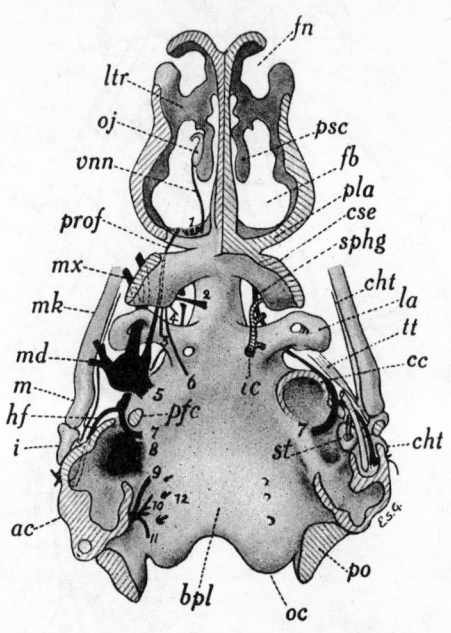

FIG. 264.

Reconstruction of chondrocranium of embryo *Trichosurus vulpecula*, 17·5 mm. long ; dorsal view. On left side dorsal parts removed by horizontal cut ; on right side cut at more ventral level (except root of facial nerve). *ac*, Auditory capsule ; *bpl*, basal plate ; *cc*, cochlear region ; *cht*, chorda tympani ; *cse*, commissura spheno-ethmoidalis ; *fb*, fenestra basalis ; *fn*, fenestra nasalis ; *hf*, hyomandibular branch of facial ; *i*, incus ; *la*, lamina ascendens ; *ltr*, lamina transversalis anterior ; *m*, malleus ; *md*, mandibular branch ; *mk*, Meckel's cartilage ; *mx*, maxillary branch ; *oc*, occipital condyle ; *oj*, organ of Jacobson ; *pfc*, prefacial commissure ; *pla*, planum antorbitale (lamina infracribrosa) ; *po*, pila occipitalis ; *prof*, profundus ; *psc*, paraseptal cartilage ; *sphg*, sphenopalatine ganglion ; *st*, stapes ; *tt*, m. tensor tympani ; *vnn*, vomero-nasal nerve. Nerves black and numbered.

aginous extensions from the wall of the capsule. Reptiles have only one main turbinal fold supported by the inturned edge of the paries nasi ; while in Birds there is developed in addition another upper turbinal above it. In the Mammals, and especially in the Ditremata possessed of a well-developed sense of smell, these folds acquire much greater importance. Besides the lower maxillo-turbinal corresponding to the reptilian, there are naso-turbinals in front and ethmo-turbinals projecting forwards from the more posterior and median wall, Fig. 262.

The general history of the nasal capsule would seem to be as follows : Two lateral processes spread outwards from each trabecula ventrally : the cornu at its anterior extremity and the antorbital process farther back. The former is not much developed in Pisces ; but the latter encloses the olfactory foramen by growing round outside the olfactory nerve and fusing above with the septum nasi. The antorbital process expands vertically to form the planum antorbitale separating nasal from orbital cavity. In Tetrapods the cornu forms the anterior transverse lamina of the solum nasi, and fusing laterally with the outer edge of the tectum completes a zona annularis surrounding the nasal cavity. This anterior lamina also separates ventrally the external from the internal nasal openings. As the nasal cavity is enlarged in Amniotes the planum antorbitale tends to bulge more and more, and retreat backwards, the lengthening antorbital process extending alongside the septum as a paraseptal cartilage underlying Jacobson's organ. A narrow fissure remains between paraseptal and septal cartilages, which in Mammalia is bridged posteriorly by a broad fusion. The paraseptal cartilage may then be interrupted behind and even also in front of Jacobson's organ. In Mammalia, the ventral edge of the planum antorbitale forms the posterior transverse lamina now fused to the median septum, and the enlarged primitive olfactory foramen becomes subdivided into the many openings of the cribriform plate.

The auditory capsules of the Gnathostomata usually develop from independent cartilages which soon fuse with each other and with the parachordals and envelop the membranous labyrinth.

In the Selachii the ventral floor originates as a lamina basiotica chondrifying in continuity with the parachordal (Sewertzoff, 384; van Wijhe, 397; Goodrich, 349); but, according to van Wijhe, the rest of the capsule is derived from two independent cartilages—one antero-lateral appearing over the ampullae of the anterior and horizontal semi-circular canals, and the other, postero-lateral, over the ampulla of the posterior semicircular canal. These soon meet and complete the capsule, except for its inner wall which grows up chiefly from the parachordal, leaving foramina for the endolymphatic duct and the 8th nerve.

Stöhr and de Beer in *Salmo* (388, 422) and Pehrson in *Amia* (372) describe the origin of the auditory capsule from an independent ventro-lateral otic cartilage which becomes connected below with the parachordal, Figs. 250, 253. This primitive ventral connexion, the commissura basicapsularis anterior, corresponding to the lamina basiotica of the Selachian, appears very early, is present from the first in *Gasterosteus*, according to Swinnerton (389), and at least in the form of a procartilaginous commissure in other fish. The otic cartilage grows round the labyrinth; but the inner wall of the capsule remains membranous in Teleostomes. A long basicapsular or metotic fissure remains behind the commissure separating the capsule from the basal plate.

This fissure is usually more or less completely obliterated by fusion of the plate with the capsule in later stages, Fig. 255; but its fate differs in different forms. It is always closed above the vagus nerve by the junction of the pila occipitalis with the capsule. In Pisces the fissure is obliterated leaving a foramen for the 9th nerve and a jugular foramen for the 10th and posterior cerebral vein (see further, p. 261).

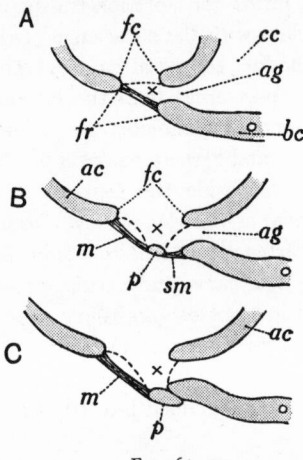

FIG. 265.

Diagrams showing relations of *fenestra cochleae* and *fenestra rotunda* in Reptilia, A, and Mammalia, B and C; transverse sections of vestibular region of pars cochlearis of left auditory capsule, *ac*, and parachordal basal plate, *bc*. ×, Recessus scalae tympani occupied by saccus perilymphaticus; *ag*, aquaeductus perilymphaticus leading to cranial cavity, *cc*; *fc*, fenestra cochleae; *fr*, fenestra rotunda closed by secondary tympanic membrane, *m*; *p*, processus intraperilymphaticus (from front edge of f. cochleae), cutting off a portion of membrane, *sm*, as in B; or fused to edge of basal plate as in C.

It is characteristic of the Tetrapoda that the independent first rudiments of the cartilaginous auditory capsule (single on each side in the Amphibia, anterior and posterior in the Amniota) spread round the labyrinth, leaving in addition to the usual apertures for the 8th nerves and the ductus endolymphaticus two constant and important fenestrae, Figs. 263, 265-6-7-8. One, on the outer side of the capsule, is the fenestra ovalis or vestibulae; it is closed by a membrane in which fits the columella auris or stapes (p. 451); the other is the more ventral and posterior fenestra cochleae (perilymphatica) in the region of the opisthotic bone, or of the exoccipital in modern Amphibia (Parker, 358-9; Gaupp, 504).

This primary fenestra is situated opposite the free edge of the basal plate, which is here separated from the capsule by what remains of the front end of the basicapsular fissure, the recessus scalae tympani. A space is thus delimited opening above into that region of the general cavum capsularis known as the cavum vestibulare, inwards and above the basal plate by the secondary foramen perilymphaticum (aquaeductus perilymphaticus) into the cavum cranii, and outwards below the basal plate by the fenestra rotunda. Into this space passes the saccus perilymphaticus, sending a ductus (aquaeductus cochleae) to open through the perilymphatic foramen into the subarachnoid spaces below the brain, and abutting through the fenestra rotunda against a thick closing membrane, the membrana tympani secundaria. Pressure exerted at the fenestra ovalis by the base of the columella or stapes is compensated by the bulging outwards of the secondary tympanic membrane usually situated close to the wall of the tympanic cavity. The edge of the basal plate separates the two secondary foramina in the Amphibia, Figs. 260-61, 266-7, and the outer fenestra rotunda may be suppressed in the more aquatic forms.

Except in the Monotremata (*Echidna*, Gaupp, 511), the primary fenestra cochleae becomes subdivided in the Mammalia into two by the growth of a bridge from the wall of the capsule (processus recessus), the upper and inner opening leading to the foramen perilymphaticum, the lower and outer to the fenestra rotunda, Fig. 265. The membrana tympanica secundaria now is attached to the rim only of the fenestra rotunda instead of partly to the edge of the basal plate as in the Reptile (Gaupp, 506, 511; Rice, 376; Versluys, 769; Fischer, 496; Brock, 326; de Beer, 422a).[1]

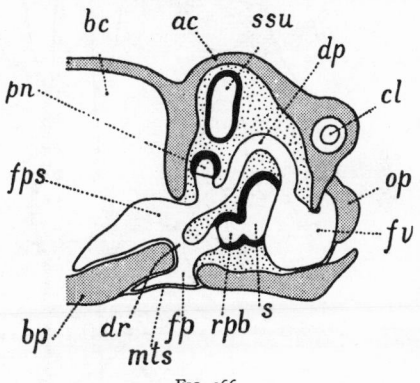

Fig. 266.

Diagrammatic transverse section of auditory capsule of larval *Rana* (partly from H. S. Harrison, 1902). *ac*, Auditory capsule; *bc*, brain-cavity; *bp*, basal plate; *cl*, lateral semicircular canal; *dp*, ductus perilymphaticus; *dr*, ductus reuniens; *fp*, fenestra rotunda; *fps*, ductus perilymphaticus; *fv*, spatium sacculare projecting through fenestra ovalis (vestibuli); *mts*, membrana tympanica secundaria; *op*, operculum in membrana tympanica; *pn*, pars neglecta (in adult a rod of cartilage lateral to it subdivides the fenestra cochleae between the two perilymphatic canals); *rpb*, pars basilaris; *s*, sacculus; *ssu*, sinus superior utriculi.

While the Amphibian auditory capsule appears to develop from a single independent otic cartilage (Stöhr, 386-387; Platt, 374), in the Amniota, at all events in Birds (Sonies, 385) and Mammals (Noordenbos, 506; Terry, 390), an anterior basiotic element

---

[1] This description does not quite agree with that generally adopted. Gaupp concluded that the membrana tympani secundaria is not homologous in Reptiles and Mammals. The name fenestra cochleae has here been retained for that opening in the floor of the pars cochlearis of the capsule which can be homologised throughout the Tetrapoda; it leads into the recessus scalae tympani. In Mammals where the cochlear region is greatly expanded this fenestra enlarges, the processus recessus grows across below it, and the recessus becomes continuous with the cavity of the pars cochlearis. The fenestra rotunda, often misnamed f. cochleae, is in all Tetrapods the lateral opening of the recessus closed by the same membrane. The recessus may become confluent with the jugular foramen, and the 9th nerve may pass through it in Reptiles.

forms the pars cochlearis, and a postero-lateral element contributes the pars canalicularis. The fissura basicapsularis is more or less obliterated, an anterior basicapsular commissure forming in front of the recessus scalae tympani, and often a posterior commissure behind.

**The Primitive Nerve Foramina.**—Primitively the olfactory nerves pass from the brain cavity into the nasal capsules through large olfactory

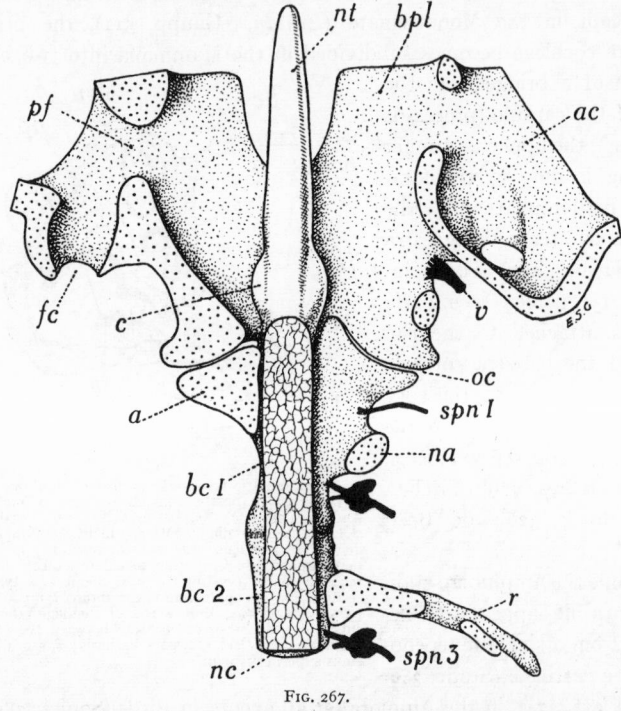

FIG. 267.

*Salamandra maculosa*, late larva. Partial reconstruction of posterior portion of skull, and first two vertebrae; dorsal parts removed by horizontal cut, at lower level on left. *a*, Articular region of atlas; *ac*, auditory capsule; *bc*, body of vertebra; *bpl*, parachordal basal plate; *c*, vestige of centrum (last occipital ?); *fc*, fenestra rotunda; *na*, neural arch; *nc*, cut end of notochord, and *nt*, its tip in basicranial fenestra; *oc*, occipital joint; *pf*, fenestra perilymphatica; *r*, rib; *spn*, spinal nerve; *v*, vagus.

foramina, one on either side of the median septum. Each foramen, bounded below by the free edge of the planum antorbitale, is enclosed by the growth upward and outside the nerve of the planum to join the tectum and septum above, Figs. 246, 263. This opening persists as the olfactory foramen in all Gnathostomes except the Mammalia (p. 258); but becomes modified in those Teleostomes which develop an extensive interorbital septum. In all forms with a tropibasic skull there is a tendency for the anterior part of the cranial cavity to be narrowed and

reduced from below upwards by the enlarging orbits and the formation of
the septum, and for the bulk of the brain to be pushed backwards. In
the higher Teleostei this process is carried to an extreme; the orbital
walls meeting in the middle line, the cranial cavity is obliterated in front
and the brain retreats far back. Since the nasal sacs remain forward and
the olfactory lobes retreat with the brain, the olfactory nerves become
much lengthened and come to pass on either side of the thin septum

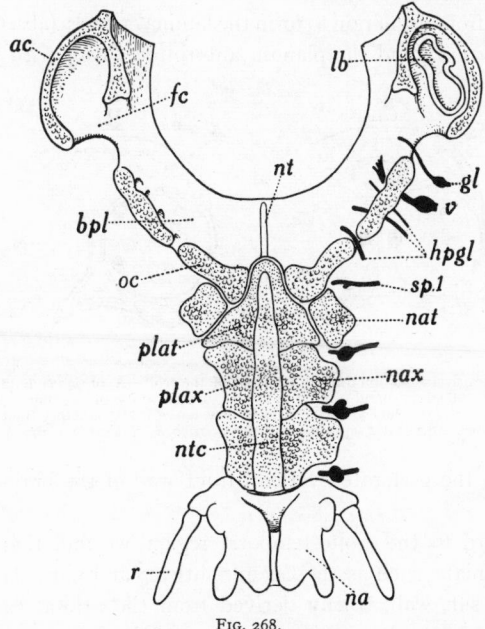

FIG. 268.

*Lacerta.* Diagrammatic reconstruction of portion of occipital region of skull and of first four
vertebrae of a late embryo; dorsal parts removed by horizontal cut, except from 4th vertebra. Nerves
in black on right.  *ac,* Portion of auditory capsule; *bpl,* basal plate; *fc,* fenestra cochleae;  *gl,*
glossopharyngeal; *hpgl,* hypoglossal; *lb,* portion of labyrinth; *na,* neural arch; *nat,* neural arch of
atlas, and *nax,* of axis; *nt,* notochord; *ntc,* notochordal 'cartilage'; *oc,* occipital arch; *plat,*
pleurocentrum of atlas; *plax,* pleurocentrum of axis; *r,* rib; *sp¹,* first spinal nerve.

through the anterior corner of the orbit to reach the nasal sacs, Fig.
269 B.   Each nerve then leaves the cranial cavity by a foramen olfactorium evehens, and, passing between the oblique muscles, pierces the
planum antorbitale through a foramen olfactorium advehens. Intermediate conditions in the formation of the septum and subdivision of the
olfactory foramen are found in the Cypriniformes, Fig. 287 (Sagemehl,
378; Gaupp, 343).[1]   Another and divergent form of specialisation

[1] The explanation given above is that of Sagemehl.  Gaupp regarded the
passage of the olfactory nerves through the orbit as due rather to the fenestra-

has long been known in the Gadiformes, where the septum is formed below the brain-cavity, which persists as a narrow channel running forward to the nasal sacs. Here the olfactory lobes remain close to the sacs, and it is the olfactory tracts of the brain which are drawn out into slender strands while the nerves are short, Fig. 269 A (Goodrich, 35).

In Birds, where the orbits are also very large, the olfactory nerves may likewise pass through the anterior corner of the orbits.

In the Mammalia the original olfactory foramen becomes subdivided by extensions from its margin to form the lamina cribrosa (absent, however, in *Ornithorhynchus*), and the planum antorbitale fusing with the median

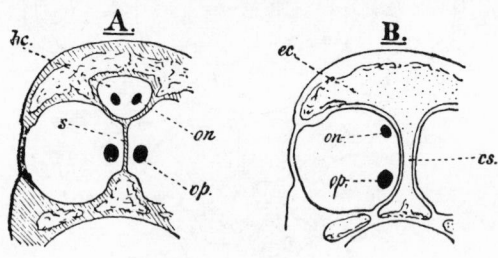

FIG. 269.

Diagrams of a transverse section through the front of the orbit—A, of *Gadus*, B, of *Perca*—to show the position of the olfactory nerves and tracts. *bc*, Brain-cavity of cranium; *cs*, cartilaginous interorbital septum; *ec*, ethmoid cartilage; *on*, olfactory nerve in B, olfactory tract in A; *op*, optic nerve; *s*, membranous interorbital septum. (From Goodrich, *Vert. Craniata*, 1909.)

septum forms the perforated vertical front wall of the brain-case in the Ditremata.

With regard to the orbito-temporal region, we find that whereas in the lower Craniata, such as the Chondrichthyes and most Amphibia, the cartilaginous side wall, chiefly derived from the orbital cartilage, Fig. 249, is so completely developed that the cranial nerves issue by separate foramina, there is a tendency in the higher groups for the wall to remain or become membranous. Increasingly large fenestrae are thus formed, and the cartilage may be reduced to a framework of slender bars (Lacertilia), though the individual foramina may be to a considerable extent replaced later by apertures in bones, with which, however, we are not concerned at present (cf. Figs. 249, 259, 274).

It will be understood that, since the side wall of the cranium occupies

tion of the lateral wall of the orbito-nasal canal at the side of the lengthening median septum. De Beer has recently suggested that the nasal septum lengthens backwards, carrying with it the olfactory foramen, while the planum antorbitale remains in front, leaving as it were the nerve exposed in the orbit (422).

the same general morphological position as the neural arches farther back, it bears the same topographical relation to the segmental cranial nerves as these do to the spinal nerves.   In other words, the ventral and dorsal roots issue separately, and the ganglia on the latter lie primitively outside the wall (this applies to the otic and occipital region as well).   In Pisces the ganglia of the trigeminal and facial nerves may retreat into a recess in the cranial wall through the foramina (p. 273).

It is a fundamental character of the Craniate skull that the auditory capsule lies morphologically between the facial and the glossopharyngeal nerves.   The foramen for the facial (main branch : palatine + hyomandibular) is closed off in the Gnathostomes, by a prefacial commissure extending from the basal plate to the capsule, Figs. 270-71. This commissure, separating the 7th from the 5th nerve, may be lost in certain Chondrichthyes (Scyllioidei and some others), and disappears in the Teleostomi.   But it is constant in Tetrapods with few exceptions (such as the adult frog).   Primitively it is situated in front of the base of the auditory capsule ; but

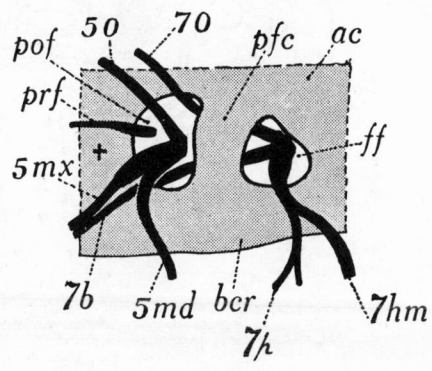

FIG. 270.

Diagram of portion of left orbito-temporal region of a Selachian skull showing relation of exit of cranial nerves to pila antotica, marked with a + ; prefacial commissure, *pfc*, auditory capsule, *ac*, and basis cranii, *bcr*.   *50*, Ophthalmic, *5mx*, maxillary, and *5md*, mandibular branches of trigeminal : *70*, ophthalmic, *7b*, buccal, *7p*, palatine, and *7hm*, hyomandibular branches of facial ; *prf*, profundus nerve ; *ff*, facial foramen ; *pof*, pro-otic foramen.

in the Amphibia becomes overgrown by the capsule, and in these the 7th nerve appears to pass through the cavity of the capsule, owing seemingly to the failure of its wall to chondrify in this region, Figs. 272-3 (see further, p. 278).   In the Reptiles to a slight extent the capsule may extend below it (Rice, 376) ; in the Mammals the prefacial commissure is so much undermined by the cochlear region of the capsule that the nerve seems to pass through a foramen in its upper wall (see further, p. 272).

It has already been explained (p. 244) how, owing to the formation of a pila antotica and connexions with the capsules, the orbital cartilage separates a primitive fenestra pseudoptica in front from a fenestra pro-otica behind.   Through the former issue the 2nd and 3rd nerves ; through the latter the profundus, trigeminal, abducens, and lateral line branches of the facial (when present in Pisces and Amphibia).   The 4th nerve is

usually enclosed in a special foramen ; but it may, as in Lacertilia, issue
through the anterior fenestra, or through the posterior fenestra as in

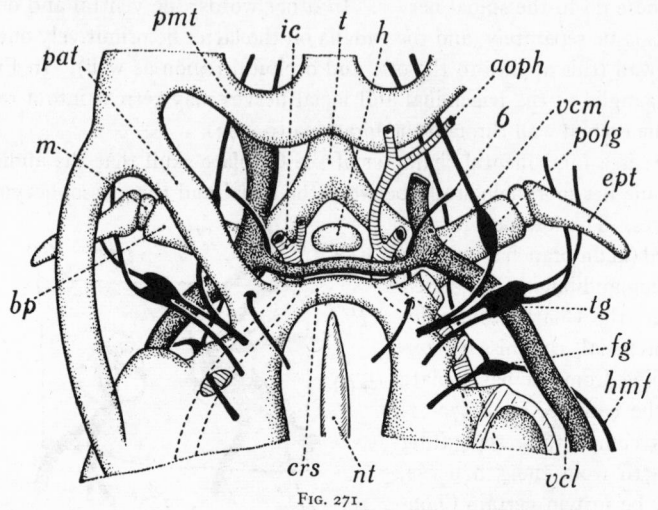

FIG. 271.

Enlarged view of orbito-temporal region of diagram, Fig. 263. *crs*, Crista sellaris (acrochordal) ;
*fg*, facial ganglion ; *h*, hypophysis ; *ic*, internal carotid ; *nt*, notochord in fenestra basicranialis
posterior ; *pat*, pila antotica ; *pmt*, pila metoptica : *pofg*, profundus ganglion ; *t*, fused trabeculae ; *tg*,
trigeminus ganglion ; *vcl*, vena capitis lateralis ; *vcm*, vena capitis medialis. Other letters as in Fig. 263.

**Mammalia.** In some Urodeles the 4th nerve comes to pierce the parietal
bone (Gaupp, 514). By the extension of the orbital cartilage to join the

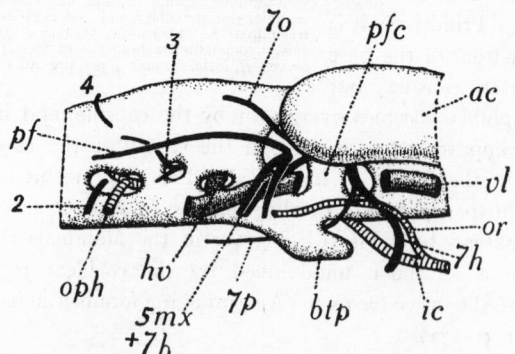

FIG. 272.

Diagram illustrating structure of orbito-temporal region in early stage of embryo Urodele ; left-
side view. Cranial nerves numbered : *5mx*, maxillary branch of trigeminal ; *7b*, buccal ; *7o*, ophthalmic branches of facial ; *pf*, profundus ; *vl*, vena capitis lateralis interrupted to show prefacial
commissure, *pfc* ; *oph*, ophthalmic artery ; *or*, orbital or stapedial artery ; *hv*, hypophysial vein.

neighbouring cartilages the wall may be completed and all the nerves
come to pass through separate foramina, as in the Elasmobranchii. But,

in the Teleostomi, the orbital wall is usually much less completely chondrified, the fenestrae remain, and even the pila antotica ceases to be formed (absent in Amioidei, Teleostei, see Figs. 283, 284). The orbito-nasal fissure remains as a small foramen, allowing the profundus nerve to pass out of the orbit on to the surface of the snout in Pisces.

In the Reptilia the orbital wall is usually much less complete, especially in the Lacertilia and Ophidia. The optic foramen is closed by a pila preoptica in front and a pila postoptica behind, cutting off the fenestra postoptica for the 3rd nerve. The trigeminal (with the profundus) may alone pass through the diminished fenestra prootica (*Crocodilus*, Shiino, 597), the 4th nerve then issuing through a small foramen above; and the 6th bores its way, so to speak, through the base of the pila antotica.[1]

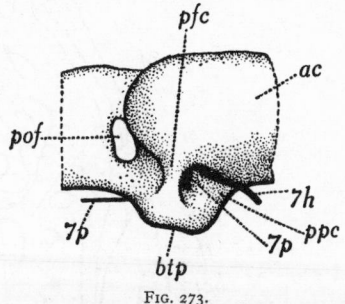

FIG. 273.

Diagram illustrating relations in orbito-temporal region of cartilages and facial nerve in late stage of embryo Urodele; left-side view. *ac*, Auditory capsule; *btp*, basitrabecular process; *pfc*, outer portion of prefacial commissure; *pof*, pro-otic foramen; *ppc*, postpalatine commissure; *7h*, hyomandibular; *7p*, palatine branches of facial.

The profundus nerve in the Tetrapods either passes by the orbito-nasal foramen directly into the nasal capsule, as in the Amphibian, or reaches the capsule from the orbito-nasal fissure by the olfactory foramen, as in Reptiles.[2] In the capsule the nerve gives off a branch which issues laterally through the foramen epiphaniale, and a branch which passes forward to the foramen apicale (see p. 266 for Mammalia).

For the 8th nerve there are usually two foramina on the inner wall of the auditory capsule; but, as mentioned above, a fenestration, already seen in *Amia*, leads to the membranous condition of this wall in Teleosts. The foramina for the 9th and 10th nerves through the occipital region have already been described. They issue through the remains of the fissura metotica; and although the 9th usually passes out separately, in

---

[1] The pila antotica may disappear in Ophidia.

[2] Primarily the orbito-nasal branch of the profundus enters the capsule through the olfactory foramen, laterally to the olfactory nerve. In Pisces and Amphibia, owing to the opening for the profundus becoming cut off from the olfactory foramen by the extensive fusion of the vertical side wall (orbital cartilage) with the planum antorbitale, the orbito-nasal foramen leads directly from orbit to capsule. The less developed spheno-ethmoidal commissure in Amniota arches over a large orbito-nasal fissure through which the profundus runs to the olfactory foramen, passing across the corner of the brain-cavity in Mammals.

Amphibia and Mammalia a jugular foramen serves for both. A varying number of segmental hypoglossal foramina remain for the roots of the 12th nerve.

**The Chondrocranium in the Mammalia.**—Certain special features distinguishing the Mammalia remain to be considered (Matthes, 544). Con-

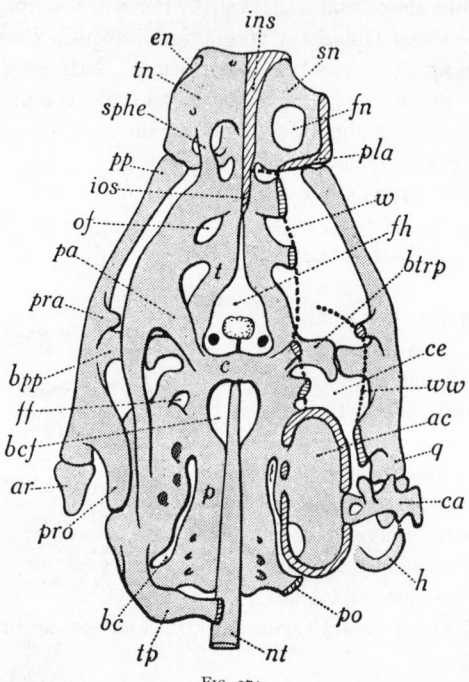

FIG. 274.

Diagram of the chondrocranium and first two visceral arches of a primitive *Tetrapod*; dorsal view. On left a horizontal cut has removed dorsal parts. *ac*, Auditory capsule; *ar*, articular end of Meckel's cartilage; *bc*, basicapsular fissure; *bcf*, basicranial fenestra; *bpp*, basal process; *btrp*, basi-trabecular process; *c*, crista sellæ; *ca*, columella auris; *ce*, cavum epiptericum; *en*, external nostril; *ff*, facial foramen; *fh*, foramen hypophyseos containing pituitary body and internal carotids; *fn*, internal nostril; *h*, top of hyoid cornu; *ins*, median internasal septum; *ios*, median interorbital septum; *nt*, notochord; *of*, optic foramen; *p*, parachordal plate; *pa*, pila antotica; *pla*, planum antorbitale; *po*, pila occipitalis; *pp*, palatine process of palatopterygoid; *pra*, processus ascendens; *pro*, processus oticus; *q*, quadrate; *sn*, solum nasi; *sphe*, commissura spheno-ethmoidalis; *t*, trabecula; *tn*, tectum nasi; *tp*, tectum posterius; *w*, limit of cranial cavity; *ww*, limit of cavum epiptericum.

siderable doubt exists as to the development of trabeculae in mammals. Although typical paired trabeculae were described by Parker in the pig (561), this observation has not been confirmed in this or other forms. Certainly the base of the prechordal cranium appears as a rule in mammals in two regions: as paired islands of cartilage lateral or postero-lateral to the hypophysis (Gaupp, 511; Fawcett, 489-92; Noordenbos, 506), and as a median rod extending from the hypophysis to between the nasal sacs.

Later the posterior cartilages join across and spread so as to floor the pituitary fossa, and unite with the anterior rod in front and the basal plate behind. The paired posterior elements have been considered as trabeculae by Levi (364), Fawcett, and others ; but Noordenbos compares them to

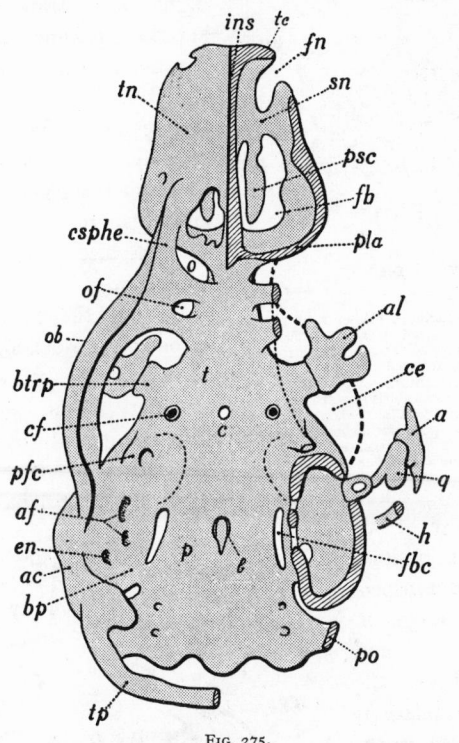

FIG. 275.

Diagram of the *chondrocranium* of a *placental mammal* ; dorsal view, with lateral parts somewhat flattened out. On left side dorsal parts removed by horizontal cut. *a*, Articular (malleus) ; *af*, foramina for auditory nerve ; *al*, ascending lamina of ala temporalis (epipterygoid) ; *b*, posterior basicranial fenestra ; *bp*, posterior basicapsular commissure ; *btrp*, basitrabecular process (prac. alaris) ; *c*, hypophysial foramen ; *ce*, cavum epiptericum (limited by thick broken line laterally, and dotted line medially) ; *cf*, carotid foramen (closed laterally by trabeculo-cochlear commissure) ; *en*, foramen endolymphaticum ; *fbc*, fissura basicapsularis ; *h*, hyoid ; *ins*, internasal septum ; *o*, orbito-nasal fissure ; *ob*, orbital (ala orbitalis), with pila preoptica and pila postoptica enclosing optic foramen, *of* ; *p*, parachordal basal plate ; *q*, quadrate (incus) ; *t*, trabecular plate ; *c*, cupula anterior ; *tn*, tectum nasi ; *tp*, tectum posterius. Other letters as in Fig. 274.

the polar cartilages of van Wijhe. They lie, however, at first between the internal carotids. Certainly this region of the skull in mammals is difficult to interpret. Whereas in all other Craniates the internal carotids primitively enter the cranial cavity from below on the median or inner side of the trabeculae, in the mammals the relative position of these parts seems at first sight to be reversed, since the carotids pass laterally to the central 'polar' or posterior 'trabecular' plate just described, and the carotid foramina are later completed by the growth from the trabecula of a commissura alicochlearis or trabeculo-cochlearis anterior, passing on the outer (lateral) side of the artery to join the cochlear region of the auditory capsule, Figs. 275-8. The unlikely view has been held by Voit that this region of the carotid in the mammal is not homologous with the internal carotid of other Craniates, a loop having been formed and the old vessel replaced by one on the outside. The commissura alicochlearis would then be secondary (Voit, 394; Toeplitz, 391). Gaupp, who describes paired trabeculae in the hypophysial region in *Echidna*, maintains that the internal carotid has cut its way

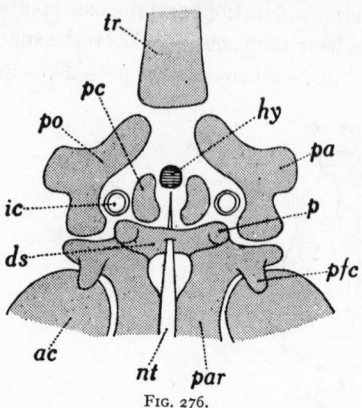

FIG. 276.

Diagram of cartilaginous elements of base of skull of *Mammal*; dorsal view. *ac*, Auditory capsule; *ds*, dorsum sellae (acrochordal cartilage); *hy*, hypophysis; *ic*, internal carotid; *nt*, notochord; *p*, point of attachment of pila antotica in Monotreme; *pa*, processus alaris (basitrabecularis); *pc*, cartilage on floor of sella turcica; *pfc*, prefacial commissure; *po*, posterior trabecular element (=polar cartilage?) sending comm. alicochlearis backwards; *tr*, anterior trabecular element.

through the base of the trabecula to a position more lateral. But inspection of early stages in *Ornithorhynchus* [1] and Marsupials favours the view that the relations of the parts are essentially the same in Mammals as in other Craniates; and that in the former the basal pituitary region has been broadened, the carotids have been separated by the cartilaginous floor of the pituitary fossa now developed from separate elements (polar of Noordenbos, and trabeculae

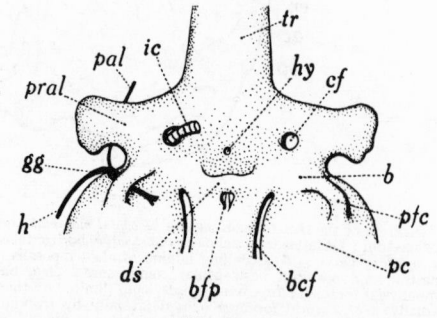

FIG. 277.

Diagrammatic reconstruction of central region of base of skull of *Placental Mammal*; dorsal view of later stage than that shown in Fig. 276. *b*, Anterior lateral region of parachordal which joins acrochordal and polar cartilages; *bcf*, basicapsular fissure; *bfp*, basicranial fontanelle; *cf*, carotid foramen; *gg*, geniculate ganglion on facial nerve; *h*, hyomandibular, and *pal*, palatine branches of facial; *hy*, vestige of foramen hypophyseos; *pral*, processus alaris (pr. basitrabecularis); *pc*, cochlear region of auditory capsule.

[1] The trabeculae seem to be distinctly lateral to the carotids in the early procartilaginous stage in *Ornithorhynchus* (E.S.G.).

of other authors), and that the anterior trabeculo-cochlear commissure (commissura alicochlearis) really represents the original base of the trabecula (that region sometimes developed from a separate 'polar'

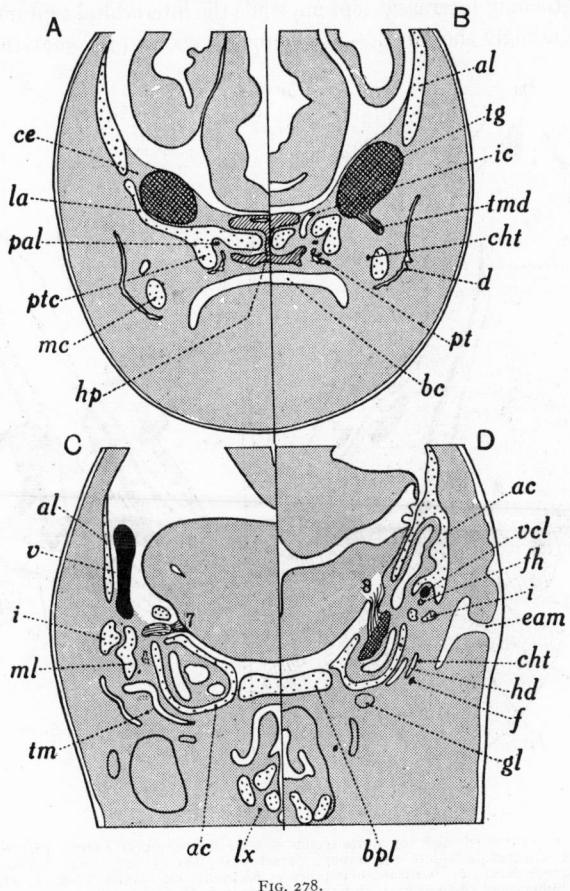

Fig. 278.

*Perameles nasuta.* Embryo of 7 mm. head-length. A–D, Four transverse half-sections of head; A, most anterior, D, most posterior. *ac,* Auditory capsule ; *al,* ala orbitalis ; *bc,* buccal cavity ; *bpl,* basal parachordal plate ; *ce,* cavum epiptericum ; *cht,* chorda tympani ; *d,* dentary ; *eam,* external auditory meatus ; *f,* hyoid branch, and *fh,* hyomandibular branch of facial nerve ; *gl,* glossopharyngeal ; *hd,* hyoid cornu ; *hp,* hypophysial stalk piercing basal plate ; *ic,* internal carotid ; *la,* lamina ascendens (pr. ascendens) ; *lx,* larynx ; *mc,* Meckel's cartilage ; *ml,* malleus ; *pal,* palatine nerve ; *pt,* pterygoid ; *ptc,* pterygoid cartilage ; *tg,* trigeminal ganglion ; *tm,* tympanic membrane ; *tmd,* mandibular nerve ; *v,* vein ; *vcl,* vena capitis lateralis.

element, see p. 237). In Placentals especially it appears to have been pushed outwards, and so come to unite more with the capsule than with the basal plate. According to this interpretation the trabeculae in the Mammalia preserve their usual position relative to the carotids, though it is possible that these have become to some extent surrounded by the trabecular cartilage; certainly cartilage develops between them, Fig. 276.

In the ethmoid region, the nasal capsule extends backwards along the lengthening internasal septum, while the interorbital septum becomes correspondingly shortened. As Gaupp has shown (343, 509), the planum

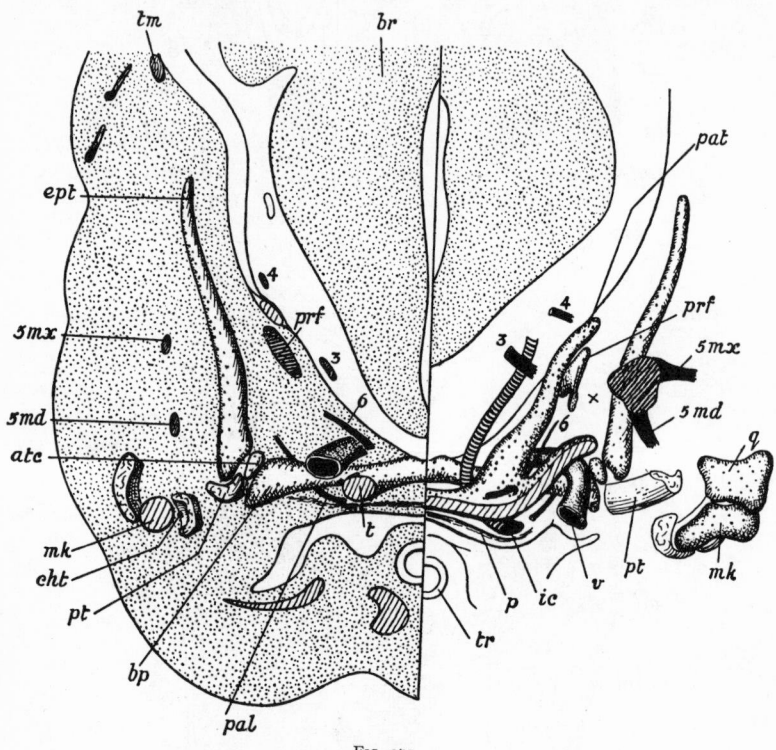

FIG. 279.

Partially reconstructed thick transverse section of head of late embryo *Lacerta*, posterior view cut through base of trabecula on left, and through parachordal plate on right. *atc*, Pterygoid cartilage (meniscus pterygoideus) ; *bp*, basitrabecular process ; *br*, brain ; *cht*, chorda tympani ; *ept*, processus ascendens (epipterygoid cartilage) ; *ic*, internal carotid ; *mk*, Meckel's cartilage ; *p*, parasphenoid ; *pal*, palatine nerve ; *pat*, pila antotica ; *prf*, profundus ; *pt*, pterygoid ; *q*, quadrate ; *t*, cut end of trabecula ; *tm*, taenia marginalis ; *tr*, trachea ; *v*, vena capitis lateralis ; 3, 4, 5, 6, cranial nerves.

antorbitale forms now an oblique floor below the olfactory lobes (lamina infracribrosa). The cartilaginous cranial wall comes thus to include a small space, originally part of the orbit in the Reptile, which forms the extreme corner of the brain-cavity into which the orbito-nasal foramen now directly opens. The orbito-nasal branch of the profundus nerve thus passes through the cranial cavity to reach the cribriform plate and enter the nasal capsule, Figs. 264, 275, 281, and p. 258.

The optic foramen is closed by a pila preoptica and a pila postoptica (radix anterior and posterior of the 'ala orbitalis') in the Placentalia; but in the Monotremata and the Marsupialia the pila postoptica fails to develop. Consequently in these a large fenestra pseudoptica arises by the confluence of the foramen opticum with the foramen postopticum, Figs. 264, 275, 282.

**Cavum epiptericum.**—More important is the disappearance in Mammalia of the lateral cranial wall farther back which leads to the inclusion within the cranial cavity of a considerable space lying outside it in the skull of the lower Tetrapods (Gaupp, 343, 506, 508). Between the side wall of the chondrocranium on the inside and the palatoquadrate with its processus ascendens on the outside there is enclosed a space partially floored by the basitrabecular and basal processes and named by Gaupp the cavum epiptericum which it is important to recognise. It has one anterior, one lateral, and one posterior opening. Originally an extracranial space, it is derived from the posterior region of the orbit. Through it pass the internal jugular vein, the orbital and facial arteries, and the profundus, trigeminal and facial nerves, whose ganglia lie typically in it, Figs. 271, 274, 279, 280 A.

The anterior opening serves for the entrance of the internal jugular vein (v. capitis lateralis) or its branches, and the exit of the profundus nerve (also usually the abducens and trochlear nerves), which, therefore, passes out anteriorly to the ascending process. The more posterior lateral opening, between the ascending and the otic processes, serves for the exit of the maxillary and mandibular branches of the trigeminal (together with the superficial ophthalmic and buccal branches of the facial in Dipnoi and those Amphibia in which these lateral line nerves persist) and the branches of the facial artery, Fig. 261. The posterior opening, bounded below by the palatobasal articulation and above by the otic process, lets through the palatine nerve below, and the hyomandibular branch of the facial and internal jugular vein behind; it also lets in the facial artery. This opening, then, is the cranio-quadrate passage (p. 412). The disposition of these various structures entering and leaving the cavum epiptericum remains fundamentally unchanged throughout the Dipnoi and Tetrapoda, though considerably modified in many forms. The cavum epiptericum remains well defined in those Reptiles which have a well-developed upstanding epipterygoid, such as the Rhynchocephalia and Lacertilia; but tends to merge again with the orbit in those where the processus ascendens is reduced, such as the Aves, the Chelonia, and Crocodilia among Reptilia, and the Amphibia and lower forms (see further, Chapter VII.).

In the mammal, as the brain expands, the original side wall behind the optic region ceases to chondrify, and is reduced to a mere membrane through which pass the nerves into the cavum epiptericum. The latter

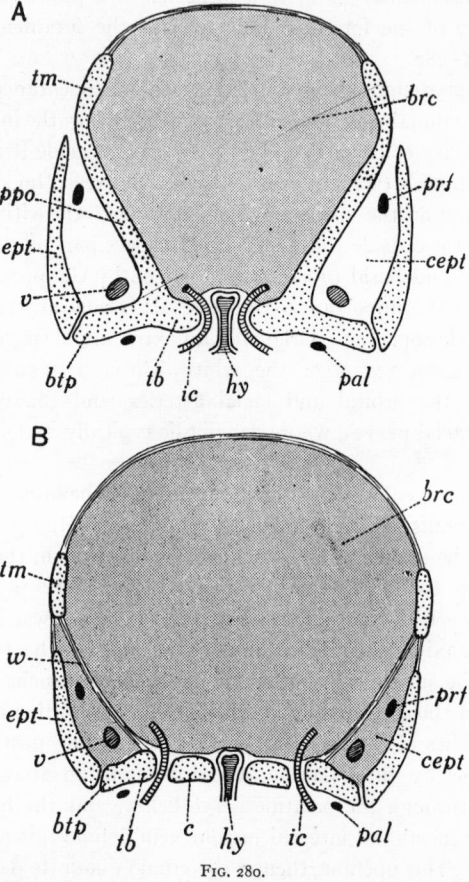

FIG. 280.

Diagrammatic transverse sections of orbito-temporal region of skull to show inclusion of extra-cranial cavum epiptericum of Reptile, A, in cranial cavity of Mammal, B. *brc*, Primitive brain-cavity; *btp*, basitrabecular process; *c*, cartilaginous floor of sella turcica; *cept*, cavum epiptericum; *ept*, processus ascendens (reptilian epipterygoid, mammalian lamina ascendens); *hy*, hypophysial stalk; *ic*, internal carotid; *pal*, palatine nerve; *ppo*, pila antotica; *prf*, profundus nerve; *tb*, trabecula; *tm*, taenia marginalis; *v*, vena capitis lateralis; *w*, membrane representing original side wall.

is now a part of the cranial cavity, since a new lateral wall becomes established at the level of the processus (Gaupp, 508; Broom, 327a, b). This new wall is represented by the lamina ascendens of the ala temporalis (p. 270), and a membrana spheno-obturatoria stretching from it, which may later become ossified. Thus the old nerve foramina, now mere holes in the inner membrane, are replaced by new fissures and foramina in the outer wall ; these become clearly defined when it is ossified. They are known as the sphenoidal fissure or foramen lacerum anterius, for the profundus (together with the 3rd, 4th, and 6th nerves) anterior to the lamina ascendens, the foramen rotundum for the maxillary branch of the trigeminal nerve

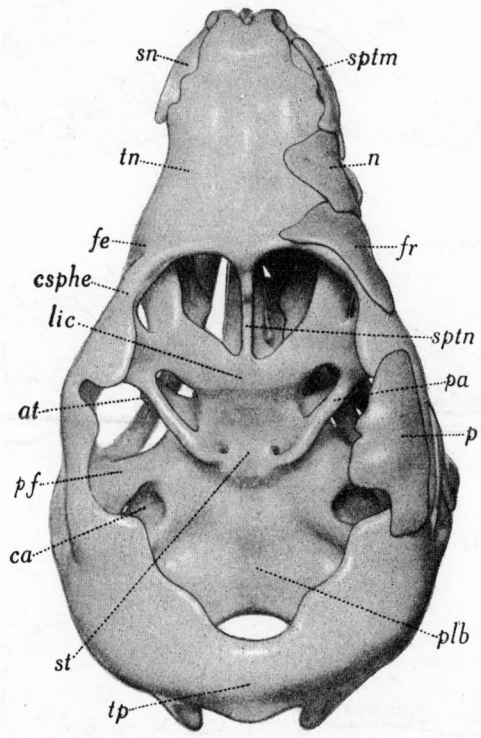

FIG. 281.

Dorsal view of skull of embryo *Echidna aculeata*, var. typica (from Gaupp-Ziegler model).   Dermal bones on right.   *at*, Ala temporalis ;   *ca*, cavity of cochlear region of auditory capsule ;   *csphe*, commissura spheno-ethmoidalis of orbital cartilage ;   *fe*, foramen epiphaniale ;   *fr*, frontal ;   *lic*, lamina infracribrosa ;   *n*, nasal ;   *p*, parietal ;   *pf*, prefacial commissure ;   *pa*, pila antotica ;   *plb*, planum basale ;   *sn*, solum nasi ;   *sptm*, septomaxillary ;   *sptn*, septum nasi ;   *st*, hind wall of sella turcica *tn*, tectum nasi ;   *tp*, tectum posterius.

either through or in front of the lamina, and the foramen ovale for the mandibular branch farther back.

There is no better evidence of the fundamentally primitive character of the chondrocranium in Monotremes, in spite of its specialisations, than the fact described by Gaupp (**511**) and Wilson (**398**), that they alone among mammals preserve complete the pila antotica (taenia clino-orbitalis) of the original wall, Figs. 281-2.   This pila has disappeared in the Ditremata, its last vestiges being perhaps represented by certain small cartilages found above the Gasserian ganglion in *Lepus*, *Felis*, and other mammals, Figs. 275, 282 (Voit, 394-5 ; Terry, 390).

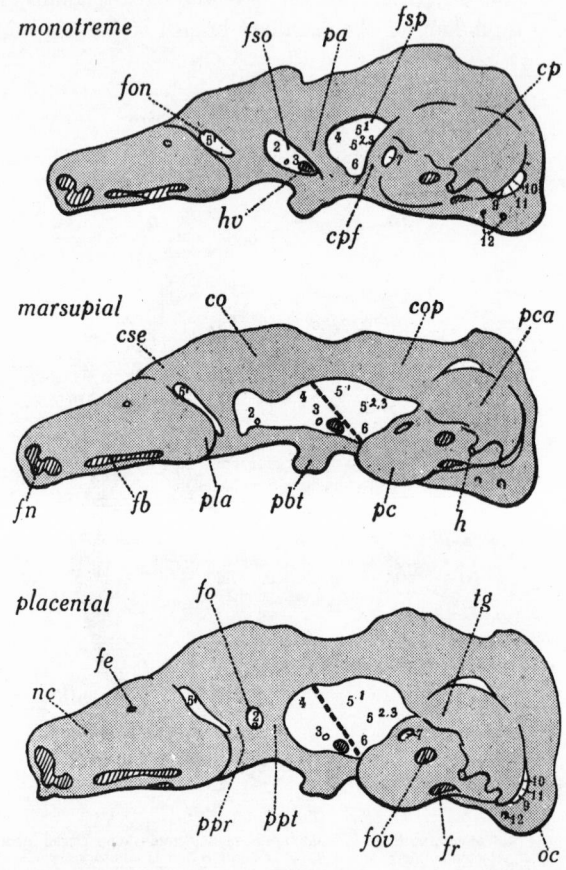

FIG. 282.

Diagrams of chondrocranium in *Mammalia*, left-side view. Exit of cranial nerves marked by Nos. 2-12. *co*, Orbital cartilage ; *cop*, commissura orbito-parietalis ; *cp*, crista parotica ; *cpf*, comm. prefacialis ; *cse*, comm. spheno-ethmoidalis ; *fb*, fenestra basalis ; *fe*, foramen epiphaniale ; *fn*, fenestra narina ; *fo*, fenestra optica ; *fon*, fissura orbito-nasalis ; *fov*, fenestra ovalis ; *fr*, fenestra rotunda ; *fso*, fenestra pseudo-orbitalis ; *fsp*, fenestra pro-otica ; *h*, laterohyal ; *hv*, hypophysial vein ; *nc*, nasal capsule ; *oc*, condyle ; *pa*, pila antotica, represented by broken line in Marsupial and Placental ; *pbt*, processus alaris or basitrabecularis ; *pc*, pars cochlearis, and *pca*, pars semicircularis of auditory capsule ; *pla*, planum antorbitale ; *ppr*, pila preoptica ; *ppt*, pila metoptica ; *tg*, tegmen tympani.

**Ala temporalis.**—The validity of this explanation of the fate of the cavum epiptericum in the mammalian skull depends to a great extent on our interpretation of the homology of the ala temporalis. The more hori-

zontal region of this structure (processus alaris) is developed as an outgrowth from the posterior trabecular rudiment, Figs. 275, 276-8. The
5th nerve and its ganglia and the vena capitis lateralis lie above it ; the
palatine arises from the facial behind it, and passes forward (joining a
sympathetic nerve) as the vidian nerve below it. It thus has the same
morphological relation to surrounding structures as the basitrabecular
process of lower Gnathostomes, and is doubtless homologous with it
(Gaupp, 508). This conclusion is generally accepted. But Broom sees in the
mammalian lamina ascendens (later alisphenoid bone) the homologue of
the Reptilian epipterygoid, Fig. 280, while Gaupp considered this lamina
to be a new development scarcely begun in the Monotreme. The chief
reason why Gaupp and others reject the homology with the processus
ascendens is because this process in lower forms always separates the
profundus from the maxillary and mandibular branches of the trigeminal
nerve ; whereas, in the Mammalia, the lamina of the ala temporalis
usually grows up between the maxillary and mandibular branches, Figs.
449, 495. But, since in many mammals (both Marsupials, Fig. 264,
and Placentals, Fig. 497) the lamina may pass also between the maxillary
branch and the profundus, so as to enclose the latter in a foramen
rotundum, the difference may be more apparent than real.[1] It may be
supposed that the mammalian processus ascendens spread backward so
as to pass on both sides of the maxillary nerve, and that then the anterior
limb disappeared while the posterior persisted. Moreover, the lamina
ascendens frequently develops separately from the basal processus alaris
(Broom: in Marsupials. Levi, Fawcett: in Man. Wincza, Noordenbos, and
others : in other Placentals). These facts, together with the evidence
from the adult skull of the Theromorpha that the alisphenoid bone of the
Mammal is derived from the epipterygoid of the Reptile, strongly support
the view that the ala temporalis is formed of two elements : the basitrabecular process from the cranium and the processus ascendens (the
only remains in this region of the palatoquadrate bar ; see Chapter VII.).

Other characteristics are found in the otic region of the mammalian
chondrocranium. Speaking generally, the brain and brain cavity are
greatly enlarged ; and as the brain bulges more and more at the sides,
the auditory capsules, instead of standing upright, acquire a more horizontal position below the cranium (already seen in Theromorph Reptiles).
Accompanying the great development of the cochlea this part of the
capsule encroaches on the basal plate. Nevertheless, the pars cochlearis

---

[1] According to Fuchs (503), who supports Broom's view, the processus
ascendens in young stages of *Didelphys* occupies the position of the reptilian
epipterygoid ; but in later stages, at all events, it surrounds the maxillary
nerve as in many other mammals (Esdaile, 722 ; Toeplitz, 391).

chondrifies as a rule separately from the plate (Broom, 327b; Noordenbos, 370; de Beer, 442a), and doubtless belongs not to the basal plate, as Gaupp supposed, but to the capsule itself, Fig. 278. As already explained, it undermines the prefacial commissure, which comes to lie above it.[1] The facial nerve, issuing from the primary foramen below the commissure, bears a geniculate ganglion, gives off the palatine branch, which issues from the cavum epiptericum below, and continues as the hyomandibular branch round the capsule in a sulcus facialis. Posteriorly the sulcus is overhung by the crista parotica, anteriorly in the Ditremata by a new formation the tegmen tympani (Parker, Van Kampen, 741; see p. 465). The nerve leaves the sulcus by the primary stylo-mastoid foramen behind the region where the hyoid joins the crista, Fig. 277.

The side of the brain-case in the auditory region may be considerably strengthened by a cartilaginous extension from the orbito-parietal commissure to form a large 'parietal plate'. This may join the tectum synoticum, and between them the capsule is left a fissure (foramen jugulare spurium) for the passage of branch of the jugular vein.

**Orbito-temporal Region.**—There remain to be considered in various groups certain important specialisations of the orbito-temporal region. The fundamental constant relations of the cartilages to certain nerves and blood-vessels must first of all be understood, Figs. 245-7.

The jugular vein (p. 535) runs back close to the lateral wall of the skull, passing from the orbit, where it receives the hypophysial vein in front of the pila antotica. It passes dorsally to the subocular shelf (basitrabecular process), medially to the ascending process of the palato-quadrate, then through the cranio-quadrate passage (p. 412). The internal carotid passes forwards below the basal plate (partly enclosed in a para-basal canal between the plate and the parasphenoid in those forms where this bone is well developed); and, having given off an orbital artery which escapes outwards through the cranio-quadrate passage, the internal carotid passes inwards and upwards into the cranial cavity between the trabecula and the hypophysis, Figs. 261, 263.

The basitrabecular process, typically developed in Lacertilia, Figs. 263, 271, but present in a more or less modified form in all Tetrapoda, Osteichthyes, and probably also in Chondrichthyes, is anterior to the palatine nerve, which passes down behind it and then forwards below it, Fig. 284. As suggested by Veit (392-3), this process has probably been derived phylogenetically from that region of the subocular shelf, immediately in front

---

[1] A small space lodging the facial ganglion, known as the cavum supra-cochleare, originally outside the cranial cavity, may become included in it by the ossification of its outer wall.

of the palatine nerve, which occurs in most Selachii as an outward extension of the trabecula. In these fish the shelf may extend backwards and
enclose a foramen for the orbital artery and also more rarely a foramen
for the palatine nerve, Fig. 284. As a rule, however, this nerve passes
down outside the edge of the shelf. In most of the higher Teleostomes
the basitrabecular process is reduced and no longer meets the basal process of the palatoquadrate; but in *Lepidosteus*, among living forms, in
Crossopterygii (*Megalichthys*, Watson, 644; *Eusthenopteron*, Bryant, 465),
Coelacanthini (Stensiö, 605-6), and primitive Chondrostei and Amioidei

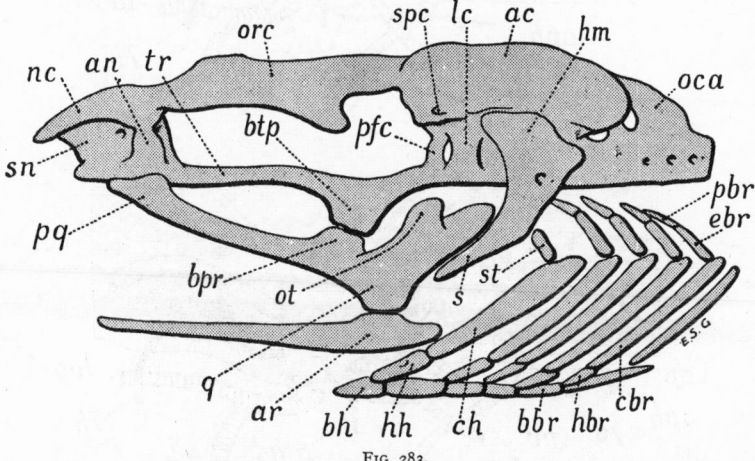

FIG. 283.

Diagram of chondrocranium and visceral arches of primitive Teleostome leading to Holostean type.
*ac*, Auditory capsule; *an*, antorbital process; *ar*, articular region; *bbr*, basibranchial; *bh*, basihyal;
*bpr*, basal process; *btp*, basitrabecular process; *cbr*, ceratobranchial; *ch*, ceratohyal; *ebr*, epibranchial; *hbr*, hypobranchial; *hh*, hypohyal; *hm*, hyomandibular; *lc*, lateral commissure; *nc*,
nasal capsule; *oca*, occipital arch; *orc*, orbital; *ot*, otic process; *pfc*, prefacial commissure; *pbr*,
pharyngobranchial; *pq*, palatine region of palatoquadrate; *q*, quadrate region; *s*, symplectic region;
*sn*, septum nasi; *spc*, spiracular canal through postorbital process; *st*, stylohyal; *tr*, trabecula.

it seems to have been well developed and to have articulated with the
pyterygoid region of the palatoquadrate, Fig. 283 (Chapter VII.).

**Trigemino-facialis Chamber.**—Having described these relations, we
may now deal with the trigemino-facialis chamber. Allis has given
this name to a space occurring in the side wall of the skull of Pisces
immediately in front of the auditory capsule (406-7). It is typically
developed in the higher Teleostomi, and may be described in the
Teleost. In Scomber, for instance (Allis, 404), is found a short horizontal canal in the pro-otic with anterior and posterior openings. The
jugular vein (v. capitis lateralis) passes through it from in front; the
orbital artery passes through it from behind. Out of its anterior
opening issue the trigeminal nerve with the lateral-line branches of

Heterodontus

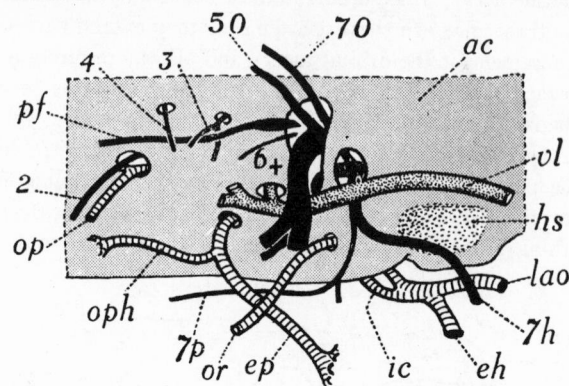

Squalus

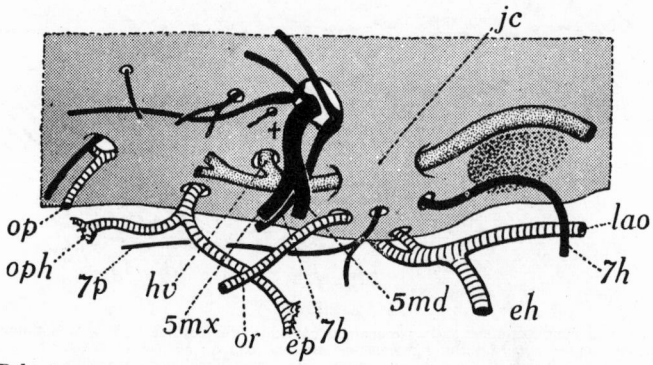

Polypterus

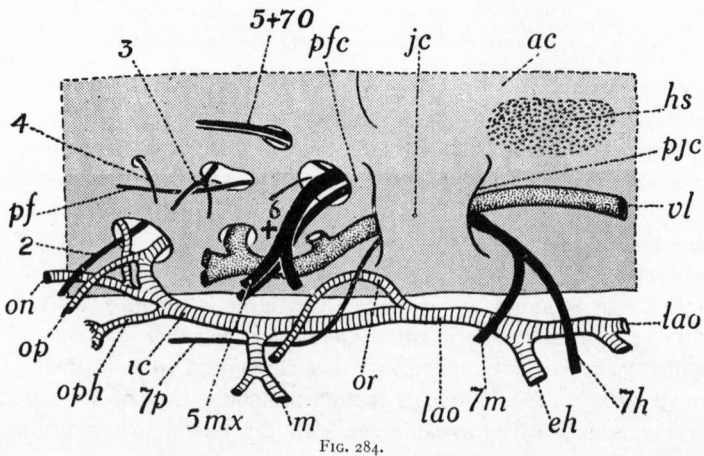

FIG. 284.

Lepidosteus

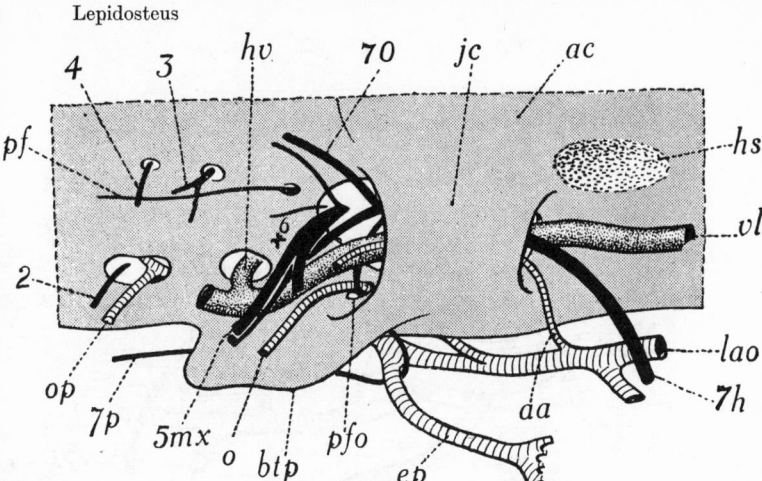

Amia embryo

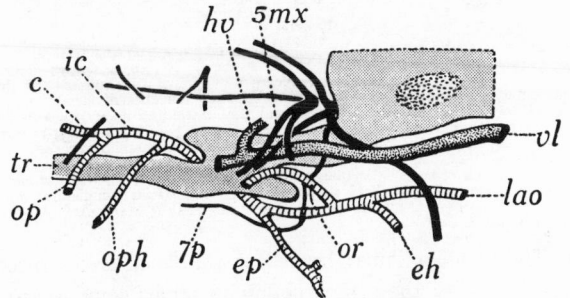

Amia, late stage

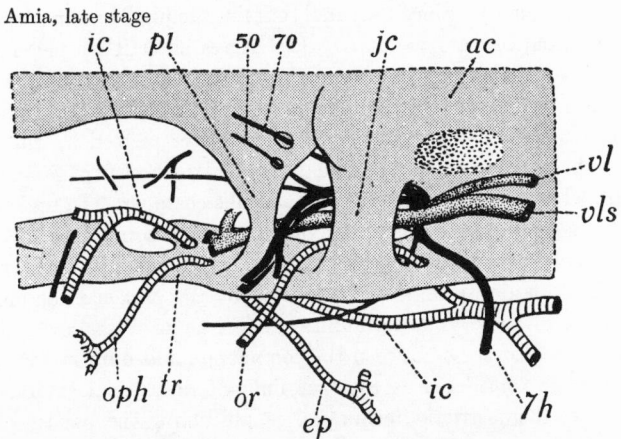

FIG. 284.

Salmo

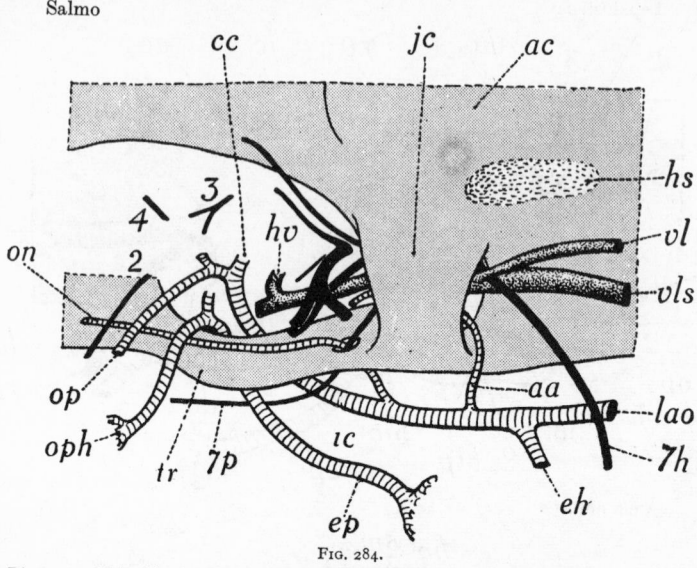

Fig. 284.

Diagrams of left side of orbito-temporal region of skull of fishes, showing relation of cartilages (stippled) to nerves (black), veins (dark), and arteries (cross-lined). Nerves: 2, Optic; 3, oculomotor; 4, trochlear; 5*mx*, maxillary, and 5*o*, ophthalmic branches of trigeminal; 6, abducens; 7*h*, hyomandibular, 7*m*, mandibular, 7*p*, palatine; 7*o*, superior ophthalmic branches of facial; *pf*, profundus. Arteries: *aa*, *o*, and *on* (orbito-nasal) seem to represent the orbital and its branches in *Lepidosteus* and *Salmo*; *eh*, efferent epibranchial of hyoid arch; *ep*, efferent pseudobranchial; *c*, cerebral; *cc*, circulus cephalicus; *ic*, internal carotid; *lao*, lateral aorta; *m*, mandibular; *op*, optic; *oph*, ophthalmic; *or*, orbital. Veins: *hv*, Hypophysial; *vl*, vena capitis lateralis and medialis = jugular or head vein; *vls*, inner branch of same. Cartilages: *ac*, Auditory capsule; *hs*, articular facet for hyomandibular; *jc*, wall of jugular canal or lateral commissure; *pfc*, prefacial commissure; *pfo*, palatine foramen; *pjc*, posterior opening of jugular canal; *pl*, pila lateralis; *tr*, trabecula. A + marks pila antotica. (Goodrich and de Beer.)

the facial. The hyomandibular branch of the facial issues through its posterior opening (with the sympathetic and ramus communicans from facial to trigeminal). Since the canal contains the jugular vein it is called a jugular canal or pars jugularis. The nerves enter it by piercing the bony wall separating the canal from the cranial cavity, and on the inner face of this wall is a recess lodging the trigeminal and facial ganglia. This recess, limited internally by the dura mater pierced by the nerve roots, is the pars ganglionaris. The pars jugularis and pars ganglionaris make up what Allis calls the trigemino-facialis chamber. To understand its morphology we must briefly describe it in other forms, Figs. 283-4.

In Selachii the main branches of the trigeminal and facial nerves emerge by foramina primitively separated by the prefacial commissure. The ganglia of these and the auditory nerve lie in a shallow acustico-trigemino-facialis recess between the commissure and dura mater, which latter may be considered as the true limit of the cranial cavity. The ganglia are, then, strictly intramural in position. The palatine nerve branches off outside the facial foramen.   The vena capitis lateralis, in early stages, runs freely above the subocular shelf and outside the auditory capsule, but later becomes enclosed in many Selachians (*Squalus*, Fig. 184) in a short jugular canal apparently formed by the upward growth of the hinder region of the subocular shelf which fuses above the vein with the auditory capsule (de Beer, 421).   Meanwhile the shelf has also grown up so as to separate the original facial opening into an anterior palatine and a posterior hyomandibular foramen separated by a postpalatine commissure.   Selachians show a condition in which the pars jugularis is still separated from the pars ganglionaris by the cranial wall (prefacial commissure).

*Lepidosteus* (Allis, 421 ; Veit, 392 ; de Beer, 421) shows an interesting structure in this region.   It develops a prepalatine (basitrabecular process) and postpalatine subocular shelf.   The two combine to close the palatine foramen, and grow up outside the vena capitis·lateralis and nerves to join the capsule, thus forming a commissura lateralis or outer wall of the pars jugularis.   This lateral commissure is in many Teleostomes strengthened by a lateral wing of the parasphenoid.   The prefacial commissure is no longer developed in *Lepidosteus*, and the pars jugularis thus becomes confluent with the pars ganglionaris.   The chamber then contains the vein which runs through it, the orbital artery which enters the palatine foramen, and the ganglia of the trigeminal and facial nerves.   The branches of the trigeminal (and lateral-line branches of the facial) issue from its anterior opening, the palatine through its floor, the hyomandibular branch through its posterior opening.   In *Amia* also the jugular canal and trigemino-facial recess are confluent ; but in Teleostei they again become separated by the ossification of the intervening membrane, Fig. 733.

The recess and jugular canal in *Polypterus* (Allis, 410 ; Lehn, 542 ; de Beer, 421) and Palaeoniscoidei (Stensiö, 218) are in about the same condition as in Selachii ; but in modern Chondrostei the prefacial commissure seems to have been lost (de Beer, 421a).

To sum up concerning the trigemino-facialis chamber of the Actinopterygii.   It is formed by the confluence of an intramural recess (pars ganglionaris) with an extramural jugular canal (pars jugularis) due to the disappearance of the cartilaginous cranial wall which separates them in lower Pisces.   Its outer wall is formed by the upgrowth of the subocular shelf.   In Teleostei the two parts become secondarily separated by a bony septum.

The orbito-temporal region in the Dipnoi and Tetrapoda has evolved along different lines; for in these, as explained elsewhere (p. 267), there is formed a cavum epiptericum containing the jugular vein, orbital artery, trigeminal and facial ganglia.   But although it happens to contain the same parts as the trigemino-facial chamber, and to be to some extent floored by the basitrabecular process, the cavum epiptericum differs radically from the chamber in being a purely extracranial space limited externally by the palatoquadrate arch.

Nevertheless, there is developed in the modern Amphibia a structure somewhat resembling the piscine chamber. For in these Tetrapods there

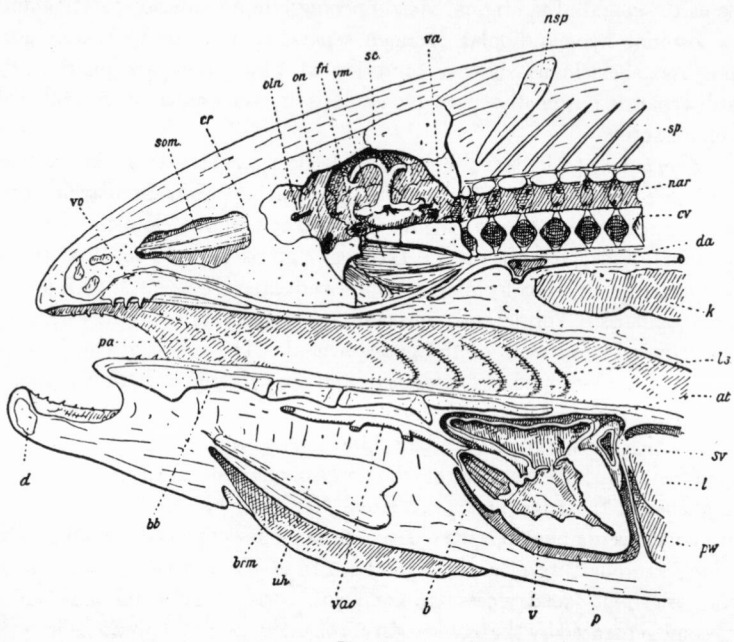

FIG. 285.

Median longitudinal section through the head of *Salmo salar*, L. (Modified, after Bruch.) *at*, Atrium; *b*, bulbus arteriosus; *bb*, basibranchial, *brm*, branchiostegal membrane; *bs*, branchial slit; *cr*, cranial cartilage; *cv*, vertebral centrum; *d*, dentary; *da*, dorsal aorta; *fn*, facial nerve; *k*, kidney; *l*, liver; *nar*, neural arch; *nsp*, enlarged radial; *oln*, olfactory nerve; *on*, optic nerve; *p*, pericardium; *pa*, parasphenoid; *pw*, septum between pericardial and abdominal coelom; *sc*, anterior vertical semicircular canal; *som*, superior oblique muscle of eye; *sp*, neural spine; *sv*, sinus venosus; *uh*, urohyal; *v*, ventricle—valves separate its cavity from that of atrium above and bulbus in front; *va*, vagus nerve; *vao*, ventral aorta; *vm*, rectus muscle of eye in eye-muscle canal; *vo*, prevomer. (From E. S. Goodrich, *Vert. Craniata*, 1909.)

is a subocular shelf forming a 'prepalatine' basitrabecular process and a postpalatine commissure in the floor of the cavum epiptericum and enclosing the palatine nerve in a foramen. As the auditory capsule extends very far forwards it overhangs the prefacial commissure and fuses with the subocular shelf, so enclosing the hyomandibular branch of the facial nerve in a canal lateral to the true facial foramen (Urodela, Figs. 261, 272-3). The basitrabecular process disappears in Anura, leaving the palatine nerve free in front of the postpalatine commissure.

**Myodome in Pisces.**—Of considerable interest is the myodome, a space developed in the orbito-temporal and otic regions of the skull of Teleostomes for the accommodation of lengthened recti muscles of the eye. Strictly speaking, this space is the posterior myodome, since a similar anterior myodome is hollowed out for the oblique muscles in the ethmoid region by the enlargement of the orbito-nasal canal (p. 245). The structure and origin of the myodome has been studied by many modern anatomists

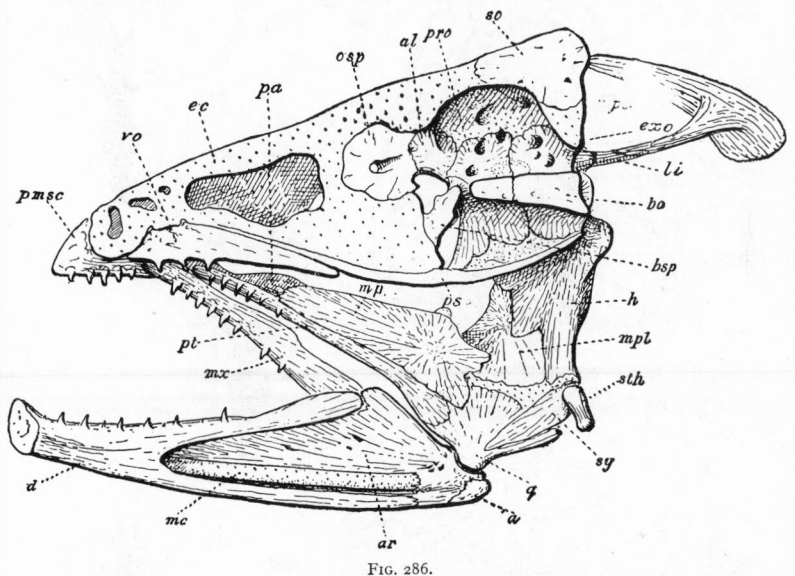

FIG. 286.

Skull of *Salmo salar*, L., cut longitudinally. (After Bruch.)  *a*, Angular; *al*, pterosphenoid; *ar*, articular; *bo*, basioccipital; *bsp*, basisphenoid; *d*, dentary; *ec*, ethmoid cartilage; *exo*, exoccipital; *h*, hyomandibular; *li*, ligament; *mc*, Meckel's cartilage; *mpl*, metapterygoid; *mp*, mesopterygoid; *mx*, maxilla; *osp*, orbitosphenoid; *p*, post-temporal; *pa*, palatine; *pmsc*, premaxilla; *pro*, pro-otic; *ps*, parasphenoid; *pt*, pterygoid; *q*, quadrate; *so*, supraoccipital; *sth*, stylohyal; *sy*, symplectic; *vo*, prevomer. (From E. S. Goodrich, *Vert. Craniata*, 1909.)

(Gegenbaur, **516**; Sagemehl, **378**; Gaupp, **343**; de Beer, **421-2**; and more especially Allis, **402, 404-5, 409, 413**).

When fully developed, as in *Salmo*, the myodome in the dry skull is a large space between the floor of the brain-case (pro-otic and basioccipital) and the parasphenoid; it opens behind, and communicates in front with the orbits, Figs. 285-7. The myodome is supposed to have originated by the penetration into the enlarged opening for the pituitary vein of recti muscles originally inserted on the outer surface of the orbital wall. First the external (posterior) rectus, and later the internal (anterior) rectus, passed into the cranium at the side of the hypophysial fossa, dorsally to the trabecula and anteriorly to the pila antotica (so-called dorsal myodome).

The enlargement of this incipient myodome involves the disappearance of the pila antotica (p. 261) and confluence with the trigemino-facialis

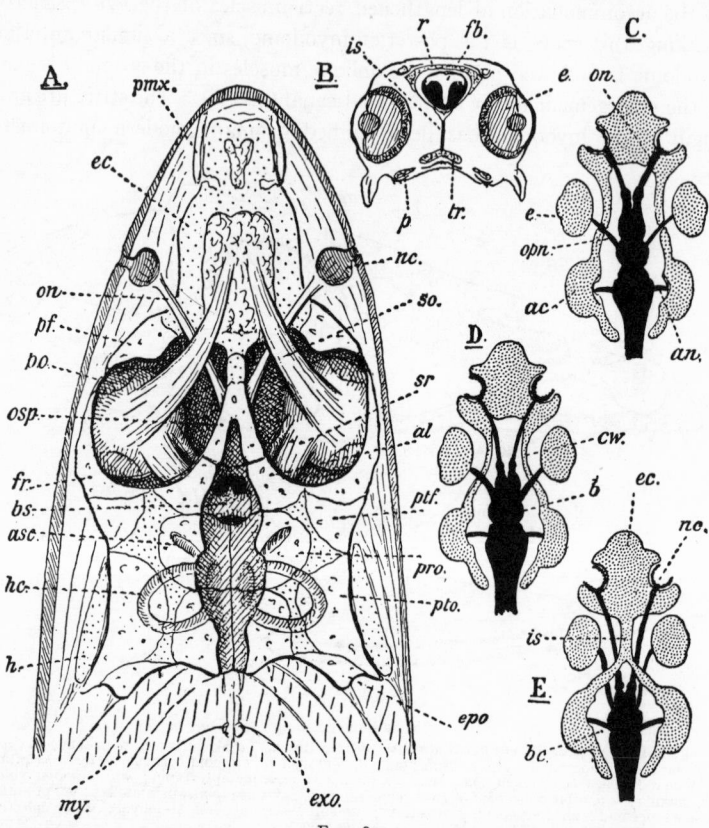

FIG. 287.

A, *Salmo salar*, L. ; longitudinal section through the head exposing the sense-organs, and brain-cavity viewed from above (after Bruch) ; B, transverse section of the head of a young *Salmo trutta*, L., in the region of the fore-brain ; C, D, and E, three diagrams showing the development of the inter-orbital septum. *ac*, Auditory capsule ; *al*, alisphenoid ; *an*, auditory nerve ; *asc*, cavity for anterior semicircular canal ; *b*, optic lobe ; *bc*, brain-cavity ; *bs*, basisphenoid ; *cw*, cranial wall ; *e*, eye ; *ec*, ethmoid cartilage ; *epo*, epiotic { *exo*, exoccipital ; *fb*, fore-brain ; *fr*, frontal ; *h*, hyomandibular ; *hc*, cavity for horizontal semicircular canal ; *is*, interorbital septum ; *my*, myotome ; *nc*, nasal capsule ; *on*, olfactory nerve ; *opn*, optic nerve ; *osp*, orbitosphenoid ; *p*, palatine ; *pf*, prefrontal ; *pmx*, premaxilla ; *po*, ossification of optic capsule ; *pro*, pro-otic ; *ptf*, postfrontal ; *r*, cranial roof ; *so*, superior oblique muscle ; *sr*, superior rectus muscle ; *tr*, trabecula. (From E. S. Goodrich, *Vert. Craniata*, 1909.)

chamber (p. 277).[1]  Extending their insertions further the muscles pass down through the hypophysial fenestra, and push their way backwards

[1] Owing to the confluence of myodome and chamber, the palatine nerve appears to pass through the former on its way down to its external foramen situated laterally to the original edge of the subocular shelf.  The muscles enter the myodome ventrally to the jugular vein.

between the cranial floor and the parasphenoid (ventral myodome). In their course from the orbit the muscles remain at first outside the dura mater, then pass below the pro-otic bridge (p. 386), the right and left myodomal cavities being separated only by a median membrane, Figs.

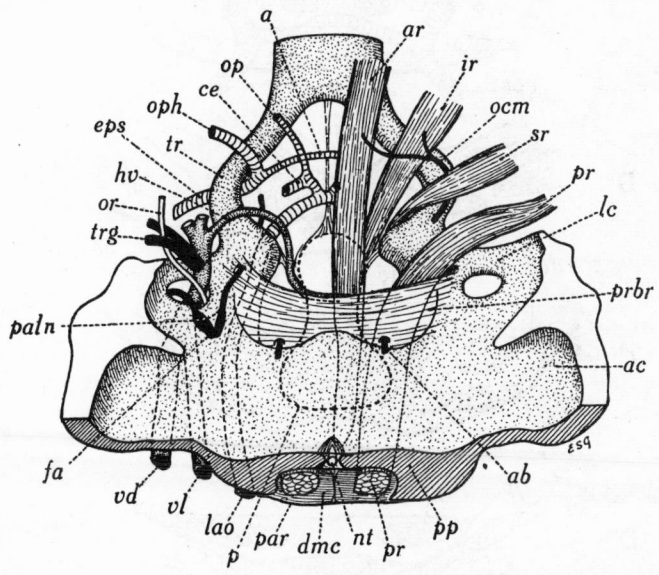

FIG. 288.

*Salmo fario*, embryo 22 mm. long. Reconstruction of orbito-temporal region of base of skull; blood-vessels on left, eye-muscles on right. Dorsal view. *a*, Transverse connexion between efferent pseudobranchial vessels; *ab*, n. abducens; *ac*, auditory capsule; *ar*, anterior rectus muscle; *ce*, cerebral artery; *dmc*, dorsal chamber of posterior myodome; *eps*, efferent pseudobranchial artery; *fa*, n. facialis; *hv*, hypophysial vein; *ir*, inferior rectus muscle; *lao*, lateral aorta; *lc*, lateral commissure; *nt*, tip of notochord in reduced basicranial fenestra; *ocm*, n. oculomotorius; *op*, optic artery; *oph*, ophthalmic artery; *or*, orbital artery; *p*, dotted outline of pituitary body passing below pro-otic bridge; *paln*, n. palatinus; *par*, parasphenoid; *pp*, parachordal; *pr*, posterior rectus muscle; *prbr*, membranous extension of pro-otic bridge; *sr*, superior rectus muscle; *tr*, trabecula; *trg*, n. trigeminus; *vd*, outer lateral vein; *vl*, inner lateral vein.

288-9. Such in brief is supposed to have been the history of the posterior myodome.

*Amia* has a myodome less developed than that of typical Teleosts (Sagemehl, **378**; Allis, **402**; Pehrson, **372**; de Beer, **421**). The cavity is confluent with the trigemino-facialis chamber, but only the external rectus muscle penetrates over the trabecula, and this but for a short way below the pro-otic bridge. In Teleosts (*Salmo*) the external rectus reaches farther back even to below the occipital region, and the internal rectus follows in a ventral compartment of the myodome separated from the dorsal by a horizontal septum usually membranous. The myodome is much less developed and even absent in some Teleosts (Siluridae, Anguilli-

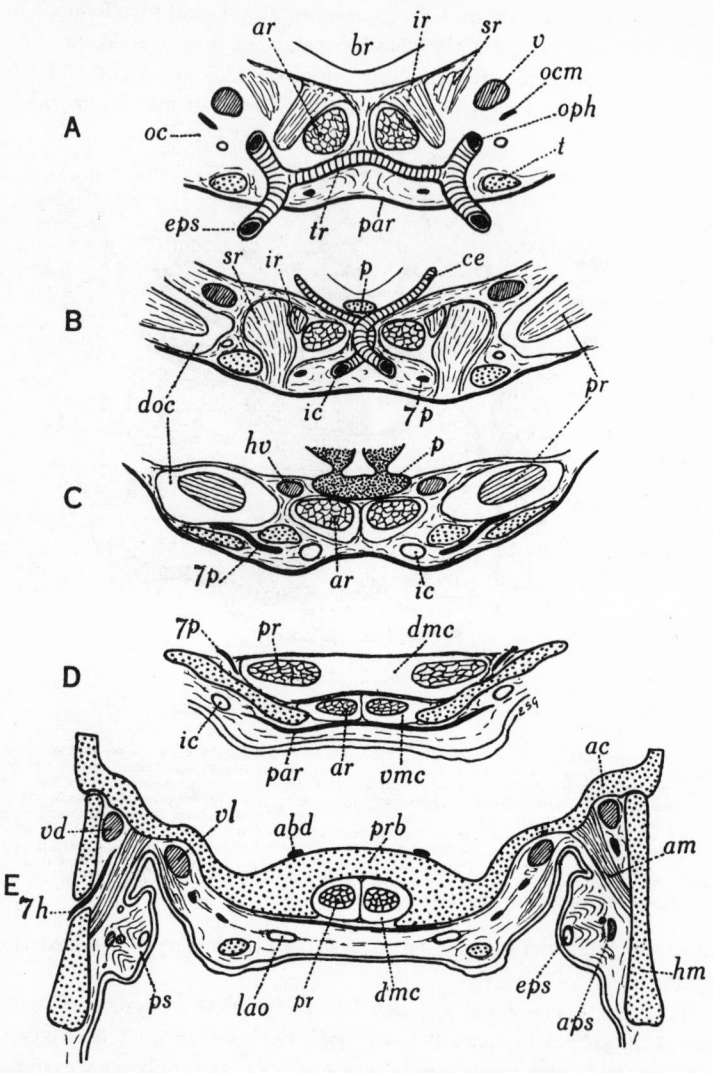

FIG. 289.

*Salmo fario*, embryo 28 mm. long. Series of transverse sections of basal region of head showing relations of myodome. A, Most anterior, E, most posterior section. *abd*, Abducens; *ac*, auditory capsule; *am*, adductor muscle; *aps*, afferent pseudobranchial vessel; *ar*, anterior rectus muscle; *br*, brain; *ce*, cerebral artery; *dmc*, dorsal chamber of myodome—*doc*, its opening into orbit; *eps*, efferent pseudobranchial vessel; *hm*, hyomandibula; *hv*, hypophysial vein; *ic*, internal carotid; *ir*, inferior rectus; *lao*, lateral dorsal aorta; *oc*, orbital cavity; *ocm*, oculomotor; *oph*, ophthalmic artery; *p*, pituitary body; *par*, parasphenoid; *pr*, posterior rectus; *prb*, pro-otic bridge; *ps*, pseudobranch; *sr*, superior rectus; *t*, trabecula; *tr*, transverse anastomosis; *v*, head vein; *vd*, vena capitis lateralis; *vl*, secondary vein; *vmc*, ventral chamber of myodome; *7h*, hyomandibular, and *7p*, palatine branches of facial.

formes, some Gasterosteiformes, Gadiformes) ; but there can be little
doubt that in these forms it has been lost. It is also absent or very little
developed in *Polypterus, Lepidosteus,* and the modern Acipenseroidei ;
yet, since it has been described in Palaeoniscoidei (Stensiö, **218**), Semionotidae (Woodward, **664** ; Frost, **500**), and Saurichthyidae (Stensiö, **134**), it
very probably is an ancestral structure common to all the Actinopterygii (see p. 385).[1]

**Conclusion.**—From the description given above it will be seen that the
chondrocranium of Gnathostomes consists essentially of a posterior basal
plate to which the auditory capsules become attached, and an anterior
trabecular region connected with the nasal capsules. Further, that the
primitive side wall is derived from an orbital cartilage which joins the
basal plate by means of a pila antotica. To these structures belonging to
the neurocranium proper becomes connected the visceral palatoquadrate
arch by an otic process to the auditory capsule above and a basal process
to the trabecular region below (palatobasal or ' basipterygoid ' articulation). On such a fundamental plan is built the skull of all Gnathostomes (with the possible exception of the palatobasal articulation in
Chondrichthyes).

## DERMAL BONES OF THE HEAD IN OSTEICHTHYES [2]

Covering the whole body, head, trunk, tail, and fins of Chondrichthyes are closely set dermal denticles ; moreover, these penetrate by

[1] In spite of Stensiö's contention, it is not generally accepted that a true
myodome existed in the Osteolepidoti and Coelacanthini.

[2] For the convenience of the reader a list of the names and synonyms of
the chief bones of the head is given below :

Cranial dermal covering bones : Nasal, frontal, parietal, premaxillary
(premaxilla), maxillary (maxilla), lacrimal (lachrymal), prefrontal, postfrontal, intertemporal, supratemporal (squamosal, suprasquamosal, supra-
mastoid), squamosal (mastoid, supratemporal ; the names squamosal and
supratemporal have been interchanged, but it is now generally agreed to call
the upper more dorsal bone supratemporal, and the lower outer bone squamosal) ; jugal (malar), quadratojugal (paraquadrate of Gaupp in Crocodile,
quadrato-maxillary of Gaupp in Stegocephalia, etc.), postorbital, tabular
(epiotic), post-parietal (dermo-supraoccipital, which with the tabulars may
form a transverse row of bones sometimes called supratemporals), septomaxillary (may penetrate into nasal capsule). Certain of these dermal bones
may have ingrowths invading the chondrocranium : the prefrontal may then
be called lateral ethmoid, ectethmoid ; the postfrontal, sphenotic ; the supratemporal, pterotic.

Paired dermal bones of opercular fold and lower jaw : Opercular, preopercular, subopercular, interopercular, dentary (dentale), angular, supra-angular
(surangular), splenial (opercular), postsplenial (preangular), prearticular
(goniale), coronoid (complementary), lateral gulars (become branchiostegal

the mouth to the inner margin of the lips where they are modified into teeth, and may spread further over that part of the lining of the buccal cavity which is derived from the stomodaeum, and may also penetrate through the gill-slits to the inner surface of the gill-bars (p. 441). Similarly, denticles or their derivatives cover the head in Ostracodermi, and, in those forms where underlying skeletal dermal plates are developed, these are found especially on the head region where they may form large shields arranged in definite patterns. In the same way the bony covering of the head, so characteristic of the Osteichthyes and their descendants the Tetrapoda, is formed of plates originally of just the same histological structure as the body scales and of the same complex origin. They are made up by the combination of superficial denticles with underlying bony plates separately developed in the lower layers of the dermis. In the early and more primitive Teleostomes (Osteolepids) and Dipnoi (*Dipterus*) the head plates, like the body scales, are of cosmoid structure ; but the outer cosmoid layer tends to disappear, leaving in later forms and their modern survivors only bone (p. 304). The early and more primitive Actinopterygii likewise started with head plates similar in structure to the ganoid scales ; and in this group also the plates soon become simplified, losing the outer ganoine and retaining only the deeper bony layers (p. 294). The denticles may also be present (Goodrich, 35).

Primitively these scales and plates in Osteichthyes formed a complete covering to the head, leaving only openings for the mouth, nostrils, paired eyes, pineal eye, spiracles, and gills. They acquire a larger size than the body scales either by growth or by fusion, and are usually more rigidly connected with each other ; allowing, however, for the necessary motion of parts, such as the lower jaw and opercular fold covering the openings of the branchial slits. The chief dermal bones are relatively few in number

---

rays). Median dermal bones : Internasal or rostral (median ethmoid), interfrontal, interparietal (probably not homologous in fishes and Tetrapods), intergular.

Paired dermal bones of palate : Prevomer (vomer, anterior paired vomer), palatine, ectopterygoid (transverse, transpalatine), endopterygoid (mesopterygoid, pterygoid of Tetrapod). Median parasphenoid (parabasal basitemporal, vomer of mammal).

Ossifications of chondrocranium : supraoccipital, exoccipital (lateral occipital, pleuroccipital), basioccipital, opisthotic (paroccipital), pro-otic (otosphenoid, together with opisthotic probably = mammalian petrosal or periotic), epiotic of Teleostome, basisphenoid, orbitosphenoid, presphenoid of doubtful occurrence, mesethmoid, pleurosphenoid (' alisphenoid ', laterosphenoid of Crocodile and bird), pterosphenoid of Teleostome. Endochondral bones of palatoquadrate are the quadrate, metapterygoid, autopalatine, and epipterygoid = alisphenoid of mammal.

and disposed according to a regular and bilaterally symmetrical pattern. A fundamental plan can be made out common to all the Osteichthyes and even to the Tetrapoda, although variable in detail and subject to much modification owing to divergent specialisation in various groups. For the identification and comparison of individual bones and the successful tracing out of homologies in spite of such modifications, it is important to notice that the distribution of the lateral-line organs and

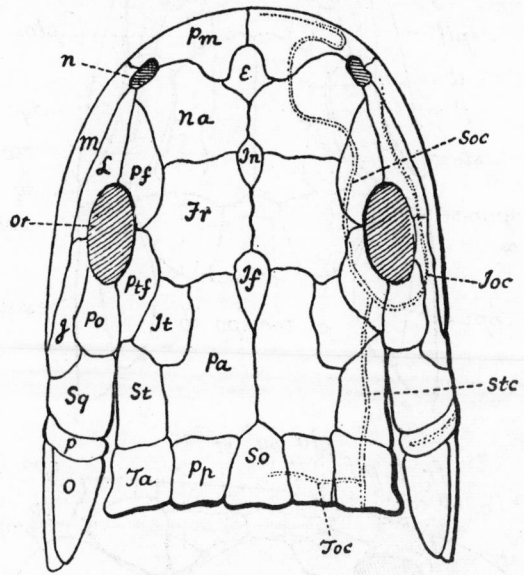

FIG. 290.

Diagram of fundamental plan of roofing-bones of skull in *Pisces*. Dorsal view of primitive representative of Osteichthyes (E. S. Goodrich, *Linn. Soc. J. Zool.*, 1925). *E*, Ethmoid or median rostral; *Er*, frontal; *If*, interfrontal; *In*, internasal; *Ioc*, infraorbital canal; *J*, jugal; *L*, lacrimal; *M*, maxillary; *N*, external nostril; *Na*, nasal; *O*, opercular; *Or*, orbit; *P*, preopercular; *Pa*, parietal; *Pf*, prefrontal; *Pm*, premaxillary; *Po*, postorbital; *Pp*, postparietal; *Ptf*, postfrontal; *So*, dermal supraoccipital; *Soc*, supraorbital canal; *Stc*, postorbital and temporal canal; *Sq*, squamosal; *Ta*, tabular; *Toc*, transverse occipital canal. Course of lateral-line canals shown on right side.

course of the lateral-line canals are on the whole remarkably constant in all the aquatic Gnathostomes. The organs also conform to a common plan with supratemporal, transverse occipital, supraorbital, infraorbital, postorbital, jugal, preopercular, oral and mandibular canals on the head (Chapter XIV.). Now, just as the lateral-line canal of the trunk comes to pierce a row of scales, so the canals of the head become embedded in dermal bones ; consequently a relation becomes established between a canal and certain particular bones lying along its course. Although subject to minor alterations among more specialised forms, and although the lateral-line

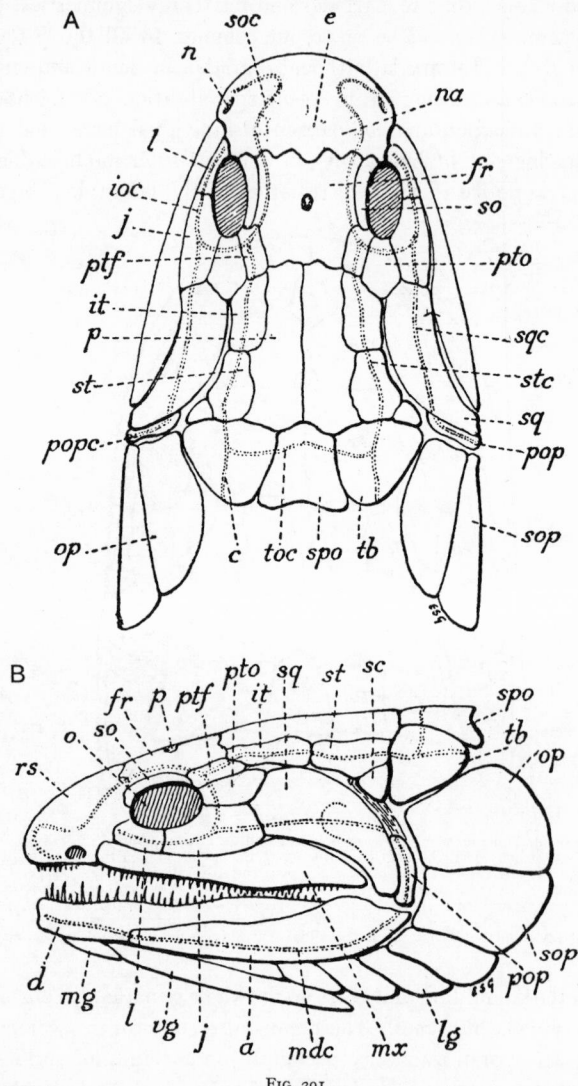

Fig. 291.

Restoration of head of *Osteolepis macrolepidotus*, dorsal view, A; left-side view, B. Course of lateral-line canals in bones shown in dotted lines (E. S. Goodrich, *Linn. Soc. J. Zool.*, 1919). *a*, Angular; *c*, main trunk canal; *d*, dentary; *e*, ethmoid included in rostral shield; *fr*, frontals fused and enclosing pineal foramen; *ioc*, infraorbital canal; *it*, intertemporal; *j*, jugal; *l*, lacrimal; *lg*, lateral gular; *mdc*, mandibular canal; *mg*, median gular; *mx*, maxillary; *n*, nostril; *na*, nasal included in rostral shield; *o*, orbit; *op*, opercular; *p*, pineal opening; *pop*, preopercular; *popc*, preopercular canal; *ptf*, postfrontal; *pto*, postorbital; *rs*, rostral shield; *sc*, plate overhanging hyomandibular; *so*, supraorbital; *soc*, supraorbital canal; *sop*, suboperclar; *spo*, dermal supraoccipital; *sq*, squamosal; *sqc*, jugal canal; *st*, supratemporal or pterotic; *stc*, postorbital and temporal canal; *tb*, tabular; *toc*, transverse occipital canal; *vg*, ventral paired gular.

system may frequently become secondarily freed from the bones when these sink below the surface in higher forms, yet the disposition of the canals is of much value in determining the homologies of the cranial bones in the lower fish and amphibians. Many of the dermal bones also become closely associated with certain parts of the underlying chondrocranium and visceral arches.

The general plan of the dermal bones of a hypothetical primitive fish is shown in Fig. 290. A double series of paired nasals, frontals, and parietals form a roof to the chondrocranium. A prefrontal, postfrontal, lacrimal, postorbital, and jugal complete the orbit; while the margin of the upper jaw is strengthened by the premaxillary and maxillary bearing teeth. The external nostril is apparently on the ventral surface of the snout. Over the occipital region lies a row of bones containing a median occipital and paired postparietals and tabulars. An intertemporal and supratemporal overhang the space occupied by the jaw muscles, which is covered at the side by one or more 'cheek plates' (squamosal and quadratojugal ?). The latter cover the quadrate region. The lower jaw has a marginal dentary bearing teeth, a large angular passing

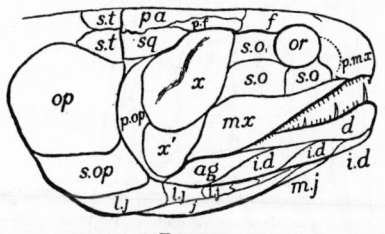

FIG. 292.

Restoration of head of *Rhizodopsis sauroides* (after Traquair, from A. S. Woodward, *Outlines of Vert. Palaeont.*, 1898). *ag*, Angular; *f*, frontal shield; *i.d*, infradentaries ; *j*, paired inferior gular; *l.j*, lateral gulars; *m.j*, median inferior gular ; *pa*, parietal; *p.f*, postfrontal; *s.o*, suborbital plates ; *sq*, supratemporal; *s.t*, tabular and dermal supraoccipital; *x*, squamosal ? ; *x′*, quadratojugal ?

back over the articulation, and probably a supra-angular as well. In front of the angular should perhaps be added infradentaries.

The hyoid region, behind the spiracle, has a preopercular over the hyomandibula, and a series of bones supporting the opercular fold which reaches forwards ventrally between the rami of the lower jaw ; these are the opercular, subopercular, interopercular, and lateral gulars. Paired ventral gulars and a median anterior gular fill up the space between them.

Such are the chief covering bones, most of which can be identified in the majority of primitive fish. But there are other elements less constant but nevertheless to be considered as primitive. These are a number of plates on the snout between the premaxillaries and nasals, of which a median ethmoid or rostral is the most important, and an occasional small internasal and interfrontal which together with the occipital are probably the remains of the median series of trunk scales continued on to the head.

**Teleostomi.**—As an example of a primitive Teleostome we may take *Osteolepis* (Pander, 1860; Huxley, **533**; Traquair, **619**; A. S. Woodward, **231**; Gregory, **523**; Watson and Gill, **648**; Goodrich, **518**). In all essentials it agrees with our hypothetical form, Fig. 291.

The cheek, however, is covered by a single bone instead of by two as in some Osteolepids, and *Holoptychius, Glyptopomus,* and the Rhizodontids, *Rhizodopsis,* and *Eusthenopteron,* Fig. 292.

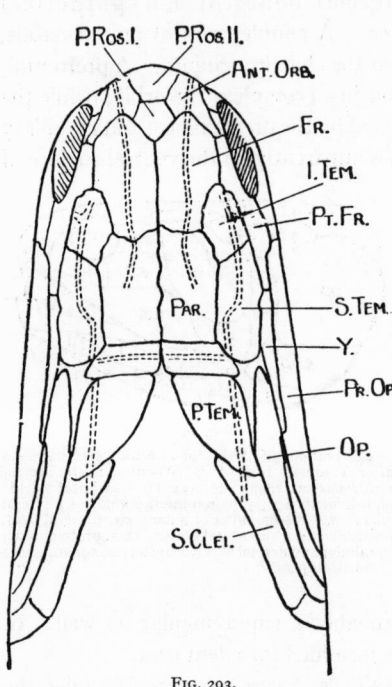

The Coelacanthini have departed considerably from the primitive plan (Huxley, **533**; A. S. Woodward, **663**; Wellburn, **649**; Stensiö, **605, 218**; Watson, **645**). They are remarkable for the extension of the parietals and frontals apparently at the expense of some of the neighbouring bones, the large size of the operculum, and absence of lateral gulars and pineal foramen. According to Stensiö two nasal apertures are present on the nasal (?) in *Axelia.* Two conspicuous series of five or more parafrontals border the frontal and nasal regions. A transverse row of six bones represents the postparietal and tabular series. All the Crossopterygii seem to have been distinguished by the formation of a transverse joint between frontals and parietals allowing for some bending in this region (Watson, **644-5**).

Fig. 293.

Dorsal view of skull of *Cheirolepis trailli,* Middle Old Red Sandstone, Scotland; restored (from D. M. S. Watson, *Proc. Zool. Soc.,* 1925). *Ant.Orb,* Antorbital (nasal); *Fr,* frontal; *I.Tem,* intertemporal; *Op,* opercular; *P.Ros.I, P.Ros.II,* postrostrals; *P.Tem,* posttemporal; *Par,* parietal; *Pr.Op,* preopercular; *Pt.Fr,* postfrontal; *S.Clei,* supracleithrum; *S.Tem,* supratemporal; *Y,* a dorso-lateral bone.

While the Actinopterygii conform in essentials to the fundamental plan, yet they have become specialised in a manner which diverges from that adopted by the Crossopterygii on the one hand and the Dipnoi on the other, perhaps in association with the development of hyostylic jaws, and the shifting of the nostrils on to the side of the snout. There is no intertemporal. Like the Coelacanthini and Dipnoi they have lost the pineal foramen.

The most primitive structure is, of course, displayed by the early fossil Chondrostei (Traquair, 614, 616, 620; A. S. Woodward, 663 ;

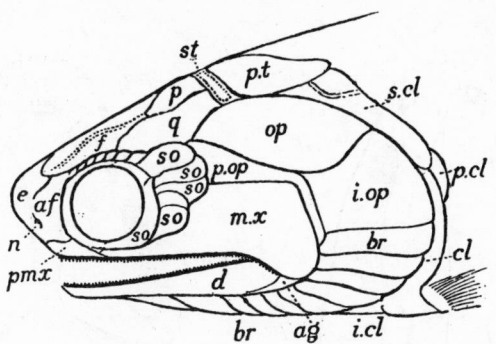

FIG. 294.

Restoration of head of *Palaeoniscus macropomus* (after Traquair, from A. S. Woodward, *Outlines of Vert. Palaeont.*, 1898). *af*, Prefrontal; *ag*, angular; *br*, lateral gulars (branchiostegal rays); *cl*, cleithrum; *d*, dentary; *e*, rostral; *f*, frontal; *i.cl*, clavicle; *i.op*, subopercular; *m.x*, maxillary; *n*, nostril; *op*, opercular; *p*, parietal; *p.cl*, postcleithrum; *pmx*, premaxillary; *p.op*, preopercular; *p.t*, post-temporal; *q*, supratemporal (pterotic); *s.cl*, supracleithrum; *so*, circum- and post-orbitals ; *st*, postparietal (+tabular ?).

Watson, 646 ; Stensiö, 218). The Palaeoniscoidei differ from the Osteolepids in the absence of a median occipital, and of large paired ventral gulars, and in the characteristic modification of the bones on the cheek. Here the maxilla is greatly expanded, and above it is a peculiar bent plate which probably represents the squamosal and preopercular. In the Devonian *Cheirolepis* these appear to be separate, Figs. 293 - 4. The rostrals, of which several are still present in Palaeoniscids, become much reduced in other Actinopterygii. In these the double nostrils are generally between the nasal and antorbital, and the latter disappears in the Teleostei. All the dermal plates have a covering of ganoine in Palaeoniscoidei.

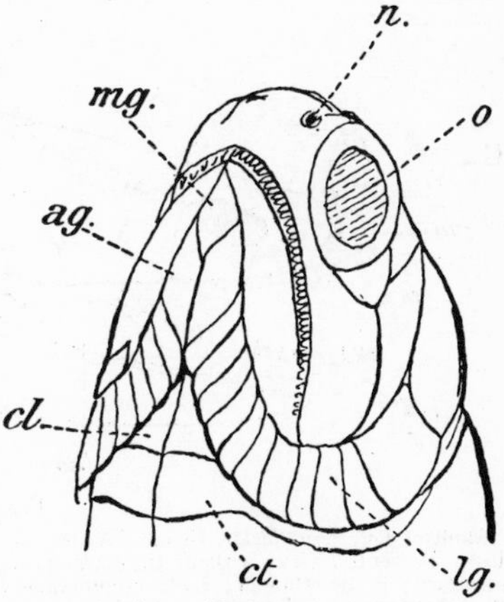

The dermal head plates of *Polypterus* have been studied by Traquair (613), Pollard (575), Allis (410), and others, and generally compared to those of the Osteolepids,

FIG. 295.

Oblique ventral view of the head of *Gonatodus punctatus*, Ag.; Calciferous Sandstone, Wardie. (After Traquair.) *ag*, Enlarged anterior lateral gular; *cl*, clavicle; *ct*, cleithrum; *lg*, lateral gular; *mg*, median gular; *n*, nostril; *o*, orbit. (From Goodrich, *Vert. Craniata*, 1909.)

with which extinct fishes Huxley believed the Polypterini to be allied (533). But *Polypterus* resembles the Palaeoniscids much more

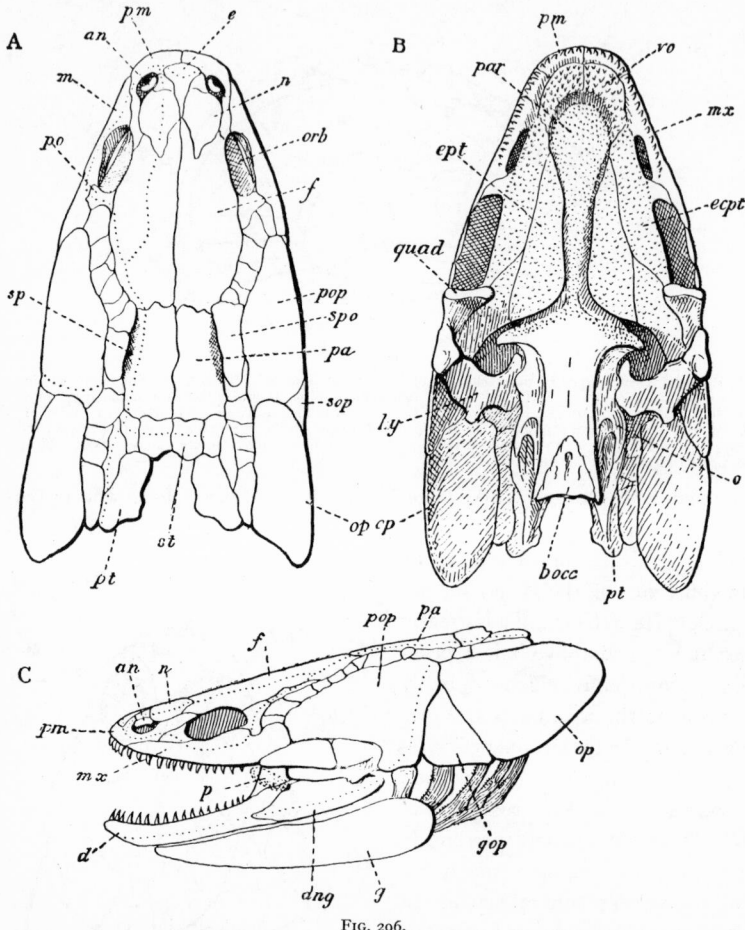

FIG. 296.

Skull of *Polypterus bichir*, Geoffr. A, Dorsal, and C, lateral view (modified from J. Müller and Allis) ; B, ventral view, without the lower jaw. *an*, Adnasal ; *ang*, angular ; *bocc*, basioccipital ; *d*, dentary ; *e*, mesethmoid ; *ecpt*, ectopterygoid ; *ept*, endopterygoid ; *f*, frontal ; *g*, paired gular ; *gop*, suboperculum ; *hy*, hyomandibular ; *m*, maxilla ; *n*, nasal ; *o*, opisthotic ; *op*, opercular ; *orb*, orbit ; *p*, labial cartilage (dotted) ; *pa*, parietal ; *par*, parasphenoid ; *pm*, premaxilla ; *po*, postorbital ; *pop*, preopercular ; *pt*, post-temporal ; *quad*, quadrate ; *sop*, suboperculum ; *sp*, spiracle ; *spo*, spiracular plate ; *st*, postparietal ; *vo*, vomer? A dotted line indicates the course of the lateral-line canal. (From Goodrich, *Vert. Craniata*, 1909.)

closely in the number and disposition of the plates, as it does in so many other characters (Goodrich, 35, 520). A ganoid layer covers their surfaces. The supratemporal appears to have fused with the parietal ;

there is the same bent plate extending over the hyoid and lateral temporal regions (certainly representing the preoperculum, and probably the squamosal as well). The rostral region is very similar, and a series of small plates extend from the orbit to the supratemporal, overlying the spiracular opening ('spiracular ossicles'). The median and lateral gulars have disappeared with the exception of two large ventral plates [1] (Goodrich, 35, 520).

Still more modified are the Acipenseroidei, Figs. 298, 434. Accompany-

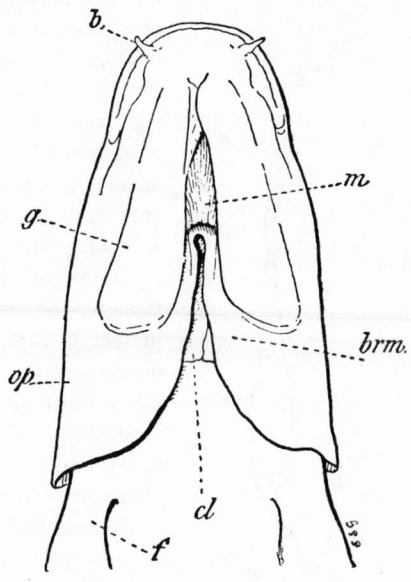

FIG. 297.

*Polypterus lapradii*, Stdr. Ventral view of head. *b*, Barbel; *brm*, branchiostegal membrane; *cl*, clavicle; *f*, pectoral fin; *g*, paired gular plate; *m*, intergular membrane; *op*, opercular region. (From Goodrich, *Vert. Craniata*, 1909.)

ing the development of a large rostrum and the reduction of the mouth, jaws, and teeth, the plates round the orbit are reduced, the rostral plates replaced by numerous ossicles, and the cheek plates, median gular, and angular lost. *Chondrosteus* of the Lias still has several lateral gulars, but in living genera these have disappeared and the opercular bones are more or less vestigial (Traquair, 620). Moreover, in Sturgeons the sucking mouth has very reduced jaws and no teeth in the adult. Although the

[1] Since the maxillary in *Polypterus* is traversed by the infraorbital lateral-line canal, and develops medially to the lip fold, Allis and Sewertzoff believe it to be a suborbital.

roofing bones are well developed, they, like all the exoskeleton, have lost all trace of ganoine.

The Saurichthyidae (Belonorhynchidae) are a specialised group which seem to be allied to the Palaeoniscidae and Acipenseroidei. They possess a very elongated rostrum and lower jaw, large frontals and supratemporals, but reduced parietals and no median or lateral gulars (A. S. Woodward, 663 ; Stensiö, 134).

The Holostei show great diversity of detail in the covering bones of the head. The more primitive forms (Amioidei) have not departed much from our fundamental plan, Figs. 299-301. The bones are still superficial, except the prefrontal, though the original ganoine present in early fossils tends to disappear and is quite lost in the modern *Amia*. The transverse series of occipital plates is reduced to two, the cheek plates are lost, and the hind end of the maxilla is freed (a supramaxillary (cheek plate ?) is attached to its upper border). The opercular bones have become established as a set of four present in all Holostei except in very specialised forms. These are a large preopercular attached to the hyomandibular and quadrate, below it an interopercular

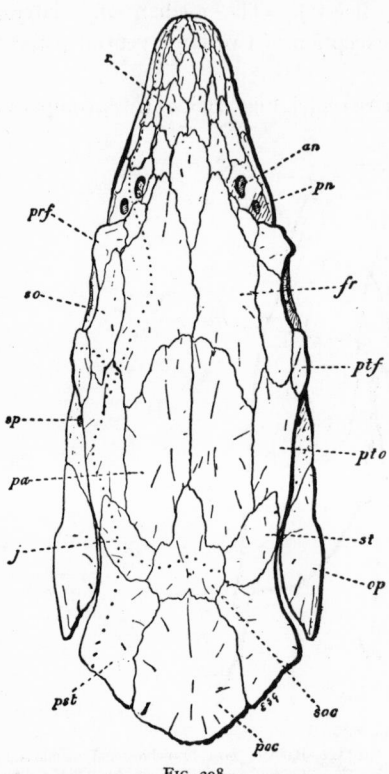

FIG. 298.

Skull of *Acipenser sturio*, L. ; dorsal view. A dotted line indicates the lateral line according to Collinge. *an*, Anterior nostril ; *fr*, frontal ; *j*, junction of postorbital, occipital, and trunk branches of lateral-line system ; *op*, opercular ; *pa*, parietal ; *pn*, posterior nostril ; *poc*, postoccipital ; *prf*, prefrontal ; *pst*, posttemporal ; *ptf*, postfrontal ; *pto*, pterotic ; *r*, rostral plates ; *so*, supraorbital ; *soc*, supraoccipital ; *sp*. spiracle ; *st*, tabular ? (From Goodrich, *Vert. Craniata*, 1909.)

of doubtful homology, a broad opercular, and a subopercular. The median gular is well developed in Amioidei ; but the lateral gulars are very narrow and have become converted into the so-called branchiostegal rays characteristic of the Holostei (Franque, 1847 ; Shufeldt, 85 ; Bridge, 429 ; Allis, 401-3).

The highly specialised Pycnodontidae have a remarkable and inconstant arrangement of the bones. Median plates separate the parietals, and numerous small plates cover the occipital region, the snout, and the space between the rami of the lower jaw (Woodward, 231, 663).

The modern *Lepidosteus,* which appears to be a specialised derivative of the Semionotidae (Traquair), with a long snout carrying the nostrils

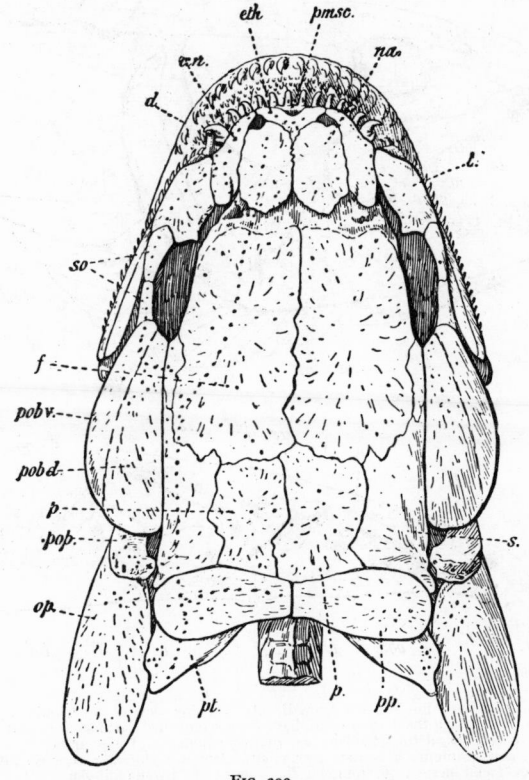

FIG. 299.

Dorsal view of the skull of *Amia calva,* L. (after Allis). The course of the lateral-line system is indicated by a dotted line on the left side. *an,* Adnasal ; *d,* dentary ; *eth,* mesethmoid ; *f,* frontal ; *l,* lachrymal or first suborbital ; *na,* nasal ; *op,* opercular ; *p,* parietal ; *pmsc,* premaxilla ; *pobd* and *pobv,* dorsal and ventral postorbitals ; *pop,* preopercular ; *pp,* postparietal ; *pt,* post-temporal ; *s,* pterotic (supratemporal) ; *so,* suborbitals. (From Goodrich, *Vert. Craniata,* 1909.)

at its extremity, is also much modified (J. Müller, 1846 ; Balfour and Parker, 2 ; Collinge, 476 ; Regan, 577). The premaxillaries extend over a great part of the snout and the maxillaries are represented by series of small bones. Small plates cover the cheek. Owing to the forward position of the articulation of the jaws, Fig. 302, the opercular apparatus is strangely modified, the preopercular being reduced and situated in front of the enlarged interopercular.   However, the homology of these bones is still doubtful, the posterior bone which contains the 'hyomandibular' lateral-line canal being considered by many to be the

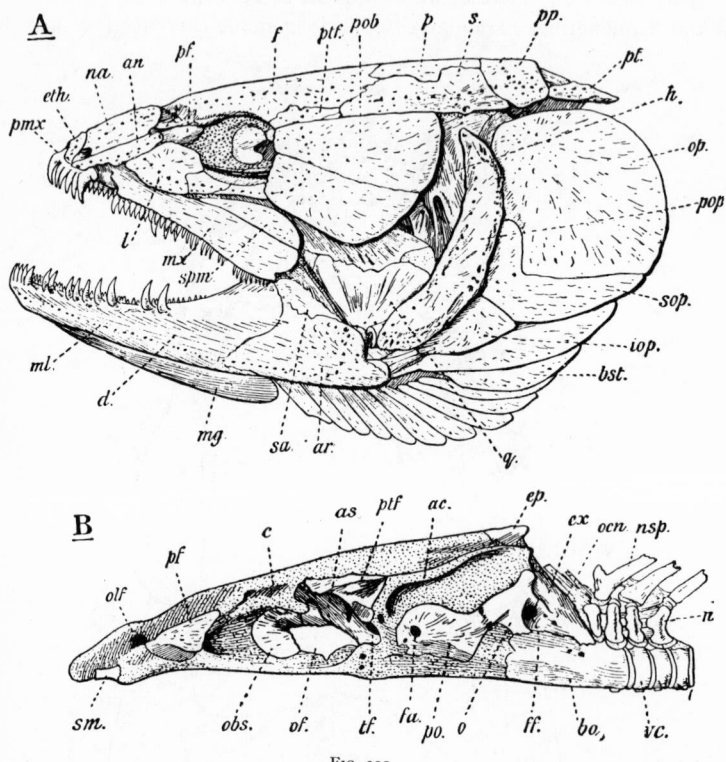

FIG. 300.

*Amia calva*, L. (after Allis, slightly altered).  A, Left-side view of the skull ;  B, left-side view of the cranium, from which the dermal bones have been removed.  Cartilage is dotted.  *ac*, Auditory capsule ;  *an*, adnasal ;  *ar*, derm-articular ;  *as*, pterosphenoid ;  *bo*, basioccipital ;  *bst*, branchiostegal ray ;  *c*, cartilaginous cranium ;  *d*, dentary ;  *ep*, epiotic ;  *eth*, mesethmoid ;  *ex*, exoccipital ;  *f*, frontal ; *fa*, foramen for facial nerve ;  *ff*, foramen for vagus ;  *h*, hyomandibular ;  *iop*, interopercular ; *l*, lacrimal ;  *mg*, median gular ;  *ml*, lateral line in mandible ;  *mx*, maxilla ;  *n*, neural arch ;  *na*, nasal ;  *nsp*, neural spine ;  *o*, opisthotic ;  *obs*, orbitosphenoid ;  *ocn*, foramen for spino-occipital nerve ;  *of*, vacuity with optic foramen in front ;  *olf*, olfactory capsule ;  *op*, opercular ;  *p*, parietal ; *pf*, prefrontal ;  *pmx*, premaxilla ;  *po*, pro-otic ;  *pob*, postorbital ;  *pop*, preopercular ;  *pp*, postparietal ;  *pt*, post-temporal ;  *ptf*, postfrontal ;  *q*, quadrate ;  *s*, pterotic ;  *sa*, supra-angular ; *sm*, 'septomaxillary' ;  *sop*, subopercular ;  *spm*, supramaxilla ;  *tf*, trigeminal foramen ;  *vc*, vertebral centrum.  (From Goodrich, *Vert. Craniata*, 1909.)

preopercular, Fig. 302.  The ganoine layer is well developed on all the superficial dermal bones.

Lastly, in the Teleostei the thin covering of ganoine, still present in the extinct Leptolepidae, soon disappears altogether, and the dermal bones tend to sink more and more below the soft tissues.   This leads in

higher forms to the subdivision of those which harbour lateral-line canals
into deep-lying plates and independent, more superficial, narrow grooved
'canal bones' (Goodrich, 35).     The latter remain near the surface
forming more or less complete chains of ossicles protecting the canals,
Fig. 303 (Bruch, 1862 ; Allis, 403-5 ; Cole, 475).    The supratemporal

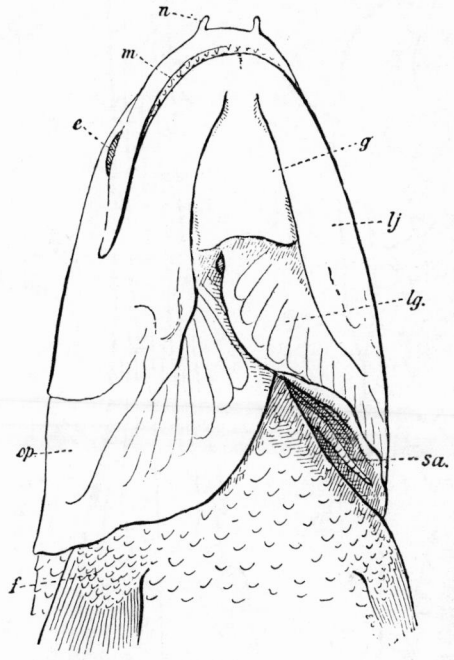

FIG. 301.

Head of *Amia calva*, L. ; oblique ventral view.  *e*, Eye ;  *f*, pectoral fin ;  *g*, median gular plate ;
*lg*, lateral gulars or branchiostegal rays ;  *lj*, lower jaw ;  *m*, mouth ;  *n*, nostril ;  *op*, operculum ;
*sa*, serrated appendage.  (From Goodrich, *Vert. Craniata*, 1909.)

(pterotic) invades the posterior region of the auditory capsule as the
prefrontal (sphenotic) does in front (p. 376).

The tabulars and postparietals become reduced and finally disappear
(except in so far as they may be represented by canal bones).    The lower
jaw retains only a small angular behind (the supra-angular has perhaps
fused with the articular).    A median gular persists very rarely (*Elops*,
Fig. 304).

While in Cypriniformes the roofing bones may still be superficial
(forming a posterior shield in combination with the post-temporal
and supracleithral in some Siluridae), in most Teleosts the frontals and

parietals sink deeply below the soft tissues and prolongations of the

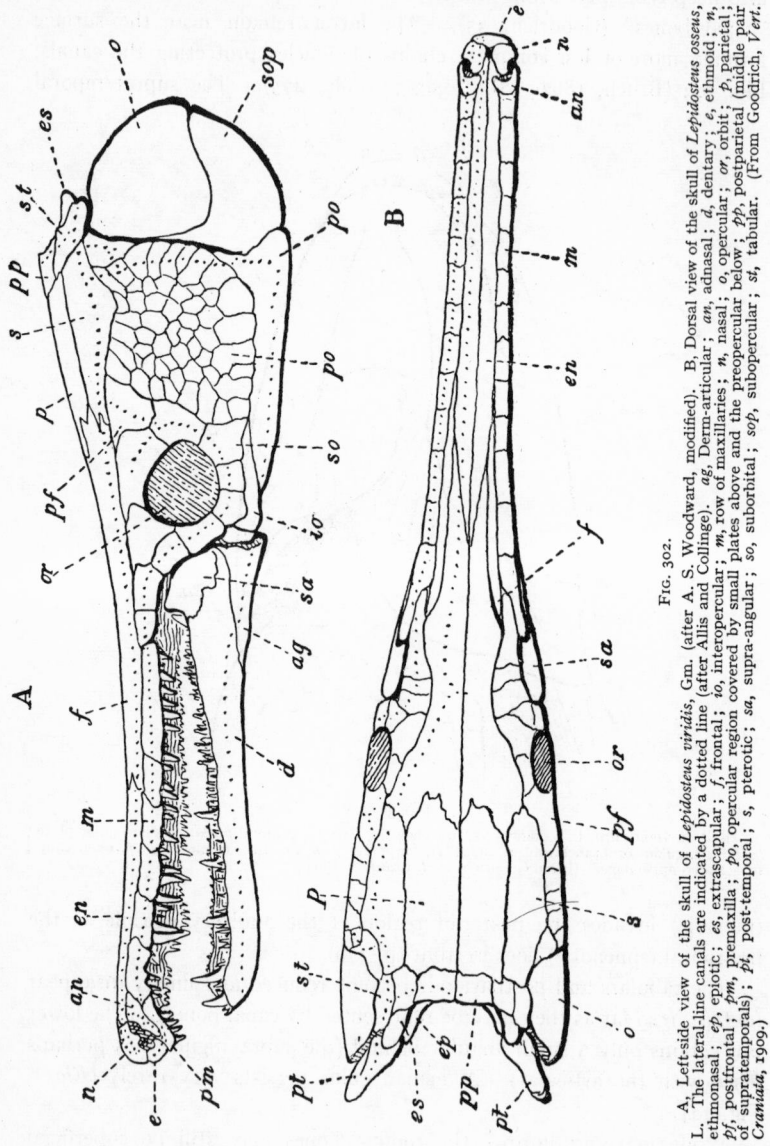

FIG. 302.

A, Left-side view of the skull of *Lepidosteus viridis*, Gm. (after A. S. Woodward, modified). B, Dorsal view of the skull of *Lepidosteus osseus*, L. The lateral-line canals are indicated by a dotted line (after Allis and Collinge). *ag*, Derm-articular; *an*, adnasal; *d*, dentary; *e*, ethmoid; *n*, ethmonasal; *ep*, epiotic; *es*, extrascapular; *f*, frontal; *io*, interopercular; *m*, row of maxillaries; *n*, nasal; *o*, opercular; *or*, orbit; *p*, parietal; *pf*, postfrontal; *pm*, premaxilla; *po*, opercular region covered by small plates above and the preopercular below; *pp*, postparietal (middle pair of supratemporals); *pt*, post-temporal; *s*, pterotic; *sa*, supra-angular; *so*, suborbital; *sop*, subopercular; *st*, tabular. (From Goodrich, *Vert. Cranida*, 1909.)

anterior myomeres, Figs. 303, 305. Ordinary scales may then secondarily extend over the greater part of the head in higher Acanthopterygii. In these also the parietals usually become separated by the supraoccipital (Sagemehl, 378; Bridge, 434; Boulenger, 426; Ridewood, 578-81; Gegenbaur, 516; Allis, 405; Goodrich, 35; etc.).

The marginal jaw bones often become much specialised in Teleosts. In Siluroids the maxilla may be reduced to a nodule supporting the cartilaginous axis of the barbel. Most of the higher groups have enlarged premaxillaries bordering the mouth, and the maxillaries modified into a toothless bone lying behind it separately articulated to the ethmoid

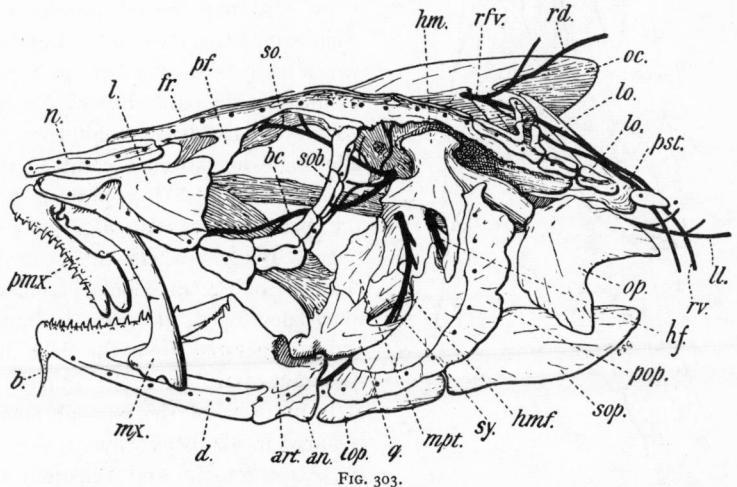

FIG. 303.

Left-side view of skull of *Gadus morrhua*, showing branches of facial nerve, and course of lateral-line system (by a series of dots), partly after Cole. *an*, Angular; *art*, articular; *b*, barbel; *bc*, buccal branch of facial supplying suborbital canal; *d*, dentary; *fr*, frontal; *hf*, hyoidean branch; *hm*, hyomandibula; *hmf*, hyomandibular branch of facial supplying its lateral-line canal; *iop*, interopercular; *l*, 'lachrymal'; *ll*, lateral-line branch of vagus; *lo*, lateral-line ossicles; *mpt*, metapterygoid; *mx*, maxilla; *n*, nasal; *oc*, crest of supraoccipital; *op*, opercular; *pf*, prefrontal; *pmx*, premaxilla; *pop*, preopercular; *pst*, post-temporal; *q*, quadrate; *rd*, branch supplying region of dorsal fin; *rfv*, dorsal recurrent branch of facial; *rv*, branch supplying region of pectoral fin; *so*, superior ophthalmic branch supplying supraorbital canal; *sob*, suborbital; *sop*, subopercular; *sy*, symplectic.

region of the skull, and no longer forming the margin of the mouth, Figs. 286, 303.

**Palate in Teleostomi.**—The dermal bones on the palate are more constant than the outer covering bones. Most of them can easily be traced from the earliest Osteichthyes to the Tetrapoda. Originally they were doubtless developed as basal plates to support patches of teeth, and similar bones occur regularly on the inner surface of the lower jaw and even in many Teleostomes spread over the inner surface of the gill bars. The teeth, however, may be lost in specialisation. These internal dermal bones, of course, never develop a cosmoid or a ganoid layer.

Below the chondrocranium is the median parasphenoid, found in

Crossopterygii below the orbito-temporal region only, Fig. 306 B (Bryant, 465 ; Watson, 644 ; Stensiö, 606) ; but extending farther back in Actinopterygii, Figs. 296, 307, sometimes even beyond the occipital region as in Acipenseroidei. It tends to develop a strong transverse process supporting the basitrabecular process of the basisphenoid region, and another more posterior lateral process or wing[1] supporting the outer wall of the trigemino-facialis chamber (p. 277).

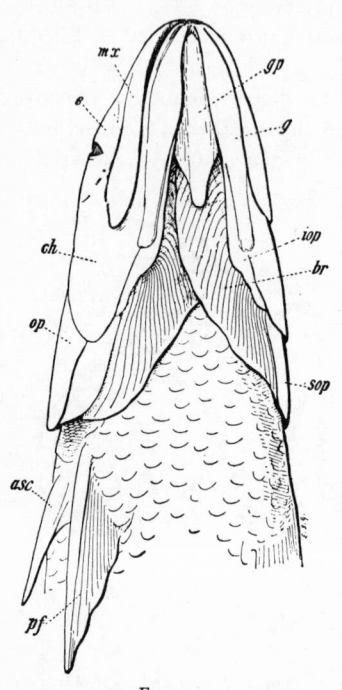

FIG. 304.

Head of *Elops saurus*, L.; oblique ventral view. *asc*, Axillary scale ; *br*, branchiostegal ray ; *ch*, preopercular region ; *e*, fold of skin over eye ; *g*, lower jaw ; *gp*, gular plate ; *iop*, interopercular region ; *mx*, maxilla ; *op*, opercular ; *pf*, pectoral fin ; *sop*, subopercular. (From Goodrich, *Vert. Craniata*, 1909.)

Primitively the parasphenoid closely adheres to the basis cranii, though allowing the internal carotids to reach the fenestra hypophyseos by the parabasal canals, Fig. 308 ; [2] but in Teleosts where the ventral chamber of the myodome becomes much developed, it may become widely separated from the floor of the brain-cavity (p. 279). Immediately in front of the parasphenoid is found in all Osteichthyes (except the Acipenseroidei and Teleostei) a pair of prevomers, underlying the ethmoid region and generally strongly toothed (p. 284). *Acipenser* and the Teleostei are distinguished by the possession of a median prevomer, Fig. 286 ; since, however, it shows signs of paired origin in *Salmo* (Gaupp, 343) and is stated by Walther (630) to arise from paired rudiments in *Esox*, this bone probably represents the two prevomers fused.

[1] This wing is often called the ' process ascendens ', inappropriately since this name is applied to. a dorsal process of the palatoquadrate (p. 423).

[2] When the bony parasphenoid is developed below the basis cranii there become enclosed between them the internal carotid arteries running forwards to the fenestra hypophyseos and the accompanying sympathetic nerves in so-called parabasal canals (Gaupp, 508, Fig. 308). The palatine nerve may also enter the canal and continue forward between the basitrabecular process and the basipterygoid process of the parasphenoid in a prolongation of the parabasal canal, which may be distinguished as the Vidian or basipterygoid canal (enclosing Vidian nerve and palatine artery, see p. 272).

The remaining internal dermal bones are developed on the visceral arches, and many of them are closely associated with corresponding cartilage bones in these arches.   On the anterior end of the palatoquadrate is a dermal palatine generally much toothed (accessory palatines may

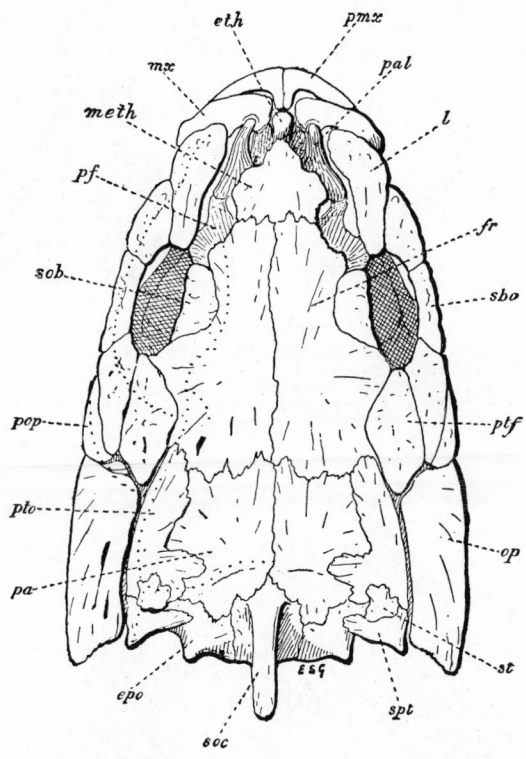

FIG. 305.

Dorsal view of the skull of *Cyprinus carpio*, L.   A dotted line indicates the lateral-line canals on the left side.   *epo*, Epiotic; *eth*, pre-ethmoid (rostral) ; *fr*, frontal ; *l*, lacrimal ; *meth*, mesethmoid ; *mx*, maxilla ; *op*, opercular ; *pa*, parietal ; *pal*, palatine ; *pf*, prefrontal ; *pmx*, premaxilla ; *pop*, preopercular ; *ptf*, postfrontal ; *pto*, pterotic ; *sob*, supraorbital ; *soc*, supraoccipital ; *spt*, tabular ? *st*, anterior supratemporal.   (From Goodrich, *Vert. Craniata*, 1909.)

occur as in *Amia*, Fig. 429).   Further back the palatoquadrate bears several ' pterygoid ' bones, of which three are typically present throughout the Teleostomes.   These are a large pterygoid (endopterygoid), an ecto-pterygoid joining it to the maxilla, and a metapterygoid.   The first two are dermal bones, usually toothed ; the metapterygoid is developed as a cartilage bone (Parker, 560 ; Gaupp, 343 ; and others).   This metaptery-goid is primitively articulated to the basitrabecular process (p. 421).   The

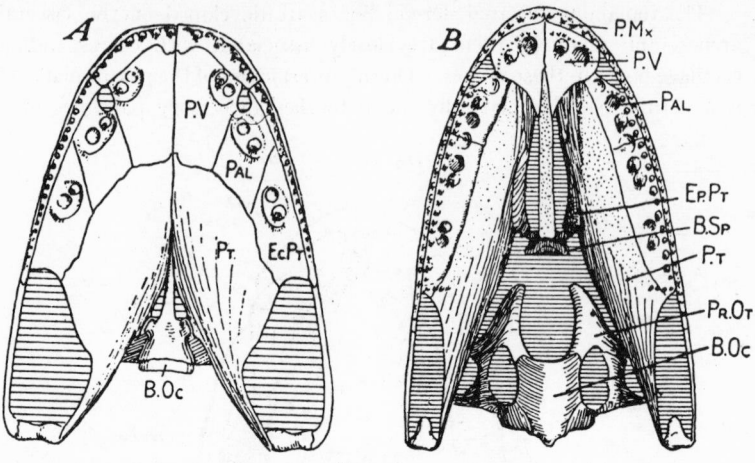

FIG. 306.

Ventral view of skull of A, *Baphetes Kirkbyi*, Middle Coal Measures, Fifeshire ; B, *Eusthenopteron*, Upper Old Red Sandstone, Canada (from D. M. S., Watson, *Tr. Roy. Soc.*, 1926).  *B.Oc*, Basi-occipital ;  *B.Sp*, basisphenoid ;  *Ec.Pt*, ectopterygoid ;  *Ep.Pt*, epipterygoid ;  *Pal*, palatine ;  *P.Mx*, premaxillary ;  *Pr.Ot*, pro-otic ;  *Pt*, pterygoid ;  *P.V*, prevomer.   Parasphenoid covers and projects forwards from basisphenoid.   Internal nostril between *P.V* and *Pal*.

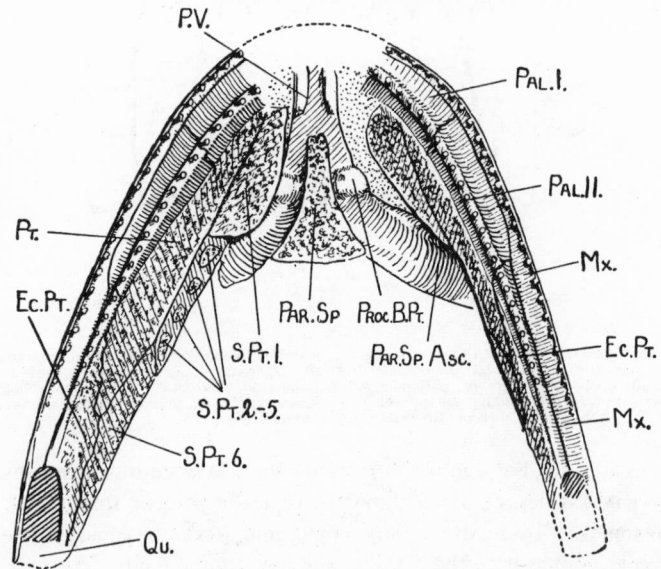

FIG. 307.

*Elonichthys binneyi* : ventral view of palate (from D. M. S. Watson, *Proc. Zool. Soc.*, 1925). *Ec.Pt*, Ectopterygoid ;  *Mx*, maxillary ;  *P.V*, prevomer ;  *Pal.I., II.*, palatines ;  *Par.Sp*, parasphenoid ; *Par.Sp.Asc.*, ascending ramus of parasphenoid ;  *Proc.B.Pt*, basipterygoid process ;  *Pt*, pterygoid : *Qu*, quadrate ;  *S.Pt.*1-6, suprapterygoids (1 = autopalatine, 6 = metapterygoid).

metapterygoid is toothed in *Polypterus* (van Wijhe, **654**; Pollard, **575**;

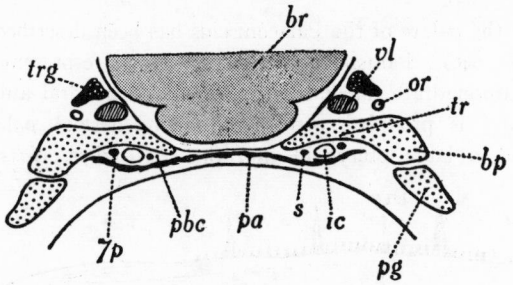

FIG. 308.

*Lepidosteus osseus*, embryo 18 mm. long. Transverse section of base of skull at level of basal processes, *bp*, of trabeculæ, *tr*. *7p*, Palatine nerve ; *br*, brain ; *ic*, internal carotid ; *or*, orbital artery ; *pa*, parasphenoid ; *pbc*, posterior parabasal canal ; *pg*, palatoquadrate ; *trg*, trigeminal ganglion ; *s*, sympathetic nerve ; *vl*, vena capitis lateralis.

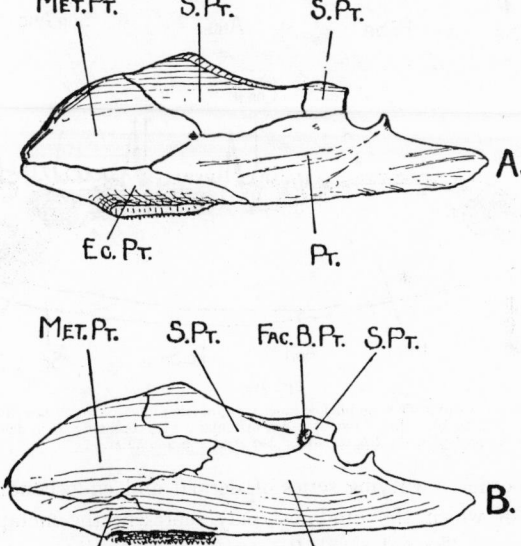

FIG. 309.

*Nematoptychius greenocki*, palatoquadrate apparatus. A, Outer view of right side; B, inner view of left side (from D. M. S. Watson, *Proc. Zool. Soc.*, 1928). *Ec.Pt*, Ectopterygoid ; *Fac.B.Pt*, facet of basal process for articulation with basipterygoid (basitrabecular) process ; *Met.Pt*, metapterygoid ; *Pt*, Pterygoid ; *S.Pt*, suprapterygoid.

Allis, **410**), and it is probable that here also there are really two elements to which the same name metapterygoid has been given : a dermal bone (usually absent), and a corresponding cartilage bone (always present, p. 299).

Recently the palate of the Palaeoniscids has been described (Stensiö, **218**; Watson, **646**). Parasphenoid and prevomers are present as usual; and the palatoquadrate (in addition to the endochondral autopalatine, and quadrate) is provided with one or two dermal palatines, an ectopterygoid, a large pterygoid, and (in *Elonichthys*, Watson) along

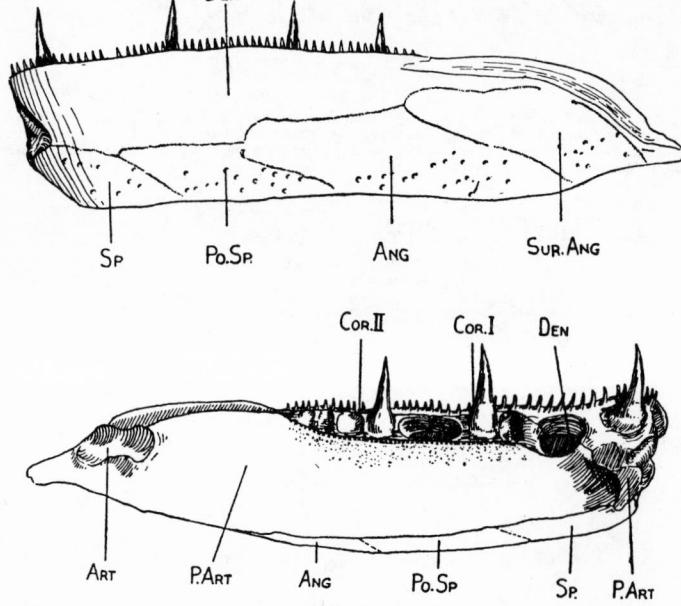

FIG. 310.

*Megalichthys*: above outer view, and below inner view, of left ramus of lower jaw (from D. M. S. Watson, *Tr. Roy. Soc.*, 1926). *Ang*, Angular; *Art*, articular; *Cor*, coronoid; *Den*, dentary; *P.Art*, prearticular; *Po.Sp*, postsplenial; *Sp*, splenial; *Sur.Ang*, supra-angular.

its medial border a varying series of dermal and endochondral suprapterygoids, of which the hindmost may represent the metapterygoid, Figs. 307, 310. The palate of *Polypterus* must be interpreted in the light of these discoveries.[1]

**Lower Jaw.**—Our knowledge of the structure of the lower jaw in fishes is by no means complete, and the nomenclature of its constituent

---

[1] Van Wijhe considers that the ectopterygoid of *Polypterus* contains a palatine element; Allis, **410**, that the bone usually called vomer is a dermal palatine. It is possible that the prevomers, already reduced in some Palaeoniscids, are absent in *Polypterus*, the so-called 'vomer' belonging to covering bones of the palatoquadrate.

bones is in some confusion. In the early forms there are numerous bones, while in modern Teleostei they are reduced to three by the disappearance of some and the fusion of others. These three are the 'dentary', 'articular', and 'angular'. The lower jaw of the early primitive Teleostomes (Crossopterygii) closely resembled that of the more primitive Tetrapoda (Stegocephalia), and was covered externally by the dentary, supra-angular, and angular; below by the splenial, and internally by the prearticular; while the Meckelian fossa was roofed over by the coronoid. The angular and splenial seem to be the enlarged posterior and anterior elements of a series of external infradentaries (Traquair, 615; Bryant, 465; Watson and Day, 647) several of which were present in *Rhizodopsis*, *Eusthenopteron*, and some Osteolepids; and the coronoid the posterior element of a more dorsal internal series, Figs. 292, 309. Most of the chief elements are still present in Coelacanthini (Stensiö, 605; Watson, 645) and Palaeoniscioidei (Traquair, 614, 616, 618; Stensiö, 218; Watson, 646). They become much reduced in the Acipenseroidei, only the dentary remaining usually in *Acipenser*. The Amioidei (Sagemehl, 378; Allis, 402; Regan, 577; van Wijhe, 654; Bridge, 429) preserve in addition to the dentary, angular, and supra-angular, a series of toothed coronoids, Figs. 300, 431. The large posterior bone generally called 'splenial' seems to be the prearticular. *Lepidosteus* differs not in essentials from *Amia* (Collinge, 476; Regan, 577; van Wijhe, 654; Parker, 566). It has been mentioned above that in Teleosts the number of bones is much reduced; the coronoids have disappeared and even the 'angular' may vanish. The so-called articular is made up of an endochondral articular fused to an outer dermal element usually called 'derm-articular'. The latter corresponds in position to the large angular of Amia and is probably its homologue; in that case the 'angular', which develops from an endochondral and a dermal element (Ridewood, 578-9), has been wrongly named. The 'dentary' is also of compound origin, being formed of a true dermal dentary and a small anterior element probably representing the mento-Meckelian (Parker, 560; Schleip, 584; Gaupp, 343).

**Dipnoi.**—The Dipnoi form a well-defined group which can be followed from the Old Red Sandstone to the present day. (Agassiz, 1833–44; Pander, 1858; Hancock and Atthey, 1868 and 1871; Miall, 1878; Traquair, 617; A. S. Woodward, 663; Günther, 1871; Bridge, 433; Dollo, 119; Watson and Gill, 648.) In general build the early forms approach the Osteolepids; but even in the earliest known genus, *Dipterus*, the characteristic specialised dentition was already established with powerful grinding compound toothed plates, accompanied by a shortening of the jaws and reduction of the marginal teeth. The Dipnoan head is broad and depressed, the snout blunt with ventral external and internal nostrils, the orbit small and about midway, the cheek region narrow, and the operculum far forward. There is no pineal foramen, and no open spiracle. The head of *Dipterus* is well covered with dermal plates; and these are provided with an external layer of typical cosmine like that on the cosmoid body scales (Pander, 1860; Goodrich, **36, 519**). This layer disappears in later forms as the bones sink below the skin, and, except in such Devonian genera as *Dipterus* and *Scaumenacia*, the lateral-

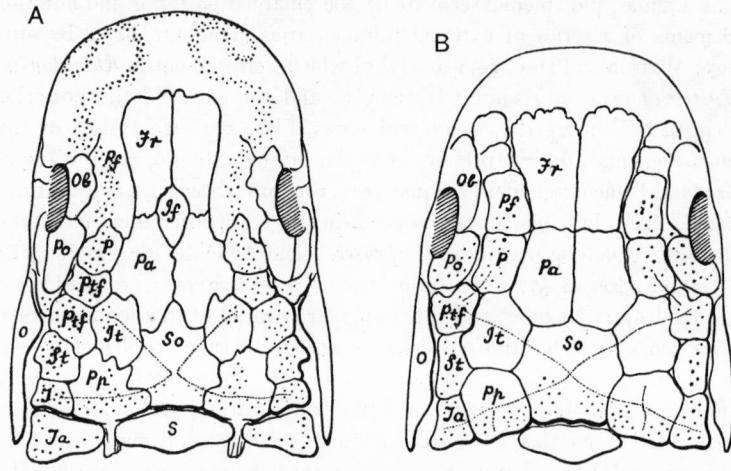

Fig. 311.

Diagrams of dorsal view of head of A, *Dipterus*, and B, *Scaumenacia*, showing dermal roofing-bones and pores of lateral-line system. *Fr*, Frontal; *If*, interfrontal; *It*, intertemporal; *O*, opercular; *Ob*, supraorbital; *P*, lateral plate; *Pa*, parietal; *Pf*, prefrontal; *Po*, postorbital; *Pp*, postparietal; *Ptf*, postfrontals; *S*, median postoccipital through which runs transverse lateral-line canal; *So*, median posterior plate or occipital; *St*, supratemporal; *T*, pretabular; *Ta*, tabular. Snout covered with plates more or less fused.

line canals are no longer enclosed. The much-reduced dermal bones of modern Dipnoi are deeply sunk, and, together with the lateral-line canals, are secondarily covered by large scales, which have spread over them from the trunk (K. Fürbringer, **25**; Goodrich, **35**). The disposition of the bones can be seen in the appended Figs. 311-12, 318-19. The cranial roof is remarkable for the large number of elements composing it in early forms, especially at the sides, and for the presence and increasing dominance of a series of median bones, perhaps remnants of a median series of scales extending along the trunk (Woodward, **231**; Whiteaves, **229**; Watson and Day, **647**; Watson and Gill, **648**; Goodrich, **519**).

The roof of the skull in early Dipnoi is distinguished by the presence, in addition to the usual paired frontals and parietals,[1] of a large median occipital, separated by paired intertemporals (?) and postparietals from lateral rows of small elements extending from the prefrontal to the tabular region and harbouring the supraorbital, postorbital, and temporal lateral-line canals. In *Dipterus*, *Scaumenacia*, and probably other Devonian genera, a transverse posterior occipital bone containing the occipital canal appears to represent, together with the anterior median occipital, the median occipital of the Osteolepids ; this bone, however, seems to

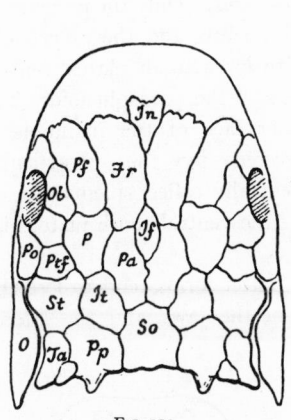

FIG. 312.

*Ctenodus* : restoration of dorsal view of skull (partly from Watson and Gill ; E. S. Goodrich, *Linn. Soc. J. Zool.*, 1925). Lettering as in Fig. 311.

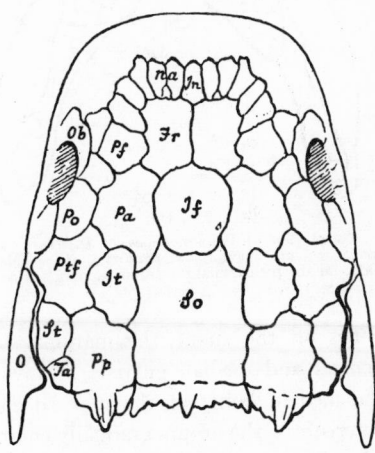

FIG. 312a.

*Sagenodus* : restoration of dorsal view of skull (partly from Watson and Gill ; E. S. Goodrich, *Linn. Soc. J. Zool.*, 1925). Lettering as in Fig. 311.

have been only loosely connected with the cranial shield of the Dipnoi. The bones on the snout of large specimens of *Dipterus platycephalus* become fused into a shield, much as in many Osteolepids, which shield probably represents premaxillaries, maxillaries, nasals, and ethmoid. *Dipterus* is also provided with the usual bones round the orbit and an inner set of small circumorbitals. Two small bones appear to have been present on the cheek. A large angular, small post-splenial, splenial, and toothless dentary covered the lower jaw, Fig. 313. The opercular flaps were supported by opercular, subopercular, and lateral gular bones ; while a median and two ventral gulars filled the space between them (Watson

---

[1] These are considered by Watson, Day, and Gill to be the nasals and frontals ; while the parietals they suppose to have been included in the median occipital, which, however, shows no trace of compound origin, Fig. 319 C. *Scaumenacia* has large frontals and parietals meeting normally without the intervention of an interfrontal, Fig. 312.

and Gill, **648**). Dipterus is the only Dipnoan preserving the gulars. There is a remarkable resemblance to the Osteolepids in this region of the head.

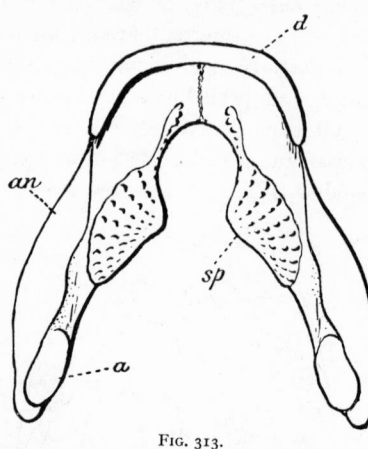

FIG. 313.

Dorsal view of the lower jaw of *Dipterus*. *a*, Articular; *an*, angular; *d*, dentary; *sp*, splenial tooth on the prearticular? (From Goodrich, *Vert. Craniata*, 1909.)

Reduced toothed premaxillary and maxillary bones may be made out in *Dipterus* (Watson and Day, **647**). Its palate seems to be nearly as specialised as in *Ceratodus*. Only the prevomers, with teeth, and the pterygoids, with large tooth plates, remain besides the parasphenoid. The inner face of the mandible is covered by the prearticular (generally called splenial), bearing the ventral tooth plate, Fig. 313.

Later forms tend to lose the bones on the snout, the marginal bones of the jaws, and the lateral ventral and median gulars. Meanwhile the median bones of the roof, so characteristic of the group, gradually enlarge. Already in the Upper Carboniferous *Sagenodus* the interfrontal meets the occipital; in *Ceratodus*, the most primitive of living Dipnoi, there remain above, in addition to the very large occipital and more anterior 'ethmoid' plate (probably interfrontal), only an elongated lateral plate (occupying the position of the frontal, parietal, and intertemporal, etc.), a postfrontal (postorbital ?), and an outer plate covering the quadrate region (probably supratemporal, but often called squamosal). At the side is a small sub- and postorbital, an opercular, a much-reduced subopercular. The lower jaw retains only the angular and so-called dentary (probably

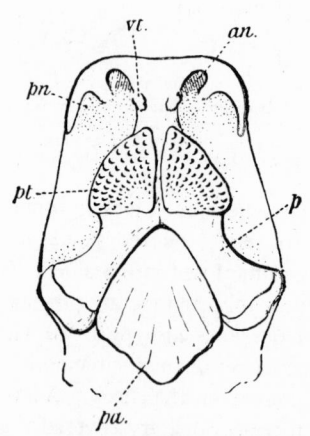

FIG. 314.

Ventral view of the palate of *Dipterus* restored. *an*, Anterior nostril; *p*, palatopterygoid bone; *pa*, parasphenoid; *pn*, posterior nostril; *pt*, palatine tooth; *vt*, vomerine tooth. (From Goodrich, *Vert. Craniata*, 1909.)

splenial; Watson and Gill, **648**) on its outer surface. *Protopterus* and *Lepidosiren* are still further

specialised in that the roofing has almost disappeared, the narrowed
lateral plates alone remaining superficial posteriorly, while the median
occipital ('fronto-parietal') has sunk below the muscles and spread

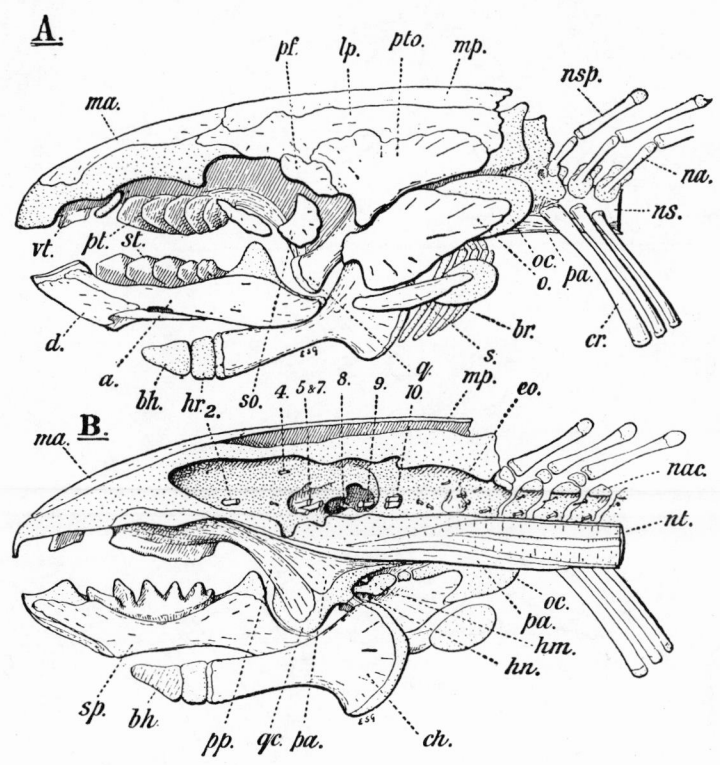

FIG. 315.

*Ceradotus Forsteri*, Krefft. A, Outer view of left half; B, inner view of right half. *a*, Angular;
*bh*, basihyal; *br*, fifth branchial arch; *ch*, ceratohyal; *cr*, 'cranial' rib; *d*, dentary; *eo*, 'exoccipital'; *hm*, hyomandibular; *hn*, hyomandibular nerve; *hr*, hypohyal; *lp*, lateral plate;
*ma*, median anterior, and *mp*, median posterior plate; *na*, neural arch; *nac*, cartilage of neural
arch; *ns*, notochordal sheath; *nsp*, neural spine; *nt*, notochord; *o*, opercular, and *oc*, its cartilage;
*pa*, parasphenoid; *pf*, postfrontal; *pp*, pterygo-palatine; *pt*, palatine tooth; *pto*, pterotic (?),
and *q*, its downward process covering the quadrate cartilage, *qc*; *s*, subopercular; *so*, suborbital;
*sp*, splenial (prearticular?); *st*, splenial tooth; *vt*, vomerine tooth. (From Goodrich, *Vert. Craniata*,
1909.)

over the brain-case (Wiedersheim, 653; Bridge, 433; Goodrich, 35),
Fig. 317.

The living Dipnoi, then, are highly specialised; but their extinct
predecessors, more especially the Devonian *Dipterus*, approach the Osteolepids in general structure and in the disposition of the bones on the head.
In the early Dipnoi, the fundamental plan of the covering bones can be

recognised, though the homology of many of the elements cannot be
determined with certainty. The two groups converge in this as in so

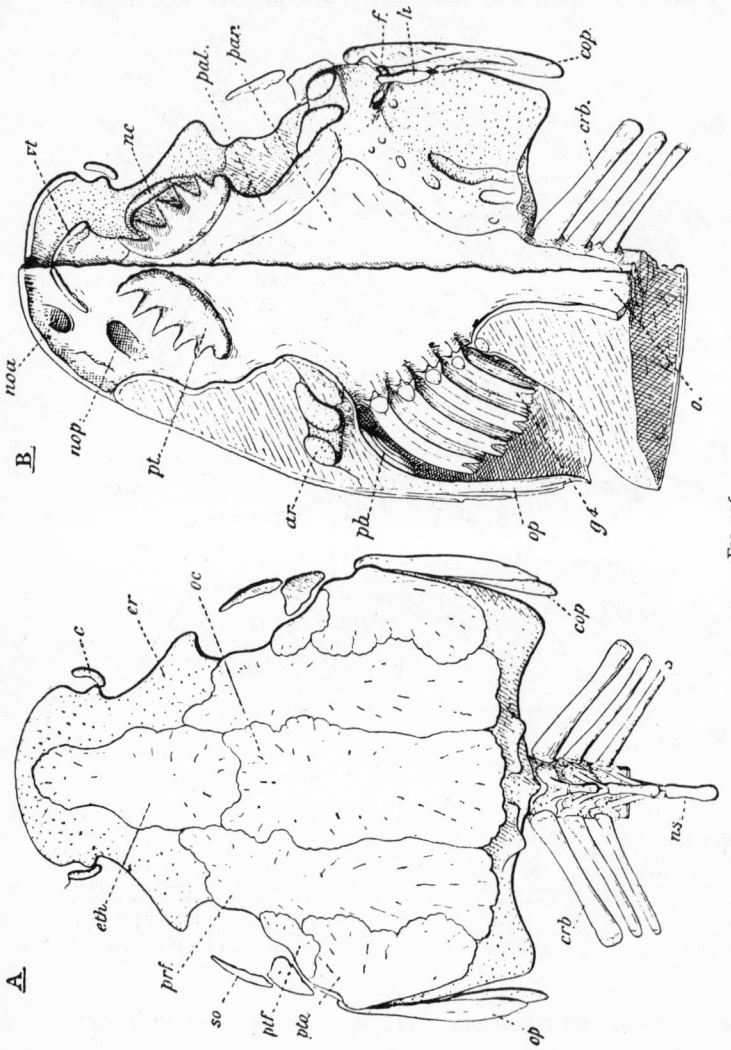

FIG. 316.

*Ceratodus Forsteri*, Krefft. A, Dorsal view of the skull; B, ventral view of the head; on the left the lower jaw has been removed and the gills cut across, on the right the skeleton has been exposed. *ar*, Articular facet of quadrate; *c*, labial cartilage; *cop*, opercular cartilage (hyoid rays?); *cr*, cartilaginous cranium; *crb*, cranial rib; *eth*, anterior median plate (ethmoid); *f*, hyomandibular branch of facial nerve; *g⁴*, fourth gill; *h*, vestigial hyomandibular; *nc*, nasal cartilage; *noa*, anterior 'external' nostril; *nop*, posterior internal nostril; *ns*, supraneural spine; *o*, oesophagus; *oc*, posterior median plate (occipital); *op*, operculum; *pal*, palatopterygoid bone; *par*, parasphenoid; *pb*, pseudobranch; *prf*, lateral plate (prefrontal?); *pt*, palatine tooth; *ptf*, postfrontal; *pto*, pterotic; *so*, suborbital; *ut*, vomerine tooth. (From Goodrich, *Vert. Craniata* 1909.)

many other characters. Whether the multiplicity of the bones contributing to the roof of the skull in *Dipterus* is secondary, or a reminiscence
of a primitive condition when the head was covered with small scales
like those on the trunk, cannot at present be determined.

## TETRAPODA : DERMAL BONES OF SKULL

**Skull of Amphibia.**—The dermal covering of the head in Tetrapoda is very similar to that of early Osteichthyes, from which it has doubtless been derived. Only in the hinder and ventral region are there any important differences ; for there is no evidence in the Tetrapod, even in the most primitive yet discovered, of any opercular or gular plates.

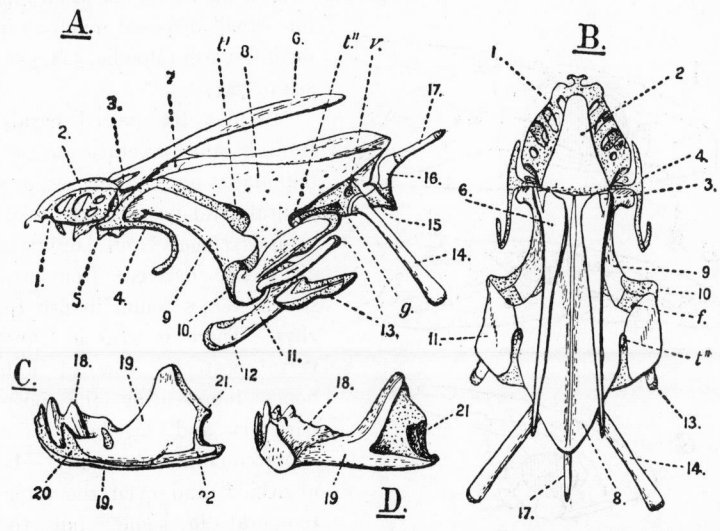

FIG. 317.

*Lepidosiren paradoxa*, Fitz. (after Bridge). A, Left-side view, and B, dorsal view of the skull ; C, outer view of the left, and D, inner view of the right ramus of the lower jaw. 1, Nasal capsule ; 2, ethmoid ; 3 and 7, process of pterygo-palatine ; 4, antorbital cartilage ; 5, palatine tooth ; 6, lateral (dermal lateral ethmoid) ; 8, occipital (fronto-parietal) ; 9, pterygo-palatine ; 10, quadrate ; 11, squamosal ; 12, ceratohyal ; 13, subopercular and opercular ; 14, cranial rib ; 15, parasphenoid ; 16, neural arch ; 17, supraneural spine ; 18, splenial tooth ; 19, splenial ? ; 20, Meckel's cartilage ; 21, articular cartilage ; 22, angular ; *f*, foramen for facial, *g*, for glosso-pharyngeal, *t*, for trigeminal, and *v*, for vagus nerve.

Either they were never developed in the ancestor, or were lost before the Amphibian stage was reached.

**Stegocephalia.**—The primitive condition is best seen in the Stegocephalia, which include the earliest known Tetrapods from the Carboniferous Epoch (v. Meyer, 1847 ; Fraas, **497** ; Miall, 1874 ; Cope, 1869 ; Williston, **657-61, 95** ; Bransom, **427** ; Broom, **448** ; Moodie, **548-9** ; Burmeister, 1840 ; Huxley, 1862-9 ; Ammon, 1889 ; Fritsch, **23** ; Jaekel, **51** ; Gaudry, **28** ; Thévenin, **610** ; Watson, **631, 644** ; A. S. Woodward, **231** ; and others). Here the superficial bones overlie the endoskeletal skull and jaws built on the autostylic plan (p. 409). Dorsally they form a roof firmly fixed to the chondrocranium, spreading laterally round the orbits and over the temporal space occupied by the jaw muscles, attached to the marginal bones of the upper jaw and outer end of the quadrates, and further buttressed by the paroccipital processes of the opisthotics. The roofing was thus complete, pierced only by external nostrils, orbits, and pineal foramen, Figs. 318-21. That the bones in many forms were still superficial is evidenced by their ornamented surface, and the frequent presence of well-marked grooves indicating the course of lateral-line canals disposed much as in primitive fish (Moodie, 548, 550; see p. 741).

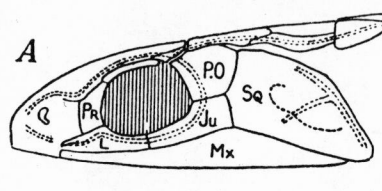

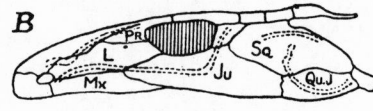

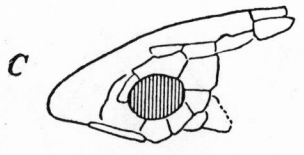

FIG. 318.

Left lateral view of skull of: A, Osteolepis; B, Palaeogyrinus; and C, Dipterus (from D. M. S. Watson, *Tr. Roy. Soc.*, 1926). Compare Figs. 291, 319, 311.

Besides the paired nasals, frontals, and parietals, are premaxillaries and maxillaries, prefrontals and postfrontals, postorbitals, jugals, and lacrimals, all easily derived from the similar bones found in fish (p. 287). There is also a transverse posterior row of four bones representing the postparietals and tabulars. The supratemporal can also be identified, and even the intertemporal in some; but the bones on the cheek are less easy to compare with those in primitive Teleostomes, possibly because the latter have a hyostylic suspension of the jaws in which the quadrate region is less developed. In the Tetrapod this part is covered by a squamosal and quadratojugal presumably derived from the cheek bones of the fish (cf. Figs. 291, 318). The lateral temporal roof covered a space for jaw muscles open to the orbit in front, and opening behind by the post-temporal foramen as in fish. The tabular usually projects at the hinder outer corner of the cranial shield, overhanging a notch in the posterior margin of the squamosal marking, no doubt the position of the tympanum (p. 483). This tympanic notch is of course a new feature in the Tetrapod skull. Such is the general plan of the dermal bones in Stegocephalia. It resembles somewhat that of early Dipnoi, but more closely that of primitive Teleostomes, not only in its completeness, but also in the elements which compose it. Indeed it affords the strongest evidence for the origin of land vertebrates from a fish-like ancestor in which this general plan had already been well established.

Certain special features remain to be considered. A constant and

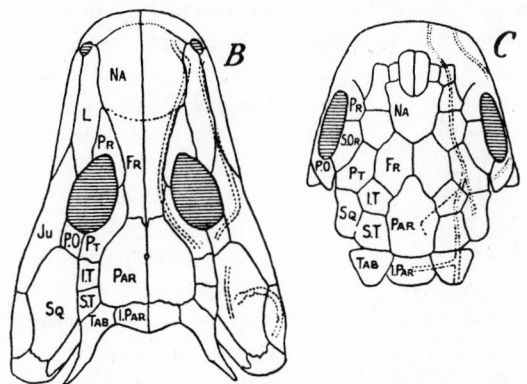

Fig. 319.

Dorsal view of B, skull of *Palaeogyrinus decorus*, Carboniferous, and C, *Dipterus valenciennessi*, Middle Old Red Sandstone, Caithness (from D. M. S. Watson, *Trans. Roy. Soc.*, 1926). In C, *Fr*, parietal (=frontal of Watson); *Par*, dermal occipital (=parietals fused of Watson); *Na*, frontals fused (=nasals of Watson). Cf. Fig. 311.

unexplained difference between Osteichthyes and Tetrapoda is that the pineal foramen is between the frontals in the former, and between the parietals in the latter.

In Osteichthyes the homologue of the lacrimal bone of Tetrapods

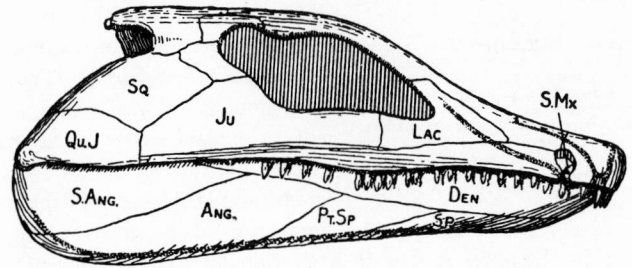

Fig. 320.

*Orthosaurus pachycephalus*, right lateral aspect of skull and lower jaw (from D. M. S. Watson, *Tr. Roy. Soc.*, 1926). *Ang*, Angular; *Den*, dentary; *Ju*, jugal; *Lac*, lacrimal; *Pt.Sp*, postsplenial; *Qu.J*, quadratojugal; *S.Ang*, supra-angular; *S.Mx*, septomaxillary; *Sp*, splenial; *Sq*, squamosal.

appears to be the dermal element at the anterior ventral edge of the orbit, lodged between the prefrontal and the jugal and belonging to the circumorbital series, Figs. 291, 318. When the ancestors of Tetrapods took to terrestrial life the necessity arose to keep the surface of the eye moist out of water, hence eyelids were developed and certain skin glands were specialised as lacrimal glands. A duct was formed to remove excess of fluid. In modern Tetrapods this lacrimal duct develops as a groove of the outer skin which closes and sinks in (Amniota), or as a solid ingrowth which is nipped off and hollowed out (Amphibia), so as to form a tube leading from the orbit to just inside the external nostril. The duct thus

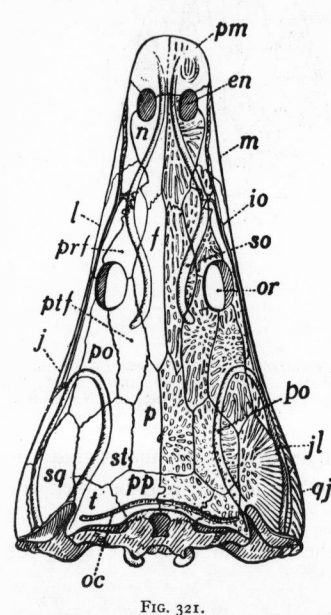

FIG. 321.

Dorsal view of skull of *Trematosaurus Brauni* (from H. Burmeister, 1849, modified). Dermal bones: *f*, Frontal; *j*, jugal; *l*, lacrimal; *m*, maxillary; *n*, nasal; *p*, parietal; *pm*, premaxillary; *po*, postorbital; *pp*, postparietal; *prf*, prefrontal; *ptf*, postfrontal; *qj*, quadratojugal; *sq*, squamosal; *st*, supratemporal; *t*, tabulare. Lateral-line grooves: *io*, Infraorbital; *jl*, jugal; *oc*, transverse occipital; *po*, postorbital; *so*, supraorbital. *en*, External nostril; *or*, orbit.

comes to pierce the later developed lacrimal bone, and open below it into the nasal cavity. In the more primitive Stegocephalia and Reptilia the lacrimal extends from orbit to nostril, and in *Micropholis*, according to Watson (633), this bone has a longitudinal groove indicating that the duct was still superficial. Many Stegocephalia and most of the higher Tetrapods have the lacrimal excluded from the nostril by the junction of the nasal and maxillary; and it may also be excluded from the orbit by the prefrontal and jugal (Gregory, 524).

The occurrence of an intertemporal in certain Rachitomi (*Trimerorhachis*, Williston, 660; *Palaeogyrinus, Micropholis*, Watson, 633, 644), Branchiosauria (*Melanerpeton*, Credner, 484), and again in the primitive reptile (?) *Conodectes* (*Seymouria*), Fig. 333 (Williston, 95; Watson, 643), is difficult to explain except as a survival of the similar bone found in Osteolepids and Dipnoi. Of the transverse row of bones over the occipital region the outer is doubtless the tabular; but the exact phylogenetic connexion between the paired postparietals of the Tetrapod and the similarly placed median occipital of Crossopterygii is uncertain. In many Teleostomes (Coelacanthini, Palaoniscoidei, etc.) the postparietal elements are paired, while in Dipnoi (p. 305) there is a median occipital as well. Possibly there were here five bones of which the middle one has been lost in the Tetrapods. Both the postparietal and the tabular may spread on to the occipital surface, and the latter usually sends down

a posterior plate which joins and may partially cover the paroccipital
process of the opisthotic.

More anterior median bones sometimes occur recalling those of the
Dipnoi (p. 304). Thus a median internasal (interfrontal) is described in

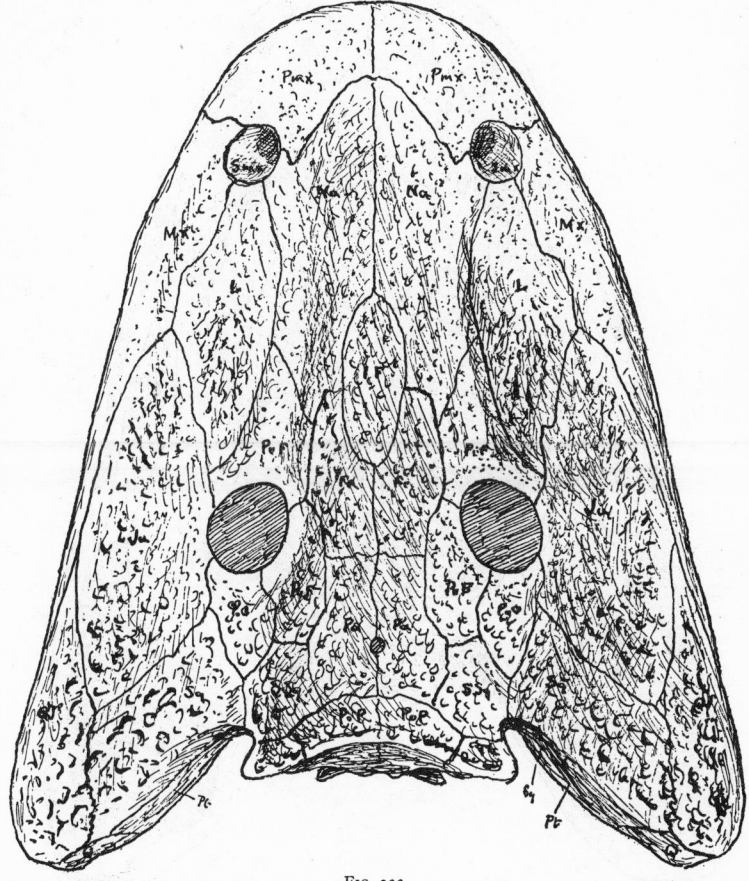

FIG. 322.

Dorsal view of skull of *Eryops megacephalus* (from R. Broom, *Am. Mus. Nat. Hist.*, 1913).

*Ricnodon, Sclerocephalus,* and *Eryops,* Fig. 322, among Stegocephalia, and
a small rostral (internasal) in *Micropholis.*

Little change, except in shape and proportion, occurs in the roofing
of the skull in Embolomeri, Rhachitomi, and Stereospondyli. It becomes
narrow and elongated in *Cricotus* and *Archegosaurus,* or broad as in
*Eryops.* Some show a foramen between the premaxillaries (*Trematops,*

*Zatrachys*), perhaps due to the presence of a gland; others have the roof pierced (as in some Crocodilia) for the accommodation of two tusks of the lower jaw. In *Trematops* the roof is excavated backwards from the

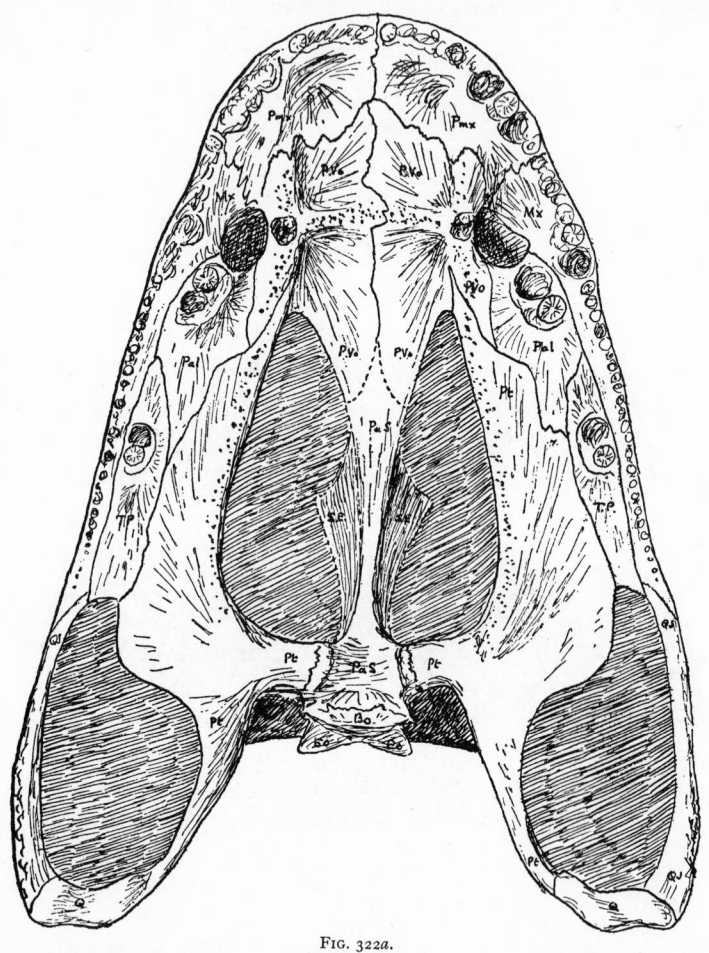

FIG. 322a.

Ventral view of skull of *Eryops megacephalus*, Permian, N. America (from R. Broom, *Bull. Am. Mus. Nat. Hist.*, 1913).

nostril, and forwards from the tympanic notch; and the notch is then closed behind by the union of the tabular with the squamosal (Williston, 660-61).

The Branchiosauria have a broad flattened skull, approaching in general appearance that of the modern Amphibia, of which they may possibly be the ancestors (Fritsch, **23**; Credner, **484**; Case, **474**; Moodie,

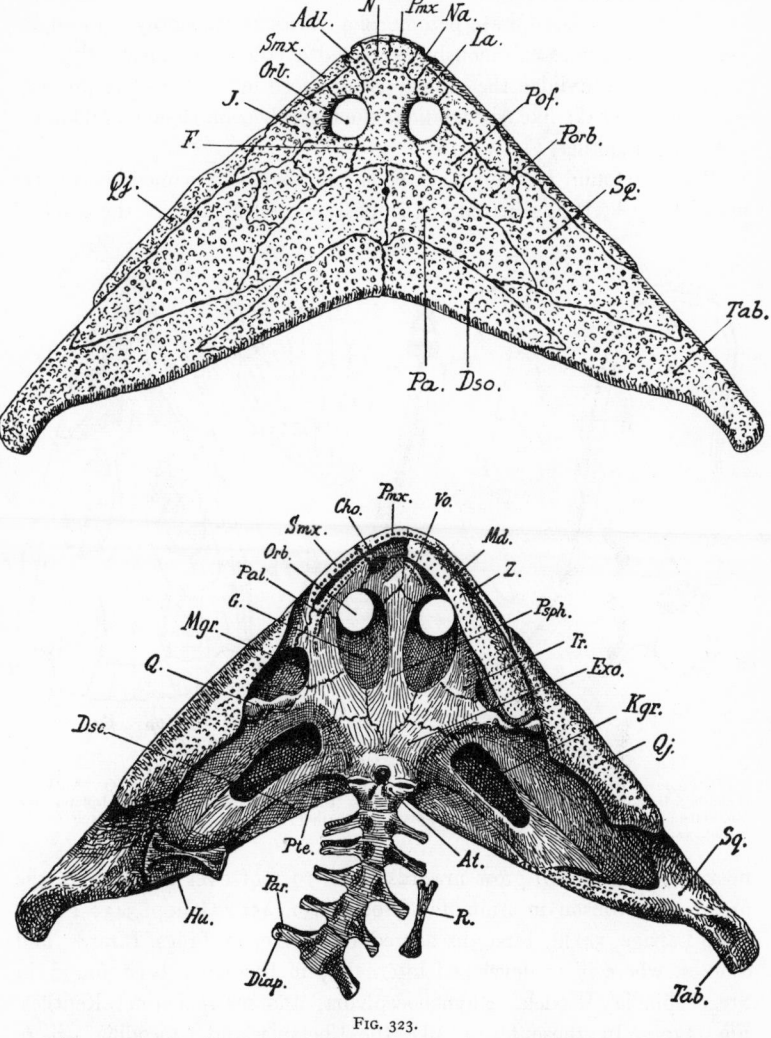

FIG. 323.

*Diplocaulus magnicornis.* Permian of Texas. Dorsal and ventral views of skull (from O. Abel, 1920). *Adl*, Lacrimal (adnasal); *At*, atlas; *Diap* and *Par*, transverse process of vertebra; *Dso*, postparietal; *Exo*, exoccipital; *F*, frontal; *G*, palatal groove; *Hu*, humerus; *Kgr*, groove for m. retractor mandibulae; *La*, prefrontal (lacrimal); *N*, nasal; *Na*, external nostril; *Md*, lower jaw; *Mgr*, groove for m. adductor mandibulae; *Orb*, orbit; *Pa*, parietal; *Pal*, palatine; *Pmx*, premaxillary; *Pof*, postfrontal; *Porb*, postorbital; *Pte*, pterygoid; *Psph*, parasphenoid; *Q*, quadrate; *Qj*, quadratojugal; *R*, rib; *Smx*, maxillary; *Sq*, squamosal; *Tab*, tabular; *Tr*, ectopterygoid; *Vo*, prevomer; *Z*, maxillary teeth.

**549**; Bulman and Whittard, **465a**). The orbits are enlarged and also the corresponding vacuities in the palate, Fig. 325. The endochondral bones seem to be much reduced or absent.

The skull of the Ceraterpetomorpha varies considerably. In Diplocaulidae it becomes enormously expanded at the sides posteriorly, Fig. 323; in Urocordylidae the tabular is produced into a horn-like process; while, in the snake-like Aistopodidae the bones become slender and loosely connected together, Fig. 323a A.

There is found in many Tetrapods a dermal bone named the septomaxillary.[1] It is situated at the postero-ventral edge of the external

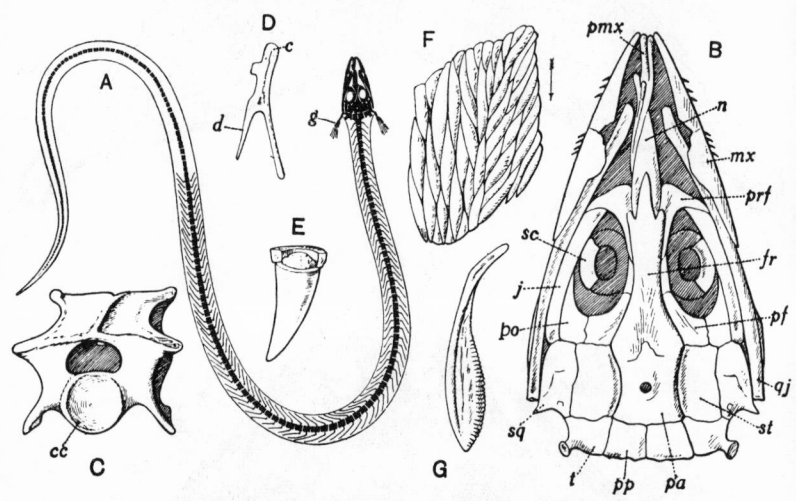

FIG. 323a.

*Dolichosoma longissimum,* L. Permian, Bohemia; restored (from A. Fritsch, 1885). A, Whole skeleton; B, skull, dorsal view; C, vertebra; D, rib; E, tooth; F, scales; G, cloacal plate. *mx,* Maxillary; *pa,* parietal; *pf,* postfrontal; *pmx,* premaxillary; *sc,* scleral plate. Other letters as in Fig. 321.

nostril, and tends to grow inwards so as to roof over and protect the organ of Jacobson in Amniota (Broom, **439, 451**; Gaupp, **343**; Fuchs, **502**; Lapage, **541**). First discovered by Parker in Frogs, Lizards, and Snakes, where it is developed internally, it has since been found in Stegocephalia, Urodela, Rhynchocephalia, and many extinct Reptiles, Fig. 320. In those forms, like the Chelonia and Crocodilia, where Jacobson's organ is ill-developed it does not occur. Often it is conspicuous on the outer surface of the skull in Theromorpha (Therocephalia,

[1] The little anterior paired bone found in certain Teleostomes, such as *Amia,* and often called the septomaxillary, is an endochondral ossification of the floor of the nasal capsule. It does not seem to be homologous with the true septomaxillary of Tetrapods, and is of quite different origin, Fig. 300.

Dromasauria, etc.).   In Monotremes it fuses early with the premaxillary forming an important part of its outer surface (Gaupp, **511**, in *Echidna*), and among Placentals it occurs as a separate internal bone in Armadillos (Broom, **439**).   There can be little doubt that it is an ancient bone which has persisted from the earliest Tetrapods, and has probably been derived from one of the dermal plates bordering the external nostril in their fish-like ancestors.

The study of the dermal bones of the palate confirms the view that the Stegocephalia approach the primitive Teleostomes, more especially the

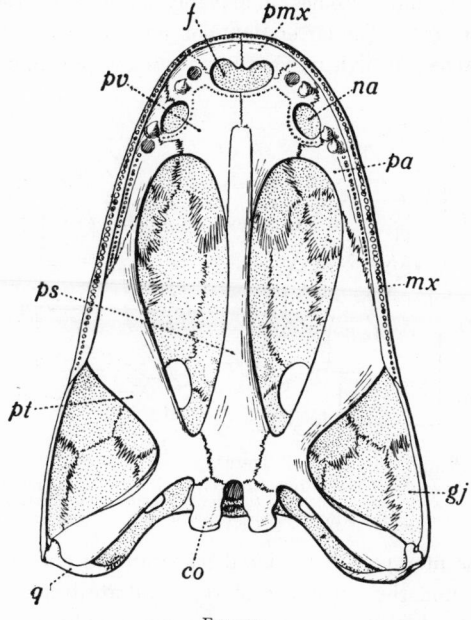

FIG. 324.

Ventral view of skull of *Cyclotosaurus robustus* (from E. Fraas, 1889).   *co*, Condyle on ex-occipital ; *f*, foramen for teeth of lower jaw ; *gj*, quadratojugal ; *mx*, maxillary ; *pa*, palatine ; *pmx*, premaxillary ; *ps*, parasphenoid ; *pt*, pterygoid ; *pv*, prevomer ; *q*, quadrate.

Osteolepids.   The Lower Carboniferous Embolomeri (Hancock and Atthey, 1869–71 ; Huxley, 1863–9 ; Watson, **631, 644**) have, instead of the typical Amphibian palate with large vacuities, an extensive bony palate formed of prevomers separating the internal nostrils, palatines, and ectopterygoids disposed as in Crossopterygians, and large pterygoids which meet in front and are separated from the slender parasphenoid only by a narrow space.   These pterygoids reach the well-developed basitrabecular processes of the basisphenoid and spread backwards over the inner side of the quadrates.   They represent the pterygoids (so-called endopterygoids) of fish (cf. *Eusthenopteron*, Fig. 306), and bear small teeth ; while large tusk-like teeth, each with a replacement tooth by its side, are present on the palatines and prevomers of these and many other Stegocephalia, Figs. 306, 322*a*.

The parasphenoid in the Embolomeri was comparatively small, closely connected with the basisphenoid posteriorly, and extending forward below the sphenethmoid as a narrow grooved blade (Watson, **644**).

In the more advanced types (Rhachitomi, Stereospondyli) the interpterygoid palatal vacuities become progressively enlarged, the parasphenoid expands behind and becomes immovably sutured to the pterygoid, Figs. 323, 324, 325. The latter does not meet its fellow in front, and becomes shortened until it no longer reaches the prevomer or even the

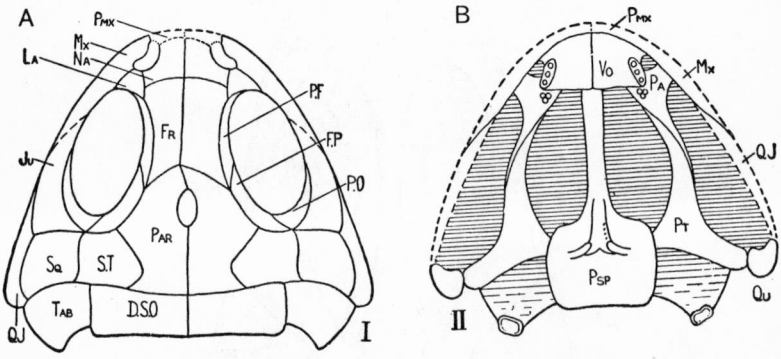

FIG. 325.

Skull of *Branchiosaurus amblystomus*, reconstructed. A, Dorsal ; B, ventral view (from Bulman and Whittard, *Proc. Zool. Soc.*, 1926). *D.S.O*, Dermal supraoccipital = postparietal ; *Psp*, parasphenoid ; *Vo*, prevomer. Other letters as in previous figures.

palatine. The pterygoid is produced backwards as a wide flange which tends to surround the inner side of the quadrate below and meet the squamosal behind, a disposition which survives only in such primitive Reptiles as *Seymouria, Pareiasaurus,* and *Varanosaurus* (Williston, **95** ; Broili, **435, 437** ; Watson, **644** ; Sushkin, **768**).

The lower jaw in the more primitive Stegocephalia has, besides the endochondral articular, a number of dermal covering bones comparable to those of primitive Teleostomes (Williston, **659, 95** ; Bransom, **427** ; A. S. Woodward ; Broom, **450** ; Watson, **632, 644**). The large dentary holds powerful teeth, the outside of the jaw is completed by an angular and supra-angular behind, and a splenial and postsplenial below (comparable to the infradentaries of early fishes). The dentary and splenial enter the symphysis. A prearticular covers the inner side, with a series of more dorsal coronoids (coronoid, intercoronoid, precoronoid) roofing the

Meckelian cavity and limiting the supramandibular fossa. These coronoids may bear teeth.

The modern Amphibia, sometimes grouped together as Euamphibia, have several cranial characters in common. The pineal foramen has disappeared ; the dermal covering bones are more or less reduced in extent, thickness, and number ; the temporal region of the roofing is absent from the orbit backwards, leaving exposed the otic bones (in Apoda, however, the small orbit may be surrounded by bone). The postfrontal, postorbital, supratemporal, tabular, postparietal, and ecto-pterygoid have disappeared.

The Urodela are in some respects the least specialised, but, except in

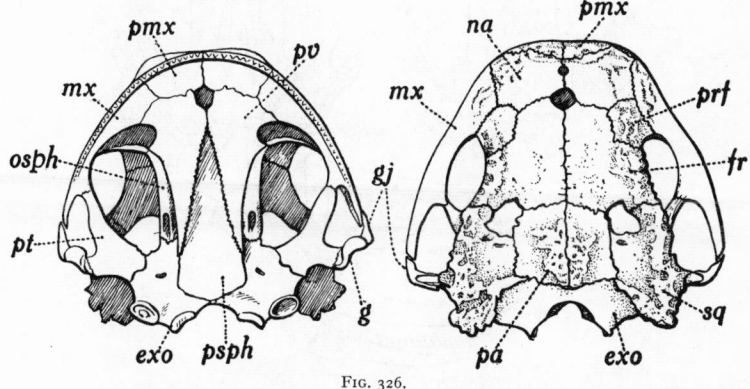

FIG. 326.

Ventral and dorsal views of skull of *Tylototriton verrucosus* (from H. Riese, 1891). *fr*, Frontal ; *g*, quadrate ; *osph*, orbitosphenoid ; *pa*, parietal ; *prf*, prefrontal. Other letters as in Figs. 290 and 324.

*Tylototriton* (Riese, 582), the margin of the roof is lost, there being neither jugal nor quadratojugal, the squamosal over the quadrate being the only dermal element left in this region, Figs. 326-8. The junction, in Sala-mandridae, of frontal and squamosal is probably secondary. In front of the orbit the lacrimal is lost (except in *Ranidens* and *Hynobius*) and the prefrontal also in *Necturus*. The nasal, frontal, parietal, premaxillary, and maxillary usually remain (Parker, 562, 573 ; Wiedersheim, 651). In the Perennibranchiata even the maxillaries and nasals are lost. The dermal bones of the lower jaw are also much reduced, there being, as a rule, only a dentary, a prearticular, and an inner tooth-bearing bone generally called splenial but more probably representing the coronoids, Figs. 327-8. An angular may also be present in Caducibranchiates. The palate in Urodela is remarkable for the width of the parasphenoid and the disappearance of the palatine, the short pterygoid being disconnected from the prevomer.

According to Winterbert (1910) the usual statement that the palatine shifts at metamorphosis and joins the vomer near the parasphenoid (Parker, Wiedersheim) is erroneous; the palatine disintegrates and the prevomer is altered by reduction at its outer border and growth at its median border.

The Anura have a still more specialised skull (Parker, 558, 559); but in them the margin remains complete with premaxillary, maxillary, and

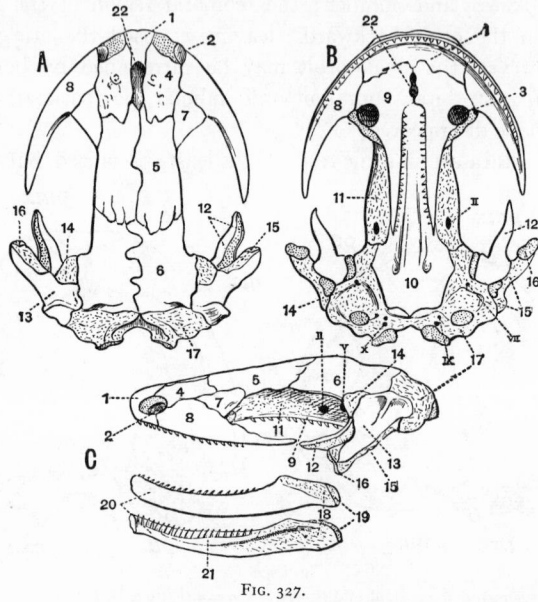

FIG. 327.

A, Dorsal; B, ventral; C, lateral views of skull of *Molge cristata* (after W. K. Parker, from S. H. Reynolds, *Vertebrate Skeleton*, 1913). Cartilage dotted, cartilage bones marked with dots and dashes, membrane bones left white. Upper view of mandible in C shows outer surface, lower shows inner surface. 1, Premaxillary; 2, anterior nares; 3, posterior nares; 4, nasal; 5, frontal; 6, parietal; 7, prefronto-lacrimal; 8, maxillary; 9, prevomero-palatine; 10, parasphenoid; 11, orbitosphenoid; 12, pterygoid; 13, squamosal; 14, pro-otic region of exoccipito-periotic; 15, calcified portion of quadrate region; 16, uncalcified portion of quadrate region; 17, exoccipital region of exoccipito-periotic; 18, calcified portion of articular region; 19, uncalcified portion of articular region; 20, dentary; 21, splenial; 22, space for glands; *II, V, VII, IX, X*, foramina for exit of cranial nerves.

quadratojugal bones. Nasals are present, also small septomaxillaries, but the superior fontanelle is covered by a single pair of bones called fronto-parietals. As a rule the sphenethmoid in front and the bones of the auditory capsules behind are exposed (the lateral temporal roofing having, of course, been lost), and the junction of the squamosal with the fronto-parietal and maxillary in such forms as *Calyptocephalus*, Fig. 329, is probably secondary.[1] The palate has enormous vacuities, and the small

[1] The bones which provide these extensions in Anura and also in *Tylototriton* have a rough outer surface resembling that of the secondary dermal ossifications on the pectoral girdle of some related forms, and are probably of the same origin.

palatine takes up a transverse position behind the prevomer.   Only two
dermal bones remain on each ramus of the lower jaw : a dentary, and a

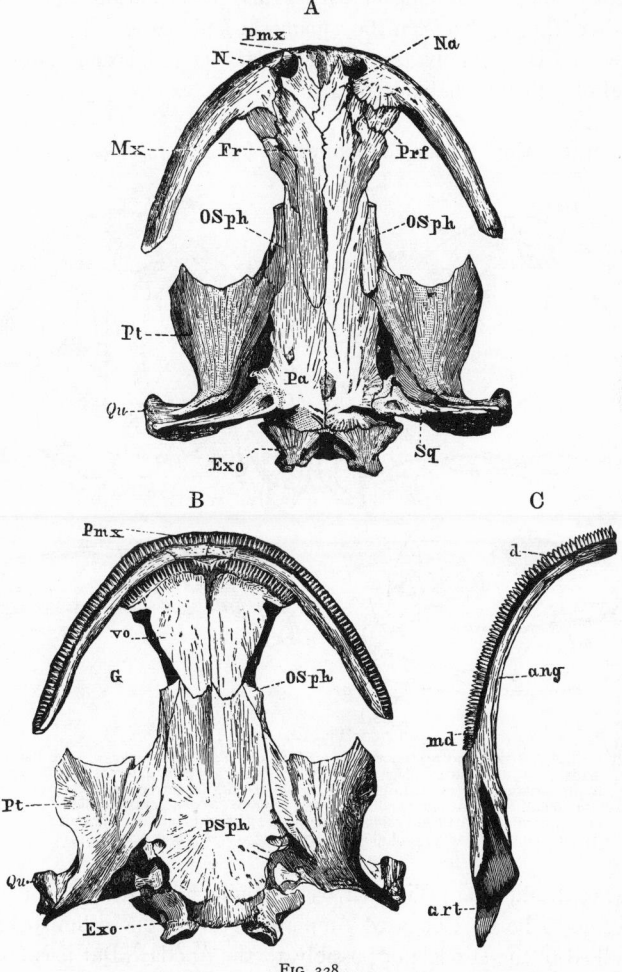

FIG. 328.

Skull of *Cryptobranchus japonicus*, v. d. Hoeven.  A, Dorsal, and B, palatal aspects ; C, lower
jaw.   *Pmx*, Premaxilla ;  *Mx*, maxilla ;  *Na*, nasal ;  *Prf*, prefrontal ;  *Fr*, frontal ;  *Pa*, parietal ;
*OSph*, orbitosphenoid ;  *Exo*, exoccipital ;  *Qu*, quadrate ;  *Sq*, squamosal ;  *Pt*, pterygoid ;  *PSph*, parasphenoid ;  *Vo*, prevomer ;  *G*, palatine vacuity ;  *N*, external nares.   (From K. Zittel, *Palaeontology*.)

larger bone which represents either the prearticular or a combination of
prearticular and angular (?).   It is often named angulosplenial.

The more complete ossification and more rigid structure of the skull
in Apoda seems to be related to their burrowing habits.   But in this

group, as in other living Amphibia, the dermal bones have been much reduced in number and the lateral temporal roof lost, Fig. 330. The apparently complete roofing in *Ichthyophis* (Wiedersheim, 652; Sarasin, 763), where the gap between the squamosal and parietal is narrowed to a mere slit, is probably due to secondary consolidation, not to the survival of a stegocephalian roof.

The interesting Upper Carboniferous fossil *Lysorophus* (Cope, 1877;

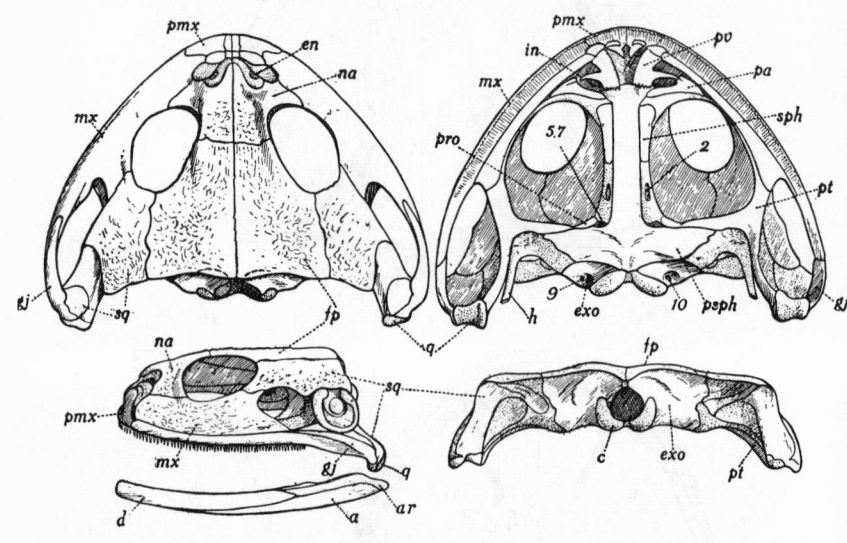

FIG. 329.

Dorsal, ventral, left-side, and posterior views of skull of *Calyptocephalus gayi* (from Parker, 1881). *a*, Angulosplenial; *ar*, articular cartilage; *c*, condyle; *d*, dentary; *en*, external nostril; *exo*, exoccipital; *fp*, frontoparietal; *gj*, quadratojugal; *h*, hyoid cornu; *in*, internal nostril; *mx*, maxillary; *na*, nasal; *pa*, palatine; *pmx*, premaxillary; *pro*, pro-otic; *psph*, parasphenoid; *pt*, pterygoid; *pv*, prevomer; *q*, quadrate cartilage; *sph*, sphenethmoid; *sq*, squamosal. Foramina: 2, of optic; 5 and 7, of trigeminal and facial; 9, of glossopharyngeal; 10, of vagus nerves.

Case, 472; Broili, 1904; Williston, 656; Moodie, 549; Huene, 531a; Sollas, 603) seems to be an elongated Amphibian with reduced limbs (Finney, 1912) allied to the Urodela or possibly to the Apoda. But it is far more primitive than any modern Amphibian, and retains the tabular and supra-temporal on the skull, and a supra-angular on the lower jaw. Moreover, the chondrocranium was more fully ossified, with supra- and basioccipital, and an orbitosphenoid (posterior pillar of Sollas).

**Dermal Bones of the Skull in the Amniota.**—The classification of the larger groups included in the Class Reptilia presents great difficulties, but ever since the pioneer work of Baur (414-17), Cope (479, 480), and

Osborn (554), the structure of the dermal roofing of the skull has been recognised as of the greatest value in tracing out the affinities of the Reptiles not only with each other, but also with the Birds on the one hand and the Mammals on the other (Broom, 459; Gaupp, 505; Versluys, 626; Williston, 655, 95; Woodward, 231; Boas, 424). It is now admitted that the early primitive Reptilia had a complete roofing like that of Stegocephalia and primitive Osteichthyes, pierced only for orbits, nostrils, and pineal eye; and further, that secondary openings have been formed

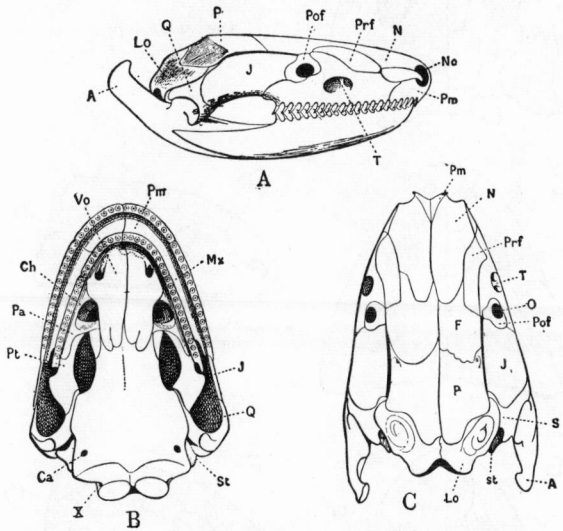

FIG. 330.

Skull of *Ichthyophis glutinosa*, × 3. A, Lateral; B, ventral; C, dorsal view. *A*, Posterior process of the os articulare; *Ca*, carotid foramen; *Ch*, choana or posterior nasal opening; *F*, frontal; *J*, jugal; *Lo*, exoccipital; *Mx*, maxilla; *N*, nasal; *No*, nostril; *O*, orbit; *P*, parietal; *Pa*, palatine; *Pm*, premaxilla; *Pof*, postfrontal; *Prf*, prefrontal; *Pt*, pterygoid; *Q*, quadrate; *S*, paraquadrate (squamosal); *St*, stapes; *T*, tentacular groove; *Vo*, vomer; *x*, exit of vagus nerve. (After Sarasin, from Parker and Haswell, *Zoology*.)

in this roofing in different ways in the various diverging phylogenetic lines. Thus have arisen openings variously called vacuities, foramina, or fossae, leaving where necessary buttresses or arches to strengthen the skull, support the jaws and quadrates, and delimit the orbits. It is agreed that there are at least three main types of dermal roofing: (1) with one lateral temporal fossa; (2) with two lateral temporal fossae, one superior and the other inferior; (3) with no fossa at all, Fig. 331. The latter 'stegocephalian' condition is found in those primitive Carboniferous Permian and Triassic Reptiles which retain the original complete roofing intact, usually with all or most of the original dermal bones (Microsauria,

Seymouriomorpha, Cotylosauria). Such primitive forms, in which the whole skull is built on essentially the same plan as in Stegocephalia, may be provisionally included in the Division Anapsida (Williston) ; probably

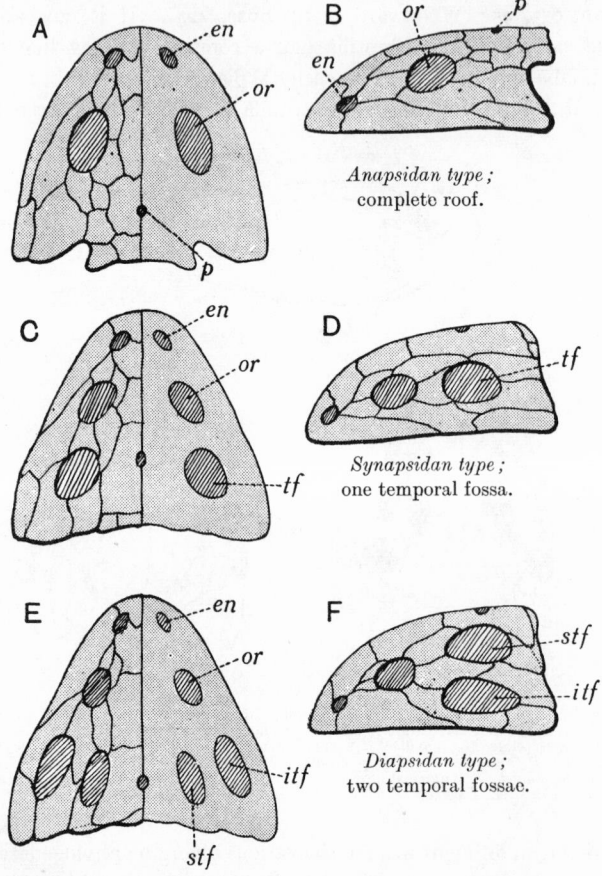

A

*en*

*or*

B

*or*    *p*

*en*

*Anapsidan type ;*
complete roof.

C

*en*

*or*

*tf*

D

*tf*

*Synapsidan type ;*
one temporal fossa.

E

*en*

*or*

*itf*

*stf*

F

*stf*

*itf*

*Diapsidan type ;*
two temporal fossae.

FIG. 331.

Diagrams showing three principal types of cranial roof in *Tetrapoda*. Dorsal views on left, lateral views on right. *en*, External nostril ; *or*, orbit ; *p*, pineal foramen ; *itf, stf, tf*, inferior, superior, and single lateral temporal fossae.

a polyphyletic assemblage containing scarcely differentiated early representatives of several divergent groups. The Microsauria still have a frankly stegocephalian structure and are often included in the Amphibia (Baur, 420 ; Moodie, 549).

Of all the Permian Reptiles hitherto discovered, *Seymouria (Conodectes)* is perhaps the most primitive (Cope, **481-2**; Williston, **661**; Watson, **643**; Sushkin, 1925). Not only is the roofing complete, but it still pre-serves an intertemporal (as mentioned above), a bone which has disappeared in other forms, Figs. 332-3. Its palate is more reptilian, the internal nostrils being near the middle line and the parasphenoid relatively small. There are well-developed basipterygoid (basitrabecular) articulations.[1] The pterygoid still spreads under and behind the quadrate to meet the squamosal.

The occiput shows a tripartite condyle, and a post-temporal fossa reduced by downgrowths of the tabular and post-parietal (as in Rhachitomi). The lower jaw retains the postsplenial and three coronoids.

The Cotylosauria are more distinctly reptilian. (Seeley, **586**; Williston, **95, 661**; Huene v. Branson, **428, 530**; Case, **466, 470, 473**; Watson, **637, 639, 643**; Broom, **444, 449, 452, 460**.) The quadrate becomes more vertical, the supratemporal may disappear, and likewise the tympanic notch (Pareiasauria, Captorhinomorpha). The descending flange of the postparietal and tabular may almost obliterate the post-temporal opening (Captorhinomorpha, Diadectomorpha). All these Cotylosaurians, and especially the Procolophonida, have a more reptilian palate

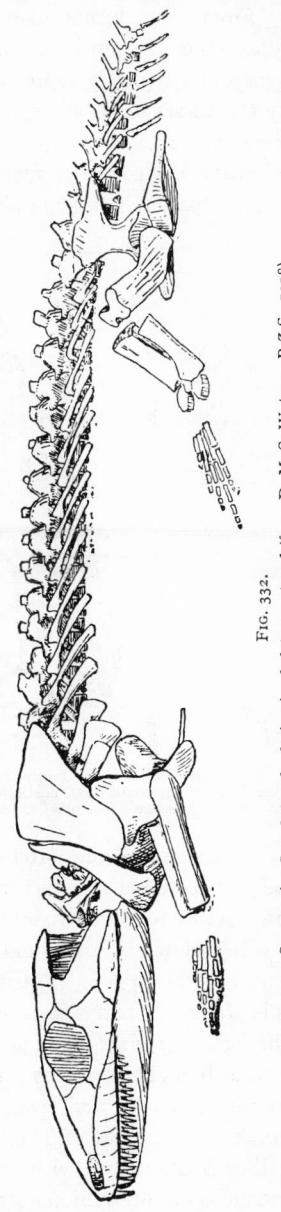

Fig. 332.

*Seymouria (Conodectes) bayloriensis,* skeleton restored (from D. M. S. Watson, *P.Z.S.,* 1918).

---

[1] A small bone intervenes between the basitrabecular process and the pterygoid (Watson, **643**). It may represent the meniscus pterygoideus of Rhynchocephalia (Howes and Swinnerton, **528**), Lacertilia (Gaupp, **506**), and Chelonia (Fuchs, **503**) in an ossified condition. Possibly this element is the remains of the endochondral metapterygoid of Teleostomes (Broom, **455**). According to Sushkin *Seymouria* is a Stegocephalian, 1925.

with pterygoids converging anteriorly, and with a pronounced ventral flange, Fig. 334.

From some ' Anapsidan ' must have evolved the other two chief types—the ' Synapsidan ' and the ' Diapsidan ' (Osborn, 554). The Synapsida, typically represented by the Theromorpha, are distinguished by the possession of a single temporal fossa, Fig. 340. The cranial roof bones are at first complete ; but the supratemporal remains only in primitive Pelycosauria, such as *Varanosaurus*, Fig. 336. The tabulars and postparietals become plastered on to the posterior occipital surface,

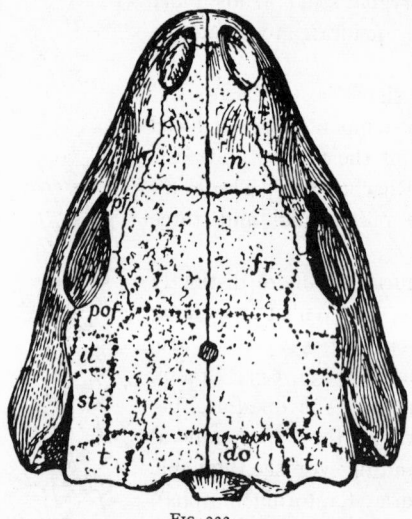

FIG. 333.

Dorsal view of skull of *Conodectes (Seymouria) bayloiensis*. Cotylosaur skull. *n*, Nasal; *l*, lacrimal; *pf*, prefrontal; *pof*, postfrontal; *fr*, frontal; *ti*, intertemporal; *do*, postparietal (dermo-occipital); *t*, tabulare. (From Williston, *Osteology of Reptiles*, 1925.)

the latter bones being often fused to form a median interparietal ; and the post-temporal openings tend to become reduced. The single temporal fossa seems to have originated between the postorbital and jugal, and is still enclosed by these and the squamosal in Pelycosauria and Deino-cephalia, Figs. 336-8. But in more advanced forms it extends upwards as in Mammalia and is then bounded above by the parietal (Dicynodontia, Theriodontia), Figs. 340, 342. The transition to the usual Mammalian type is brought about by the enlargement of the fossa, and loss of the prefrontal, postfrontal, postorbital, and quadratojugal (already much reduced or vestigial in Theriodonts). The tabular is finally lost, or in-distinguishably fused with the parietal, while the two postparietals may remain as an interparietal often fused with the supraoccipital.

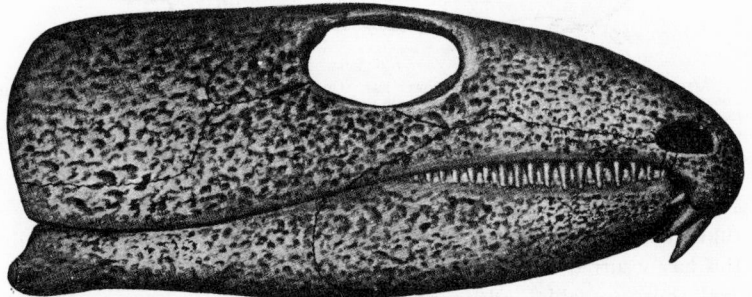

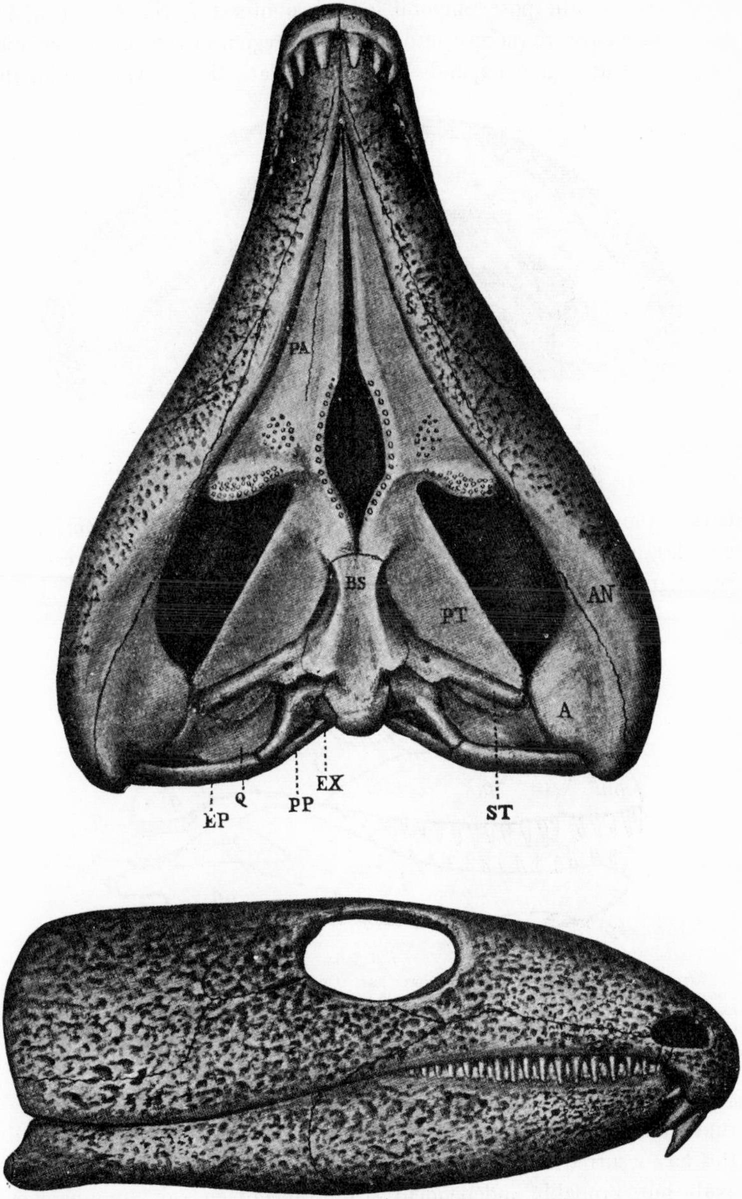

FIG. 334.

Ventral and right-side view of skull of *Labidosaurus hamatus* (from Williston, 1910).   *A*, Articular;
*AN*, angular; *BS*, basisphenoid (+ parasphenoid?); *EP*, tabular; *EX*, exoccipital; *PA*, palatine;
*PP*, postparietal; *PT*, pterygoid; *Q*, quadrate; *ST*, stapes.

Meanwhile the post-temporal fossa is obliterated, the post-temporal bar being as it were merged into the hinder region of the brain-case, Fig. 343. As this region expands to accommodate the growing brain, the

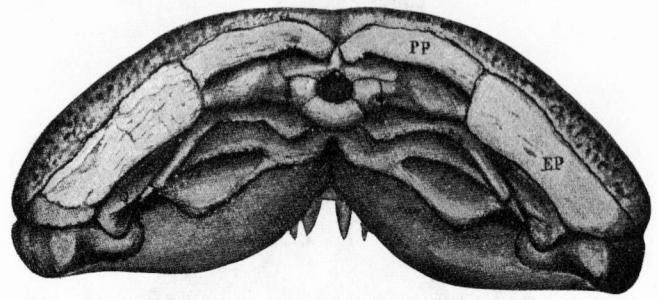

FIG. 335.

Posterior view of skull of *Labidosaurus hamatus* (from Williston, 1910). *EP*, Tabular; *PP*, postparietal.

parietals and squamosal spread over its surface below the powerful jaw muscles, and are withdrawn from the more superficial layers representing the original roofing. Lastly, in the Mammalia, the postorbital bar is inter-

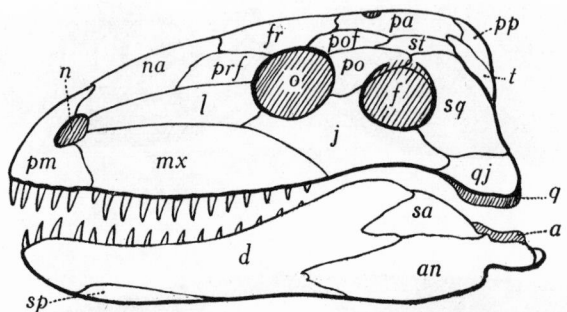

FIG. 336.

*Pelycosauria.* Diagram of skull and lower jaw. Openings in cranial roof : *f*, Lateral temporal fossa ; *n*, external nostril ; *o*, orbit ; *if*, inferior temporal fossa ; *pf*, pineal foramen ; *pl*, preorbital fossa ; *sf*, superior temporal fossa ; *q*, quadrate ; *a*, articular. Dermal bones : *an*, Angular ; *co*, coronoid ; *d*, dentary ; *fr*, frontal ; *ip*, interparietal (fused postparietals) ; *j*, jugal ; *l*, lacrimal ; *mx*, maxillary ; *na*, nasal ; *pa*, parietal ; *pm*, premaxillary ; *po*, postorbital ; *pof*, postfrontal ; *pp*, postparietal ; *prf*, prefrontal ; *qj*, quadratojugal ; *s*, probably squamosal ; *sa*, supra-angular ; *sm*, septomaxillary ; *sp*, splenial ; *sq*, squamosal ; *st*, supratemporal.

rupted, leaving the orbit confluent with the lateral temporal fossa (already this has occurred in the Cynodont *Bauria*, Fig. 499 [Broom, 443-5, 451, 458], but probably independently). Strangely enough, an analogous postorbital bar is re-formed in many mammals by the junction of the frontal with the jugal (later Ungulates, Primates, *Tupaja*).

The canal, arched over by the squamosal, at the side of the occipital region of the skull in Monotremes, is supposed to represent a vestige of the post-temporal opening occupying about the same position in Reptiles, Fig. 403.

Other orders of reptiles besides the Theromorpha have a single lateral

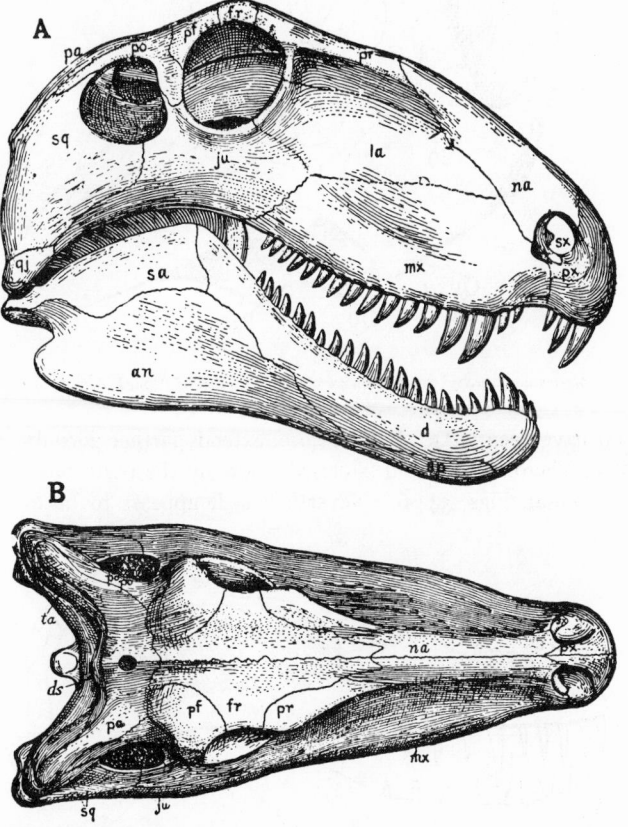

FIG. 337.
Skull of *Sphenacodon*; A, left-side, and B, dorsal view (from Williston, *Osteology of Reptiles*, 1925).

temporal fossa.  Among these are the Sauropterygia (including Mesosauria), Placodontia, Thalattosauria, and Ichthyosauria, and the important question arises whether in all or any of these the fossa is the same as that of the Theromorpha and Mammalia, or has been independently acquired, Fig. 344.

The temporal opening in the Sauropterygia (and Placodontia, which are probably allied to them) is large and bounded by the postfrontal, postorbital, squamosal, and parietal (the supratemporal, tabular, and post-

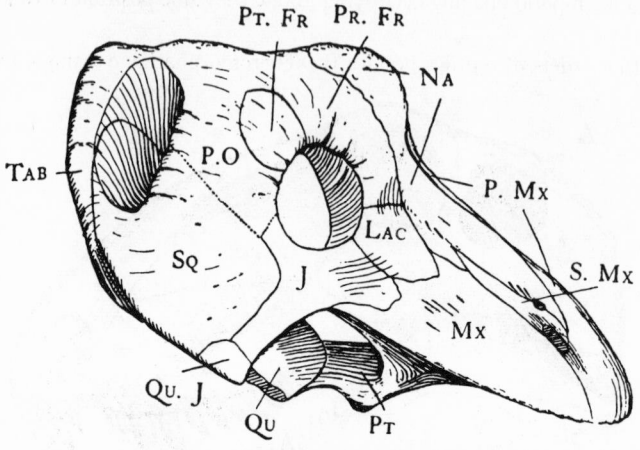

Fig. 338.

*Mormosaurus seeleyi*, right-side view of skull (D. M. S. Watson, *P.Z.S.*, 1914).

parietal have been lost). It, therefore, extends farther dorsally than in primitive Theromorpha, and is closed below by the postorbital meeting the squamosal, Figs. 344-6. Nevertheless, it appears to be essentially

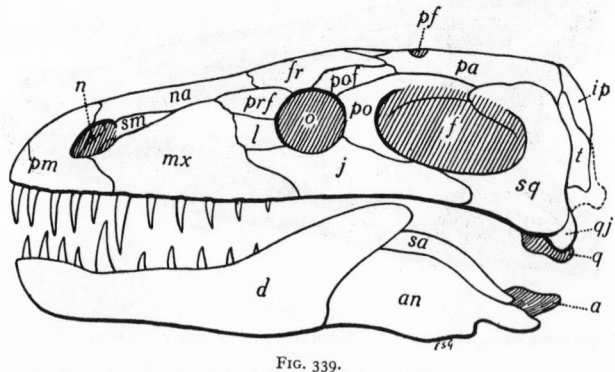

Fig. 339.

*Therocephalia.* Diagram of skull and lower jaw. Lettering as in Fig. 336, p. 328.

the same fossa, though some authors claim that it has had a separate origin (Versluys, **626**; Broom, **456**, **459**).

A single temporal fossa, usually of small size, occurs in the Ichthyosauria. Here the original reptilian roofing bones are complete excepting for the postparietal and tabular,[1] and the fossa lies between the parietal above and the postfrontal and supratemporal below, Figs. 348-9, 350.

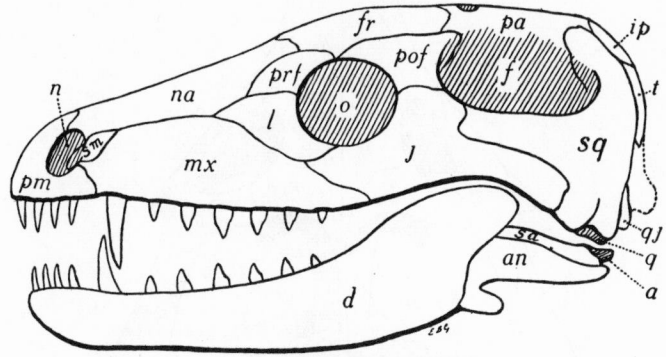

FIG. 340.

*Cynodontia.* Diagram of skull and lower jaw. Lettering as in Fig. 336, p. 328.

The affinities of this group are still very obscure. The great elonga-tion of the snout, the enlargement of the orbit and consequent reduction of the posterior roofing and other characteristic features, appear to be

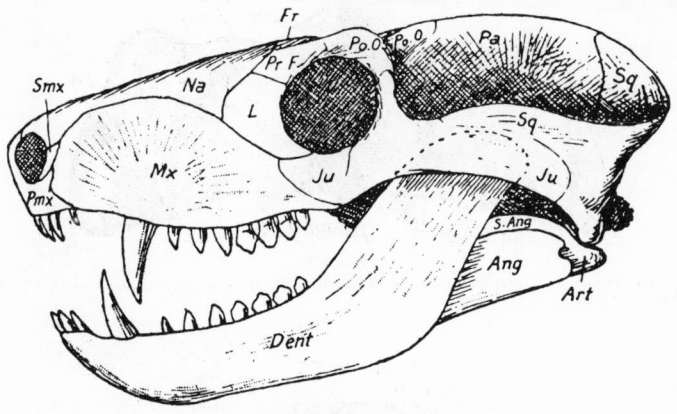

FIG. 341.

*Thrinaxodon,* left-side view of skull and lower jaw, restored (from R. Broom, *P.Z.S.,* 1911).

adaptations to an aquatic and predaceous mode of life, and are less pronounced in some of the early Triassic forms (Merriam, 547). The fossa

[1] According to Broom (447, 456, 459) it is the supratemporal which is lost and the tabular preserved, not only in Ichthyosauria, but also in *Youngina* and Lacertilia.

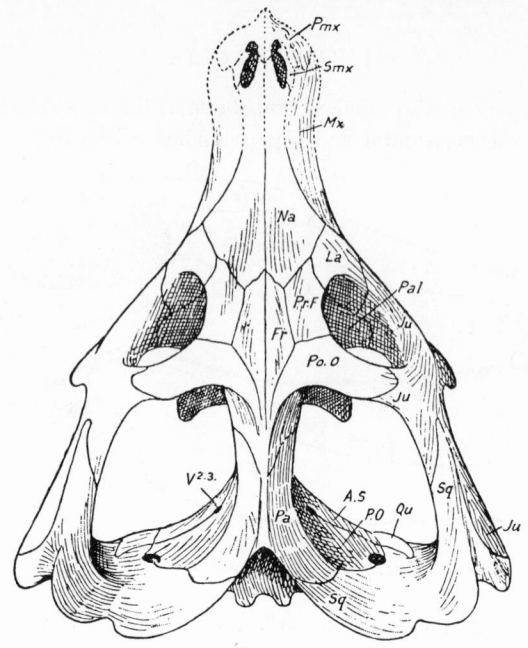

Fig. 342.

*Gomphognathus minor*, dorsal view of skull, restored (from R. Broom, *P.Z.S.*, 1911).

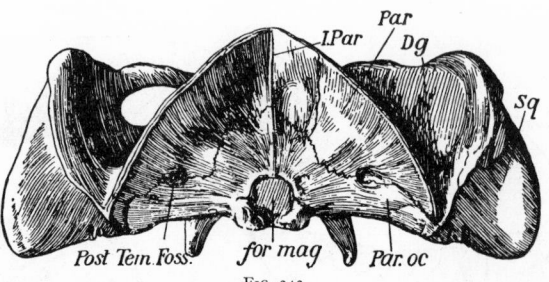

Fig. 343.

*Diademodon browni*, posterior view of skull (from D. M. S. Watson, *Ann. Mag. N.H.*, 1911)
Dg, Digastric groove.

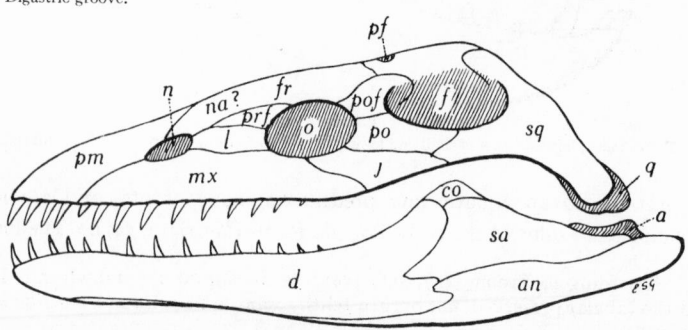

Fig. 344.

*Plesiosauria*. Diagram of skull and lower jaw. Lettering as in Fig. 336, p. 328.

in these is larger than in the later fossils, and appears not to differ essentially from that of other Synapsida.

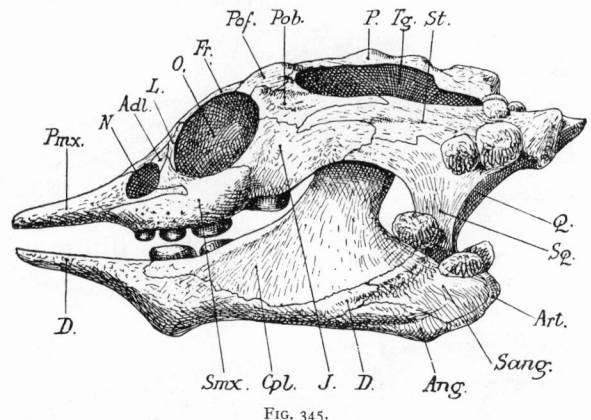

FIG. 345.

*Placochelys placodonta*, Trias of Hungary; left-side view of skull (after O. Jaekel, from O. Abel, 1920). *Ang*, Angular; *Art*, articular; *Cpl*, coronoid; *D*, dentary; *O*, orbit; *Sang*, supra-angular; *Tg*, temporal fossa. Other letters as in Fig. 336.

Quite distinct from the foregoing are the Diapsida with two temporal fossae and two lateral temporal arches on each side. This group

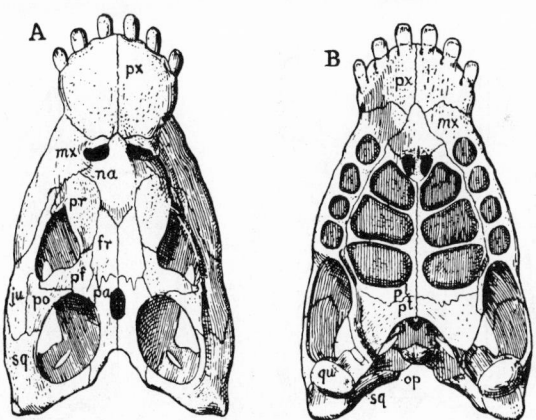

FIG. 346.

Skull of *Placodus*; A, dorsal, and B, ventral view (after Broili, from Williston, *Osteology of Reptiles*, 1925).

includes the Rhynchocephalia, Pseudosuchia, Phytosauria, Crocodilia, Pterosauria, and ' Dinosaurs ' (Saurischia and Ornithischia), and leads towards the Aves. Broom discovered *Youngina*, the earliest and perhaps the most primitive known Diapsidan, in the Permian of S. Africa (Broom, **457**). In general build the skull of this remarkable reptile resembles

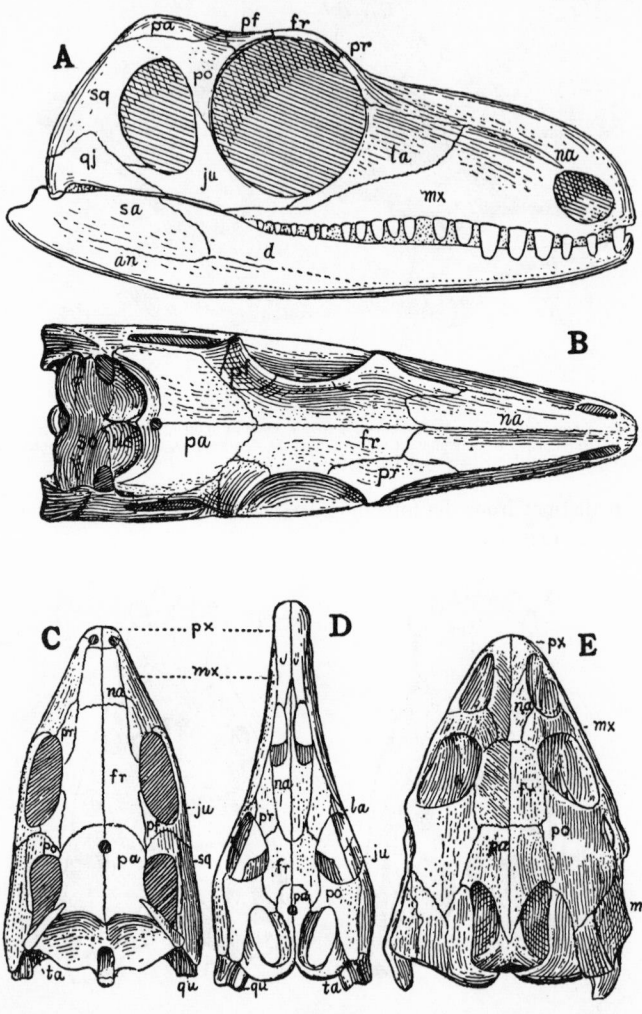

FIG. 347.

A, Left-side, and B, dorsal view of skull of *Mycterosaurus*; C, dorsal view of skull of *Araeoscelis*; D, of *Pleurosaurus*; E, of *Sauranodon* (from Williston, *Osteology of Reptiles*, 1925).

that of *Sphenodon*, but has preserved all the roofing bones except one, either tabular or supratemporal. The superior temporal fossa lies between the parietal, postorbital, and supratemporal (tabular ?); and the inferior

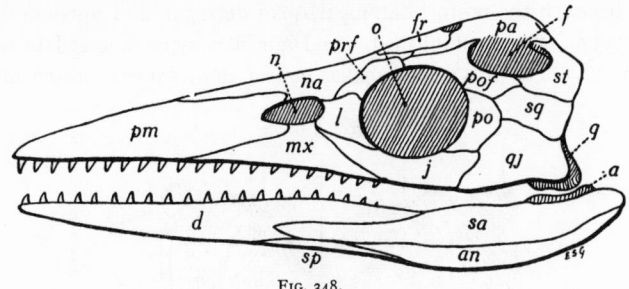

FIG. 348.

*Ichthyosauria.* Diagram of skull and lower jaw. Lettering as in Fig. 336, p. 328.

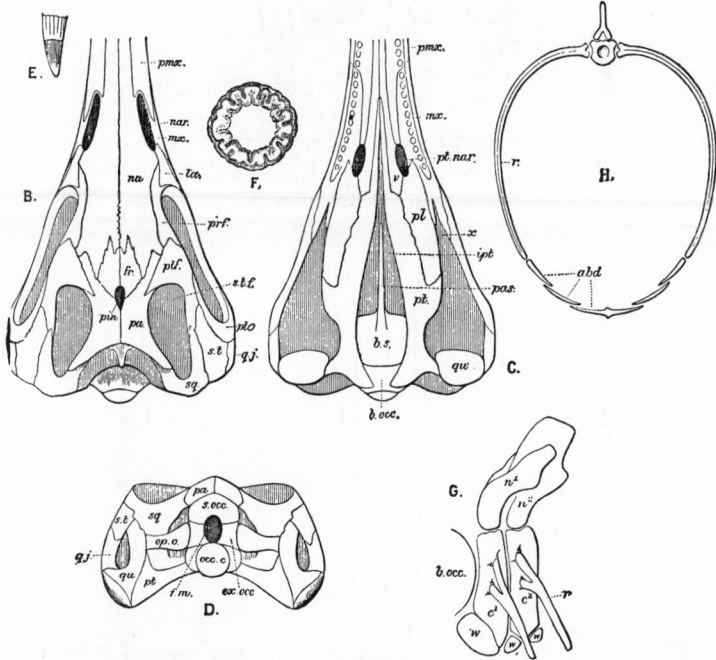

FIG. 349.

Diagrams illustrating structure of *Ichthyosaurus* (from A. S. Woodward, *Vertebrate Palaeontology*, 1898). B, C, D, dorsal, ventral, and posterior views of skull; E, tooth; F, its transverse section; G, atlas and axis; H, dorsal. *b.occ,* Basioccipital; *b.s,* basisphenoid; *d,* dentary; *ex.occ,* exoccipital; *f.m,* foramen magnum; *fr,* frontal; *ipt,* interpterygoid vacuity; *j,* jugal; *la,* lacrimal; *mx,* maxillary; *na,* nasal; *nar,* external narial opening; *occ.c,* occipital condyle; *op.o,* opisthotic; *pa,* parietal; *pas,* parasphenoid; *pin,* pineal foramen; *pl,* palatine; *pmx,* premaxillary; *prf,* prefrontal; *pt,* pterygoid; *pt.nar,* posterior nares; *ptf,* postfrontal; *pto,* postorbital; *q.j,* quadratojugal; *qu,* quadrate; *s.ag,* surangular; *s.occ,* supraoccipital; *s.t,* supratemporal (prosquamosal); *s.t.f,* supratemporal vacuity; *scl,* sclerotic plates; *spl,* splenial; *sq,* squamosal; *x,* space for ectopterygoid (?); *v,* vomer. *abd,* Abdominal ribs; *c¹,* centrum of atlas; *c²,* centrum of axis; *n¹,* paired neural arch of atlas; *n²,* single neural arch of axis; *r,* ribs; *w,* subvertebral wedge-bones (intercentra or hypocentra).

fossa between the postorbital, jugal, quadratojugal, and squamosal, Figs. 351, 353 A. Once established, the Diapsidan type diverged in various directions. The Rhynchocephalia, one of the least specialised of these

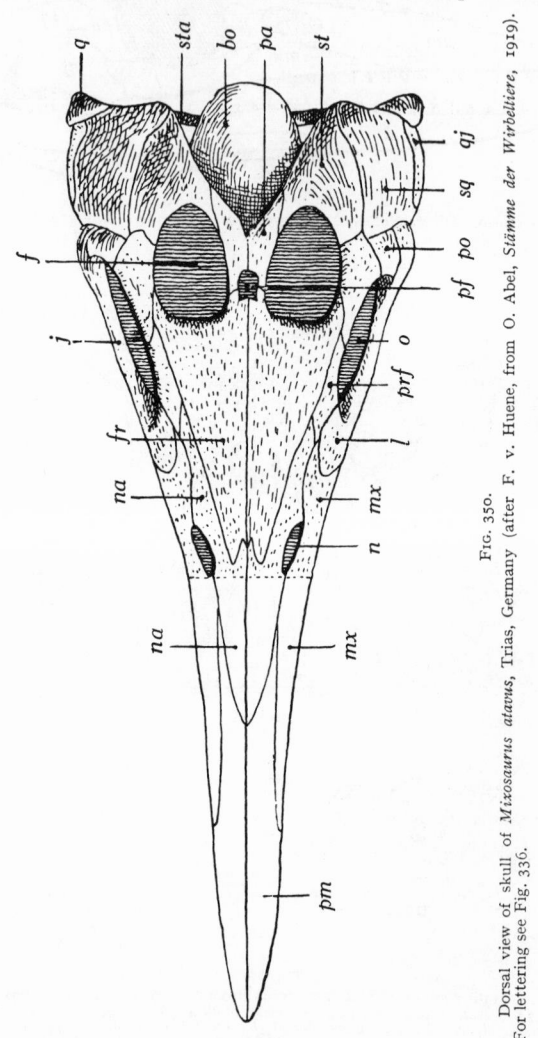

FIG. 350.

Dorsal view of skull of *Mixosaurus atavus*, Trias, Germany (after F. v. Huene, from O. Abel, *Stämme der Wirbeltiere*, 1919). For lettering see Fig. 336.

branches, survive at the present day in the single species *Sphenodon punctatum* of New Zealand (Günther, 1867; Siebenrock, 598; Ossawa, 552; Howes and Swinnerton, 528; Schauinsland, 583).

It has lost the lacrimal, postorbital, supratemporal, tabular, and post-

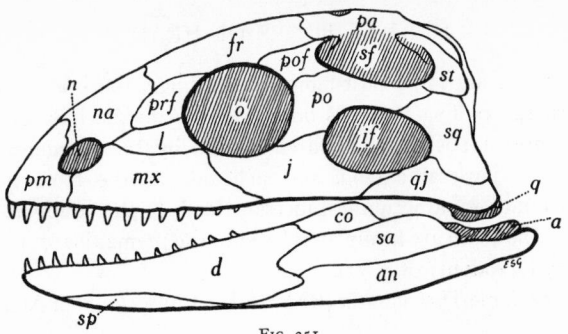

FIG. 351.

*Eosuchia.* Diagram of skull and lower jaw. Lettering as in Fig. 336, p. 328.

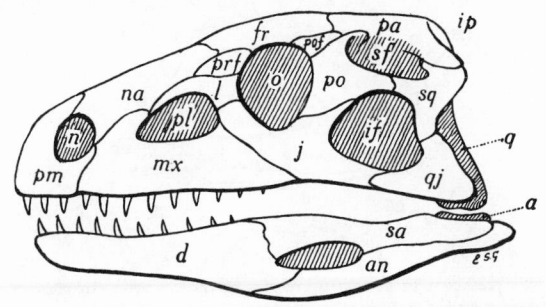

FIG. 352.

*Pseudosuchia.* Diagram of skull and lower jaw. *pl*, Preorbital fossa. Other lettering as in Fig. 336, p. 328.

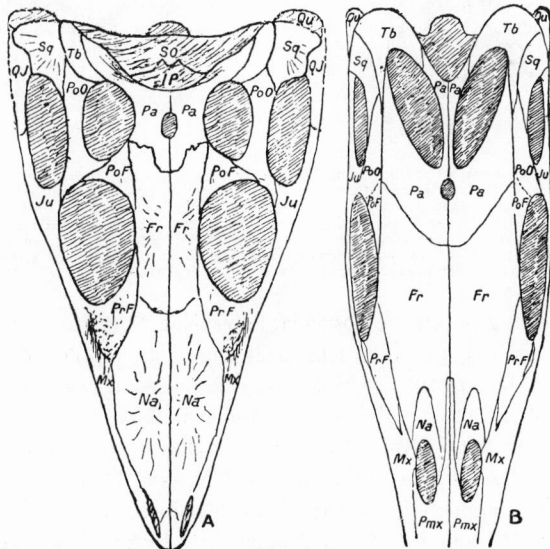

FIG. 353.

Dorsal view of restoration of skull of : A, *Youngina capensis* ; B, *Thalattosaurus alexandrae* (from R. Broom, *Proc. Zool. Soc.,* 1925).

parietal. There are large post-temporal openings, the brain-case being attached to the roofing parietals only near the middle line, as in most Lacertilia; and a post-temporal arch formed by the squamosal and a process of the parietal extends on each side to the fixed quadrate. Large outstanding paroccipital processes lend further support to the quadrate. The teeth are firmly ankylosed to the premaxillary, maxillary, and dentary (acrodont), Fig. 354.

Under the name Thecodontia (with teeth set in sockets) or Archosauria

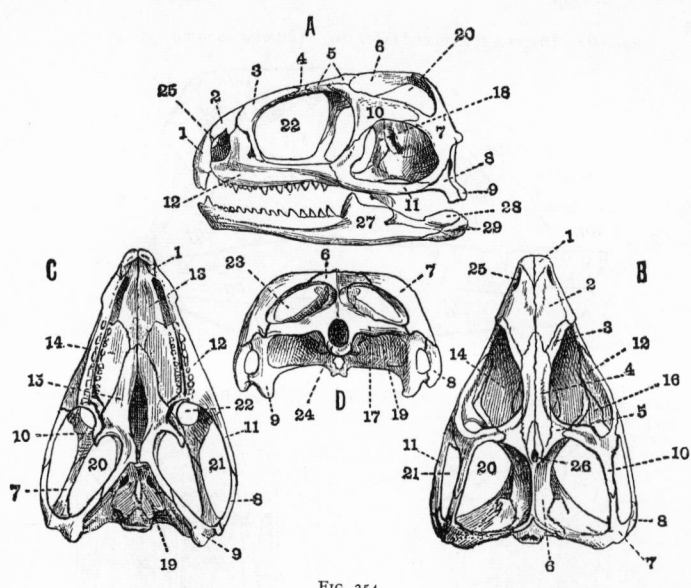

FIG. 354.

A, Lateral; B, dorsal; C, ventral; and D, posterior view of skull of *Sphenodon punctatus* (from S. H. Reynolds, *Vertebrate Skeleton*, 1913.) 1, Premaxillary; 2, nasal; 3, prefrontal; 4, frontal; 5, postfrontal; 6, parietal; 7, squamosal; 8, quadratojugal; 9, quadrate; 10, postorbital; 11, jugal; 12, maxillary; 13, prevomer; 14, palatine; 15, pterygoid; 16, transpalatine; 17, exoccipital; 18, epipterygoid; 19, basisphenoid; 20, supratemporal fossa; 21, infratemporal or lateral temporal fossa; 22, orbit; 23, post-temporal fossa; 24, foramen magnum; 25, anterior nares; 26, pineal foramen; 27, dentary; 28, supra-angular; 29, articular.

are sometimes grouped the Eosuchia, Parasuchia, 'Dinosaurs' (Saurischia and Ornithischia), and Pterosauria, all Diapsidan reptiles allied to the Crocodilia. Except the Crocodilia, they all possess a new opening in the dermal roofing between the lacrimal and maxillary, known as the pre-orbital or antorbital fossa. In most Crocodiles it appears to have been secondarily closed up, persisting, however, in some Teleosauridae. Even the superior temporal fossa may be much reduced in extent and rarely quite closed in modern Crocodiles, apparently by the deposition on the skull of new bony matter comparable to the bony dermal scutes developed

over the rest of the body. This new growth adds a secondary rough
superficial sculpturing to the skull (excepting the postorbital bar in all

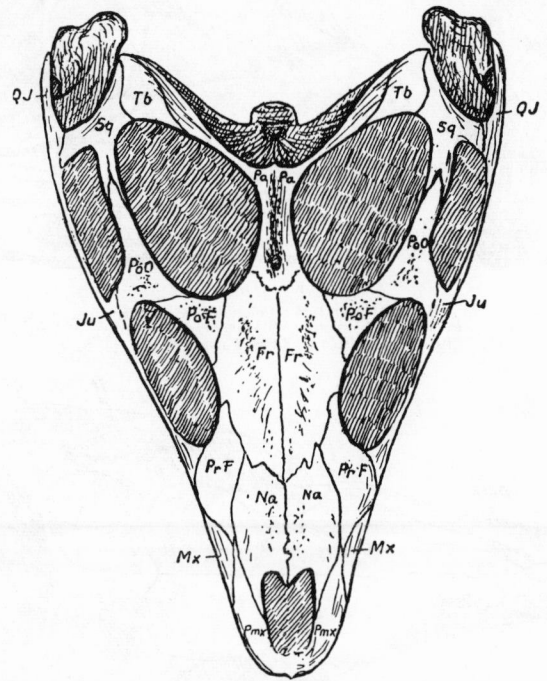

FIG. 355.

Dorsal view of skull of *Mesosuchus browni* (from R. Broom, *Proc. Zool. Soc.*, 1925).

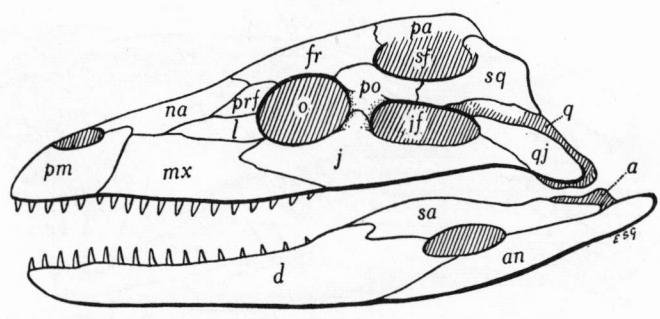

FIG. 356.

*Crocodilia.* Diagram of skull and lower jaw. Lettering as in Fig. 336, p. 328.

later forms) bearing a deceptive resemblance to the primitive sculpturing
of Stegocephalia, Figs. 356-9, and p. 354.

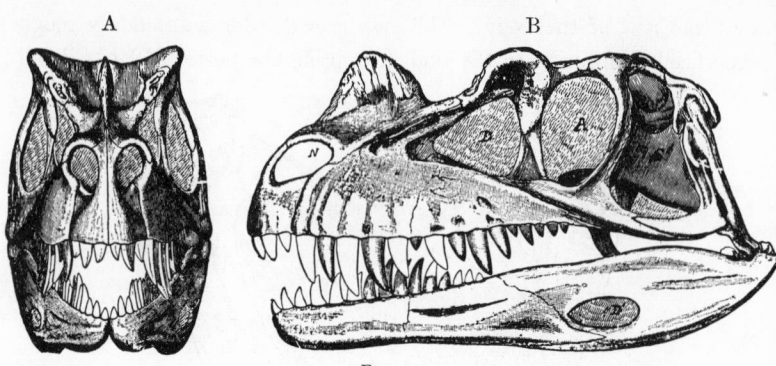

FIG. 357.

*Ceratosaurus nasicornis*, Marsh. Upper Jura : Colorado. Skull from anterior (A) and lateral (B) aspects, ⅙. *A*, Orbit ; *D*, antorbital vacuity ; *D'*, mandibular vacuity ; *N*, external nostril ; *S*, supratemporal vacuity. (After Marsh, from K. Zittel, *Palaeontology*.)

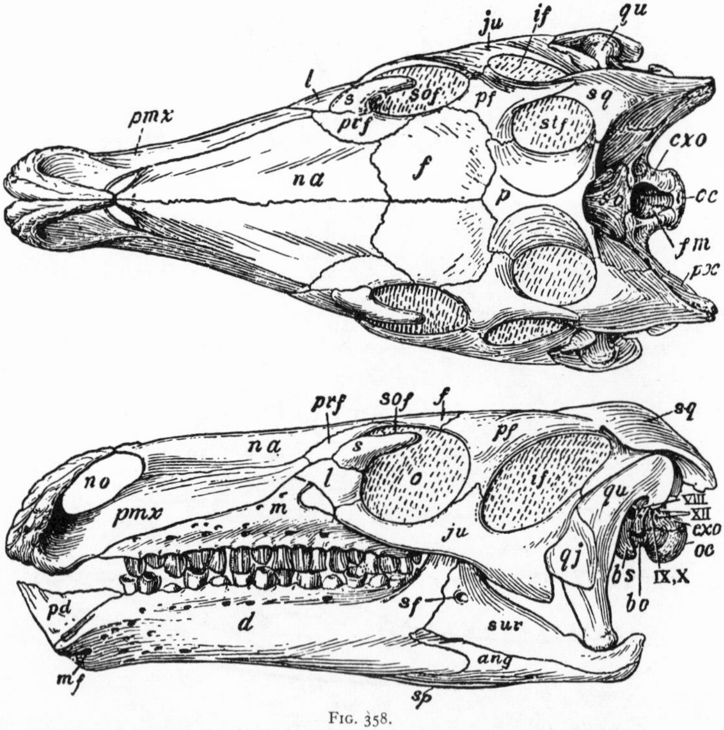

FIG. 358.

Dorsal and left-side view of skull of *Camptosaurus* (after C. W. Gilmore, '09, from O. Abel, *Stämme der Wirbeltiere*, 1919). *ang*, Angular ; *bo*, basioccipital ; *bs*, basisphenoid ; *d*, dentary ; *exo*, exoccipital ; *f*, frontal ; *fm*, foramen magnum ; *if*, inferior temporal fossa ; *ju*, jugal ; *l*, lacrimal ; *m*, maxillary ; *mf*, mental foramen ; *na*, nasal ; *no*, nasal opening ; *o*, orbit ; *oc*, occipital condyle ; *pd*, predentary ; *pf*, postfrontal ; *pmx*, premaxillary ; *poc*, opisthotic ; *prf*, prefrontal ; *qj*, quadrato-jugal ; *qu*, quadrate ; *s*, supraorbital ; *sf*, external vacuity ; *sp*, splenial ; *sq*, squamosal ; *stf*, superior temporal fossa ; *sur*, supra-angular.

The Archosauria, at all events the Crocodilia, Saurischia, Ornithischia, and Pterosauria, are further characterised by the fact that the inferior

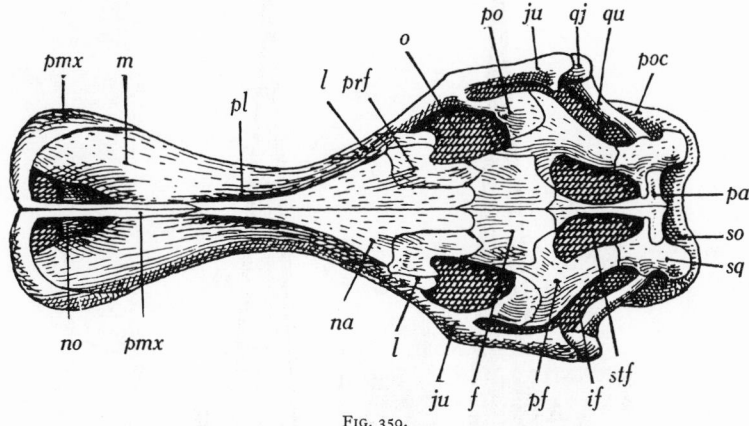

FIG. 359.

Reconstruction of skull of *Trachodon mirabilis*, Upper Cretaceous, N. America (from O. Abel, *Stämme der Wirbeltiere*, 1919). *pl*, Preorbital fossa; *po*, postorbital. Other letters as in Fig. 358.

temporal fossa is usually open behind, Figs. 356, 360-61. For the quadrato-jugal fails to join the squamosal (supratemporal ?),[1] thus exposing part of the quadrate (p. 433).

Besides the Reptilia dealt with above, which may confidently be

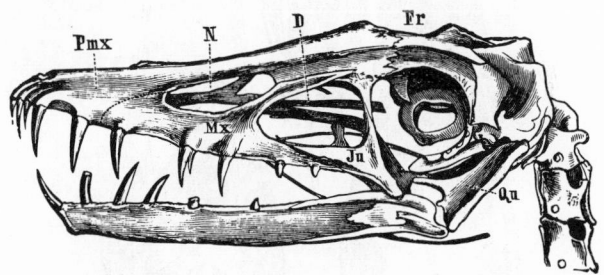

FIG. 360.

*Scaphognathus crassirostris*, Goldf. sp., Upper Jura, Eichstädt, Bavaria. *D*, Antorbital vacuity; *Fr*, frontal; *Ju*, jugal; *Mx*, maxilla; *N*, narial opening; *Pmx*, premaxilla; *Qu*, quadrate. (From K. Zittel, *Palaeontology*.)

classified into Synapsida and Diapsida, there remain certain important Orders provisionally included in the Parapsida whose position is still

---

[1] In most Archosauria and also in Rhynchocephalia only one bone persists between the parietal and the quadratojugal, and it is difficult, if not impossible, on existing evidence to decide whether it is the supratemporal or the squamosal. Both views have been held. On the whole, it seems best to call this bone the squamosal.

doubtful. The Lacertilia have a skull with a single lateral temporal fossa,

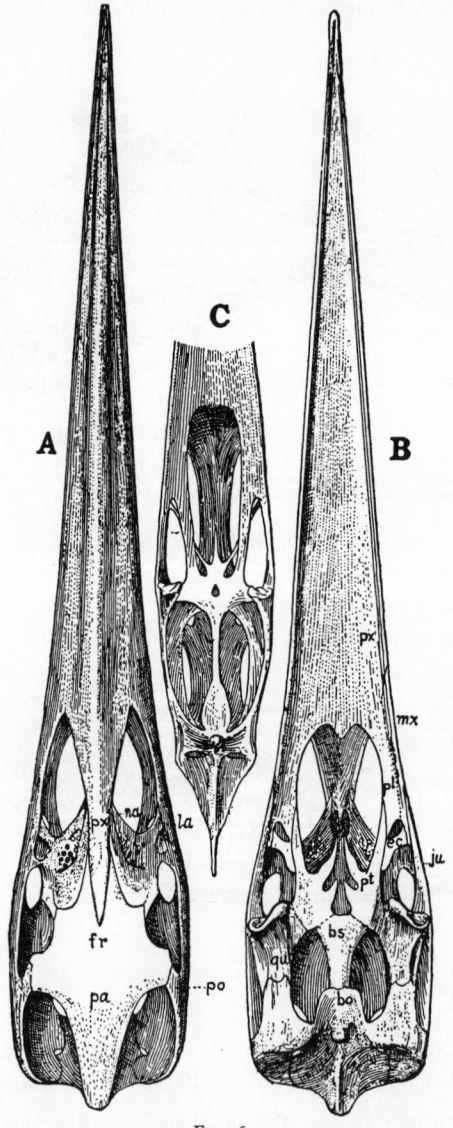

FIG. 361.

Skull of *Nyctosaurus*: A, from above, B, from below; and of *Pteranodon*: C, from below (after Eaton, from Williston, *Osteology of Reptiles*, 1925).

and the interesting question arises whether this opening corresponds to the single one in Synapsida, or to the upper fossa of the Diapsida,[1] Figs. 362-6. According to the first interpretation the lateral temporal bar of

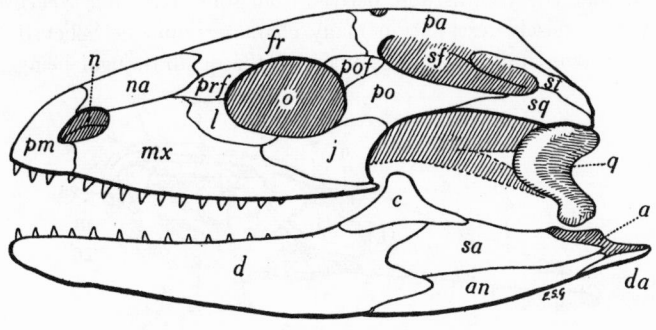

FIG. 362.

*Lacertilia.* Diagram of skull and lower jaw. Lettering as in Fig. 328.

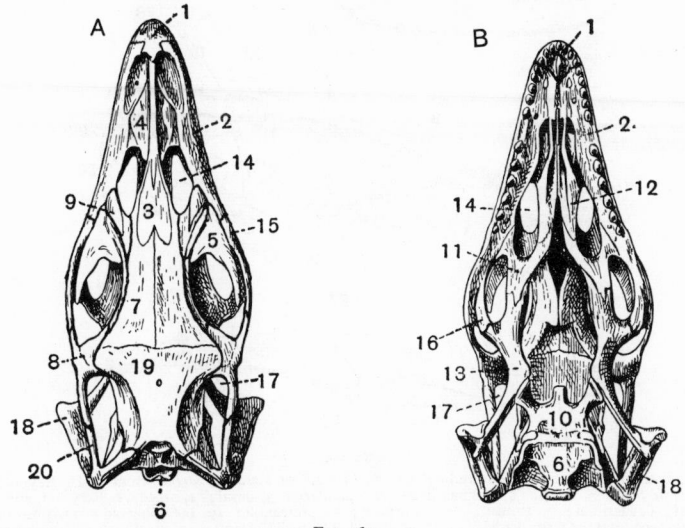

FIG. 363.

A, Dorsal, and B, ventral view of cranium of *Varanus* sp. (from S. H. Reynolds, *Vertebrate Skeleton*, 1913). 1, Premaxillary; 2, maxillary; 3, nasal; 4, septomaxillary; 5, supra-orbital; 6, basioccipital; 7, frontal; 8, postfrontal; 9, lacrimal; 10, basisphenoid; 11, palatine; 12, prevomer; 13, pterygoid; 14, anterior narial opening; 15, jugal; 16, transpalatine; 17, supratemporal fossa; 18, quadrate; 19, parietal; 20, squamosal.

the Lacertilian would represent that of the Synapsidan, and would then be formed presumably of a jugal and a quadratojugal; while, according to

---

[1] The postorbital and temporal bars may be interrupted in degenerate lizards, such as the Geckonida, and in the Amphisbaenidae they disappear.

the second, this bar would represent the upper one of the Diapsidan skull formed by the postorbital joining the squamosal. Huxley was of the opinion that the Lizards were derived from some form like *Sphenodon*, which they closely resemble in many characters, and he believed that the lower temporal bar has disappeared (the quadratojugal being now

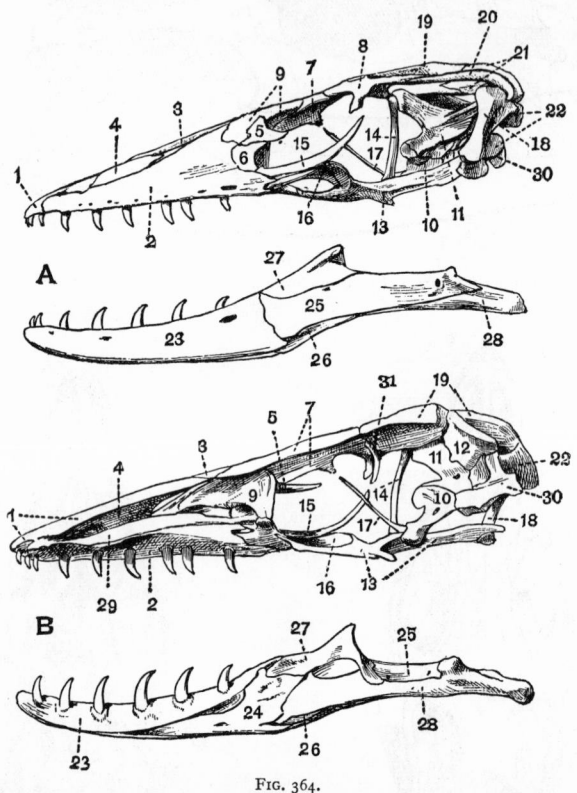

FIG. 364.

A, Lateral view, and B, longitudinal section of skull of *Varanus varius* (from S. H. Reynolds, *Vertebrate Skeleton*, 1913). 1, Premaxillary; 2, maxillary; 3, nasal; 4, septomaxillary; 5, supraorbital; 6, lacrimal; 7, frontal; 8, postorbital; 9, prefrontal; 10, basisphenoid; 11, pro-otic; 12, supraoccipital; 13, pterygoid; 14, epipterygoid (columella cranii); 15, jugal; 16, transpalatine; 17, parasphenoid; 18, quadrate; 19, parietal; 20, squamosal; 21, supratemporal; 22, exoccipital; 23, dentary; 24, splenial; 25, supra-angular; 26, angular; 27, coronoid; 28, articular (+prearticular); 29, vomer; 30, basioccipital; 31, orbitosphenoid.

represented only by a ligament), setting free the quadrate (streptostylic condition, p. 433). This view has been adopted by many (Broom, **456**; Versluys, **796**; and others). Williston (**95**) and Watson (**638**) derive the Lacertilia from some form with a single temporal fossa and a wide bar, like the Permo-Carboniferous *Araeoscelis* or the Jurassic *Pleurosaurus*, by the narrowing of the bar from below, Fig. 347. However, the affinities of these extinct genera are uncertain, and the whole ques-

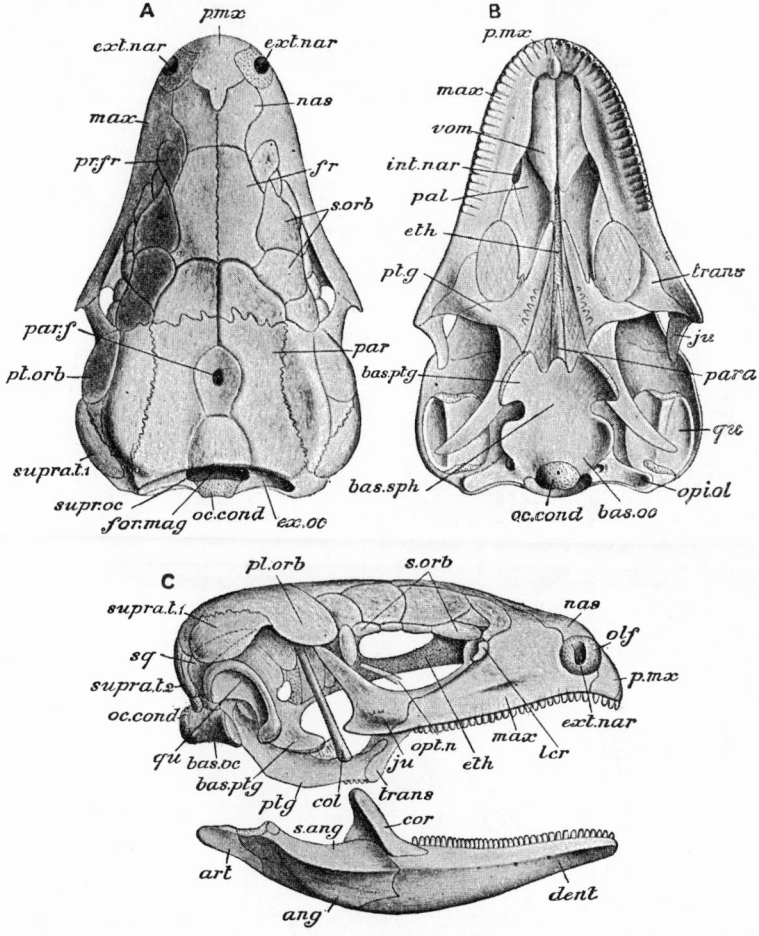

FIG. 365.

Skull of *Lacerta agilis* (from Parker and Haswell's *Zoology*, after W. K. Parker). A, From above ; B, from below ; C, from the side, showing secondary ossifications closing superior temporal fossa. *ang*, Angular ; *art*, articular ; *bas.oc*, basioccipital ; *bas.ptg*, basipterygoid processes ; *bas.sph*, basisphenoid ; *col*, epipterygoid ; *cor*, coronary ; *dent*, dentary ; *eth*, ethmoid ; *ex.oc*, exoccipital ; *ext.nar*, external nares ; *for.mag*, foramen magnum ; *fr*, frontal ; *int.nar*, internal nares ; *ju*, jugal ; *lcr*, lacrimal ; *max*, maxilla ; *nas*, nasal ; *oc.cond*, occipital condyle ; *olf*, olfactory capsule ; *opi.ot*, opisthotic ; *opt.n*, optic nerve ; *pal*, palatine ; *par*, parietal ; *para*, parasphenoid (anterior rostrum ; posterior plate fused to basisphenoid) ; *par.f*, parietal foramen ; *p.mx*, premaxillae ; *pr.fr*, prefrontal ; *ptg*, pterygoid ; *pt.orb*, postorbital ; *qu*, quadrate ; *s.ang*, supra-angular ; *s.orb*, supraorbitals ; *sq*, paraquadrate (squamosal) ; *supra.oc*, supra-occipital ; *supra.t.1*, supratemporal ; *supra.t.2*, supratemporal [2] ; *trans*, transpalatine ; *vom*, prevomer.

tion of the origin of the Lacertilia remains open for the present ; but their general resemblance to other living Diapsidan reptiles (Rhyncho-

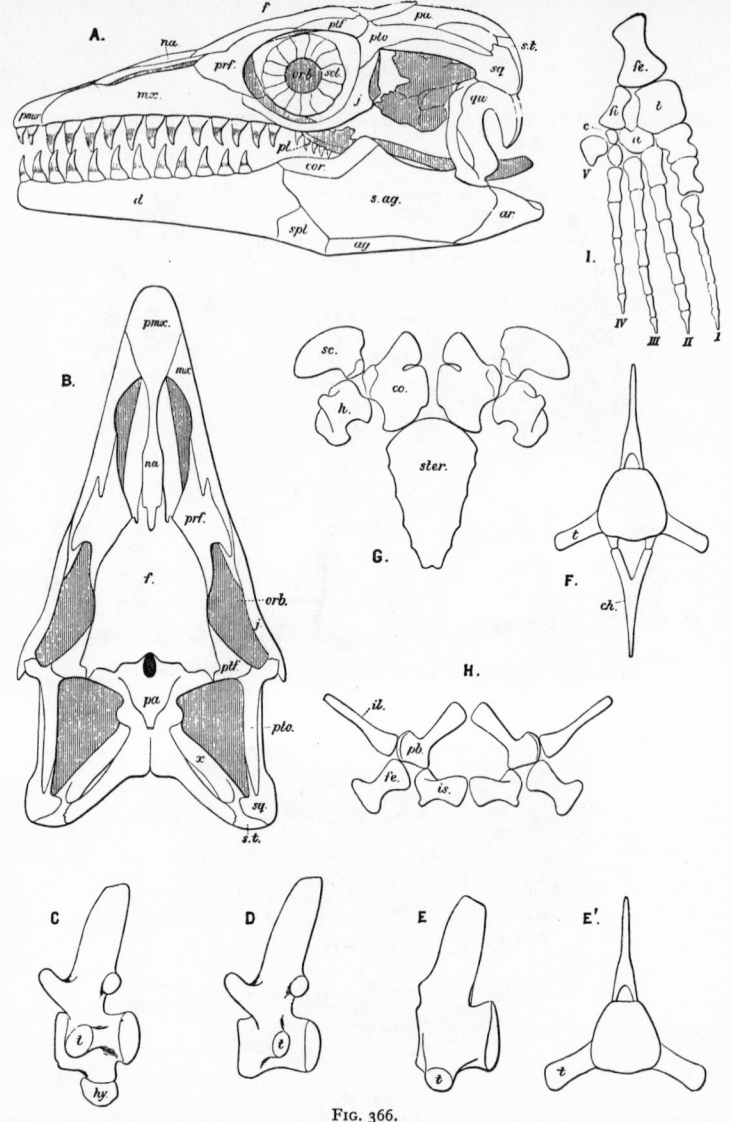

FIG. 366.

Diagram illustrating principal characters of Pythonomorpha.

A, B, *Platecarpus coryphaeus*. Skull from the lateral and superior aspects. U. Cretaceous, Kansas (slightly restored after Merriam). *ag*, Angular; *ar*, articular; *cor*, coronoid; *d*, dentary; *f*, frontal; *j*, jugal; *mx*, maxillary; *na*, nasal; *orb*, orbit; *pa*, parietal; *pmx*, premaxillary; *prf*, prefrontal; *pt*, pterygoid; *ptf*, postfrontal; *pto*, postorbital; *qu*, quadrate; *s.ag*, surangular; *s.t*, supratemporal (prosquamosal); *scl*, sclerotic; *spl*, splenial; *sq*, squamosal; *x*, exoccipital, etc.

C, *Mosasaurus camperi*. Cervical vertebra, left lateral aspect. U. Cretaceous, Maastricht, Holland. *hy*, Hypocentrum; *t*, transverse process.

D, *Ditto*. Anterior dorsal vertebra, left lateral aspect. *Ibid*. *t*, Transverse process.

E, E[1], *Ditto*. Posterior dorsal vertebra, left lateral and hinder aspects. *Ibid*. *t*, Transverse process.

F, *Ditto*. Anterior caudal vertebra, hinder aspect. *Ibid*. *ch*, Chevron bone; *t*, transverse process.

G, *Edestosaurus dispar*. Pectoral arch, ventral aspect. U. Cretaceous, Kansas (after Marsh). *co*, Coracoid; *h*, humerus; *sc*, scapula; *ster*, calcified sternum.

H, *Lestosaurus simus*. Pelvic arch. U. Cretaceous, Kansas (after Marsh). *fe*, Femur; *il*, ilium; *is*, ischium; *pb*, pubis.

I, *Mosasaurus lemonnieri*. Pelvic limb. U. Cretaceous, Belgium (after Dollo). *a*, Astragalo-central; *c*, calcaneum; *fe*, femur; *fi*, fibula; *t*, tibia; *I.-V*., the five digits, the fifth represented only by its metatarsal. (From A. S. Woodward, *Vertebrate Palaeontology*, 1898.)

cephalia, etc.), more particularly the structure of the heart (p. 572), other viscera, and hind foot (Goodrich, 517), affords strong corroborative evidence in favour of Huxley's view.    Another controversy has taken place about the homology of the two lower bones limiting the single temporal fossa

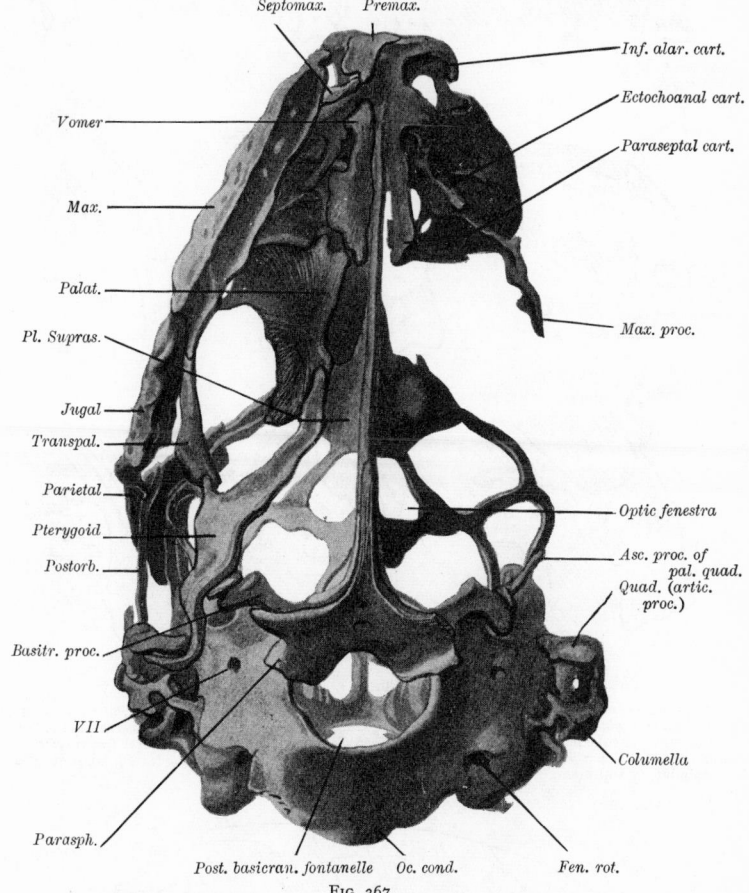

FIG. 367.

Ventral view of Gaupp-Ziegler model of skull of embryo *Lacerta agilis*, 4½ mm. in length.    (From Wiedersheim, *Comp. Anatomy*.)

behind in lizards.[1]    The outer bone, which joins the jugal, is considered by many to be the squamosal (Huxley, Boulenger, Gadow, Siebenrock, Broili, v. Huene, Broom, Jaekel, Williston, and others); it is called para-quadrate by Gaupp (505), prosquamosal by Baur (416-17) and Case, quadratojugal by Watson (638).    The inner bone next to the parietal is

[1] The homology and nomenclature of these bones is discussed by Thyng (611).

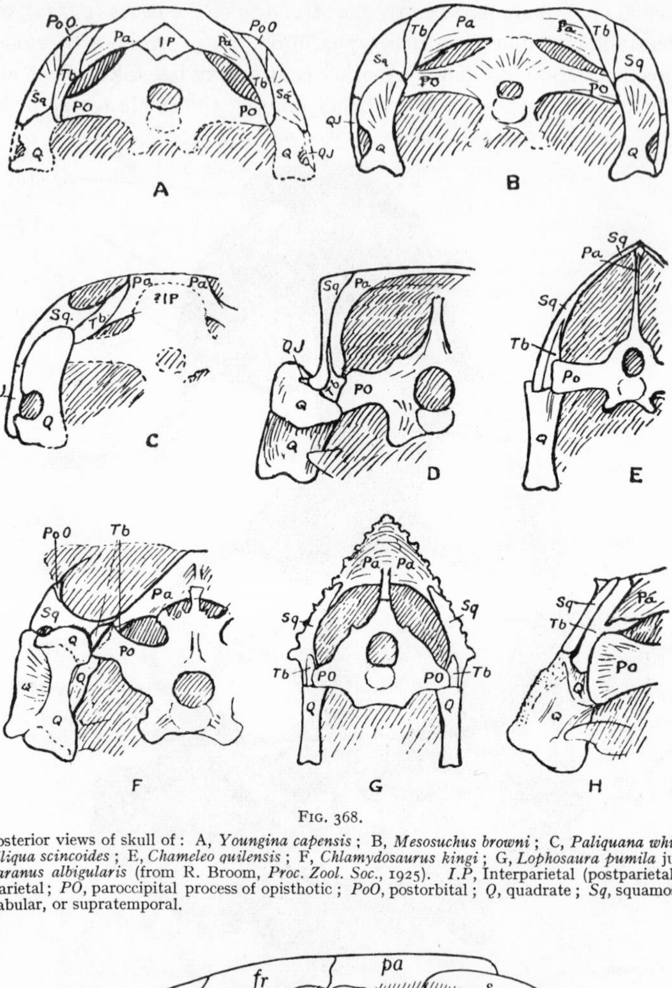

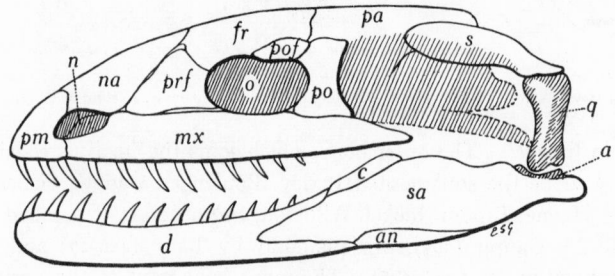

FIG. 368.

Posterior views of skull of : A, *Youngina capensis* ; B, *Mesosuchus browni* ; C, *Paliquana whitei* ; D, *Tiliqua scincoides* ; E, *Chameleo quilensis* ; F, *Chlamydosaurus kingi* ; G, *Lophosaura pumila* juv. ; H, *Varanus albigularis* (from R. Broom, *Proc. Zool. Soc.*, 1925). *I.P,* Interparietal (postparietal ?) ; *Pa,* parietal ; *PO,* paroccipital process of opisthotic ; *PoO,* postorbital ; *Q,* quadrate ; *Sq,* squamosal ; *Tb,* tabular, or supratemporal.

FIG. 369.

*Ophidia.* Diagram of skull and lower jaw. Lettering as in Fig. 336, p. 328.

called supratemporal by the majority, squamosal by Gaupp and Watson,

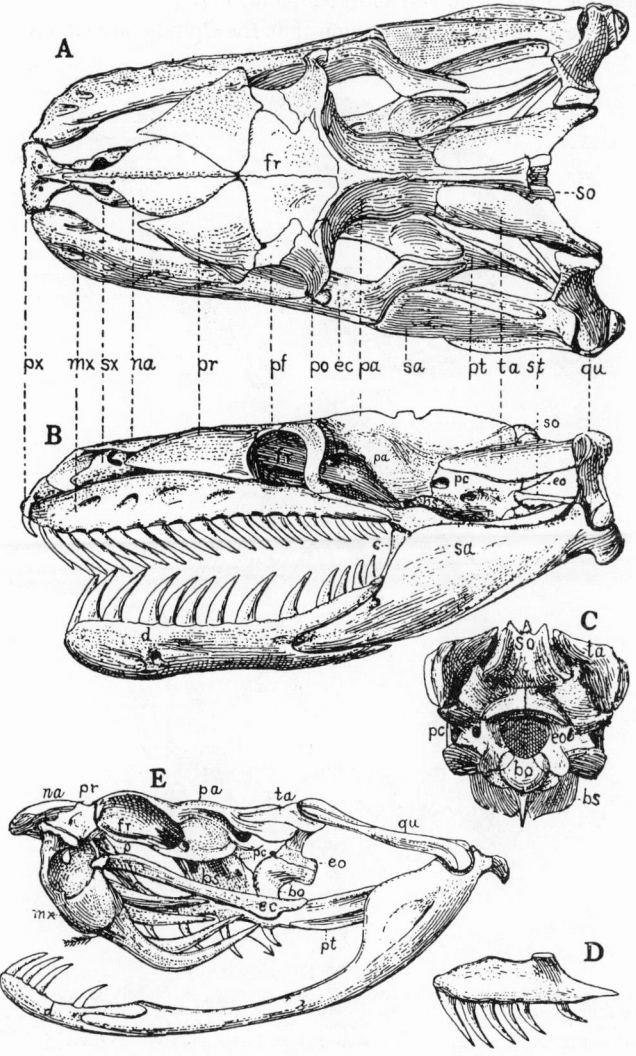

FIG. 370.

A, Dorsal, B, left-side, and C, posterior view of skull of *Python*; D, palatine of same; E, left-side view of skull of *Crotalus* (from Williston, *Osteol. of Reptiles*, 1925). *bo*, Basioccipital; *bs*, basisphenoid; *d*, dentary; *ec*, ectopterygoid; *eo*, exoccipital; *fr*, frontal; *mx*, maxillary; *na*, nasal; *p*, palatine; *pa*, parietal; *pc*, pro-otic; *pf*, postfrontal; *po*, postorbital; *pr*, prefrontal; *pt*, pterygoid; *px*, premaxillary; *qu*, quadrate; *sa*, supra-angular; *so*, supraoccipital; *st*, stapes; *sx*, septomaxillary; *ta*, tabular ?

tabular by Broom, Williston, and v. Huene.    The identity of these two bones remains uncertain, but if Huxley's view be correct they are probably the squamosal and supratemporal, Fig. 368.

If the generally accepted opinion that the Ophidia are closely related

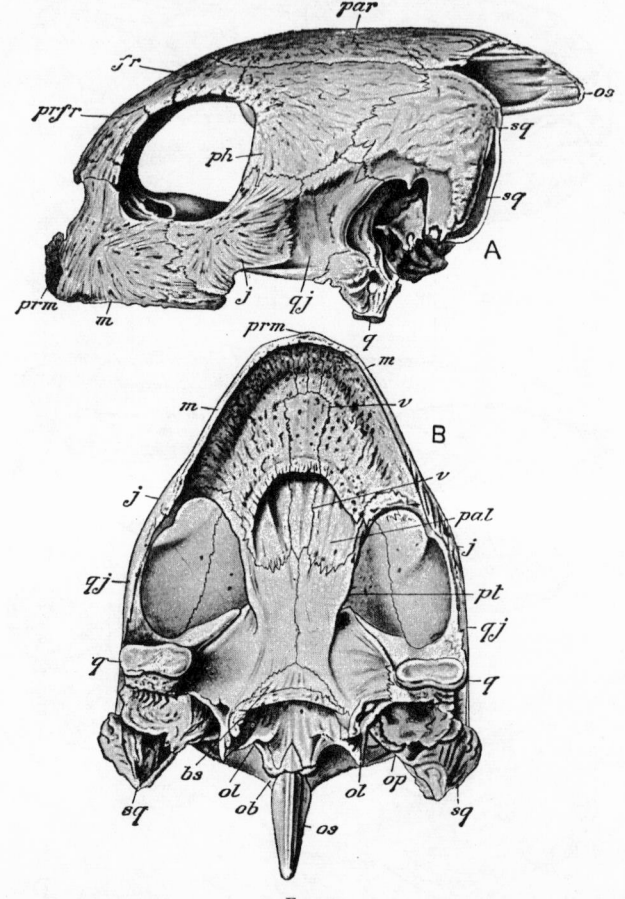

FIG. 371.

Ventral view of the skull of *Chelone mydas*.  *bs*, Basisphenoid ; *fr*, frontal ; *j*, jugal ; *m*, maxilla ; *ob*, basioccipital ; *ol*, exoccipital ; *op*, opisthotic ; *os*, supraoccipital ; *pal*, palatine ; *par*, parietal ; *ph*, postfrontal ; *prfr*, prefrontal ; *pt*, pterygoid ; *prm*, premaxilla ; *q*, quadrate ; *qj*, quadrato-jugal ; *sq*, squamosal ; *v*, vomer.  (After Hoffmann, from Parker and Haswell, *Zoology*.)

to the Lacertilia be correct, we must suppose that the temporal roofing has almost entirely disappeared, and that the fossae have been opened out completely.   The single bone which remains connecting the quadrate to the cranium above may be either a squamosal, or more probably a supratemporal, or again possibly a tabular, Figs. 369, 370.

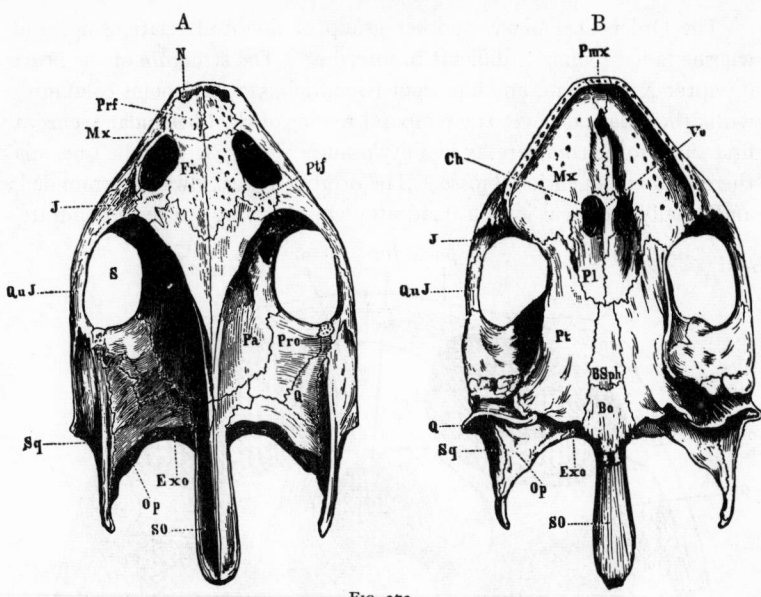

FIG. 372.

*Trionyx gangeticus*, Cuvier. Recent; India. Superior (A) and palatal (B) aspects of skull, reduced. *Bo*, Basioccipital; *BSph*, basisphenoid; *Ch*, internal nares; *Exo*, exoccipital; *Fr*, frontal; *J*, jugal; *Mx*, maxilla; *N*, external nostril; *Op*, opisthotic: *Pa*, parietal; *Pl*, palatine; *Pmx*, premaxilla; *Prf*, prefrontal+nasal; *Pro*, pro-otic: *Ptf*, postfrontal; *Q*, quadrate; *QuJ*, quadratojugal; *S*, palatine vacuity; *SO*, supraoccipital; *Sq*, squamosal; *Vo*, vomer. (From K. Zittel, *Palaeontology*.)

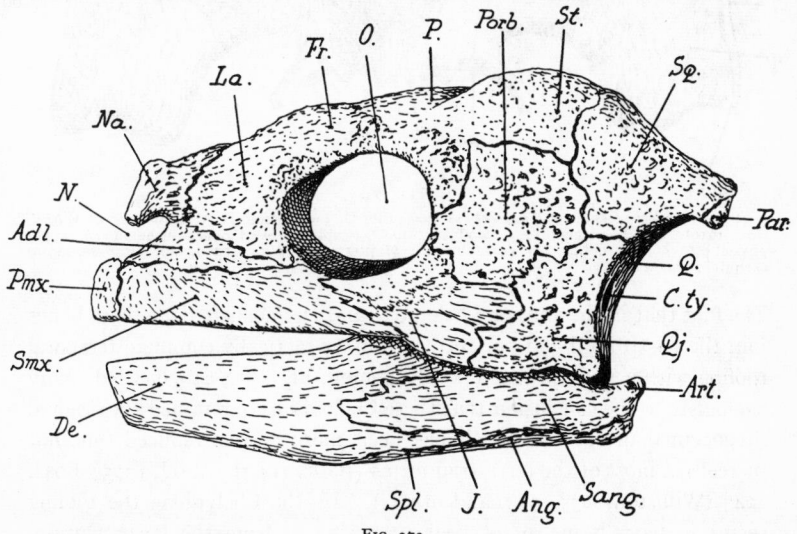

FIG. 373.

*Triassochelys dux*, Trias of Halberstadt; left-side view of skull (after O. Jaekel, from O. Abel, 1920). *Adl*, Lacrimal; *C.ty*, tympanic cavity; *La*, prefrontal; *Par*, paroccipital process; *St*, supratemporal.

The Order Chelonia is another group of doubtful relationship, and whose cranial roofing is difficult to interpret. The structure of the heart (Chapter X.), viscera, and hind foot (Goodrich, **517, 826**) point to affinity with other Diapsida; yet the temporal roofing of the Chelonidae seems at first sight to be complete as in Cotylosauria, Fig. 371. In the Chelonia there is never an enclosed fossa. The orbit is almost always surrounded, and usually the jugal joins a quadratojugal overlying the fixed quadrate.

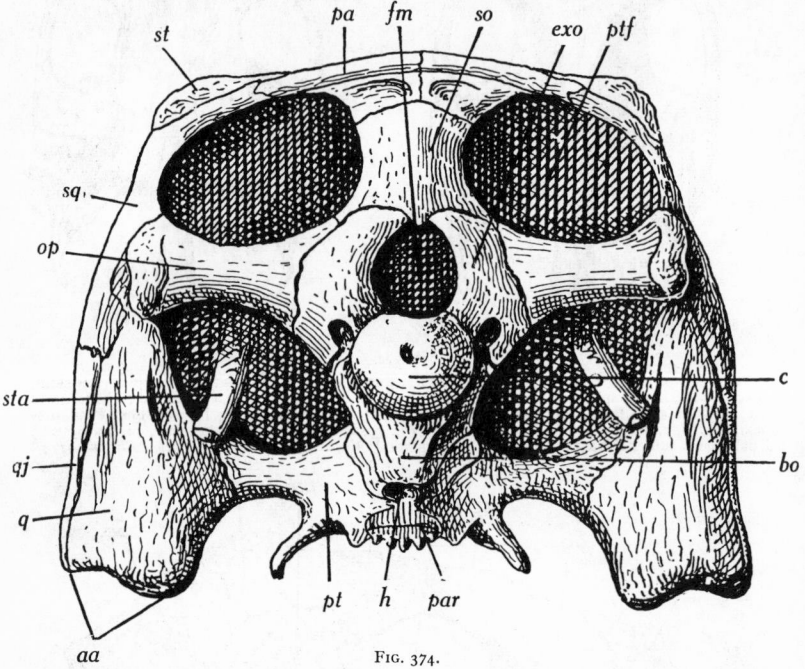

Fig. 374.

Posterior view of skull of *Triassochelys dux* (after O. Jaekel, from O. Abel, *Stämme der Wirbeltiere*, 1919). *bo*, Basioccipital; *c*, condyle; *exo*, exoccipital; *fm*, foramen magnum; *h*, hypophysial pit; *op*, opisthotic; *par*, parasphenoid; *pt*, pterygoid; *ptf*, post-temporal fossa; *so*, supraoccipital; *sta*, stapes.

The fact that in the aquatic Chelonidae and Dermochelydidae these bones join the postfrontal and parietal to form a practically complete temporal roofing with a wide post-temporal opening, Figs. 374-419, has led many zoologists to the conclusion that these Chelonia have retained the original Stegocephalian roofing, which has been more or less reduced (but not pierced) in most of the terrestrial forms (Baur, **414-16**; Rabl, 1903; Boas, **424**; Williston, **655, 95**; and others). In the Chelydidae the roofing seems to have been, so to speak, eaten away from the lower margin, while in the majority it seems to have been eaten away from behind, leaving in many only narrow postorbital and inferior bars, Fig. 372. The roofing in the most primitive known form, *Triassochelys* (Jaekel, 536), is almost as complete as in *Chelone* and contains a supratemporal

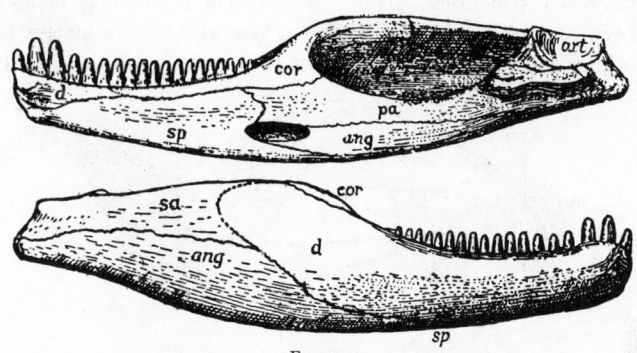

FIG. 375.

Right lower jaw of *Labidosaurus Namatus* Cope.  Inner view above, outer view below.  (From Williston, *Osteology of Reptiles*, 1925.)

in addition.  Yet, the view that this covering is the primitive one is difficult to reconcile with the fact that the bones are much reduced in number and that the pineal foramen is closed.  Not only are there no

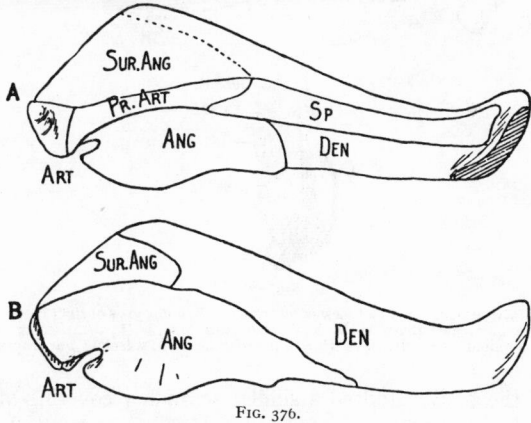

FIG. 376.

Lower jaw of *Dimetrodon*.  A, Inner view of left ramus ; B, outer view of right ramus.  (From D. M. S. Watson, *Ann. Mag. N.H.*, 1912.)  Lettering as in Fig. 377.

supratemporal (except in *Triassochelys*), postparietal, and tabular, but there is only one bone to represent the postfrontal and postorbital and one to represent the nasal prefrontal and lacrimal.  Taking into account the evidence from other parts as to the general affinities of the Chelonia (see above), it would seem more probable that the roofing is secondary and, after many of the original dermal bones had disappeared, has been reacquired (by extension of the parietal, postfrontal, and squamosal in *Chelone,* and of the parietal, jugal, and quadratojugal in *Podocnemis* (Goodrich, 517)). The remaining roofing bones may have been extended by the addition of secondary bony matter of the same nature as the dermal bony scutes so conspicuously developed over

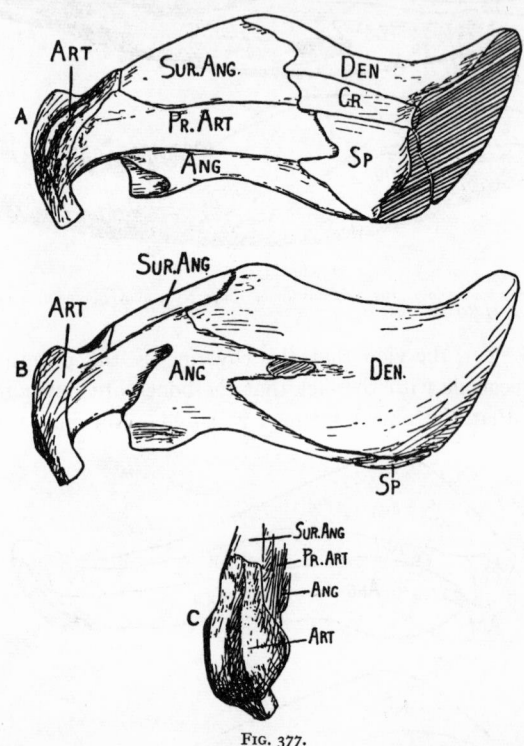

FIG. 377.

Lower jaw of *Dicynodon.* A, Inner view of left ramus ; B, outer view of right ramus ; C, posterior view of left articular region (from D. M. S. Watson, *Ann. Mag. N.H.,* 1912). *Ang,* Angular ; *Art,* articular ; *Cr,* coronoid ; *Den,* dentary ; *Pr.Art,* prearticular ; *Sp,* splenial ; *Sur.Ang,* supra-angular.

the rest of the body. Indeed a similar secondary covering of the temporal region by dermal scutes is known to occur among Lacertilia (*Lacerta,* Fig. 365), and even in Crocodilia and Anura (see above, pp. 320, 338).

The lower jaw in Reptilia preserves, besides the articular, a considerable number of the dermal bones present in Stegocephalia (Baur, 418 ; Broom, 450, etc. ; Williston, 659 ; Watson, 632 ; Gaupp, 515). In most of the more primitive forms angular, supra-angular, dentary, coronoid, splenial, and prearticular bones can be distinguished, Figs. 362, 375-7, though the latter may often fuse with the articular (Lacertilia) or disappear

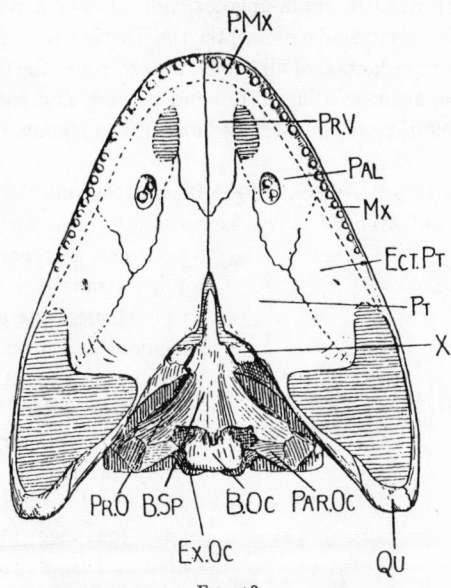

Fig. 378.

*Seymouria (Conodectes) bayloriensis*, ventral view of skull.   (From D. M. S. Watson, *P.Z.S.*, 1918.)

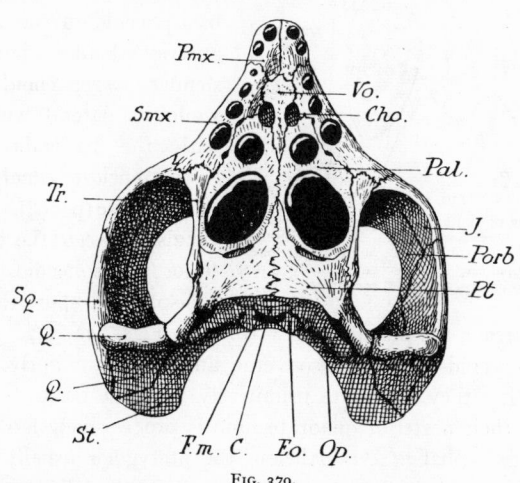

Fig. 379.

*Cyamodus tarnowitzensis*, Triassic; ventral view of skull (after O. Jaekel, from O. Abel, 1920). *C*, Median basioccipital condyle; *Cho*, internal nostril; *F.m*, foramen magnum; *Op*, opisthotic; *Porb*, postorbital; *Smx*, maxillary; *St*, supratemporal; *Tr*, ectopterygoid; *Vo*, prevomers.

(Crocodilia).   The bone generally considered as splenial no longer enters the symphysis in Lacertilia, Ophidia, Crocodilia, and Chelonia. An opening between angular, supra-angular, and dentary is characteristic of the Thecodontia. Among Theromorpha, the Theriodontia are remarkable for the progressive reduction of all the bones excepting the dentary, which increases in size, acquires a large coronoid process, and comes more and more to resemble the only remaining bone in the Mammalian lower jaw (see p. 476).

The palate of primitive Reptiles differs little from that of primitive Stegocephalia and even of early Teleostomes. The same prevomers,

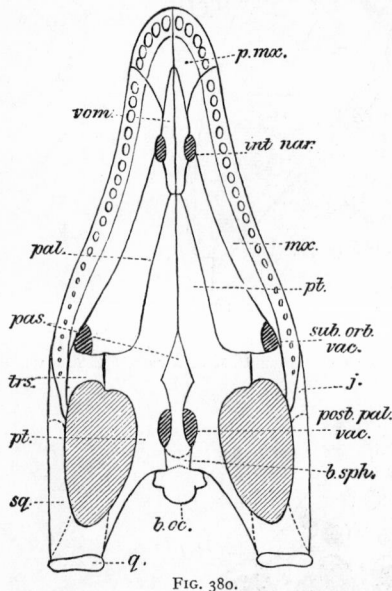

FIG. 380.

Ventral view of skull of *Plesiosaurus* (from C. W. Andrews, *Q. J. Geol. Soc.*, 1896). *int nar*, Internal nostril; *sub.orb.vac*, suborbital vacuity; *pas*, parasphenoid; *post.pal.vac*, interpterygoid vacuity; *trs*, transverse or ectopterygoid; *vom*, prevomer.

palatines, pterygoids, ectopterygoids (transverse or transpalatine bones) occur, and the median parasphenoid underlies the brain-case. All these bones may bear teeth. Considerable divergence of structure, however, occurs in the various specialised orders, Figs. 378-382, 390; see authors quoted above; Lakjer, 540a.

Usually the parasphenoid is inconspicuous and fused to the basisphenoid in the adult. Its anterior blade may form a slender 'basisphenoid rostrum', while its lateral wings fusing with the basitrabecular processes enclose canals for the vidian nerve (p. 298). Parabasal canals between the more posterior parasphenoid plate and basisphenoid allow the internal

carotids to reach the pituitary fossa (p. 298), Figs. 279, 367.

The pterygoids generally converge and meet anteriorly, diverging farther back; they articulate primitively with the basitrabecular processes, but their posterior quadrate limb is progressively less developed than in Stegocephalia. Nevertheless, the pterygoids usually reach and help to support the quadrates. A characteristic ventrally directed flange is often formed by the pterygoid and ectopterygoid combined. In Lacertilia the palatines are interpolated between the pterygoids and the prevomers, Fig. 363.

An interesting adaptation to aquatic life is seen in the higher Crocodilia, where an extensive false palate is developed carrying the choanae far back to behind the pterygoids.
The nostrils are forward near the end of the snout, so that they are the first part to emerge above water. The true internal nares extend far back, as usual separated by the prevomers. The premaxillaries, maxillaries, palatines, and pterygoids have ventral palatal plates meeting in the middle line to form a bony false palate, the floor of two long nasal canals, separated from each other by vertical downgrowths from the prevomers and pterygoids, Figs. 383, 415-16. These canals run below the true palate from the original internal nostrils to a posterior median opening opposite the glottis. In the living crocodile two fleshy folds, a dorsal velum palati and a ventral basihyal valve, serve to keep the water out of the glottis when it opens its mouth below the surface,[1] Fig. 383.

The Phytosauria have a deep median groove. Intermediate stages in the formation of the false palate are known in fossil forms, Figs. 384, 385. In *Pelagosaurus,*

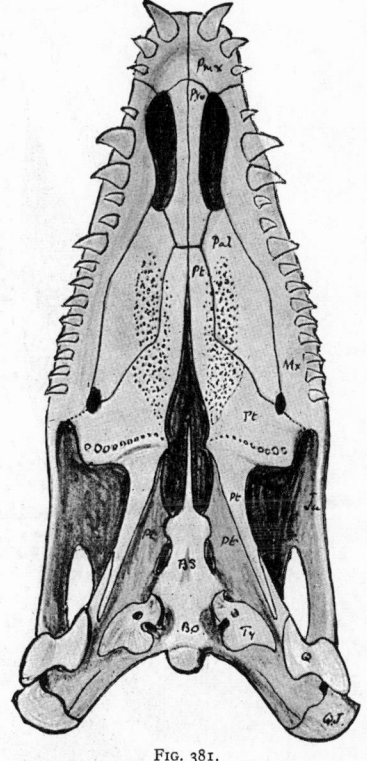

Fig. 381.

Ventral view of skull of *Dimetrodon,* restored (from R. Broom, *Bull. Am. Mus.,* 1910). *Bo,* Basioccipital ; *Bs,* basisphenoid ; *Ju,* jugal ; *Pal,* palatine ; *Pmx,* premaxillary ; *Pt,* pterygoid ; *Pv,* prevomer ; *Q,* quadrate ; *Q.J.,* quadratojugal ; *Ty,* stapes.

for instance, a premaxillary and

[1] The Eustachian tubes, also, are modified in that they sink between the basisphenoid and basioccipital into bony canals opening behind the choanae on either side of the aperture leading into a median tympanic canal. This canal, running up through the basioccipital, bifurcates and opens into a complicated system of spaces communicating with the tympanic cavities, perforating the bones of the occipital region and penetrating into the lower jaw. Since these spaces contain air they lighten this part of the heavy skull, especially when immersed. A similar system of air spaces occurs in some Dinosaurs and in Birds.

The early fossil Crocodilia have a tympanic canal, but only grooves to hold the Eustachian tubes (Teleosauridae).

maxillary false palate is already developed, but the palatines scarcely meet

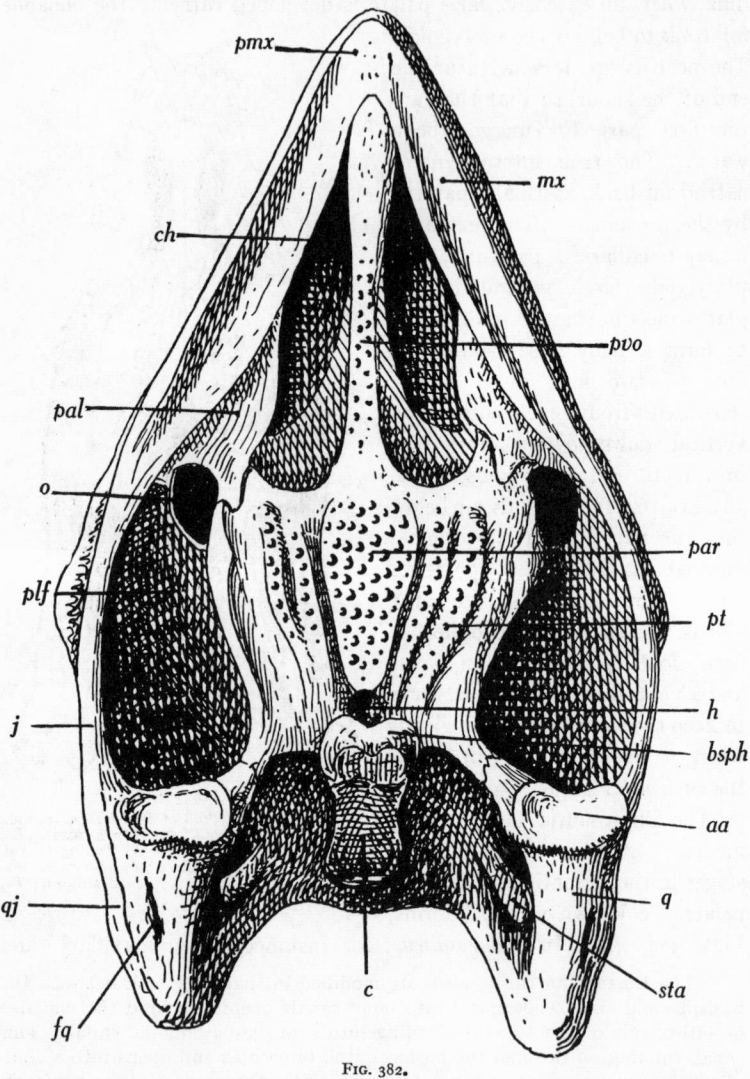

FIG. 382.

Ventral view of skull of *Triassochelys dux* (after O. Jaekel, from O. Abel, *Stämme der Wirbeltiere*, 1919). *aa*, Articular surface for lower jaw; *bsph*, basisphenoid; *fq*, quadrate foramen; *par*, parasphenoid with teeth; *plf*, lateral palatal space; *pvo*, prevomer; *sta*, stapes.

and the groove opens about midway, Fig. 385.  *Steneosaurus*, with its complete palatine region, leads to the specialised modern type.

There can be little doubt that the Class Aves is related to the Diapsidan Reptiles, is indeed closely allied to the Crocodiles and Dinosaurs.
This conclusion is firmly based on a comparison of the general anatomy
of these groups. But the avian skull is highly specialised, and the
original roofing of the Diapsidan type has been much modified, chiefly
owing to the great enlargement of the brain-case. Unfortunately the
structure of the dermal roofing in Palaeornithes is but very imperfectly
known, but there is some reason to believe that it was more complete

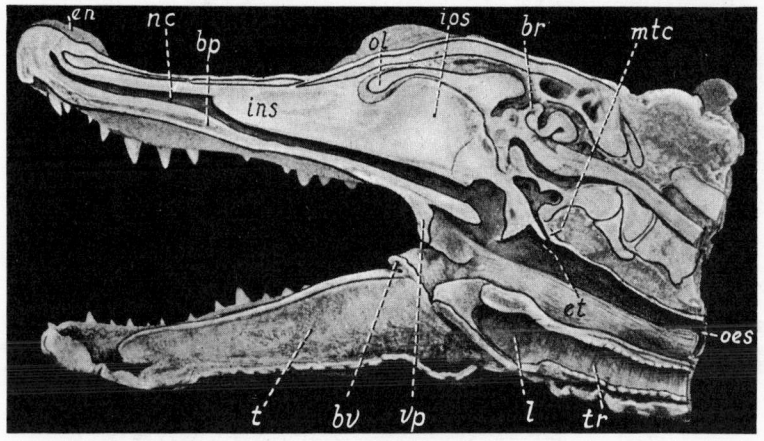

FIG. 383.

Nearly median longitudinal section of head of *Alligator mississipiensis*, showing right nasal canal,
*nc*, running above false palate, *bp*, and opening far back into pharynx opposite glottis. *br*, Brain;
*bv*, basihyal valve; *en*, position of external nostril; *et*, opening of Eustachian canal; *ins*, internasal
septum; *ios*, interorbital septum; *l*, larynx; *mtc*, median tympanic canal, leading into spaces in
skull bones communicating with tympanic cavity; *oes*, oesophagus; *ol*, olfactory lobe; *t*, tongue;
*tr*, trachea; *vp*, velum palati.

than in the Neornithes (Owen, 1863; Dames, 486). Renewed study of the
Berlin specimen of *Archaeopteryx* (*Archaeornis*) has revealed that the orbit
is completely surrounded by bone, that the inferior temporal fossa is clearly
delimited, and that there are signs of a superior temporal fossa (Heilmann,
527). Assuming, then, that it is derived from that type of Archosaurian
skull which possesses a preorbital and two lateral temporal fossae, the
roofing may be interpreted as follows in the Neornithes. The preorbital
fossa is typically present, but becomes confluent with the external nostril
in Ratitae where the nasal is small. A single bone (prefrontal or
lacrimal), pierced for the lacrimal duct, separates the fossa from the
orbit. The lower temporal bar remains complete, with jugal and quadratojugal loosely applied to the quadrate. The postorbital bar is incomplete, and represented only by a postfrontal process of the frontal. The

upper temporal bar has disappeared, leaving the temporal fossae confluent with each other and also with the orbit ; moreover, they are freely open behind owing to the wide gap between the squamosal (supratemporal ?) and quadratojugal, thus further exposing the quadrate which is loosely articulated to the brain-case (streptostylism, p. 432), Figs. 386-90.

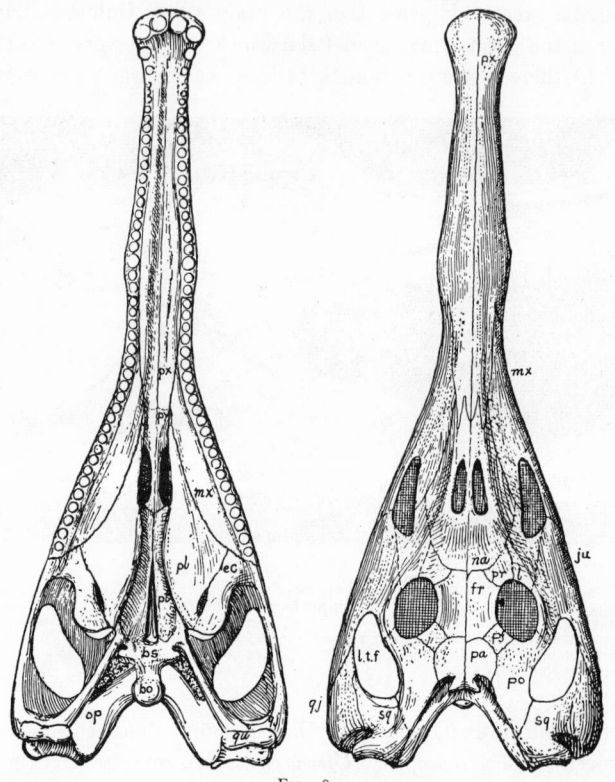

FIG. 384.

Skull of *Machaeroprosopus*, dorsal and ventral view.   (From Williston, *Osteology of Reptiles*, 1925.)

The bones of the skull tend to fuse in adult Carinates, but their boundaries can be made out in the young, and in Ratites (Parker, 556 ; T. J. Parker, 555). As in many Reptiles, but to an even greater extent, the parietals and frontals form not only the roof, but also much of the lateral walls of the large brain-case. The squamosals also come to contribute to it below them. The premaxillaries send backward processes between the nostrils. Although the lower jaw is slender it shows in the young most of the reptilian bones (articular, dentary, splenial, angular, supra-angular). A prearticular has recently been identified by Killian.

The two rami are fused at the symphysis and form together with the fused

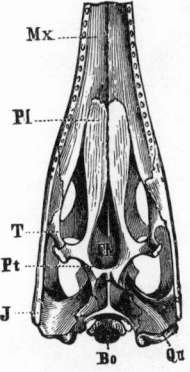

FIG. 385.

*Pelagosaurus temporalis*, Blv. sp.   Upper Lias : Curcy, Calvados.   Posterior half of skull, showing typical mesosuchian palate, ⅓.  *Bo*, Basioccipital ;  *Ch*, internal nares ;  *J*, jugal ;  *Mx*, maxilla ;  *Pl*, palatine ;  *Pt*, pterygoid ;  *Qu*, quadrate.  (From K. Zittel, *Palaeontology*.)

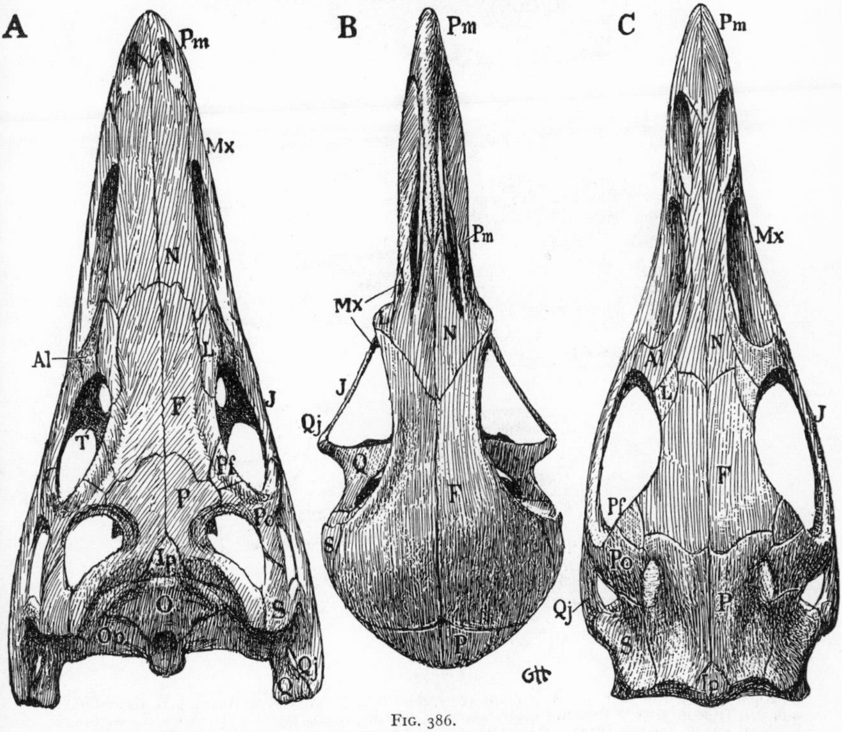

FIG. 386.

Dorsal view of skull of : A, *Euparkeria capensis* (after R. Broom) ;  B, *Columba domestica* ; C, *Archaeornis siemensi*, restored.  (From G. Heilmann, *Origin of Birds*, 1926.)

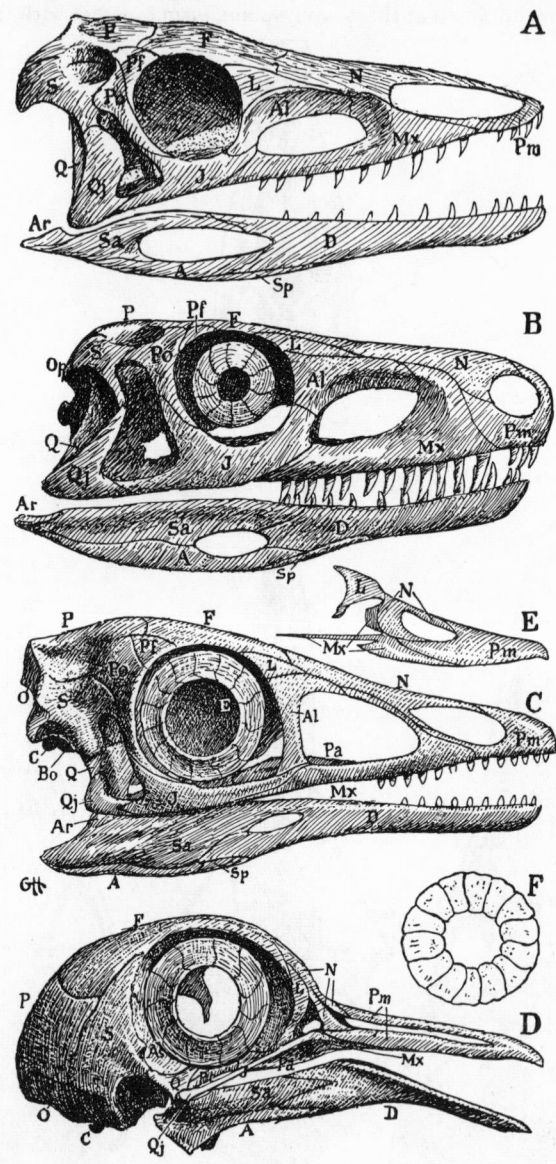

FIG. 387.

Right-side view of skull of : A, *Aëtosaurus ferratus*, Triassic (after F. v. Huene) ; B, *Euparkeria capensis*, Triassic (after R. Broom) ; C, *Archaeornis siemensi*, Jurassic, restored ; D, *Columba domestica* ; E, upper jaw of *Fuligula ferina* ; F, sclerotic ring of *Thalattosaurus alexandrae* (after Merriam). *Al*, lacrimal ; *L*, prefrontal (lacrimal in D ?) ; *S*, squamosal. (From G. Heilmann, *Origin of Birds*, 1926.)

premaxillaries the characteristic bony beak provided with a horny sheath
above and below.    There is a lateral fossa in the lower jaw, as in Crocodilia and certain related reptiles.    Except in Palaeornithes and early
fossils of the Cretaceous (*Ichthyornis, Hesperornis,* etc., Marsh, 1880), the
teeth have been lost, Fig. 226.

The palate becomes remarkably specialised (Huxley, 533; Parker, 568,·
572; Pycraft, 576).    The parasphenoid (basitemporal of Parker) is very

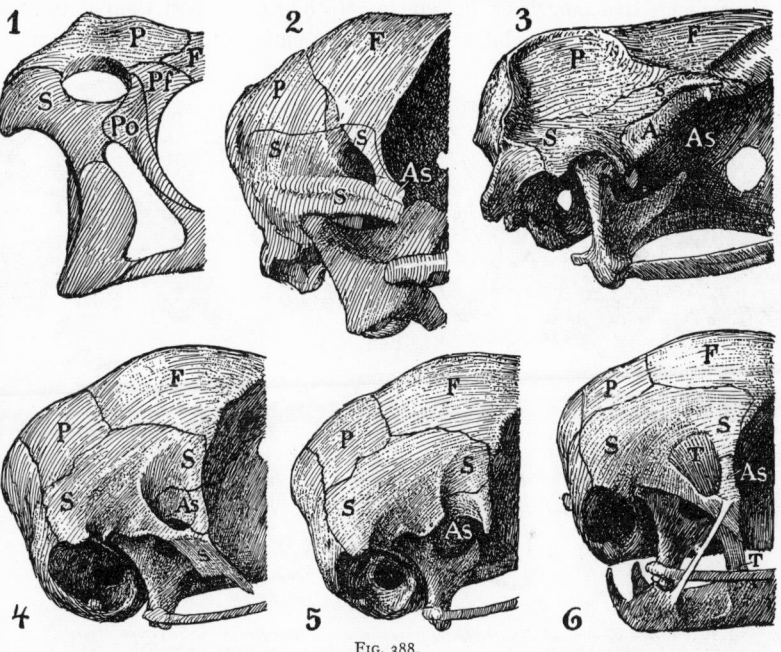

FIG. 388.

Right-side view of hind part of skull of : 1, *Aëtosaurus ferratus* (after F. v. Huene) ; 2, *Xeno-
rhynchus*; 3, *Colymbus glacialis*; 4, *Phasianus*; 5, young *Phasianus*; 6, *Gallus.   As,* Pleurosphenoid;
*F,* frontal ;  *P,* parietal ;  *Pf,* postfrontal ;  *S,* squamosal ;  *T,* temporal muscle.   (From G. Heilmann,
*Origin of Birds,* 1926.)

large, but soon fuses indistinguishably with the basisphenoid, enclosing,
as in Crocodiles, the Eustachian tubes in bony canals which open by a
median aperture.    The slender rostrum extends below the interorbital
septum.    In front the palate is, to a great extent, formed by processes
of the premaxillaries and maxillaries, the prevomers being far back,
usually fused, often very slender, and sometimes absent.    The internal
nostrils open in a deep groove.    Primitively well-developed basitrabecular
processes support the pterygoids, which articulate with the large palatines
in front (Ratitae, and more primitive Carinatae), Fig. 390 A.    In many
modern forms, however, these processes are reduced or absent, and then

both pterygoids and palatines come to rest on the parasphenoid (basisphenoid) rostrum, Fig. 391. There are no ectopterygoids.

Huxley first used the structure of the palate for the classification of Birds (533a). He distinguished four types: Dromaeognathous (Ratitae); Desmognathous (Hawks, Parrots, Ducks, etc.); Schizognathous (Gulls, Game-birds, etc.); Ægithognathous (Passeres). Later Pycraft (576) defined the dromaeognathous type, with large 'vomer' (prevomers) reaching back (except in Struthio) to support the palatines and pterygoids, with the latter bones rigidly connected with the palatines

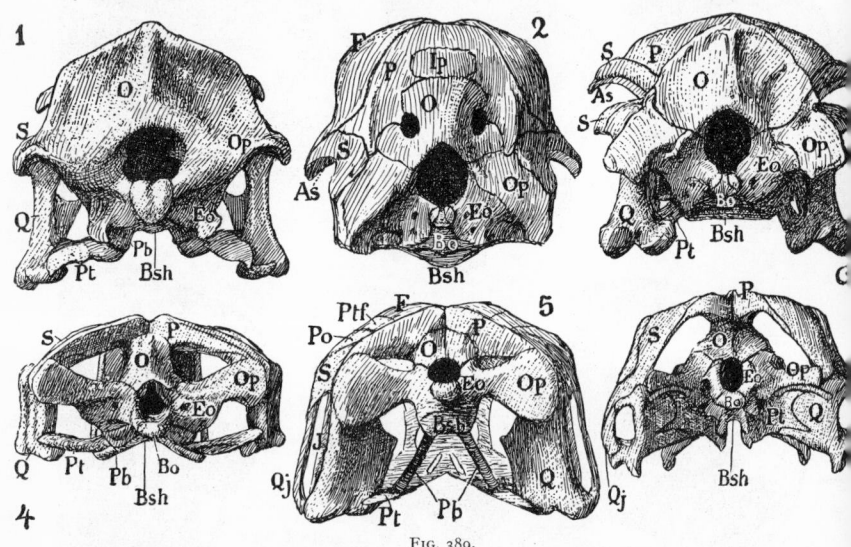

FIG. 389.

Posterior view of skull of: 1, *Hesperornis regalis*; 2, *Anser ferus*; 3, *Colymbus glacialis*; 4, *varanus*; 5, *Scaphognathus purdoni* (after E. T. Newton); 6, *Sphenodon* (after Zittel). *Pb*, Basipterygoid articulation. (From G. Heilmann, *Origin of Birds*, 1926.)

(as in most Reptilia), and with strong basipterygoid processes, as a primitive 'Palaeognathous' form of palate common to all the Ratites and the Tinamous, Fig. 390 A. The various types of palate found in other birds he defined as 'Neognathous'. In these the prevomers are small; the maxillopalatine processes contribute to the palate passing dorsally to the palatines; the latter and the pterygoids are movably connected and converge towards the parasphenoidal rostrum, Fig. 391.

**The Mammalian Palate, False Palate, and Vomer.**—Characteristic of the Mammalia is the bony false palate forming the ventral floor of two naso-pharyngeal passages separated by the vomer and opening behind by the choanae bounded in front and at the sides by the palatines. It is continued backwards in the living by a fleshy false palate which ends opposite the epiglottis, a fold supported by a cartilage in front of the glottis also characteristic of the mammal. Yet this bony false palate was already present in the related Theromorph Reptiles (Seeley, 589-91; Broom, 441-5, 458; Watson, 634, 641) and undoubtedly evolved in that

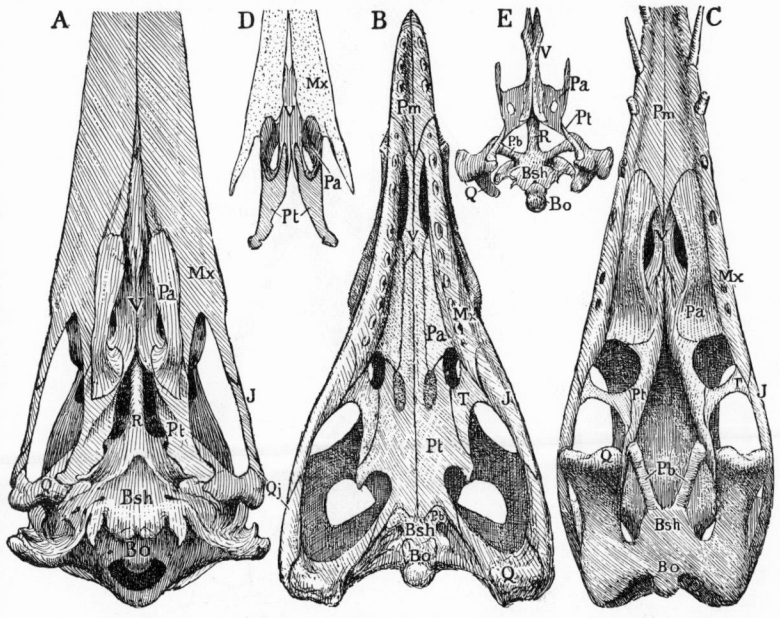

FIG. 390.

Ventral view of skull of : A, *Apteryx australis* (after Pycraft) ; B, *Ornithosuchus woodwardi* (after Broom and Newton) ; C, *Rhamphorhynchus gemmingi* (after A. S. Woodward and v. Huene) ; D, dorsal view of palate of *Apteryx* (after Pycraft) ; E, palate of *Rhea* (after Pycraft). *Bsh,* Basisphenoid +parasphenoid, *R,* its rostrum ; *Bo,* basioccipital ; *Mx,* maxillary ; *Pa,* palatine ; *Pb,* basipterygoid process ; *Pm,* premaxillary ; *Pt,* pterygoid ; *Q,* quadrate ; *T,* transverse (ectopterygoid) ; *V,* pre-vomers. (From G. Heilmann, *Origin of Birds,* 1926.)

group, whose more primitive forms have the ordinary reptilian palate, Figs. 394-6.

The Therocephalia have in front a rudimentary false palate, the naso-pharyngeal passages being represented further back by a deep groove, and in the Dicynodontia (Seeley, 588; Lyddeker, 1888; Newton, 1893; Sollas, 602; Broom, 441; Huene, 532) the maxillae and palatines tend to form palatine processes enclosing the grooves; but it is not until the Cynodontia that these processes are fully developed and join across the middle line. In this group also are found a large median vomer separating the nasal passages, pterygoids no longer reaching the quadrate, and alisphenoids passing back towards the tympanic cavities—all mammalian characters.

The secondary or false palate develops in the embryo mammal, behind the original internal nostrils on the true palate, by the growth from the sides of ridges enclosing palatal plates from the maxillae and palatines which meet ventrally and join a vertical plate of the vomer. Into the

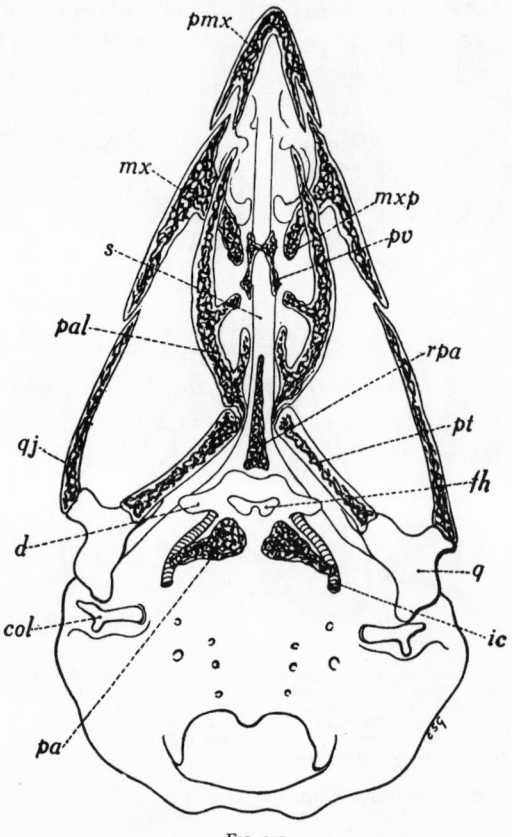

FIG. 391.

Ventral view of skull of late embryo of *Passer domesticus* showing ossification of palatal bones. *col*, Columella auris ; *d*, infrapolar cartilage ; *fh*, foramen hypophyseos ; *ic*, internal carotid ; *mx*, maxillary ; *mxp*, maxillopalatine process ; *pa*, paired posterior parasphenoidal wing ; *pal*, palatine ; *pmx*, premaxillary ; *pt*, pterygoid ; *pv*, prevomer ; *q*, quadrate ; *qj*, quadratojugal ; *rpa*, parasphenoidal rostrum ; *s*, interorbital septum.

air passages so enclosed the internal nostrils now open, only a pair of small anterior palatine foramina or naso-palatine canals remaining as parts of the original communications in front, Figs. 392, 397-9. Into these canals open Jacobson's organs (Seydel, 595; Broom, 1895–98).

The interpretation of the palate of the mammal involves the important question of the homology of the mammalian vomer still under dispute.

For long it was thought that it represented the paired vomers (prevomers) of lower forms, which typically extend between the internal nostrils, and form their postero-medial boundary.[1] But Albrecht (1883), Sutton (609), and W. K. Parker (567) concluded that the prevomers of lower forms correspond to the palatal processes of the premaxillae of most mammals. Further, Parker claimed to show that these processes appear in many of the lower Mammalia (567) as separate bones which later fuse

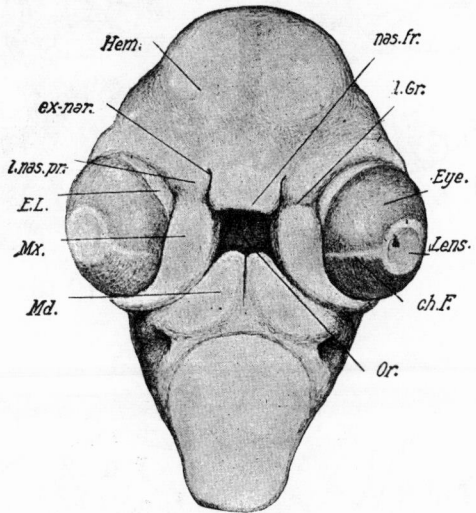

FIG. 392.

Head of chick embryo of about 5 days from the oral surface (N.L. 8 mm.) (from F. R. Lillie, *Develt. Chick*, 1919). *chF*, Choroid fissure ; *E.L*, eyelid (nictitating membrane) ; *ex-nar*, external nares ; *l.Gr*, lacrimal groove ; *l.nas.pr*, lateral nasal process ; *Md*, mandibular arch ; *Mx*, maxillary process ; *nas.fr*, naso-frontal process ; *Or*, oral cavity.

with the premaxillae, Fig. 399 A. These observations have to some extent been confirmed by Broom on the bat *Miniopterus* and by Fawcett on *Tatusia*; but as a rule the premaxillary processes develop in continuity with the premaxillaries.

Jacobson's organ, which appears to serve for smelling the liquid contents of the buccal cavity, occurs in the Amniota as a small sac, blind behind and opening in front towards the palatal surface at or near the internal nostril, Figs. 264, 399. It is derived in development from the wall of the nasal cavity, and is supported below by the paraseptal cartilage and the prevomer which underlies it, Figs. 400-1. When

[1] These usually paired bones, now known as prevomers (Broom), occur from the earliest Teleostomes ; but they fuse to a median bone in Teleostei, Chelonia, and most Birds. Even in the embryo chelonian there is evidence of paired origin (Kunkel, 540).

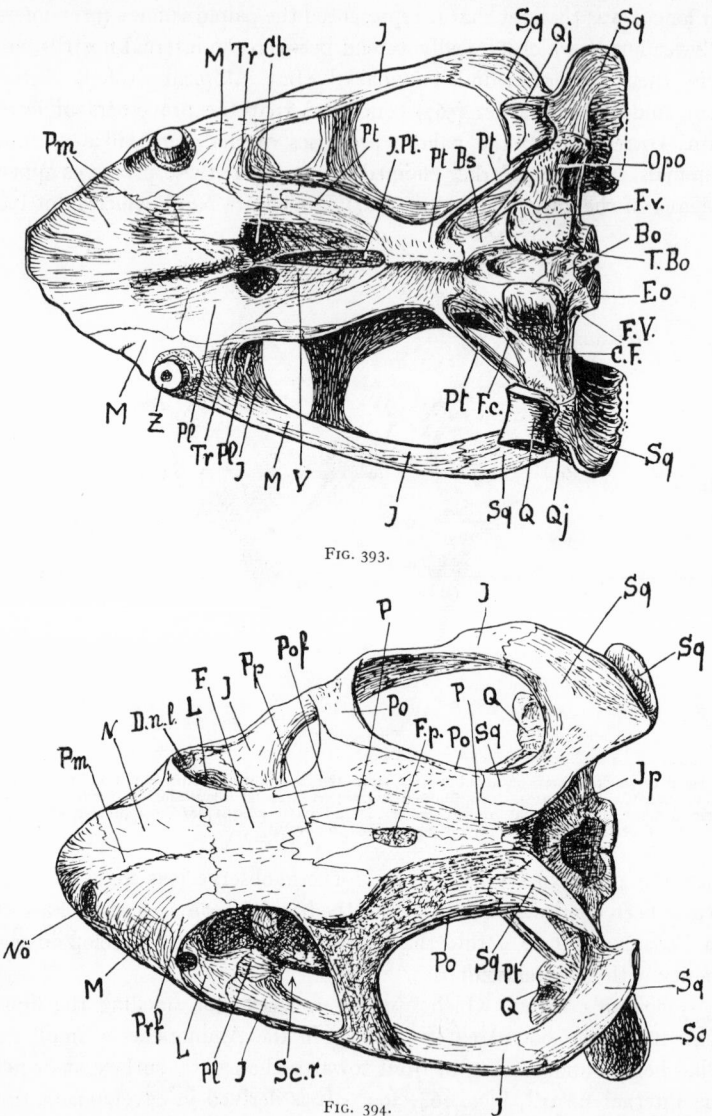

Fig. 393.

Fig. 394.

Fig. 393, ventral, and Fig. 394, dorsal aspect of skull of *Dicynodon* (from F. von Huene, *Palaeontol. Zeitschr.*, 1922). *Bo*, Basioccipital ; *Bs*, basisphenoid ; *C.F*, Canalis Fallopii, facial foramen ; *Ch*, choana, internal nostril ; *D.n.l*, ductus naso-lacrimalis ; *Eo*, exoccipital ; *Ep*, epipterygoid ; *F*, frontal ; *F.c*, carotid foramen ; *F.p*, pineal foramen ; *F.v*, fenestra ovalis ; *F.V*, vagus foramen ; *J*, jugal ; *I.p*, inter-parietal ; *I.Pt*, interpterygoidal vacuity ; *L*, lacrimal ; *M*, maxillary ; *N*, nasal ; *Nö*, external nostril ; *Opo*, opisthotic ; *P*, parietal ; *Pa*, parasphenoid ; *Pl*, palatine ; *Pm*, premaxillary ; *Po*, postorbital ; *Pof*, postfrontal ; *pp*, preparietal or interfrontal ; *Prf*, prefrontal ; *Pro*, pro-otic ; *Ps*, ' presphenoid '=basisphenoid ? ; *Pt*, pterygoid ; *P.T.F*, post-temporal fossa ; *Q*, quadrate ; *Qj*, quadratojugal ; *Sc.r*, sclerotic ring ; *Sm*, septomaxillary ; *So*, supraoccipital ; *Sq*, squamosal ; *Tb*, tabular ; *T.Bo*, tuber basioccipitale ; *Tr*, ectopterygoid ; *V*, prevomer ; *Z*, broken tooth.

Wilson and Martin (1893–94) showed that the separate 'os paradoxum' of *Ornithorhynchus* is of paired origin and occupies the same position with regard to Jacobson's organ and the paraseptal cartilage, Broom (**439, 440, 451**) homologised this bone in Monotremes and the premaxillary processes in other mammals with the prevomers, and the vomer of mammals with the parasphenoid of lower forms, Figs. 402, 404. Already in the more mammal-like Theriodontia the prevomers and

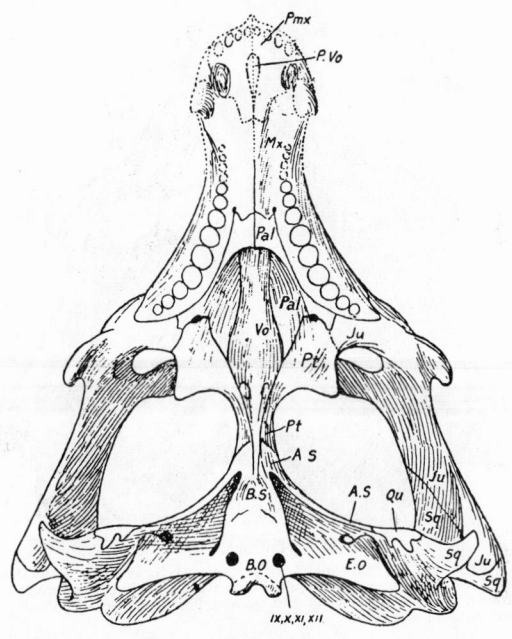

Fig. 395.

*Gomphognathus minor*, ventral view of skull, restored (from R. Broom, *P.Z.S.*, 1911). *As*, Alisphenoid; *BO*, basioccipital; *BS*, basisphenoid; *E.o*, exoccipital; *Pal*, palatine; *Pt*, pterygoid; *P.Vo*, prevomer; *Vo*, vomer. Other letters as in Fig. 396.

parasphenoid assume much the same form and position as the premaxillary processes and median vomer respectively of the mammal, Figs. 395, 413. Although Broom's interpretation has not yet been quite conclusively proved, yet there is much to be said in its favour, and it affords an explanation of the fate in the Mammalia of the parasphenoid, a bone which hitherto has generally been supposed to have unaccountably disappeared.[1]

[1] But the mammalian vomer, which does not extend backwards over the basisphenoid region, would appear to represent only the anterior rostral part of the parasphenoid situated below the median septum; the posterior plate may be separately represented, p. 370.

Another bone in the mammalian palate the homology of which has given rise to much controversy of late is the pterygoid. When Gaupp (**511, 513**) discovered a separate bone in *Echidna* ventral to that usually called pterygoid, Figs. 405, 402-3, he concluded that it is homologous with the reptilian pterygoid. The more dorsal bone he considered to represent on the one hand the mammalian pterygoid and on the other the lateral wing of the reptilian parasphenoid (see footnote, p. 369).

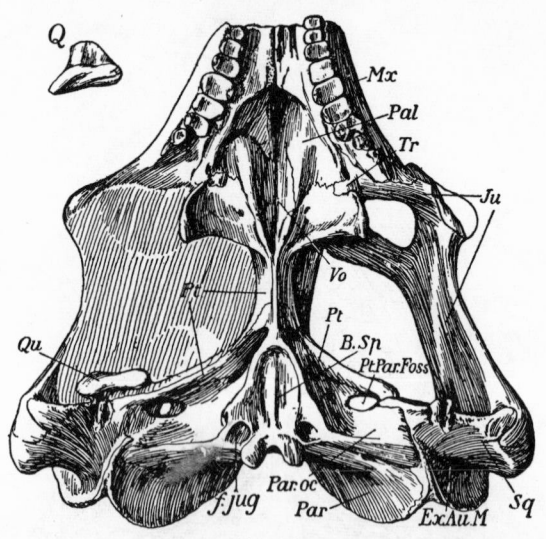

FIG. 396.

*Diademodon browni,* ventral view of skull (from D. M. S. Watson, *Ann. Mag. N.H.,* 1911). *B.Sp,* Basisphenoid; *Ex.Au.M,* external auditory meatus; *f.jug,* jugular foramen; *Pt,* pterygoid; *Pt.Par.Foss,* foramen between alisphenoid and paroccipital process of opisthotic; *Vo,* vomer; *Q,* figure of quadrate, anterior aspect.

Comparing the Monotreme with the higher mammal, the newly discovered ventral bone of the former ('Echidna pterygoid' of Gaupp) is found to correspond in position to the 'pterygoid cartilage' of the latter, Figs. 405-6. It has long been known that the 'pterygoid' bone in Mammalia may be formed of two elements, separate at all events in development (Fawcett, **488**; Lubosch, **543**); a more important dorsal element of dermal origin, and a more ventral related to the 'pterygoid cartilage' and forming the hamulus. Now this 'pterygoid cartilage', Figs. 406, 487, appears from its histological character to be of secondary nature (similar to that related to the dermal bones of the lower jaw) and to give rise to dermal bone. There are, therefore, probably two dermal elements related to the basitrabecular region in all mammals : the more dorsal 'mammalian pterygoid' of Gaupp, and the more ventral

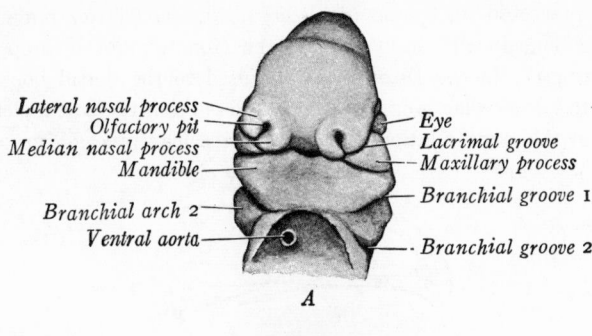

Lateral nasal process
Olfactory pit
Median nasal process
Mandible

Branchial arch 2
Ventral aorta

Eye
Lacrimal groove
Maxillary process

Branchial groove 1

Branchial groove 2

*A*

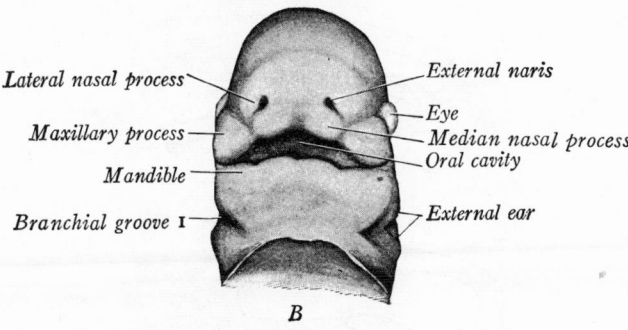

Lateral nasal process

Maxillary process

Mandible

Branchial groove 1

External naris

Eye
Median nasal process
Oral cavity

External ear

*B*

FIG. 397.

Two stages showing development of face in pig embryos. × 7. A, Ventral view of face of 12 mm. embryo; B, of 14 mm. embryo. (After Prentiss and Arey, *Text-Book of Embryology*, 1917.) Branchial grooves mark vestigial gill-slits.

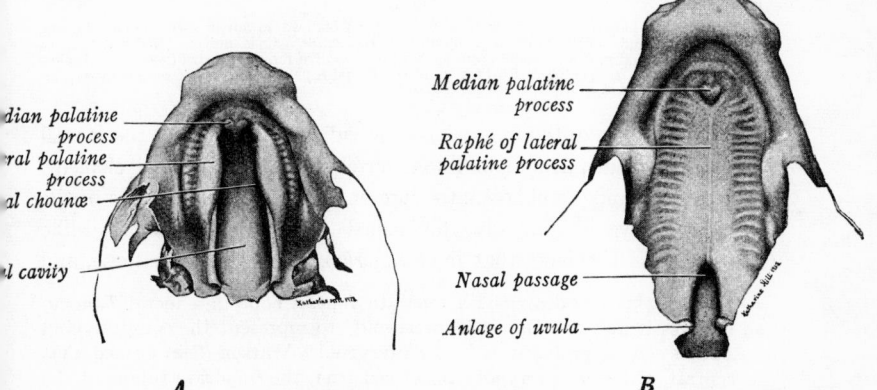

Median palatine process
ral palatine process
al choanæ

l cavity

Median palatine process

Raphé of lateral palatine process

Nasal passage

Anlage of uvula

*A*                                        *B*

FIG. 398.

Dissections to show development of hard palate in pig embryos. × 5. A, Ventral view of palatine processes of 22 mm. pig embryo, mandible removed; B, same of 35 mm. embryo showing fusion of palatine processes. (From Prentiss and Arey, *Text-Book of Embryology*, 1917.)

'Echidna pterygoid' of Gaupp (de Beer, **422a**). The latter remains as a separate bone in the adult only in the Monotremata (Gaupp, van Bemmelen, **423**); in the Ditremata it is fused to the dorsal bone and gives rise to its hamular process. Gaupp showed that the dorsal element bears much the same relation to the basitrabecular process (processus

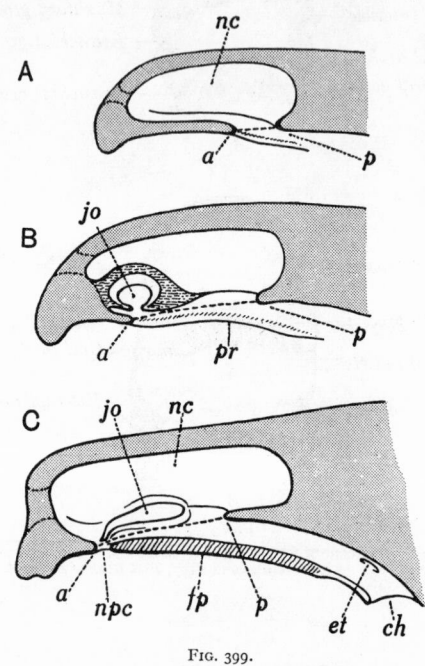

FIG. 399.

Diagrammatic longitudinal sections of anterior region of head to left of median line, showing relations of true and false palate. A, Amphibian; B, Reptile; C, Mammal. (Modified from O. Seydel, 1899.) *a* and *p*, Anterior and posterior limit of primitive internal nostril (marked by broken line); *ch*, choana; *et*, opening of Eustachian tube; *fp*, false palate; *jo*, organ of Jacobson; *nc*, nasal cavity; *npc*, nasopalatine canal; *pr*, palatine ridge.

alaris) and to the anterior parabasal or vidian canal as does the lateral wing of the parasphenoid in lower vertebrates. The ventral element, on the other hand, would seem to represent the degenerate vestige of the reptilian pterygoid (already diminished in the most mammal-like Cynodonts).[1] The facts that in *Ornithorhynchus* this bone is loose, and

---

[1] Broom (**451**) has described a separate ventral bone in a foetal *Tatusia*, and believes it and the 'Echidna pterygoid' to represent the ectopterygoid of Reptiles; more probably it is the pterygoid. Watson (**642**) argued that the ventral (Echidna) pterygoid is derived from the quadrate ramus of the epipterygoid of Cynodontia, and the mammalian pterygoid is homologous with the reptilian. Certainly the three bones (alisphenoid, dorsal, and ventral pterygoids) have not been found separate in Monotremes, where the ali-

that a slip of muscle is attached to it, may be taken as evidence in favour of this conclusion. The homology of the epipterygoid is discussed elsewhere (p. 456).

### OSSIFICATIONS OF THE CHONDROCRANIUM

**Osteichthyes.**—It has already been mentioned above that the cartilaginous skull becomes more or less thoroughly replaced and com-

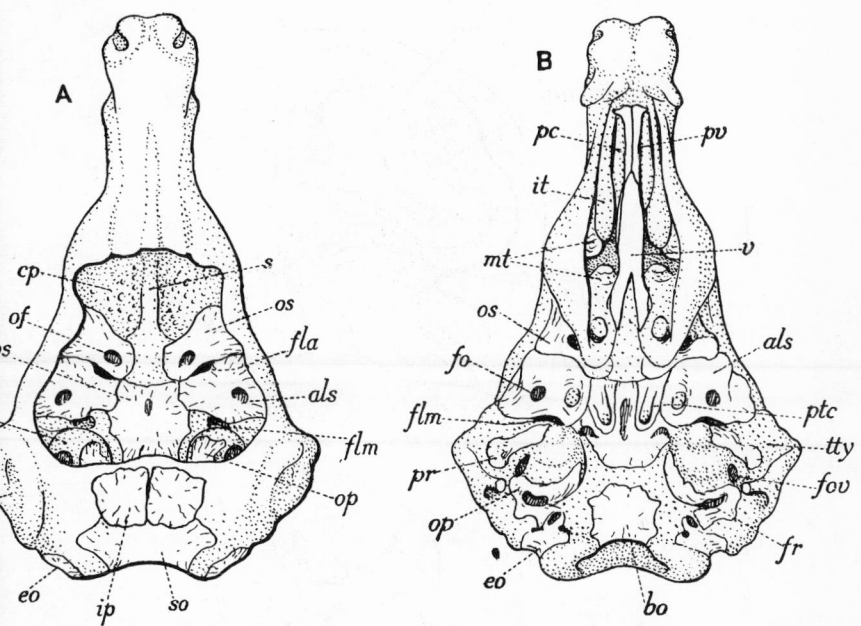

Fig. 399a.

Skull of embryo *Erinaceus europaeus*, 3 inches long (after W. K. Parker, 1885). A, Dorsal; B, ventral view. *ac*, Auditory capsule; *als*, alisphenoid; *bo*, basioccipital; *bs*, basisphenoid; *cp*, cribriform plate; *eo*, exoccipital; *fla*, foramen lacerum anterius; *flm*, f. lac. medium; *fo*, for. ovale; *fov*, fenestra ovalis; *fr*, fenestra rotunda; *ip*, 'interparietal'=postparietal?; *it*, inferior turbinal; *mt*, maxillo turbinals; *of*, optic foramen; *op*, opisthotic?; *os*, orbitosphenoid; *pc*, paraseptal cartilage; *pr*, pro-otic?; *pv*, prevomer; *ptc*, pterygoid; *s*, median septum; *so*, supra-occipital; *tty*, tegmen tympani; *v*, vomer. Cartilage dotted.

pleted by bone in the Osteichthyes. These endochondral bones spread from various 'centres' which do not correspond to the original cartilaginous elements of the skull; nor are they restricted to the

sphenoid (true epipterygoid) seems to have disappeared or fused with one of its neighbours (wing of periotic?). According to Van Kampen (1922) the mammalian pterygoid is homologous with the reptilian, but the vestige of the parasphenoid forms the processus tympanicus of the adult basisphenoid in Ditremata.

elements in which they first arise.  The ossification of the chondrocranium
and visceral arches progresses not only in the ontogeny of the individual,
but also often in the phylogeny of the main groups ;  and, speaking quite
generally, the most thoroughly bony are among the most highly specialised orders.   But, although this holds good for the highest Teleostei,
the most bony of all fishes, yet it is by no means always the case.

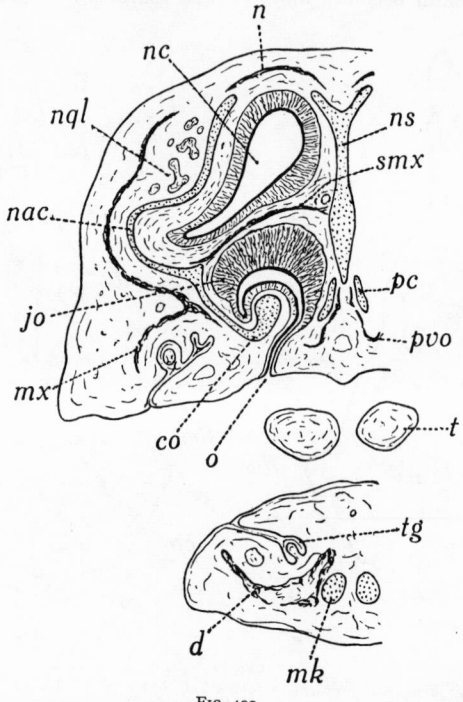

FIG. 400.

Lacerta, late embryo.  Transverse section through snout, lower jaw, and Jacobson's organ, jo.
co, Lower edge of nasal capsule ; d, dentary ; mx, maxillary ; n, nasal ; nac, nasal capsule ; nc,
nasal cavity ; ngl, nasal gland ; ns, median nasal septum ; mk, Meckel's cartilage ; o, opening of
Jacobson's organ ; pc, paraseptal cartilage ; pvo, prevomer ; smx, septomaxillary ; t, tongue ;
tg, tooth-germ.   Cartilage dotted.

Frequently in several important groups, such as the Dipnoi and Chondrostei, there may be on the contrary a progressive reduction of ossification,
and apparently a partial return to a cartilaginous condition due to the
retention or even to an increase in the adult of the cartilaginous parts
developed in the embryo (pp. 382, 389).

Taking first the Holostean Teleostomes (Amioidei, Lepidosteoidei,
Teleostei) as containing the best known and, in some ways, least specialised
forms, we find in the occipital region a basioccipital and paired exoccipital

bones, Figs. 429, 436. The former extends well forward in the basal parachordal plate ; surrounds the notochord, here practically obliterated in the
adult, and bears a posterior concave face, like that of a centrum, to which
the vertebral column is attached by ligament without distinct articulation.
In *Amia* two pairs (and in *Polypterus* one) of neural arches rest on the

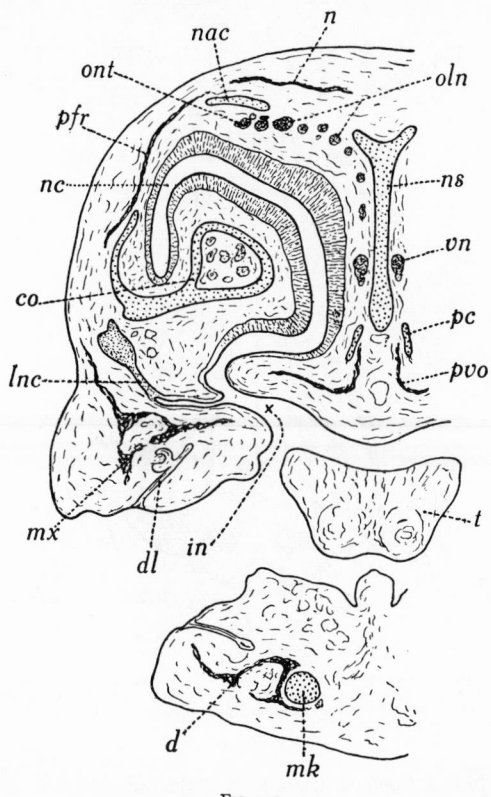

FIG. 401.

*Lacerta*, late embryo. Transverse section through head at level of internal nostril, *in. co*, Concha ;
*dl*, dental lamina ; *lnc*, lacrimonasal duct ; *oln*, olfactory nerve ; *ont*, orbitonasal nerve ; *pfr*,
prefrontal ; *vn*, vomeronasal nerve. Other letters as in Fig. 400.

hinder region of the basioccipital, which includes the corresponding
centra. The exoccipitals more or less completely enclose the foramen
magnum above and at the sides, let through hypoglossal nerves, and
define the hinder limit of the vagal foramen. In the higher Teleostei
they may have a facet for the first vertebra. A median supraoccipital
appears only in the Teleostei, where it is generally provided with a
characteristic keel projecting backwards between the right and left

anterior myomeres. The history of the supraoccipital is still obscure ; there is no good evidence that it has been derived from the median dermal occipital of lower fish (Crossopterygii, Chondrostei). It develops as an endochondral bone, and may possibly correspond to the neural spines further back. Recently, however, Watson has described a supraoccipital

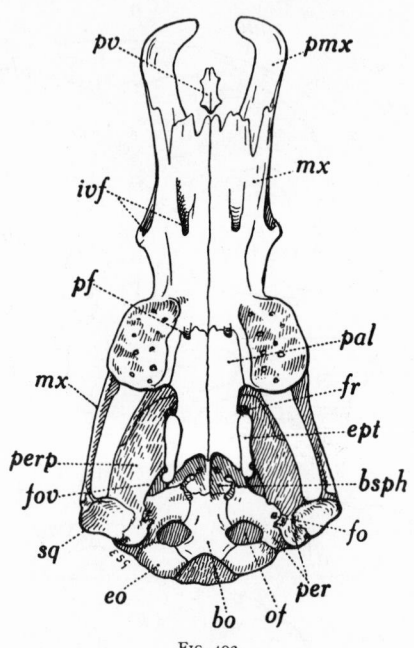

Fig. 402.

*Ornithorhynchus paradoxus*, ventral view of skull. *bsph*, Basisphenoid ; *fov*, foramen ovale ; *ivf*, infraorbital foramina ; *of*, fenestra occipitalis (for. jugulare and for. praecondyloideum) ; *pal*, palatine ; *perp*, periotic plate ; *pf*, palatine foramen ; *pv*, prevomers combined to ' dumb-bell shaped bone '. Other letters as in Fig. 403.

in an Osteolepid, a Coelacanth, and a Palaeoniscid, Fig. 408 ; it may after all be a primitive bone, perhaps homologous with that of Tetrapods.

It is well known since the work of Huxley and Parker that the auditory capsule in Teleostei is typically ossified from 5 points, Figs. 285, 429, 436. A pro-otic occupies its antero-ventral region, generally surrounding the facial foramen and lodging the anterior semicircular canal. It surrounds the jugular canal (p. 276). A postero-ventral opisthotic overlies the posterior corner reaching the vagal foramen in *Amia*. This bone varies greatly in development (Vrolick, **629** ; Sagemehl, **278** ; Allis, **401-2**) ; fairly well developed in primitive forms it becomes very large in the Gadidae, but is reduced in many Teleostei, and sometimes even absent (Mormyridae, etc., also absent in *Lepidosteus* ?).  Dorsally the capsule may become ossified by the prefrontal from in front, and the supratemporal ('squamosal') from behind, the former (sphenotic) overlying the anterior semicircular canal and the latter (pterotic) the horizontal canal.[1]  The fifth bone is the epiotic which develops dorsally on the posterior medial corner of the

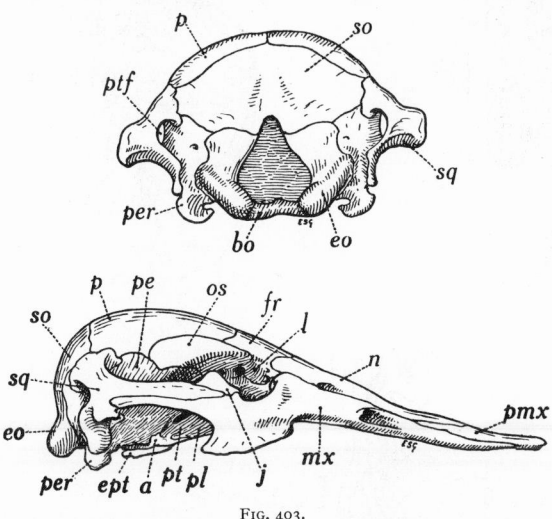

FIG. 403.

*Ornithorhynchus paradoxus*, right-side view and hind view of skull.  *a*, Alisphenoid? ; *bo*, basi-occipital ; *eo*, exoccipital ; *ept*, ventral pterygoid ; *fr*, frontal ; *j*, jugal ; *l*, lacrimal fused to *fr* ; *mx*, maxillary ; *n*, nasal ; *os*, orbitosphenoid ; *p*, parietal ; *pe*, wing of periotic ; *per*, periotic ; *pl*, palatine ; *pt*, dorsal pterygoid ; *ptf*, post-temporal foramen ; *pmx*, premaxillary ; *so*, supraoccipital ; *sq*, squamosal.

capsule over the posterior semicircular canal.  To the epiotic and opisthotic are usually attached the two limbs of the post-temporal bone by strong ligaments.  In *Amia* and *Lepidosteus* the supratemporal has not invaded the capsule (Allis, 402 ; Parker, 566).

[1] There is still some uncertainty as to the phylogenetic history of the postfrontal and the supratemporal and their true relation to their deep-lying 'perichondral' and 'endochondral' parts (sphenotic and pterotic).  Some authors consider that the fusion of the superficial plate (related to the lateral line) and the deeper ossification of the auditory capsule is secondary.  But no primitive form is known possessing a separate supratemporal and pterotic in the adult, and their separate origin in early stages of development (dermo- and auto-squamosum of Schleip, 584, and Gaupp, 343) would appear to be secondary, and may be compared to the separation of 'canal bones' from dermal bones in other parts.  The postfrontal also may develop from separate superficial and deep (autosphenotic) ossifications which fuse later, as in *Amia* and some Teleosts, or fail to fuse as in many of the higher Teleostei.  But in *Polypterus* there is only one ossification (Allis, 410 ; Lehn, 542), and no separate autosphenotic is known in primitive fossil forms.

In Teleostomes the cavity of the auditory capsule is extensive and its inner wall is chiefly membranous, especially in Teleosts.

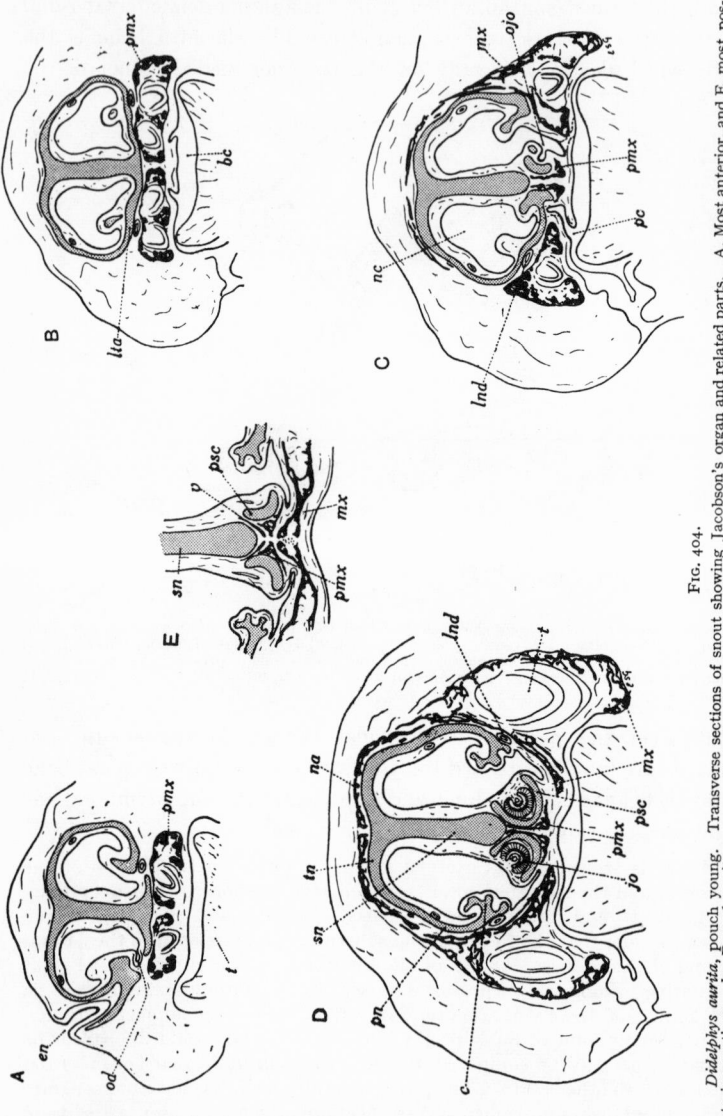

FIG. 404.

*Didelphys aurita*, pouch young. Transverse sections of snout showing Jacobson's organ and related parts. A, Most anterior, and E, most posterior sections. *bc*, Buccal cavity; *c*, maxillo-turbinal; *en*, external nostril; *jo*, organ of Jacobson; *lnd*, lacrimonasal duct; *lta*, lamina transversalis anterior; *mx*, maxillary; *na*, nasal; *nc*, nasal cavity; *od*, opening of lacrimonasal duct; *ojo*, opening of Jacobson's organ; *pc*, palatonasal canal (foramen incisivum); *pmx*, premaxillary; *pn*, paries nasi; *psc*, paraseptal or Jacobson's cartilage; *sn*, septum nasi; *t*, tongue; *tn*, tectum nasi; *v*, paired extremity of median vomer.

Anterior to the basal parachordal plate and to the pro-otics is the basisphenoid. Although arising from paired centres in the trabeculae in *Amia* (Allis, **402**), it appears as a median bone with paired wings, Figs.

286-7. In the more platybasic skulls (Cypriniformes) the basisphenoid

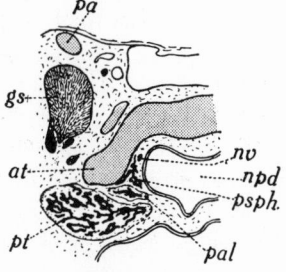

FIG. 405.

*Echidna aculeata*, var typica; portion of transverse section of left side of head passing through base of ala temporalis, *at*, and bones of palate. *gs*, Gasserian ganglion; *npd*, nasal canal; *nv*, vidian nerve; *pa*, pila antotica; *pal*, palatine; *psph*, dorsal pterygoid (= parasphenoid?); *pt*, ventral pterygoid. (From E. Gaupp, 1911.)

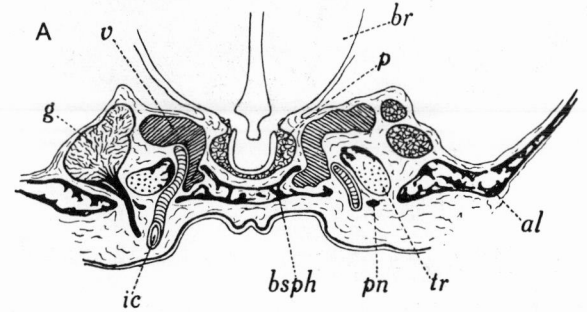

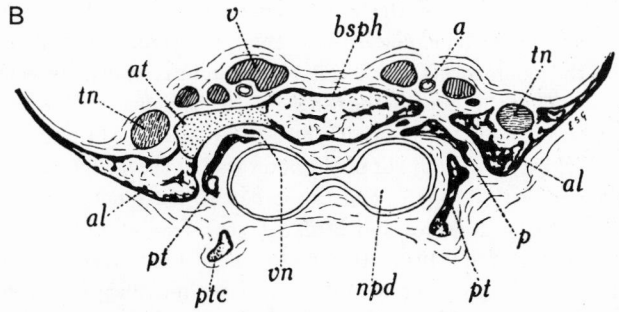

FIG. 406.

*Didelphys aurita*, pouch young. Transverse sections through head in region of basisphenoid, *bsph*. A, Through sella turcica. *br*, Brain; *ic*, internal carotid; *p*, pituitary; *pn*, palatine nerve; *tr*, trabecula. B, Section farther back through ala temporalis, *at*. *a*, Artery; *al*, alisphenoid; *npd*, nasal passage; *p*, palatine; *pt*, pterygoid; *ptc*, pterygoid cartilage; *tn*, trigeminal; *v*, vein; *vn*, vidian nerve.

is flat or U-shaped in section, but becomes Y-shaped in the majority where the interorbital septum is developed.    In fishes with a myodome and Teleosts generally it is situated in front of the pituitary fossa, and does not extend below the hypophysis as in Tetrapods, hence its homology has been doubted (Kindred adopts Hallmann's name suprasphenoid, 537).    Nevertheless, this bone appears to represent the true basisphenoid pushed forward owing to the development of the myodome and growth of the pro-otics (see p. 279).    In *Polypterus* and some more specialised Teleosts it may be absent or fused to the parasphenoid. Parker showed that the basitrabecular processes of *Lepidosteus* ossify

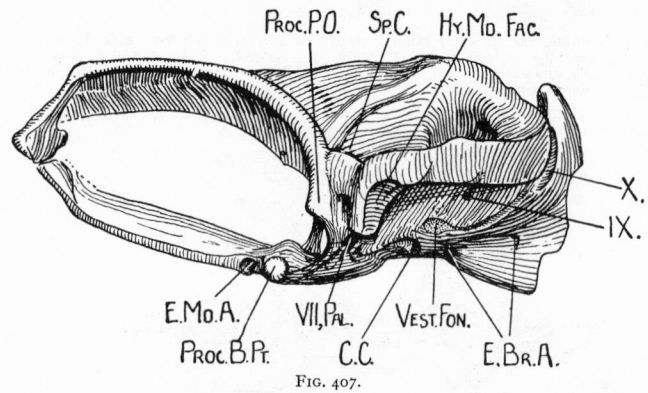

FIG. 407.
Left-side view of neuro-cranium of *Palaeoniscid* (from D. M. S. Watson, *Proc. Zool. Soc.*, 1925). *Hy.Md.Fac*, Facet for hyomandibular.    Other letters as in Fig. 408.

separately at first and later fuse with the parasphenoidal wings (566) ; doubtless the former bones represent the basisphenoids.

Resting on the wings of the basisphenoid are the paired bones generally called alisphenoids, extending between the optic foramen and the pro-otic and up to the roof to form the side walls of the brain-cavity in this region, Figs. 286-7, 436.    That this bone in the fish is not the homologue of the mammalian alisphenoid is obvious, since it is an ossification in the primitive cranial wall (orbital cartilage) and not in the outer wall of the cavum epiptericum as in the mammal (p. 437).    Nor can it be the exact homologue of the pleurosphenoid of Reptiles and Birds (p. 392) since it is not primarily developed in a pila antotica.    It must be considered as a special element, the pterosphenoid (de Beer, 421) developed as an ossification of the pila lateralis, a structure only found in the Holostei.    This pterosphenoid is, then, a bone formed in what is apparently a secondary downgrowth of the orbital cartilage (pedicel of the alisphenoid of Allis, 402), which fuses with the subocular shelf laterally to the vena capitis lateralis, and behind the exit of the profundus and abducens nerves.   Nevertheless, its more dorsal part may correspond to that of the pleurosphenoid.

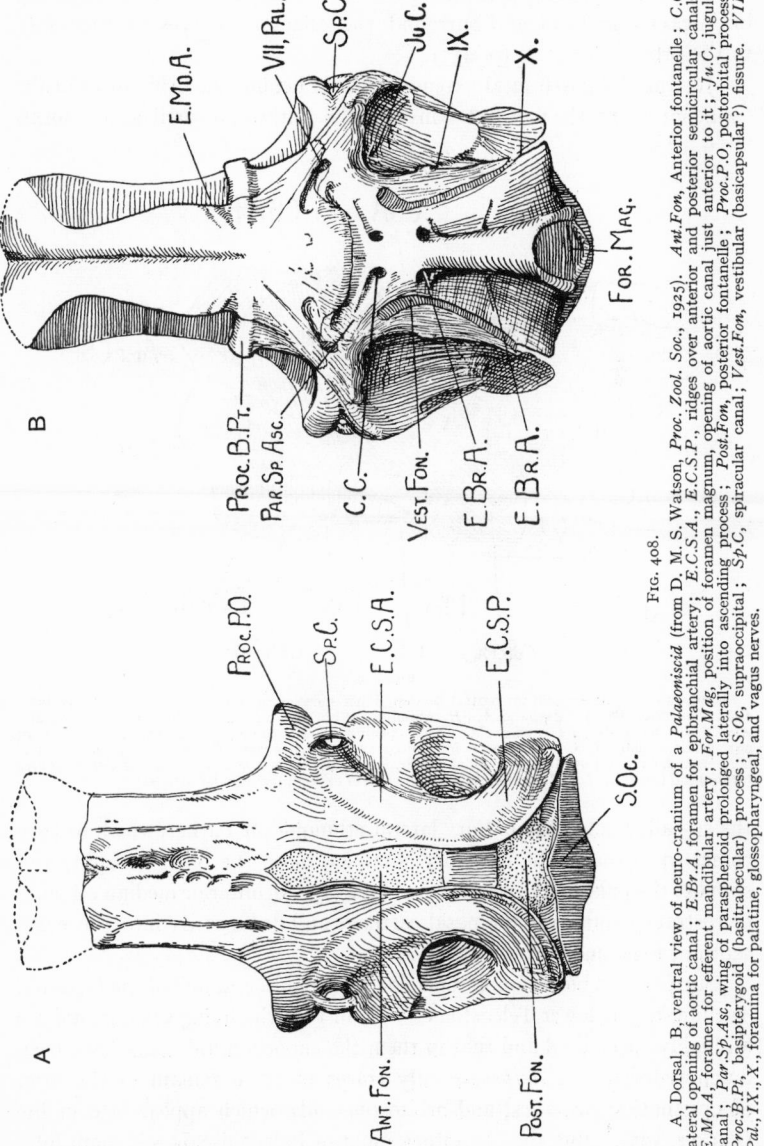

FIG. 408.

A, Dorsal, B, ventral view of neuro-cranium of a *Palaeoniscid* (from D. M. S. Watson, *Proc. Zool. Soc.*, 1925). *Ant.Fon.*, Anterior fontanelle; *C.C*, lateral opening of aortic canal; *E.Br.A*, foramen for epibranchial artery; *E.C.S.A.*, *E.C.S.P.*, ridges over anterior and posterior semicircular canals; *E.Mo.A.*, foramen for efferent mandibular artery; *For.Mag*, position of foramen magnum, opening of aortic canal just anterior to it; *Ju.C*, jugular canal; *Par.Sp.Asc*, wing of parasphenoid prolonged laterally into ascending process; *Post.Fon*, posterior fontanelle; *Proc.P.O*, postorbital process; *Proc.B.Pt*, basipterygoid (basitrabecular) process; *S.Oc*, supraoccipital; *Sp.C*, spiracular canal; *Vest.Fon*, vestibular (basicapsular?) fissure. *VII.*, *Pal.*, *IX.*, *X.*, foramina for palatine, glossopharyngeal, and vagus nerves.

In the wall of the brain-case in front of the optic foramen are developed the orbitosphenoids, of paired origin, Figs. 286-7, 436. They meet below the brain and above the parasphenoid fusing to form the interorbital septum, when such a septum is present and ossified ; and, thus, come to close the brain-cavity in front and surround the olfactory nerves on their way to the orbit in Teleosts (p. 257).

Just as the postfrontal extends inwards behind the orbit to form the ' sphenotic ', so the prefrontal invades the antorbital cartilage and forms

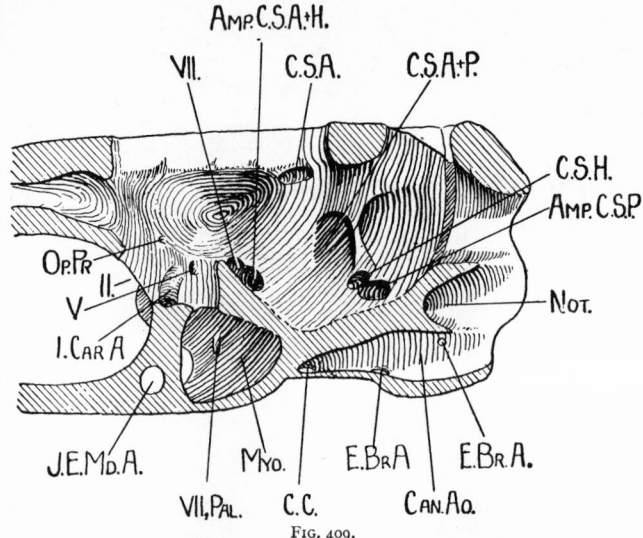

FIG. 409.

Brain-case of *Palaeoniscid* in sagittal section, inner view of right half (from D. M. S. Watson, *Proc. Zool. Soc.*, 1925). *Amp.C.S.A.+H*, Ampulla for anterior and horizontal semicircular canals ; *Amp.C.S.P*, for posterior s. canal ; *C.C*, lateral opening of aortic canal ; *C.S.A*, hole into cavity for ant. semic. canal ; *C.S.A.+P*, space for united vertical s. canals ; *C.S.H*, for posterior end of horizontal s. canal ; *Can.Ao*, aortic canal ; *E.Br.A*, foramen for epibranchial artery ; *I.Car.A*, groove for internal carotid ; *J.E.Md.A*, foramen for junction of efferent mandibular arteries.

the so-called ecto-ethmoid or ' lateral ethmoid ' of Parker, which usually comes to surround the olfactory foramen, close the orbit in front, and support the palatoquadrate below, Fig. 436. An anterior median ethmoid or rostral spreads over the nasal cartilage and downwards into the nasal septum, Figs. 299, 305.

Such are the bones found replacing the chondrocranium of the Holostei. Turning to the lower Teleostomes we find that the living Chondrostei are all highly specialised and that in them the endochondral bones have been much reduced. In *Acipenser* only traces of them remain in the form of opisthotics, pro-otics, and orbitosphenoids, which appear late in life (Parker, 565). But the chondrocranium of Palaeoniscids was more fully ossified, Figs. 407-9 (Stensiö, 218 ; Watson, 646). The occipital and

auditory regions were ossified much as in the higher forms, but the orbito-
temporal ossifications further forward seem to have been fused to a single
bone, the ' sphenoid ', apparently representing the basisphenoid, ptero-

Osteolepis

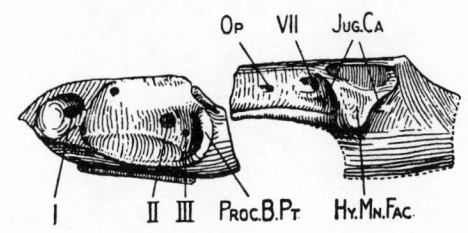

Palaeogyrinus

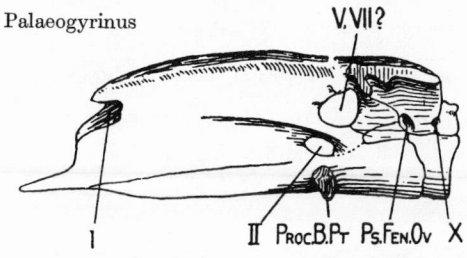

Eryops

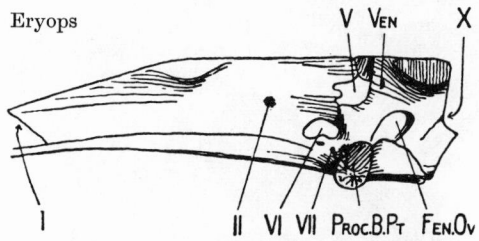

FIG. 410.

Left lateral aspects of ossified parts of brain-case of *Osteolepis macrolepidotus*, Middle Old Red
Sandstone, Banffshire; *Palaeogyrinus decorus*, Middle Carboniferous, Fifeshire; *Eryops megacephalus*,
Lower Permian, Texas (from D. M. S. Watson, *Tr. Roy. Soc.*, 1926). *Fen.Ov*, Fenestra ovalis;
*Hy.Mn.Fac*, facet for articulation of hyomandibula; *Jug.Ca*, openings of jugular canal; *Op*, superior
ophthalmic foramen; *Proc.B.Pt*, basipterygoid process; *Ps.Fen.Ov*, pit corresponding to fenestra
ovalis; *Ven*, venous foramen. I-X, cranial nerve foramina.

sphenoids (?), and orbitosphenoids (and in some the ' lateral ethmoids '
as well). The basisphenoid region was more normal than in higher forms,
and had a fossa for the pituitary body and well-developed paired basitrabecular processes for the articulation of the basal processes of the
palatoquadrates. This primitive joint persists in *Lepidosteus* (p. 421),

but is lost in *Amia* and all modern Teleostei.[1] As in so many other respects, *Polypterus* resembles the Palaeoniscids in having a large

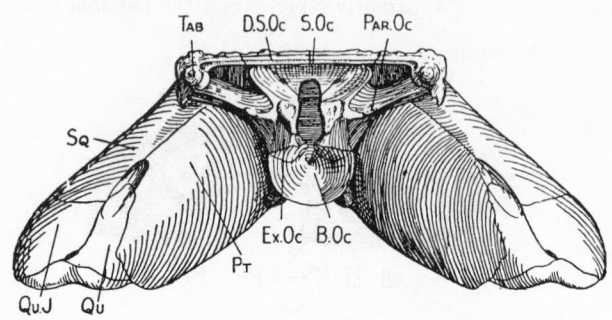

FIG. 411.

*Orthosaurus pachycephalus*; reconstruction of occipital aspect of skull (from D. M. S. Watson, *Tr. Roy. Soc.*, 1926). *B.Oc*, Basioccipital; *D.S.Oc*, dermal supraoccipital=postparietal; *Ex.Oc*, exoccipital; *Par.Oc*, paroccipital process of opisthotic; *Pt*, posterior plate of pterygoid; *Qu.J*, quadratojugal; *Qu*, quadrate; *S.Oc*, supraoccipital; *Sq*, squamosal; *Tab*, tabular.

'sphenoid' extending from the front end of the brain-cavity to the basisphenoid and even the pro-otic region (Traquair, **613**; Allis, **410**;

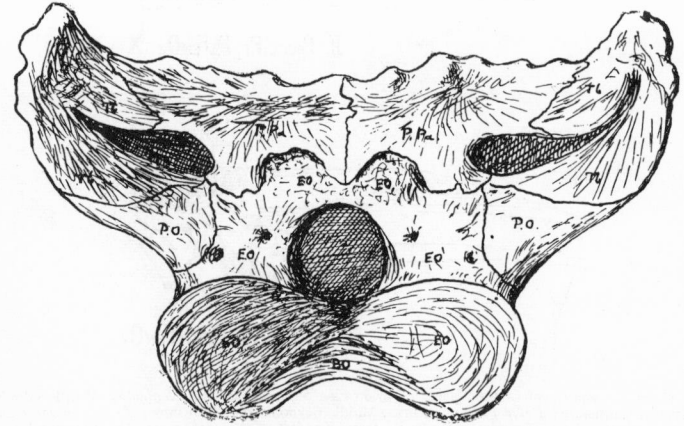

FIG. 412.

Occiput of *Eryops megacephalus*. (From R. Broom, *Am. Mus. Nat. Hist.*, 1913.)

Lehn, **542**; Budgett, **10**; Pollard, **575**). It is pierced by the olfactory optic and trigeminal foramina, and passes behind the infundibulum over the hypophysial fossa to form a 'pro-otic bridge' (see below). A well-

[1] The connexion between parasphenoid and endopterygoid in Osteoglossidae, described by Bridge, **432**, and Ridewood, **580**, is almost certainly secondary.

developed independent opisthotic has not yet been identified in either

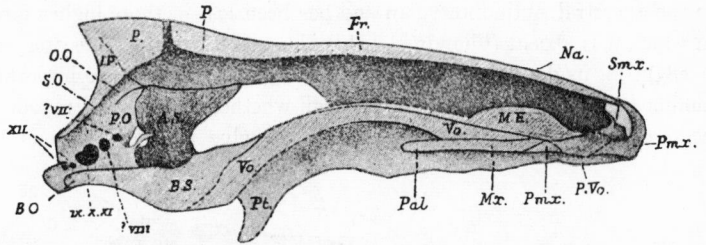

FIG. 413.

Median section of skull of *Diademodon* (after R. Broom, *Proc. Zool. Soc.*, from W. K. Gregory, *J. Morph.*, 1913). *AS*, Alisphenoid=epipterygoid; *BS*, basisphenoid; *ME*, mesethmoid; *OO*, opisthotic; *PO*, pro-otic; *P.Vo*, prevomer; *Smx*, septomaxillary; *Vo*, vomer.

Palaeoniscids or *Polypterus*; but small ossifications in the latter may perhaps represent it (Stensiö, **409**).

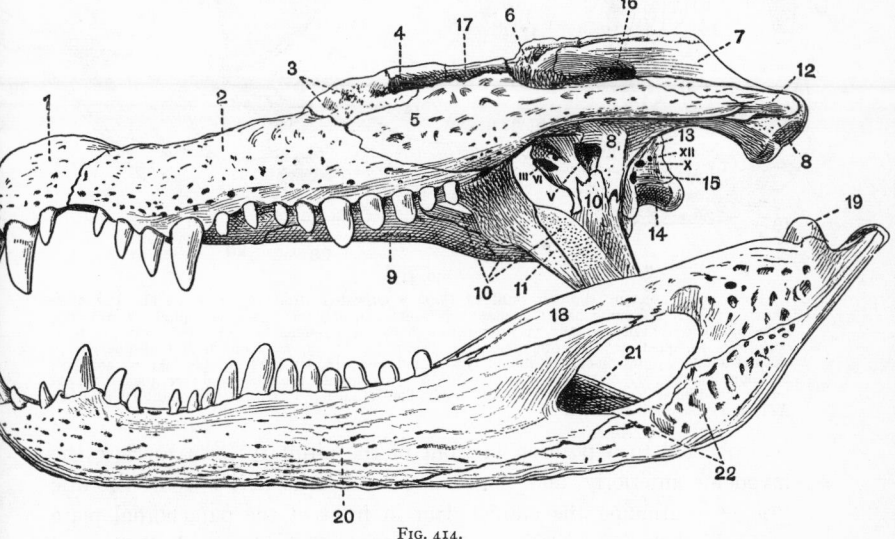

FIG. 414.

Lateral view of skull of *Caiman latirostris* (from S. H. Reynolds, *Vertebrate Skeleton*, 1913). 1, Premaxillary; 2, maxillary; 3, lacrimal; 4, prefrontal; 5, jugal; 6, postfrontal; 7, squamosal; 8, quadrate; 9, palatine; 10, pterygoid; 11, transpalatine (ectopterygoid); 12, quadratojugal; 13, exoccipital; 14, basioccipital; 15, carotid foramen; 16, external auditory meatus; 17, frontal; 18, supra-angular; 19, articular; 20, dentary; 21, coronoid; 22, angular; *III, VI*, opening for exit of oculomotor and abducens nerves; *V*, foramen ovale; *X*, pneumogastric foramen; *XII*, hypoglossal foramen.

It has recently been shown by Stensiö (**218**) and Watson (**646**) that a 'dorsal myodome' is present in the pituitary region of Palaeoniscids, but has not yet in these early fish extended backwards to form a

' ventral myodome ' below the basis cranii, Fig. 409. It must be concluded, as previously mentioned, that the myodome was already developed
in the ancestral Actinopterygian and has been lost in those higher forms
in which it is absent (Chondrostei, Lepidosteoidei, certain Teleostei ; see
p. 283) ; for its development leads in this region of the skull to important
modifications found in all Actinopterygii whether a functional myodome
be present or not.   These modifications involve the restriction of the

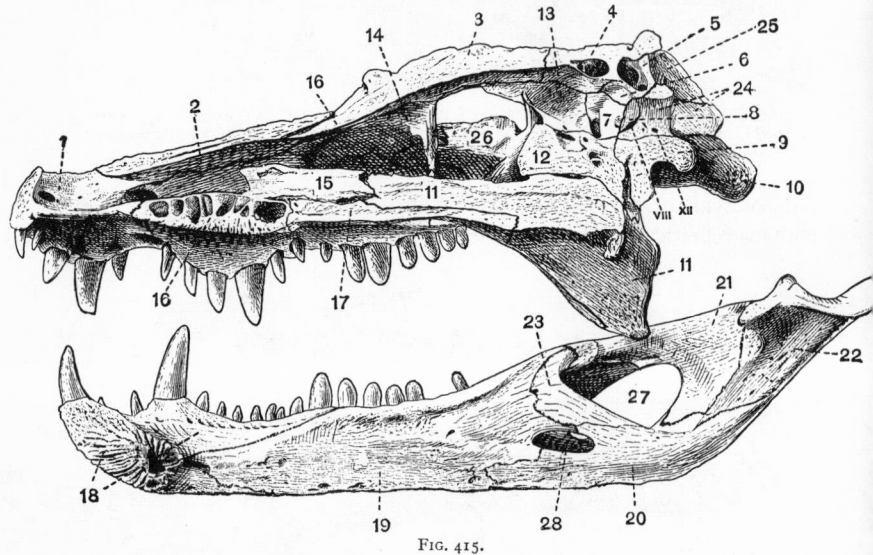

FIG. 415.

Longitudinal section through skull of *Caiman latirostris* (from S. H. Reynolds, *Vertebrate
Skeleton*, 1913).   1, Premaxillary ;   2, nasal ;   3, frontal ;   4, parietal ;   5, supraoccipital ;   7, pro-otic :
immediately in front of the figure 7 is prominent foramen for trigeminal nerve ;   8, opisthotic ;   9, basioccipital ;   10, quadrate ;   11, pterygoid ;   12, basisphenoid ;   13, pleurosphenoid (' alisphenoid ') ;
14, prefrontal ;   15, prevomer ;   16, maxillary ;   17, palatine ;   18, dentary ;   19, splenial ;   20, angular ;
21, supra-angular ;   22, articular ;   23, coronoid ;   24, exoccipital ;   25, squamosal ;   26, jugal ;   27, external mandibular vacuity ;   28, internal mandibular foramen ;   *VIII*, internal auditory meatus
*XII*, hypoglossal foramen.

basisphenoid to a position in front of the pituitary fossa to close the
myodome anteriorly, and the roofing over of its cavity by a ' pro-otic
bridge ' continuing the cranial floor in front of the parachordal plate
and behind the infundibulum.   This remarkable bridge, typically formed
by the junction of processes from the pro-otic bones, is partly preformed
in cartilage occupying the position of the acrochordal cartilage of
Tetrapods (p. 240), and is probably homologous with it.   When a ventral
division of the myodome is developed in Teleostei between the basis
cranii and the parasphenoid, its side walls are strengthened by downgrowths from the pro-otics and basioccipital (p. 279 and Figs. 286, 289).

Some interorbital septum (more or less developed and often partly membranous, p. 256) is present in Palaeoniscids and in all Holostean Teleostomes, excepting Amioidei and a few Teleosts. It is associated with

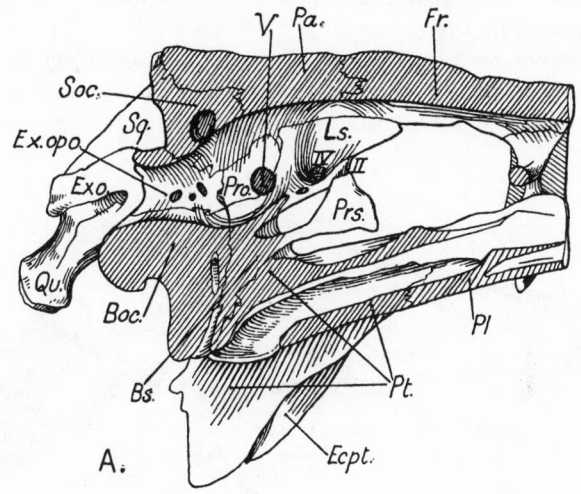

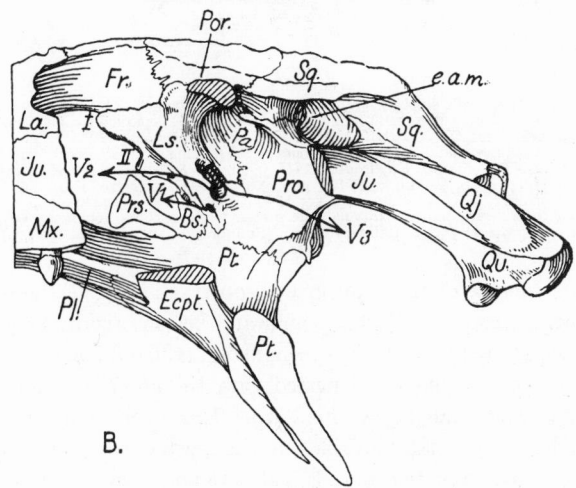

FIG. 416.

A, Inner view of left half of posterior region of skull of *Crocodilus*; B, outer view of same (from Gregory and Noble, *J. Morph. and Physiol.*, 1924). *Bs* and *Prs*, Basisphenoid; *e.a.m*, external auditory meatus; *Ls*, pleurosphenoid (laterosphenoid).

the growth of large eyes and orbits bringing the originally separate cranial side walls together in the mid-line. How far the absence of the septum

and more platybasic build of the skull in *Polypterus, Amia,* and the
Cypriniformes is primary or secondary is at present uncertain ; but there
is some reason to suppose that this condition has arisen independently in
several groups (p. 235).

The recent work of Bryant on *Eusthenopteron* (465), and more especially of Stensiö (218, 606) and Watson (644) on *Dictyonosteus, Osteolepis,*
and other related fossils, has brought to light many interesting facts

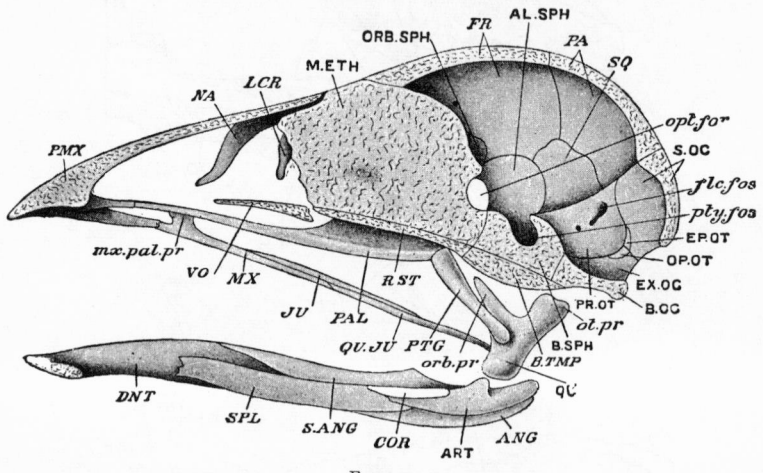

FIG. 417.

Sagittal section of a bird's skull (diagrammatic).   Replacing bones : AL.SPH, pleurosphenoid ;
ART, articular ; B.OC, basioccipital ; B.SPH, basisphenoid ; EP.OT, epiotic ? ; EX.OC, exoccipital ;
M.ETH, mesethmoid ; OP.OT, opisthotic ; ORB.SPH, orbitosphenoid ; PR.OT, pro-otic ;   QU,
quadrate ;   S.OC, supraoccipital.   Investing bones : *ANG,* angular ;   *B.TMP,* basi-temporal ;
*COR,* coronary ; *DNT,* dentary ; *FR,* frontal ; *JU,* jugal ; *LCR,* lacrymal ; *MX,* maxilla ; *NA,*
nasal ; *PA,* parietal ; *PAL,* palatine ; *PMX,* premaxilla ; *PTG,* pterygoid ; *QU.JU,* quadratojugal ; *RST,* rostrum ; *S.ANG,* supra-angular ; *SPL,* splenial ; *SQ,* squamosal ; *VO,* vomer.
*flc.fos,* Floccular fossa ; *mx.pal.pr,* maxillo-palatine process ; *opt.for,* optic foramen ; *orb.pr,* orbital
process ; *ot.pr,* otic process ; *pty.fos,* pituitary fossa.   (From Parker and Haswell, *Zoology.*)

about the structure of the skull in Crossopterygii.   While the occipital
and otic bones tend to combine behind and become rigidly attached to
the overlying cranial roofing, the sphenoid and ethmoid bones combine to
form a massive 'sphenoid' connected with the anterior roofing above
and the parasphenoid below, Fig. 410.   This orbito-temporal region
was probably somewhat movable on the posterior region, the joint
being marked between the frontals and parietals at all events in Osteolepids.   Jugular canals, basitrabecular processes, and paroccipital processes
are present.

Evidence of close affinity between the Coelacanthini and  Osteolepids
is afforded by the skull (Stensiö, 605 ;  Watson, 645) ; for both groups
appear to have the same frontoparietal hinge.   The anterior ethmoid

region was mainly cartilaginous in Coelacanths, but there is a ' sphenoid ' including the well-ossified basisphenoid.[1]  A large pro-otic (which possibly represents the combined pro-otic and opisthotic), basioccipital, exoccipital, and supraoccipital bones have been found in *Macropoma* and others. The chondrocranium of the Devonian genus *Diplocercides* was solidly ossified in both its anterior and posterior regions (Stensiö, 606).

Little is known about the condition of the cranium in early Dipnoi beyond the fact that it was more fully ossified than in later forms (Traquair, 622 ; Watson and Day, 647).  In existing genera it is almost completely cartilaginous, with only a pair of posterior bones considered to be exoccipitals (Huxley, 535 ;  Bridge, 433 ;  Wiedersheim, 653).

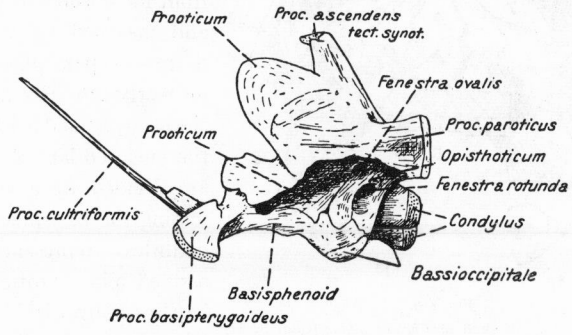

FIG. 418.

Occipital region, etc., of skull of *Tupinambis teguexin* (from Versluys, *Vergl. Anat.*, 1927).   *Proc. cultriformis* = rostrum of parasphenoid.

**Tetrapoda.**—The chief ossifications in the chondrocranium of Tetrapods were doubtless derived from those of their fish-like ancestors.  Indeed, most of the endochondral bones found even in the human skull can be traced back to the primitive Osteichthyes.  But, although there is a fundamental similarity in these ossifications throughout the Tetrapods, specialisation has led to the fusion or loss of many of them in most modern forms.  Among Amphibia it is to the early (Carboniferous and Permian) Stegocephalia that we must turn for the primitive structure, for in these the chondrocranium is much more completely ossified than in later forms and thus approaches in structure that of the early Reptiles.  The early Embolomeri, such as *Palaeogyrinus* and *Orthosaurus* (*Loxomma*), have the foramen magnum closed above by a supraoccipital, and below by a basioccipital, which forms the greater part of a hollow occipital condyle

[1] The basitrabecular processes of the basisphenoid are brought high up at the sides in the Coelacanths ;  but the depressions below them are probably not myodomes as described by Stensiö (Watson, 645).

completed at the sides by the exoccipitals, Figs. 410, 411-12. An opisthotic and a pro-otic are present in the auditory region ; the former provided with a strong paroccipital process abutting against the tabular region of the dermal roof, and probably also supporting the otic process of the quadrate. A basisphenoid lodging the pituitary fossa, and closely connected or fused to the underlying elongated parasphenoid, has pronounced basitrabecular (basipterygoid) processes with facets for the pterygoid and epipterygoid.

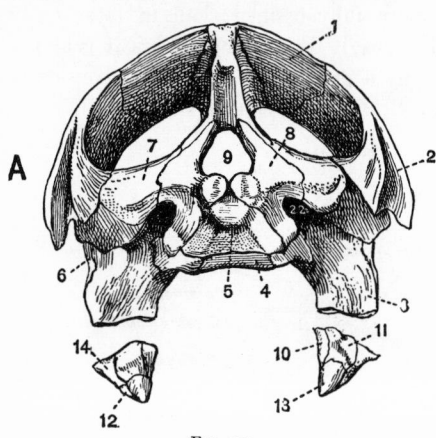

FIG. 419.

Posterior half of skull of *Chelone midas* (from S. H. Reynolds, *Vertebrate Skeleton*, 1913). 1, Parietal ; 2, squamosal ; 3, quadrate ; 4, basisphenoid ; 5, basi-occipital ; 6, quadratojugal ; 7, opisthotic ; 8, exoccipital ; 9, foramen magnum ; 10, prearticular ; 11, articular ; 12, dentary ; 13, angular ; 14, supra-angular.

Farther forward extends a large ' sphenethmoid ', surrounding the anterior region of the brain-case, pierced in front for the olfactory nerves, and sheathed below by the narrowing parasphenoid. It meets the pro-otics above and the basisphenoid below, while the enclosed lateral openings are divided by a stout bar joining the basisphenoid and doubtless representing the ossified pila antotica. This ' sphenethmoid ' bone, formed presumably by the fusion of two orbitosphenoids (ossified orbital cartilages), is of special interest since its ventral portion forms a thick low interorbital septum, indicating apparently that in these primitive Stegocephalia the skull was less platybasic than in modern Amphibia, and so approximated to the Amniote structure (Watson, 631, 644). Important also is the presence of a hypoglossal foramen in the exoccipital of such forms as *Ortho-saurus*, *Trimerorhachis*, and *Eryops*, as evidence that some at least of the hypoglossal roots, as in Amniotes, passed through this region, and therefore that this nerve probably was composed of more segmental roots than in the higher Stegocephalia and modern Amphibia (p. 226), and that the occipital region of the skull perhaps contained more skeletal segments.

The later and more specialised Stegocephalia show traces of the reduction in ossification which is so characteristic of all modern Amphibia (Fraas, 497 ; Broili, 435 ; Williston, 657-8, 660 ; Broom, 448 ; Watson, 644). The supra- and basioccipital, still present in *Eryops*, usually are no longer developed, and the occipital condyles are then paired and formed exclusively by the exoccipitals which may meet in the middle line below. There are no hypoglossal foramina (p. 226).

The modern Amphibia have lost not only the supra- and basioccipital, but also the opisthotic (except perhaps *Necturus*, where a bone occurs called 'epiotic' by Huxley, **534**). It has become either supplanted by or fused with the exoccipital. The very flat basis cranii has no basi-

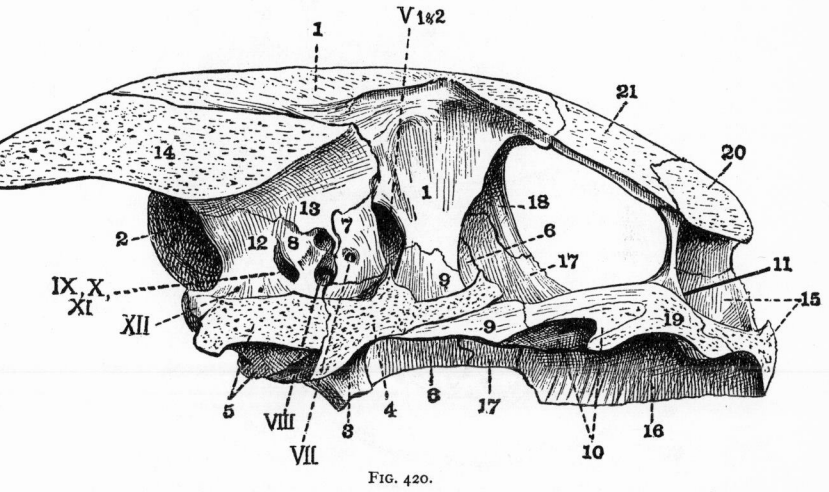

FIG. 420.

ꕯLongitudinal vertical section through the skull of *Chelone midas* (from S. H. Reynolds, *Vertebrate Skeleton*, 1913). 1, Parietal; 2, squamosal; 3, quadrate; 4, basisphenoid; 5, basioccipital; 6, quadratojugal; 7, pro-otic; 8, opisthotic; 9, pterygoid; 10, palatine; 11, rcd passed into narial passage; 12, exoccipital; 13, 14, supraoccipital; 15, premaxillary; 16, maxillary; 17, jugal; 18, postfrontal; 19, prevomer; 20, prefrontal; 21, frontal; *V, VII, VIII, IX, X, XI, XII*, foramina for the exit of cranial nerves.

sphenoid. Anterior ossifications persist either in the form of a single sphenethmoid 'girdle-bone' (Anura) or of paired orbitosphenoids (Urodela and Apoda). There are few occipital segments, no hypoglossal foramina, and the paired exoccipital condyles are widely separated, Fig. 329.

As already mentioned, the most primitive Amniota (Cotylosauria) differ but little from the early Stegocephalia (Embolomeri) in the endochondral ossifications of the occipital and auditory regions, Fig. 410. A 'sphenethmoid' still surrounds the brain-cavity in front in such forms as *Diadectes* and *Pareiasaurus* (Case, **470**; Williston, **661, 95**). It persists anteriorly in some Theromorpha (Dicynodontia) as a median bone pierced for the olfactory nerves, lodging the olfactory lobes of the brain and spreading down into the median septum, Fig. 422 (Sollas and Sollas, **602**; Broom, 1912–13). In the Theriodontia it seems to have been less developed. The occipital condyle in these Reptiles (Cotylosauria and Theromorpha) is usually distinctly tripartite (formed by the basioccipital and two ex-occipitals) and sometimes concave, as in *Pareiasaurus* (Seeley, 586).

The remainder of the Reptilia diverge considerably from this primitive structure. Except in the Ophidia (p. 237) the skull is markedly tropibasic, the interorbital septum high and thin ; consequently the sphenethmoid ossification is completely lost as in Chelonia and Crocodilia, or reduced to disconnected vestigial bones near the optic foramen and usually lost in

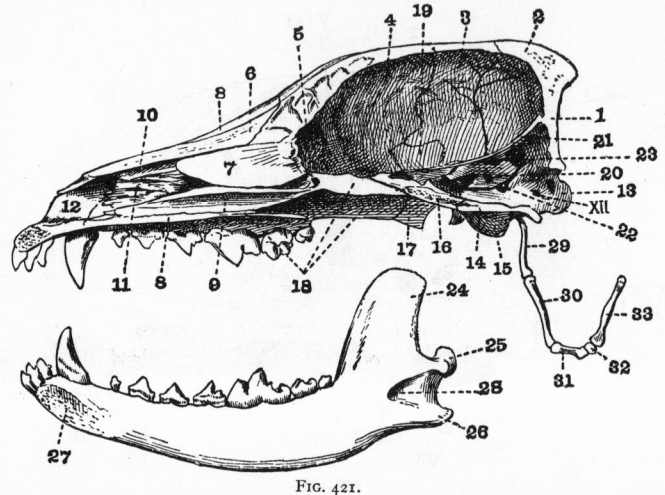

FIG. 421.

Vertical longitudinal section taken a little to left of middle line through skull of *Canis familiaris* (from S. H. Reynolds, *Vertebrate Skeleton*, 1913). 1, Supraoccipital ; 2, interparietal ; 3, parietal ; 4, frontal ; 5, cribriform plate ; 6, nasal ; 7, mesethmoid ; 8, maxilla ; 9, vomer ; 10, ethmo-turbinal ; 11, maxillo-turbinal ; 12, premaxillary ; 13, occipital condyle ; 14, basioccipital ; 15, tympanic bulla ; 16, basisphenoid ; 17, pterygoid ; 18, palatine ; 19, alisphenoid ; 20, internal auditory meatus ; 21, tentorium ; 22, foramen lacerum posterius ; 23, floccular fossa ; 24, coronoid process ; 25, condyle ; 26, angle ; 27, mandibular symphysis ; 28, inferior dental foramen ; 29, stylo-hyal ; 30, epi-hyal ; 31, cerato-hyal ; 32, basi-hyal ; 33, thyro-hyal ; *XII*, condylar foramen.

dry skulls. Such vestiges occur in *Sphenodon*, Lacertilia, and Ophidia (orbitosphenoids, 'alisphenoids' of Parker, postoptics of Cope ; Siebenrock, 599, 600).[1] Down-growing flanges of the parietals and frontals to some extent replace the ' sphenethmoid ' in supporting the sides of the brain-case.

An apparently new bone makes its appearance in the Crocodilia as an ossification of the posterior lateral wall of the brain-case (orbital cartilage, and pila antotica) extending downwards to the basisphenoid between the optic foramen in front and the trigeminal foramen behind (Parker, 570 ; Shiino, 597 ; de Beer, 421). It was called the alisphenoid by older authors, but is certainly not homologous with the Mammalian alisphenoid, since it

[1] The absence of orbitosphenoids in so many fossil Reptilia may be due to their having dropped out of the skull.

belongs to the true cranial wall and not the outer wall of the cavum
epiptericum (Gregory and Noble, 524a; and see p. 267). This bone probably
occurred in related fossil reptiles, such as the Phytosaurs (v. Huene),
and is present in Birds. It may be called the laterosphenoid (Gregory
and Noble) or better pleurosphenoid, Figs. 414-16; but it probably
represents the hinder region of the extensive sphenethmoid described
above in Stegocephalia which may be supposed to include an anterior
(true orbitosphenoid) and this posterior element. Both elements are well
developed in the avian skull, Figs. 388, 417; the pleurosphenoid occupy-

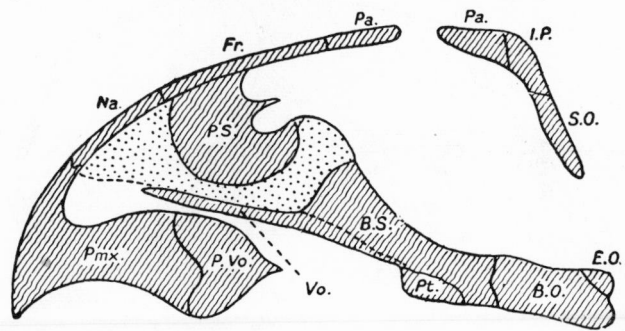

FIG. 422.

Median section of skull of *Dicynodon sollasi* (from R. Broom, *Proc. Zool. Soc.*, 1926). *Na*,
Nasal; *Fr*, frontal; *Pa*, parietal; *I.P*, interparietal; *S.O*, supraoccipital; *P.S*, presphenoid or
sphenethmoid; *B.S*, basisphenoid; *B.O*, basioccipital; *Pmx*, premaxillary; *pp*, its palatine process;
*Vo*, vomer; *Mx*, maxillary; *Pal*, palatine; *P.Vo*, prevomer; *E.O*, exoccipital. (Cp. Fig. 423.) (From
Broom, *Proc. Zool. Soc.*, 1926.)

ing a large part of the antero-lateral wall of the swollen brain-case, and
the orbitosphenoids fusing to a median ethmoid usually forming an
extensive bony interorbital septum (Parker, 557; Tonkoff, 612; Sushkin,
608; T. J. Parker, 555; de Beer, 421).

The opisthotics (paroccipitals) in Sauropsidan Reptiles usually bear
strong paroccipital processes, particularly well developed in Rhynchocephalia and Lacertilia, Figs. 354, 368, 418, 419; but they are shorter
in Crocodilia and still more reduced in Aves. The single occipital condyle
characteristic of Reptiles and Birds is still tripartite in most Chelonia,
Fig. 319, and to a less extent in Lacertilia and Ophidia; but in the other
Orders it is typically a prominent articular knob on the basioccipital
alone (Osborn, 553).

The ossifications of the Mammalian chondrocranium may be derived
from those of the Theromorpha. The characteristic dicondylic condition
arises from the primitive monocondylic[1] by the enlargement of the

[1] The condyle is more or less bilobed and paired in many of the mammal-
like Theromorpha, Fig. 343.

exoccipital and gradual withdrawal of the basioccipital element. An intermediate ∪-shaped stage, in which the two lateral condyles are still joined by a narrow articular region, occurs in Monotremes, more especially in the embryo (Osborn, 553; Gaupp, 512). In the adult Mammal the opisthotic and pro-otic are always fused to one bone, the periotic or petrosal, enclosing the membranous labyrinth. This periotic is often but loosely connected with the surrounding bones in lower forms and may

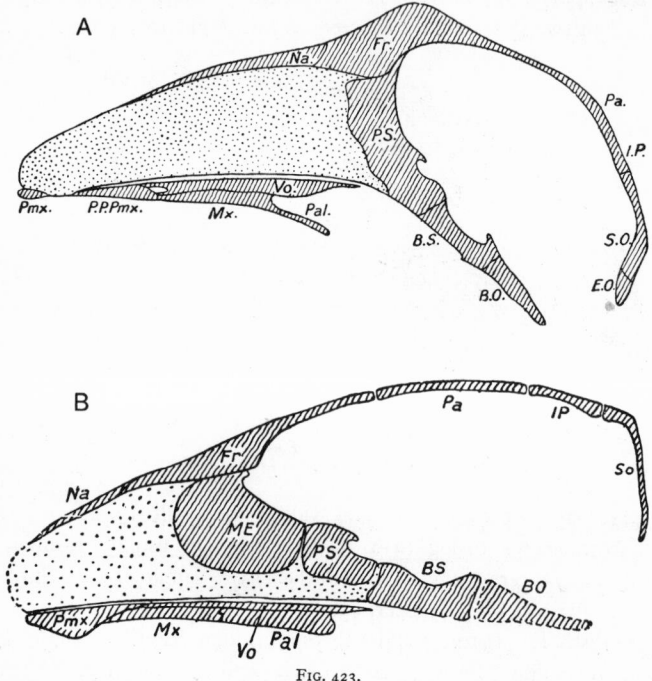

FIG. 423.

Median section of skull of A, young goat, *Capra*; B, young *Procavia capensis*. *ME*, Mesethmoid. Other letters as in Fig. 422. (From Broom, *Proc. Zool. Soc.*, 1926-7.)

fall out in macerated skulls; but in the higher mammals it may fuse with the squamosal and tympanic (='temporal bone' of Man).

There is still some doubt about the derivation of the Mammalian periotic. The earlier authors described three centres of ossification in foetal man, and Huxley named them pro-otic, opisthotic, and epiotic, believing them to be homologous with these bones in the Reptile and Fish. They all three fuse later to the single bone of the adult. Parker (567), Strong, and Thomas (1926) also describe these three early centres in other mammals. But Vrolik (628) found four centres of ossification in the calf and pig, and from three to as many as six in the human foetus. While it may safely be held that the periotic as a whole is homologous with the reptilian pro-otic and opisthotic combined, it is doubtful whether the centres so named by Huxley alone represent them, or whether each bone may develop from several secondary centres.

The paroccipital process is little developed, being represented by the posterior portion of the crista parotica (p. 272). The basisphenoid harbours the pituitary body in a deep fossa or sella turcica which may in Rodents retain its hypophysial opening ; this bone in Marsupials is pierced by the internal carotids (as in the lower Tetrapods), but in Placentals they pass to the pituitary fossa on either side of it.

In many Placentals two bones occur in the anterior region of the floor of the brain-case : one just in front of the basisphenoid has a median presphenoid region and two lateral orbitosphenoid wings ; the other and more anterior is the mesethmoid, an ossification of the anterior wall of the brain-case (including the lamina cribrosa) and median nasal septum, Figs. 421, 423 B. The latter bone arises from a median centre, while the former is formed apparently by the junction ventrally of two orbito-sphenoid ossifications. Some Placentals, however, and the Marsupials have only one bone occupying the place of presphenoid, mesethmoid, and orbitosphenoids,[1] Fig. 423 A. There appears to be no separate 'presphenoid' bone in any adult Mammal. Thus the sphenethmoid of Theromorphs would seem to be represented by a single bone in the adult skull of some Mammals ; but in many Placentals, including the Primates, there is an anterior mesethmoid in addition to the posterior ossification (fused orbitosphenoids). In these forms, then, either a new anterior ossification has appeared, or the old one has been divided into two (Broom, 462a and b).

[1] This bone develops from two orbitosphenoid centres as a rule (Parker) ; but in some Placentals there may appear an additional median anterior ossification of doubtful significance. According to Broom there is a mesethmoid and a 'presphenoid' in the Orders Tubulidentata, Pholidota ?, Hyracoidea, Rodentia, Insectivora, Carnivora, Menotyphla, Cheiroptera, Dermoptera, Primates ; but not in the Orders Xenarthra, Artiodactyla, Perissodactyla, Sirenia, Chrysochloridea, and Monotremata.

# CHAPTER VII

## SKELETAL VISCERAL ARCHES AND LABIAL CARTILAGES

## THE SKELETAL VISCERAL ARCHES

THE skeletal visceral arches of Gnathostomes, already mentioned on
p. 129, are originally quite independent of the chondrocranium proper
(neurocranium). They belong to the visceral, not to the axial skeleton,
and are developed not from skeletogenous tissue surrounding the central
nervous system and notochord, but from that which envelops the alimentary canal. Hence they are derived from splanchnic mesoblast, and
primarily lie in the pharyngeal wall, internal to the main blood-vessels
and branchial nerves, and necessarily internal to the coelom, Fig. 142
(represented in this region by the pericardial coelom, and by canals in
the embryonic gill bars, see p. 490). The skeletal arches, then, primarily
are situated internally to the dorsal aorta, cardinal veins, and lateral
aortic arches, and meet ventrally above and medially to the pericardium,
heart, and ventral aorta. The ventral junction is perhaps secondary in

ontogeny, the earliest prochondral rudiments being paired, even probably the median copulae (Gibian, 684).

Behind the mandibular and hyoid arches are the branchial arches

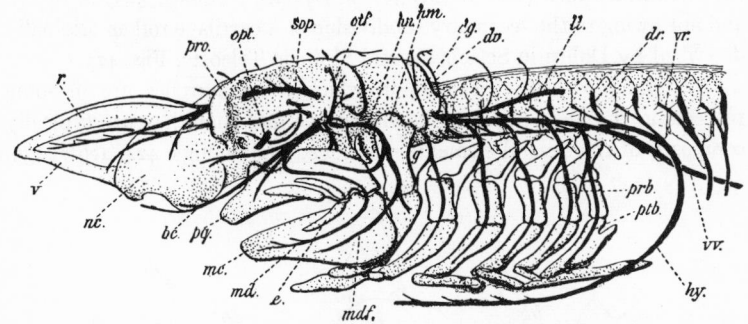

FIG. 424.

Skeleton and nerves of the head of *Mustelus laevis*, Risso (the nerves partly from Allis). *bc*, Buccal nerve; *dg*, dorsal branch of glossopharyngeal; *dr*, dorsal root of spinal nerve; *dv*, dorsal branch of vagus; *e*, labial cartilage; *g*, glossopharyngeal; *hm*, hyomandibular—the spiracle is indicated by a dotted line in front, and the prespiracular cartilage is shown in front of the spiracle; *hn*, hyomandibular nerve; *hy*, hypoglossal nerve; *ll*, lateral-line branch of vagus; *mc*, Meckel's cartilage; *md*, mandibular nerve; *mdf*, mandibular branch of facial nerve; *nc*, nasal capsule; *opt*, optic nerve; *otf*, otic branch of facial; *pq*, palatoquadrate; *prb*, pretrematic nerve; *pro*, profundus nerve; *ptb*, post-trematic nerve; *r*, dorsal rostral cartilage; *sop*, superior ophthalmic branch of trigeminal and facial; *v*, ventral rostral cartilage; *vr*, ventral root; *vv*, visceral branch of vagus. (From Goodrich, *Vert. Craniata*, 1909.)

(p. 440), loosely attached below the occipital region and vertebral column, Fig. 424. These branchial arches typically become subdivided in Pisces into dorsal pharyngeal, epibranchial, lateral ceratobranchial, and ventral hypo-

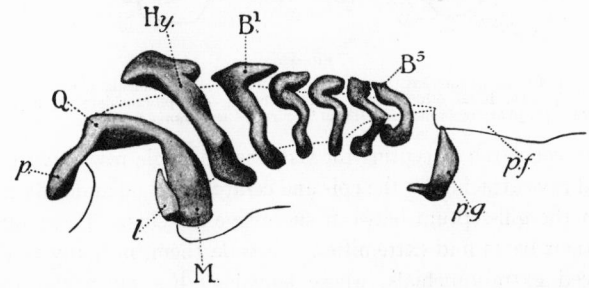

FIG. 425.

Skeleton of visceral arches and pectoral girdle of 20·5 mm. embryo of *Spinax*. (After Braus, 1906, from Kerr, *Embryology*.) *B¹*, *B⁵*, Branchial arches; *Hy*, hyoid; *l*, labial cartilage; *M*, mandibular arch; *p*, palatopterygoid bar; *p.f*, rudiment of pectoral fin; *p.g*, pectoral girdle; *Q*, knob for attachment to trabecular region of skull.

branchial segments joined together in the mid-ventral line by an unpaired basibranchial or copula. Even among fishes these elements undergo considerable modification in number and development, and it is doubtful whether the homology of the separate pieces can be traced to the branchial

arches of Amphibia and still less of higher forms, where the arches are
much altered in structure and function. The various elements appear to
develop in a continuous procartilaginous crescentic rudiment as independent chondrifications (van Wijhe, 397, in *Squalus*; Sonies, 385, in birds),
and not owing to the secondary subdivision of a cartilage rod as originally
described by Dohrn in Selachians and Stöhr in Teleosts, Fig. 425.

Beginning with the Selachii, in which the gill-arches are in some
respects in the most primitive condition, we find that they are typically
composed of the several elements mentioned above, Figs. 424, 426-7, 439.

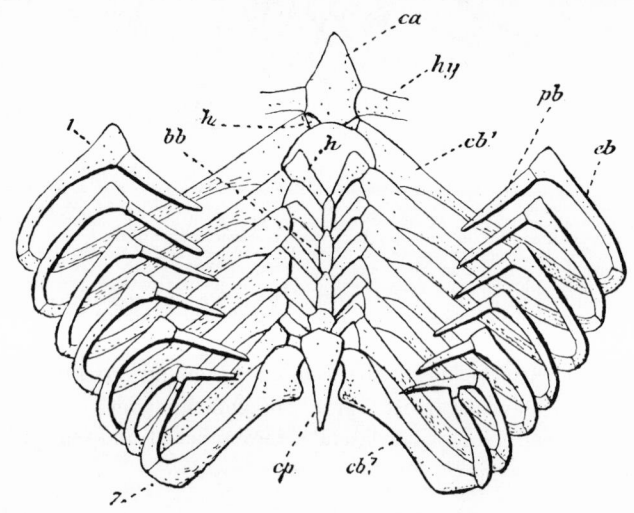

FIG. 426.

Branchial arches of *Heptanchus*. (After Gegenbaur.)  *bb*, Basibranchial;  *ca*, basihyal;  *cb*¹⁻⁷,
ceratobranchials;  *cp*, fused 6th and 7th basibranchials;  *eb*, epibranchial;  *h*, hypobranchial;
*hy*, ceratohyal;  *pb*, pharyngobranchial. (From Goodrich, *Vert. Craniata*, 1909.)

Moreover, each arch, excepting the last, bears a single row of cartilaginous
branchial rays attached to the epi- and ceratobranchial and radiating outwards in the gill-septum between successive gill-slits. These rays may
fuse at their bases and extremities. Outside them, in many Selachians,
are curved extrabranchials, whose homology has given rise to much
controversy. By some they have been considered as outer branchial
arches; [1] but Gegenbaur's view that they are merely the enlarged dorsal

[1] Rathke's view (1832) that the Cyclostomes have outer arches, and the
Gnathostomes inner arches (the outer arches being represented by the extrabranchials of Selachii), was adopted by J. Müller, Duvernoy, Stannius, Balfour,
and Gegenbaur at first. Later Dohrn established the modern view that the
arches are homologous throughout the Craniata (333), and was followed by
Goette, Gegenbaur, and others.

and ventral branchial rays is generally accepted and agrees with their structure and development (Gegenbaur, 166; Dohrn, 333).

Small outer septal cartilages (extraseptals) may also occur in the gill-septa of the Rajidae (K. Fürbringer, 681).

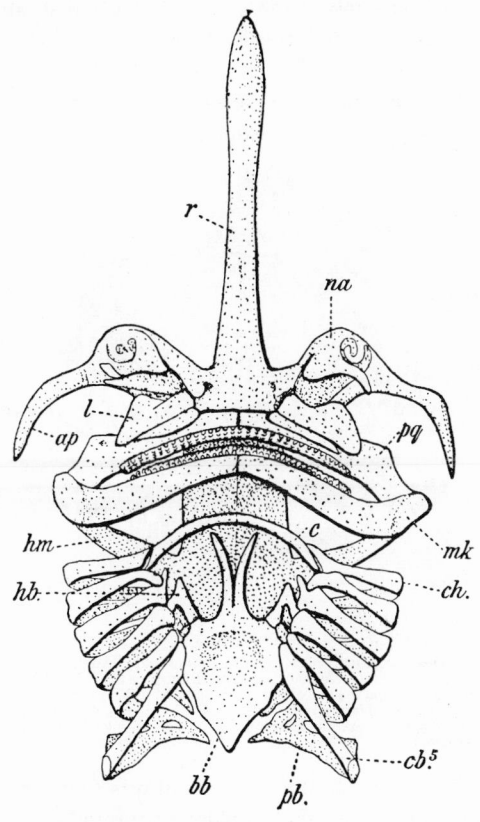

FIG. 427.

Skull and visceral arches of *Raja*, ventral view.   (After Gegenbaur.)    *ap*, Antorbital process ; *bb*, compound basibranchial ; *c*, basihyal ; *cb*⁵, fifth ceratobranchial ; *hb*, hypobranchial ; *hm*, hyomandibular ; *l*, labial ; *mk*, Meckel's cartilage ; *na*, nasal capsule ; *pb*, pharyngobranchial ; *pq*, palatoquadrate ; *r*, rostrum.   (From Goodrich, *Vert. Craniata*, 1909.)

The branchial arches in other Chondrichthyes (Cladoselachii, Dean, 154, 155; Pleuracanthodii, Fritsch, Jaekel, 186) seem to have been built on the same plan as in the Selachii.   In Acanthodii the pharyngobranchial is in two pieces (Jaekel, 690).

In the Osteichthyes the branchial arches are also of essentially the same structure, Fig. 436.   The chief modifications they undergo in these and other fishes will be dealt with farther on (p. 440).

**The Mandibular and Hyoid Arches in Pisces.**—The chief interest centres round the first two visceral skeletal arches, which become closely connected with the chondrocranium. The rudiment of the first or mandibular arch bends round the corner of the mouth and gives rise to two cartilages found in all Gnathostomes : the palatoquadrate bar above and the mandibular bar below. The latter is often called Meckel's cartilage. In Chondrichthyes these two bars meet those of the opposite side in the middle line below the snout, and form the primitive biting upper and lower jaws bearing the teeth developed on the inside of the margin of

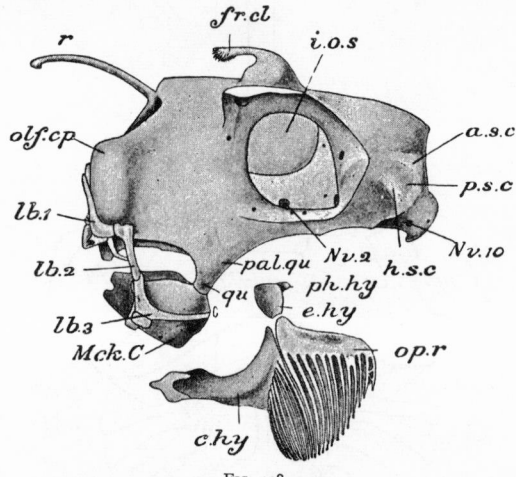

FIG. 428.

Skull of *Chimaera monstrosa*, lateral view. (From Parker and Haswell's *Zoology*, after Hubrecht.) *a.s.c*, Position of anterior semicircular canal ; *c.hy*, ceratohyal ; *e.hy*, epihyal ; *fr.cl*, frontal clasper ; *h.s.c*, position of horizontal semicircular canal ; *i.o.s*, interorbital septum ; *lb.* 1, *lb.* 2, *lb.* 3, labial cartilages ; *Mck.C*, mandible ; *Nv.* 2, optic foramen ; *Nv.* 10, vagus foramen ; *olf.cp*, olfactory capsule ; *op.r*, opercular rays ; *pal.qu*, palatoquadrate ; *ph.hy*, pharyngohyal ; *p.s.c*, position of posterior semicircular canal ; *qu*, quadrate region ; *r* rostrum.

the mouth, Figs. 424, 427. But in Osteichthyes (with the exception of the Chondrostei) and Tetrapoda the palatoquadrate bars do not meet in front, but usually and primitively become connected with the lateral ethmoid region (antorbital process), and although the quadrate region of the palatoquadrate behind always serves to support Meckel's cartilage, the more anterior pterygopalatine region becomes chiefly concerned in roofing the palate, Figs. 429, 437. Meanwhile the function of support-ing the biting teeth is taken on by the marginal dermal bones (p. 287). Meckel's cartilage is always developed in young Osteichthyes ; but, except at its articular end, loses its importance in the adult, being always functionally replaced by dermal bones. Finally in Tetrapods the primitive upper and lower cartilages no longer take an important share

in the support of the adult jaws except at their extreme posterior ends
(quadrate and articular). They are more or less completely developed

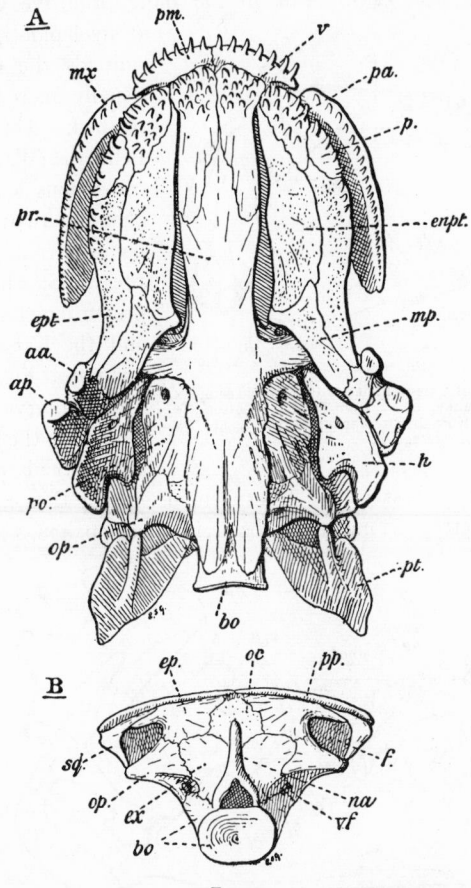

FIG. 429.

*Amia calva*, L. A, Ventral view of skull and upper jaw; B, posterior view of skull. *aa*, Articular
surface of quadrate, *ap*, of symplectic; *bo*, basioccipital; *enpt*, entopterygoid; *ep*, epiotic; *ept*,
ectopterygoid; *ex*, exoccipital; *f*, posterior temporal fossa; *h*, hyomandibular; *mp*, metapterygoid;
*mx*, maxilla; *na*, neural arch, whose centrum is fused to basioccipital; *oc*, occipital cartilage;
*op*, opisthotic; *p* and *pa*, palatine bones; *pm*, premaxilla; *po*, pro-otic; *pp*, postparietal?;
*pr*, parasphenoid; *pt*, post-temporal; *sq*, pterotic; *v*, vomer; *vf*, vagus foramen. (From Goodrich,
*Vert. Craniata*, 1909.)

in the embryo, but become greatly specialised and modified in the higher
groups (p. 423).

Both the palatoquadrate and mandibular cartilages become ossified
in varying degree in Osteichthyes, Figs. 430, 436. In the former there
is generally an anterior autopalatine, a posterior quadrate, and a meta-

pterygoid between, at all events in Coelacanthini and Actinopterygii (recalling somewhat the three calcified pieces described by Jaekel in Acanthodians, **690, 443**). But in the more primitive Crossopterygii

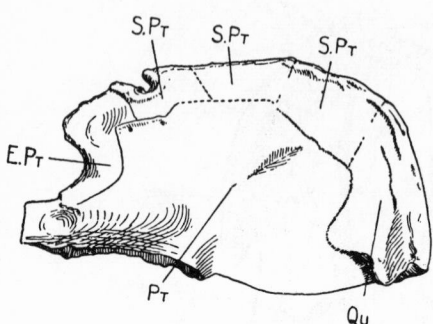

FIG. 429a.

*Megalichthys*; outer view of left palatopterygoid camplex, with palatal part broken away (from D. M. S. Watson, *Tr. Roy. Soc.*, 1926). *E.Pt*, Epipterygoid ; *Pt*, pterygoid ; *Qu*, quadrate; *S.Pt*, suprapterygoids.

(Osteolepidoti) and Palaeoniscids the cartilage was usually more completely ossified. Thus in Megalichthys (Watson, **644**) a continuous series of endochondral suprapterygoid bones extends along the pterygoid, the first representing the epipterygoid and the last reaching the quadrate, Figs. **309, 429**. The epipterygoid bone extends into the basal process and articulates with the basitrabecular process of the basisphenoid. From this condition that of the lower Tetrapoda may easily be derived (see pp. 428, 431). Meckel's

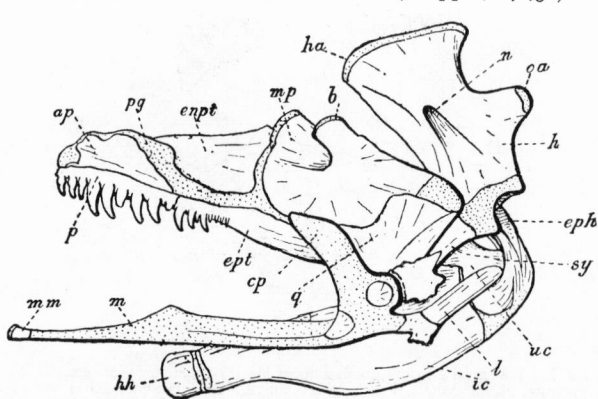

FIG. 430.

*Amia calva*, L. Skeleton of the left jaws and hyoid arch, from which the dermal bones of the lower jaw have been removed. (After Allis, slightly modified.) The cartilage is dotted. *ap*, Endochondral palatine ; *b*, otic process ; *cp*, coronoid process ; *enpt*, endopterygoid ; *eph*, epihyal ; *ept*, ectopterygoid ; *h*, hyomandibular ; *ha*, its articular head ; *hh*, hypohyal ; *ic*, ventral segment of ceratohyal ; *l*, ligament ; *m*, Meckel's cartilage ; *mm*, mento-Meckelian ; *mp*, metapterygoid ; *n*, foramen for hyomandibular nerve ; *oa*, articular head for opercular ; *p*, palatine (dermal) ; *pg*, palatopterygoid cartilage ; *q*, quadrate ; *sy*, symplectic ; *uc*, upper segment of ceratohyal. (From Goodrich, *Vert. Craniata*, 1909.)

cartilage is generally ossified in the articular region; in some, such as *Amia*, several small bones occur, Figs. **430-1**, including an endochondral articular, 'coronoid', and 'angular' (van Wijhe,

654; Bridge, 429; Allis, 402), besides an anterior mento-mandibular (mento-Meckelian). Some of these persist in the higher forms; while

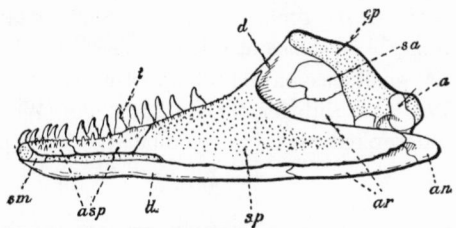

FIG. 431.

Inner view of the lower jaw of *Amia calva*, L. (After Allis.)    *a*, Articular; *an*, angular; *ar*, dermarticular (angular); *asp*, anterior coronoids; *cp*, coronoid cartilage; *d*, dentary; *sa*, supra-angular; *sm*, mento-Meckelian; *sp*, coronoid or prearticular with minute teeth; *t*, marginal tooth. (From Goodrich, *Vert. Craniata*, 1909.)

in *Saurichthys* the whole cartilage is replaced by a single bone (Stensiö, 134).

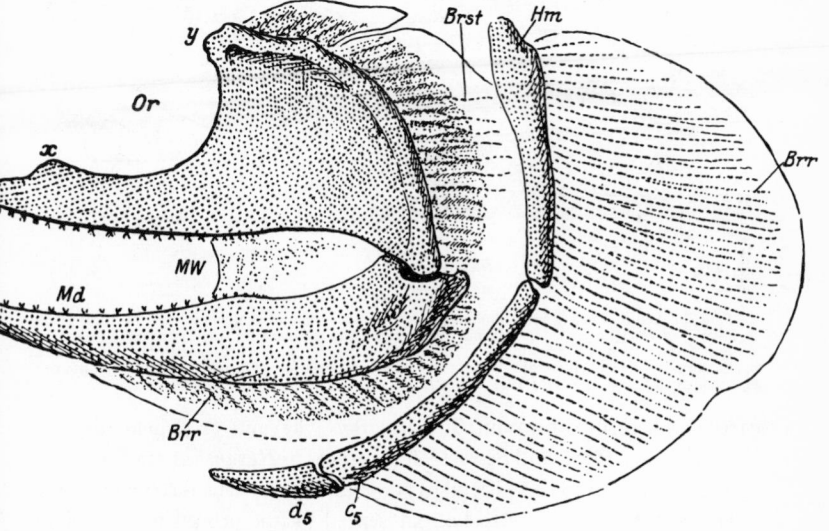

FIG. 432.

*Pleuracanthus sessilis*, L. Permian, Germany (from O. Jaekel, *Morph. Jahrb.*, 1925).   *x*, *y*, Anterior and posterior articulation of palatoquadrate with chondrocranium; *Brr*, branchial rays; *Brst*, outer dermal rays?; *c₅*, ceratohyal; *d₈*, hypohyal; *Hm*, hyomandibula; *Md*, mandibular cartilage; *MW*, skin at corner of mouth; *Or*, orbit.

Comparing the mandibular arch with the branchial in fishes it is clear that the mandibular cartilage somewhat resembles the ceratobranchial, and the palatoquadrate the epibranchial. Opinions differ as to their exact

homology. Whether they deserve the names epimandibular and cerato-
mandibular respectively is doubtful. There is no definite evidence from
ontogeny or palaeontology that the mandibular arch was ever formed of
the same elements as the branchial arches. Some evidence, however,
has been found of the existence of vestigial pharyngo-, hypo-, and basi-
mandibulars. A small median ventral cartilage has been described in
*Chlamydoselachus* (K. Fürbringer, **681**), in *Laemargus* (White, **702**), and in
Teleosts, and interpreted as a basimandibular. Small paired anterior

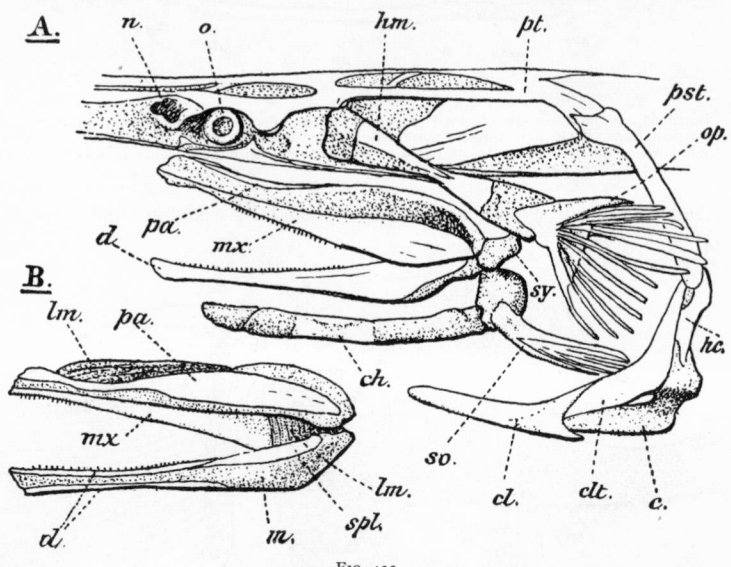

FIG. 433.

*Polyodon folium*, Lac. (After Traquair.)  A, Left-side view of skull, jaws, and pectoral girdle ;
B, inner view of right jaws.  *c*, Coracoid ; *ch*, ceratohyal ; *cl*, clavicle ; *clt*, cleithrum ; *d*, dentary ;
*hc*, postclavicle ; *hm*, hyomandibular ; *lm*, levator muscle ; *m*, Meckel's cartilage ; *mx*, maxilla ;
*n*, olfactory capsule ; *o*, optic capsule ; *op*, opercular ; *pa*, palatine ; *pst*, post-temporal ; *pt*, pterotic ;
*so*, subopercular ; *spl*, splenial ; *sy*, symplectic.  (From Goodrich, *Vert. Craniata*, 1909.)

cartilages described by White in *Laemargus* (**702**) and by Gegenbaur (**166**),
K. Fürbringer (**681**), and Sewertzoff (**594, 701**) in *Hexanchus* are considered
by the last author to be vestigial hypomandibulars. The pharyngo-mandibular Sewertzoff believes to be represented by the orbital process of the
palatoquadrate in most Selachians, and by a small dorsal cartilage discovered in the 'ethmoid ligament' of *Scaphirhynchus* by Ivanzoff (1887)
and of *Laemargus* by Sewertzoff and Disler (**594**). These homologies
cannot, however, be taken as well established.[1]

[1] Allis (**670**) sees the pharyngo-mandibular and pharyngo-hyal in the
trabecular and polar cartilages ; but there are serious objections to this view,
since these latter cartilages appear to belong to the axial skeleton (p. 238).

The same question arises with regard to the homology of some of the elements composing the hyoid arch. In Pisces in general there are two main paired elements : the dorsal hyomandibula and the more ventral ceratohyal, which seem to correspond to the epibranchial and cerato-branchial respectively. A ventral median copula or basihyal is usually well developed (p. 397) ; but is apparently fused with the first basi-branchial in Acipenseroidei, Polypterini, Amioidei, and *Lepidosteus*. Separate hypohyals are not usually found in Elasmobranchs ; though Braus has described them in an embryo *Heptanchus* (**673**), and Sewertzoff has found vestiges in the adult (**701**). Well-developed hypohyals have been

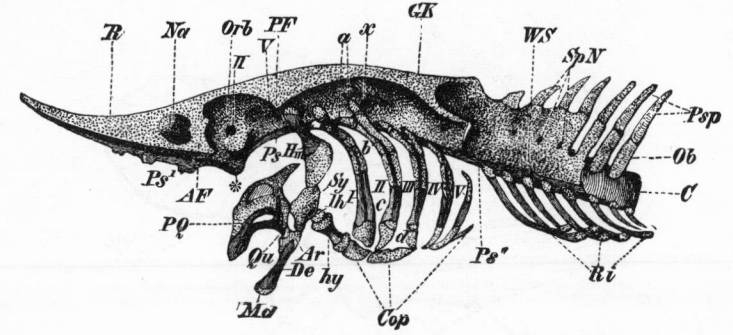

FIG. 434.

Cranial skeleton of sturgeon (*Acipenser*) after removal of exoskeletal parts. *Ar*, Articular ; *C*, notochord; *Cop*, copulae; *De*, dentary; *GK*, auditory capsule; *Hm*, hyomandibular; *hy*, hyoid; *I* to *V*, first to fifth branchial arches, with double pharyngobranchial (*a*), epibranchial (*b*), cerato-branchial (*c*), and hypobranchial (*d*); *Ih*, interhyal; *II*, optic foramen; *Md*, mandible; *Na*, nasal cavity; *Ob*, neural arches; *Orb*, orbit; *PF*, *AF*, postorbital and antorbital processes; *PQ*, palato-quadrate; *Ps*, *Ps'*, *Ps''*, parasphenoid; *Psp*, supraneural spines; *Qu*, quadrate; *R*, rostrum; *Ri*, ribs; *SpN*, apertures for spinal nerves; *Sy*, symplectic; *WS*, vertebral column; *x*, vagus foramen; *, ridge on basis cranii. (From Wiedersheim, *Comp. Anatomy*.)

found in Pleuracanthini and Acanthodii (Jaekel, **690**), Fig. 432, and are constantly present in Teleostomes living and extinct, and in Dipnoi, Fig. 436.

In the Holostei the ceratohyal has separate upper and lower ossifica-tions ; the more ventral is the main bone, and the smaller more dorsal has often been called the 'epihyal'. This name it certainly does not deserve, since it clearly forms part of the original cartilaginous ceratohyal. A rudiment of the dorsal bone has been found in Palaeoniscids (Stensiö, **218**). All the Actinopterygii have, between the hyomandibular and ceratohyal elements, a small separate segment, the stylohyal or interhyal (its presence in Palaeoniscoidei is doubtful). It has sometimes been compared to the epibranchial, but probably is a new formation. The large hyomandibular cartilage of the Holostei ossifies in two pieces—a hyomandibular bone above articulating with the auditory capsule, and a symplectic below connected with the quadrate. It is probable that the small dorsal and large ventral ossifications of the hyomandibula in *Polypterus* do not correspond to the two in other forms, Fig. 435 ; but a symplectic has been described in some Palaeoniscids (Broom; Stensiö, **218**). This symplectic becomes an independent element in the Acipenseroidei, where it may be very large ; but is lost in a few Teleosts, such as the Siluridae and Anguilliformes.

Whether the hyomandibular cartilage of fishes represents the epihyal element only, as generally held, or includes a pharyngohyal as well, can hardly be determined on the evidence available.[1] A very small cartilage

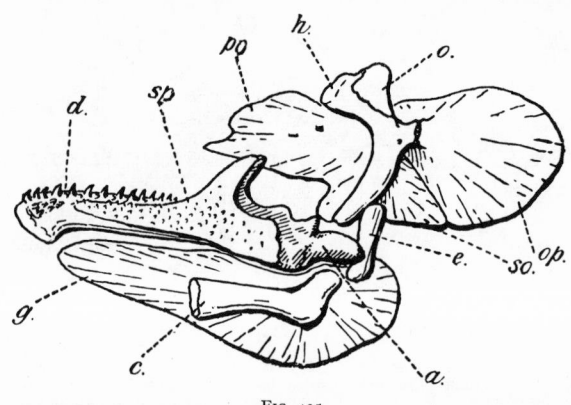

FIG. 435.

*Polypterus bichir*, Geoffr. Inner view of the lower jaw and hyoid arch. *a*, Articular ; *c*, ceratohyal ; *d*, dentary ; *e*, epihyal ; *g*, inferior gular ; *h*, hyomandibular ; *o*, small dermal ossicle ; *op*, opercular ; *po*, preopercular ; *so*, subopercular ; *sp*, coronoid or prearticular. (From Goodrich, *Vert. Craniata*, 1909.)

has been described as a vestigial pharyngohyal in *Stegostoma* by Luther (**695**), and a small pharyngohyal occurs in Holocephali (Dean, **17** ; Schauinsland, **583** ; Sewertzoff, **594, 701**), Figs. 428, 444.

We must now consider the important question of the connexion of the first two visceral arches with the chondrocranium. In all the Gnathostomes (except the Mammalia, Chapter VIII.) the lower jaw is articulated to the quadrate region of the upper jaw by means of the posterior articular end of the mandibular cartilage, ossified as the articular bone in Osteichthyes and Tetrapoda. This articulation persists in Mammals, but serves another function (Chapter VIII.). Now the mode of support

[1] The term hyomandibula has been applied to structures which are not strictly homologous : to the cartilaginous dorsal element in Selachians, to the dorsal bone in the originally continuous hyomandibular cartilage in Actinopterygii, and to that cartilage before ossification ; also to the separate dorsal cartilage (ossified in the adult) of Acipenser.

of this articulation and of the jaws, and the connexion of the first two
visceral arches with the skull, varies in different fishes (and to a less
extent in Tetrapods, p. 423).

When the palatoquadrate bar is complete it is connected in front to
the chondrocranium, by fusion as in Dipnoi (and Amphibia) or by movable
articulation as in Chondrichthyes and Teleostomes.  But this articulation

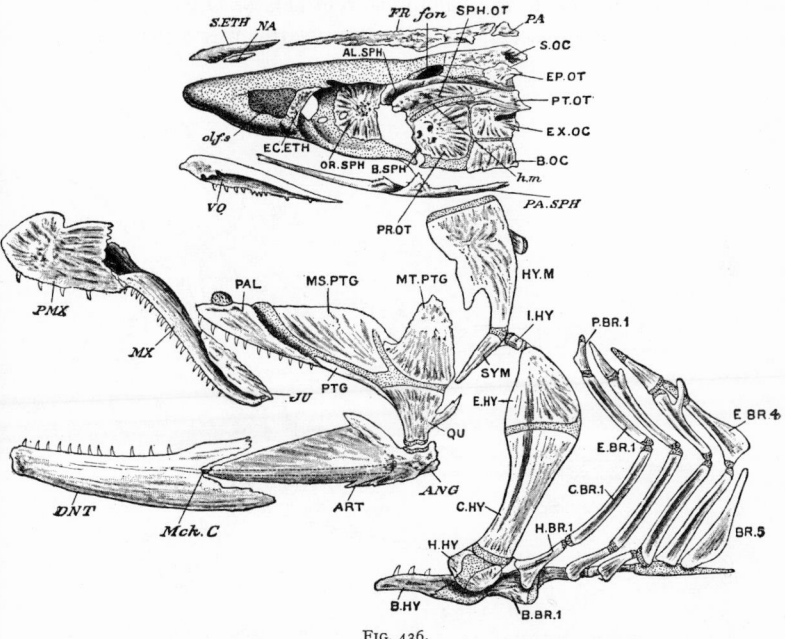

FIG. 436.

*Salmo fario.*  Disarticulated skull with many of the investing bones removed.  The cartilaginous
parts are dotted.  *fon,* Fontanelle ;  *h.m,* articular facet for hyomandibular ;  *Mck.C,* Meckel's cartilage ;
*olf.s,* hollow for olfactory sac.  Replacing bones : AL.SPH, pterosphenoid ; ART, articular ; B₄BR.1,
first basibranchial ; B.HY, basihyal ; B.OC, basioccipital ; BR.5, fifth branchial arch ; B.SPH, basisphenoid ; C.BR1. first ceratobranchial ; C.HY, ceratohyal ; EC.ETH, ecto-ethmoid ; E.BR.1, first
epibranchial ; E.HY, epihyal ; EP.OT, epiotic ; EX.OC, exoccipital ; H.BR.1, first hypobranchial ;
H.HY, hypohyal ; HY.M, hyomandibular ; I.HY, interhyal ; MS.PTG, mesopterygoid ; MT.PTG,
metapterygoid ; OR.SPH, orbitosphenoid ; PAL, palatine ; P.BR.1, first pharyngobranchial ; PTG,
pterygoid ; PT.OT, pterotic ; QU, quadrate ; S.OC, supraoccipital ; SPH.OT, sphenotic ; SYM,
symplectic.  Investing bones : ANG, angular ; DNT, dentary ; FR, frontal ; JU, jugal ; MX,
maxilla ; NA, nasal ; PA, palatine ; PA.SPH, parasphenoid ; PMX, premaxilla ; VO, vomer.  (From
Parker and Haswell, *Zoology*.)

is not necessarily the same in all fish.  In the apparently more primitive
Selachians the palatoquadrate acquires a well-marked articular process
(orbital or ethmo-palatine process) which articulates with the trabecular
basal part of the skull (palatobasal articulation (?), see p. 411), either far
back in the postorbital region as in *Scymnus,* or about the middle of the
orbit as in *Squalus* and *Notidonus,* or far forwards near the antorbital region
as in *Mustelus* or *Heterodontus* (Gegenbaur, 166), Figs. 424, 439, 440.

In these the process usually fits in a well-marked groove; but in others, such as *Scyllium*, the process is reduced and only loosely attached by the 'ethmo-palatine' ligament. In Rajidae there is no longer any definite articulation. It is characteristic of the Selachians that the bars are prolonged beyond the articulation as pre-palatine processes which, as already mentioned, meet in front.[1]

On the other hand, the palatoquadrate bars of other Gnathostomes do not typically so meet, but their anterior extremities articulate or fuse

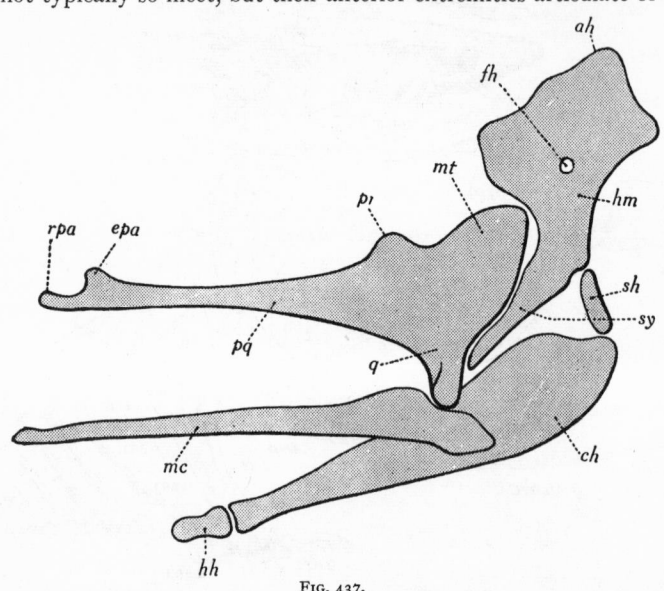

FIG. 437.

*Salmo fario*, late embryo. Left-side view of paired cartilages of first two visceral arches. *ah*, Articular head; *ch*, ceratohyal; *epa*, ethmo-palatine articular process; *fh*, foramen for hyomandibular nerve; *hh*, hypohyal; *hm*, hyomandibular; *mc*, mandibular; *mt*, metapterygoid region; *pq*, palatoquadrate; *pr*, vestigial basal process; *q*, quadrate region; *rpa*, rostropalatine articular process; *sh*, stylohyal; *sy*, symplectic region.

with the lateral region of the antorbital processes. Here in Teleostomes an articular surface is formed, simple primitively, but tending in many Teleostei to become subdivided into an anterior pre-palatine process meeting the pre-ethmoid cornu, and a posterior postpalatine process meeting the parethmoid cornu of this ethmoid region, Fig. 437. In some of the most specialised Teleostei, such as the Gasterosteiformes and Plectognathi, the posterior articulation disappears (Swinnerton, 389).

[1] If the orbital process represents, as seems probable, the basal process of other forms, then this anterior prolongation may be compared to the palatine region of the palatoquadrate of Teleostomes and Tetrapods. In Chlamydoselache it lies below and is connected with the nasal capsule (Sewertzoff, 701).

Before discussing the homology of these anterior connexions the posterior connexions of the palatoquadrate bar must be described. In Pisces the quadrate region may be directly articulated to or fused with the base and auditory region of the skull, or it may be supported away from the skull by the hyomandibula, or again it may be connected with the auditory capsule both by a dorsal articulation and by the hyomandibula. Huxley (535), who distinguished these three types of jaw suspension, named them autostylic, hyostylic, and amphistylic respectively. While the amphistylic type occurs only among the more primitive Chondrichthyes (Notidani and early Heterodonti among Selachii, Pleura-

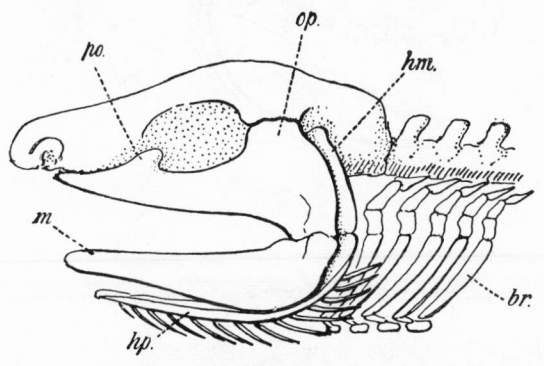

FIG. 438.

Diagram of the skull and visceral arches of an Acanthodian. *br*, Fifth branchial arch ; *hm*, hyomandibula ; *hp*, calcified plate bearing similar branchial rays (?) ; *m*, Meckel's cartilage ; *op*, otic process of the palatoquadrate ; *po*, ethmoid process. (From Goodrich, *Vert. Craniata*, 1909.)

canthodii, Acanthodii, Cladoselachii, Figs. 438-9), the hyostylic type is found in the majority of Selachii and in all Teleostomi, though not necessarily strictly homologous in these two groups.[1] Among Pisces, the true autostylic type occurs only in the Dipnoi, Figs. 441-2, and possibly in Holocephali, Fig. 444 ; but it is the type on which are built all the Tetrapoda, although it becomes much altered in the Amniota.

It should be noted that in the autostylic type the hyomandibula becomes much reduced, takes no share in the support of the jaws, and may even disappear altogether (*Protopterus, Lepidosiren*). In the hyostylic type, on the contrary, it becomes large and important, forms the chief support, and may give rise to the symplectic. The amphistylic

[1] In Gnathostomes generally the first or spiracular gill slit is early reduced from below upwards, and either closes altogether or remains only as a small dorsal spiracle (Chapter IX.): this enables the lower end of the hyomandibula to become strongly bound by ligaments to the quadrate region of the mandibular arch below the slit.

is, perhaps, the least specialised of the three types, and here the hyo-mandibular is only moderately developed.

Fully to appreciate the importance of Huxley's three types we must first of all study the autostylic more closely. In this type of suspension

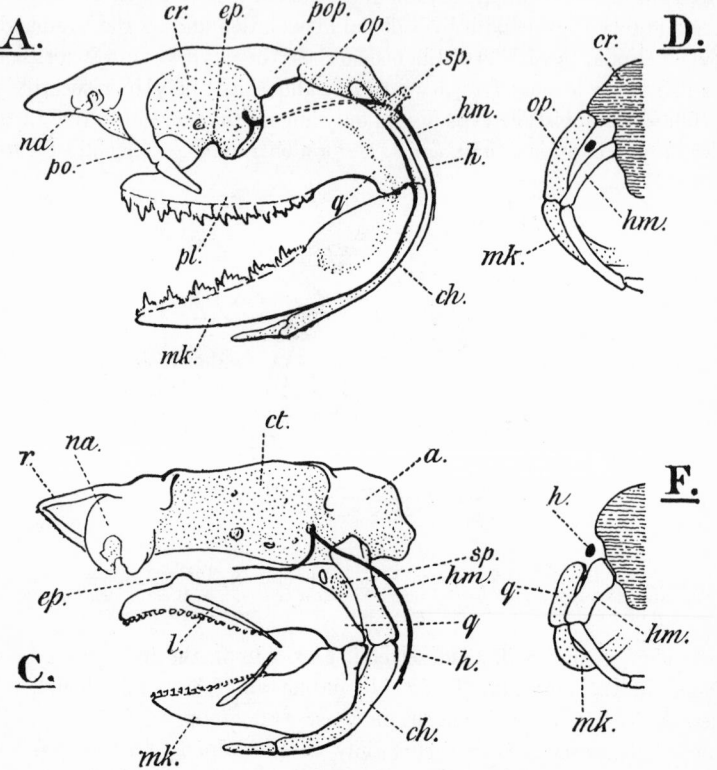

FIG. 439.

Diagrams of: A and D, an amphistylic skull (*Heptanchus*), and C and F, a hyostylic skull (*Scyllium*). A and C, left-side views; D and F, from behind (the mandibular arch being dotted, and the cranium shaded). *ch*, Ceratohyal; *cr*, cranium; *ep*, ethmoid process; *h*, hyomandibular branch of facial nerve; *hm*, hyomandibula; *l*, labial; *mk*, Meckel's cartilage; *na*, nasal capsule; *op*, otic process; *pl*, palatoquadrate cartilage; *po*, preorbital process; *pop*, postorbital process; *q*, quadrate region; *r*, rostral process; *sp*, spiracle. (From Goodrich, *Vert. Craniata*, 1909.)

the palatoquadrate bar is primitively connected with the chondro-cranium at three points (more clearly seen in the Amphibia than in the Dipnoi, Figs. 441-2, 449): by its anterior palatine process to the ant-orbital (parethmoid) process of the ethmoid region; by the basal process (or pedicle of Huxley and Parker) of its middle pterygoid part to the trabecula; and by a dorsal otic process of the posterior or quadrate part

to the auditory capsule or its postorbital process.[1]  A fourth possible connexion is through the processus ascendens of the palatoquadrate, which
is dealt with later (pp. 413, 428).  These three attachments are present
in Dipnoi and Amphibia, where the palatine process usually fuses with
the antorbital, the otic process with the auditory capsule, and the basal
process with the trabecula (in Dipnoi and Urodela, but not in Anura or

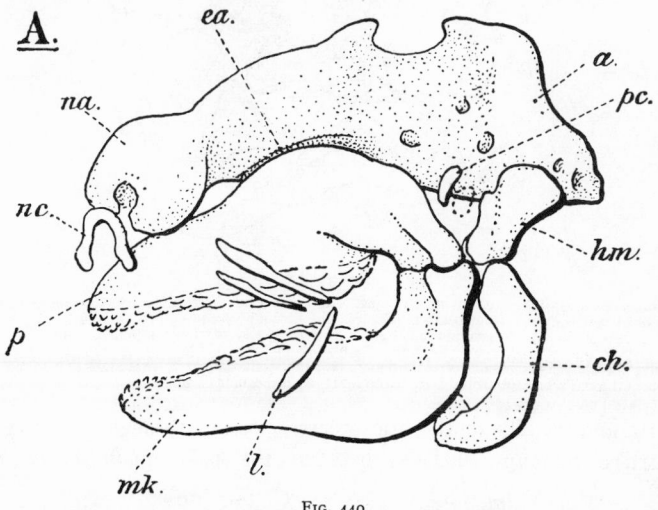

FIG. 440.

Skull, jaws, and hyoid arch of *Heterodontus* (*Cestracion*) *Philippi*, Lac. (after Parker, modified).
*a*, Auditory capsule; *ch*, ceratohyal; *ea*, ethmoid articulation; *hm*, hyomandibula; *l*, labial;
*mk*, Meckel's cartilage; *na*, nasal capsule; *nc*, nasal cartilage; *p*, palatoquadrate; *pc*, prespiracular.  A dotted ring indicates the spiracle. (From Goodrich, *Vert. Craniata*, 1909.)

Apoda).  In the Amniota and also in many Urodela the palatine process
(pterygoid process of many authors) is little developed and fails to
reach the ethmoid region (p. 425).  From the trabecula[2] there grows
out a basitrabecular process (basipterygoid process of many authors) to
meet the basal process; it is little developed in modern Dipnoi and
Amphibia, but usually prominent in Reptilia, Aves, and Mammalia
(p. 270).

The fundamental relations of these connexions to the blood-vessels
and nerves are as follows (Figs. 449, 495, 493): The palatine branch of

[1] The articulation of the otic process appears to shift along the crista
parotica or lateral edge of the capsule.  In Selachii it meets it anteriorly
at the postorbital process, and in Reptilia posteriorly where the crista forms
a paroccipital process.

[2] This basitrabecular process seems to grow out of that region of the
trabecula which is developed from the polar cartilage, p. 237.

the facial nerve passes down posteriorly to the basitrabecular and basal processes, then forwards below them. The jugular vein or vena capitis lateralis (p. 532) runs back dorsally to the basitrabecular and basal pro-

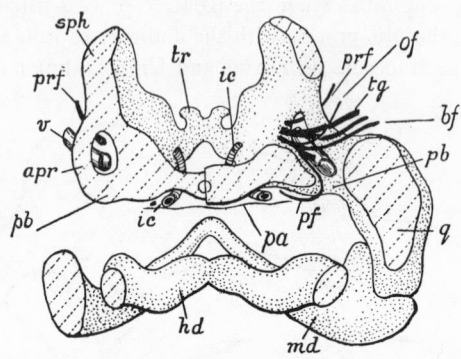

FIG. 441.

*Ceratodus forsteri*, embryo about 13 mm. long. Reconstruction from transverse sections of anterior part of head skeleton, seen from behind. On left, cut through ascending process and basal process; on right, cut farther back through quadrate. Nerves black, cartilage stippled. *apr*, Processus ascendens; *bf*, buccal; *hd*, hyoid; *ic*, internal carotid; *md*, mandibular; *of*, ophthalmic; *pa*, parasphenoid; *pb*, processus basalis of palatoquadrate; *pf*, palatine; *prf*, profundus; *q*, quadrate; *sph*, sphenethmoid region of orbital; *tg*, trigeminal; *tr*, trabecular cornu.

cesses and ventrally to the otic process, passing through the **cranio-quadrate passage** enclosed between the palatoquadrate, its two

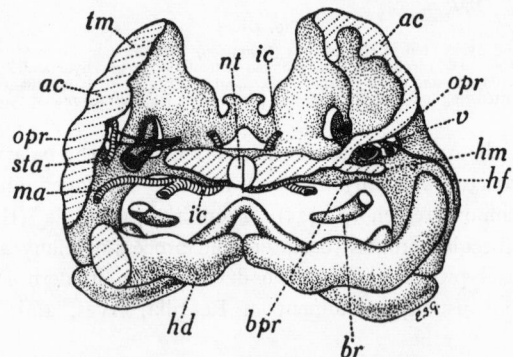

FIG. 442.

*Ceratodus forsteri*, same as in Fig. 441. On left, cut through otic process; on right, through auditory capsule. *ac*, Auditory capsule; *bpr*, basal process; *br*, branchial arch; *hf*, hyoid branch of facial; *hm*, remains of hyomandibula; *ma*, mandibular artery; *nt*, notochord; *opr*, otic process of palatoquadrate fused to capsule; *sta*, orbital or stapedial artery; *tm*, commissura orbito-parietalis; *v*, vena capitis lateralis passing through cranio-quadrate passage with artery and nerve.

processes, and the chondrocranium. The vein is accompanied by the hyomandibular branch of the facial nerve, which passes over the spiracular slit to the hyoid arch. The internal carotid passes morphologically dorsally to the spiracular slit, ventrally to the hyomandibular attachment, but gives off an orbital artery (external carotid of many authors) which runs forwards to the orbit through the cranio-quadrate passage, Figs. 241-2.

Yet another important process is present in Dipnoi and Tetrapoda. It is the processus ascendens typically developed from the pterygoid region of the palatoquadrate bar, near the origin of the basal process, as a dorsal cartilage passing vertically upwards between the profundus nerve and the maxillary branch of the trigeminal, and laterally to the vena

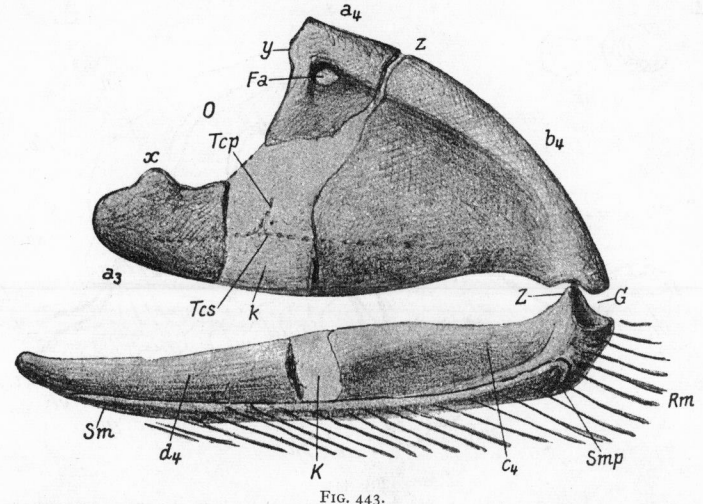

FIG. 443.

*Acanthodes bronni*, L. Permian, Germany. Outer view of left mandibular arch (from O. Jaekel, *Morph. Jahrb.*, 1925). *x, y*, Anterior and posterior articulation of palatoquadrate with chondro-cranium ; *z*, fracture ? ; $a_3$, $a_4$, $b_4$, calcifications in palatoquadrate, and $c_4$, $d_4$, in mandibular cartil-age ; *k* ; *G*, articulation ; *O*, position of orbit ; *Rm*, rays ; *Smp*, submandibular bony plate ; *Tcp, Tcs*, scales of supra- and infra-orbital lateral lines.

capitis lateralis, Figs. 449, 495. Its upper end fuses with the orbital wall of the cranium in Dipnoi, Fig. 441 (Greil, **525**). It is found neither in Chondrichthyes nor in modern Teleostomi except possibly as a vestige. Whether it occurred in early primitive Teleostomes is not yet certain, but Watson describes traces of it in an Osteolepid (**644**). In Dipnoi and Tetrapods the ascending process forms the outer wall of the cavum epitericum which is described above (p. 267).

Comparing now the amphistylic with the autostylic type, it may safely be concluded that the dorsal process of the palatoquadrate in Notidani represents the otic process, since it bears the same relation to the nerves and blood-vessels, Figs. 438-9. But it is by no means so easy to determine the homology of the anterior 'orbito-palatine' (ethmo-palatine) connexion of the Selachian. Is it formed by the basal process which has moved forwards, or by an originally anterior palatine process which has moved backwards along the base of the skull ?[1] Huxley held the former view, which on the whole seems the more probable ;[2] yet, the anterior articulation of the palatoquadrate seems to have been very far forward in such early forms as Acanthodii and Pleuracanthini (judging from the reconstructions of Jaekel, 186), if it is really the palatobasal and not an ethmoid connexion. The fact that it articulates really with the

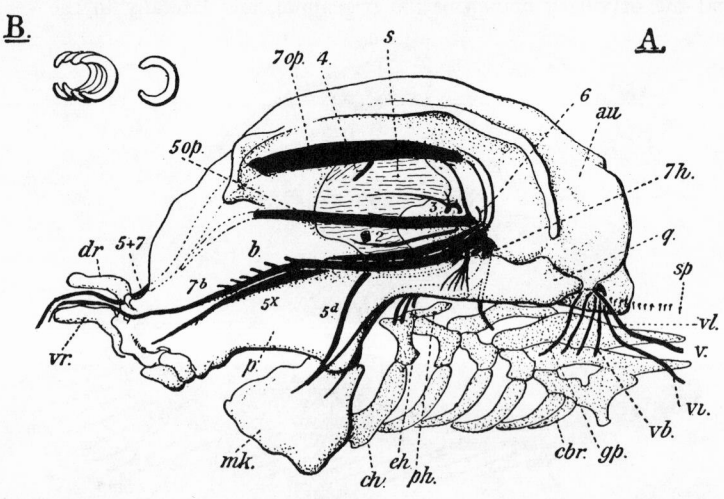

FIG. 444.

*Callorhynchus antarcticus*, Lac. A, Skeleton and nerves of the head of a young specimen (after Schauinsland's figures). *au*, Auditory capsule ; *b*, region of fusion of palatoquadrate with nasal capsule ; *cbr*, 5th ceratobranchial ; *ch*, ceratohyal ; *dr*, dorsal median rostral cartilage ; *eh*, epihyal ; *gp*, glossopharyngeal nerve ; *mk*, Meckel's cartilage ; *p*, palatoquadrate region ; *ph*, pharyngohyal ; *q*, quadrate region (otic process ?) ; *s*, interorbital septum ; *sp*, spinal nerve-roots ; *vb*, *vi*, *vl*, branchial, intestinal, and lateral-line branches of vagus nerve ; *vr*, ventral paired rostral cartilage ; 2, optic, 3, oculomotor, 4, pathetic, 5, trigeminal, 6, abducent, and 7, facial nerves. B, Calcified skeletal supports of the lateral line. (From Goodrich, *Vert. Craniata*, 1909.)

basal or trabecular and not antorbital region of the skull is strong evidence that it is a true basal process. Further study of the fossils may enable this point to be decided.

That the hyostylic type of the Selachian is derived from the amphistylic by the loss of the otic process, and accompanying shortening and strengthening of the hyomandibula, now the chief support of the jaws,

[1] Since both the palatine and the orbital processes would occupy the same position as the basal process with regard to the internal jugular vein and palatine nerve if brought sufficiently far back, these relations do not help us to decide on their homology.

[2] Allis (667, 412) believes the basal process to be represented in Selachians by a medial ridge on the hinder region of the palatoquadrate.

it is easy to suppose,[1] Figs. 439, 440. While early Heterodonti have
an otic articulation (Woodward, 703), the modern genus has lost it;
similarly the articulation is lost and the otic process much reduced in
*Chlamydoselachus* among Notidani.

A very specialised type of jaw suspension occurs in the Holocephali
(Huxley). The whole structure has been profoundly modified in connexion with the development of permanent grinding tooth plates adapted
for hard food, Figs. 428, 444. The jaws are shortened and strengthened;
the rami of the lower jaws are fused in front, while the palatoquadrate is
fused to the ethmoid and orbital region of the skull in front and to the
auditory capsule behind (Dean, 17; Schauinsland, 583). The cranio-

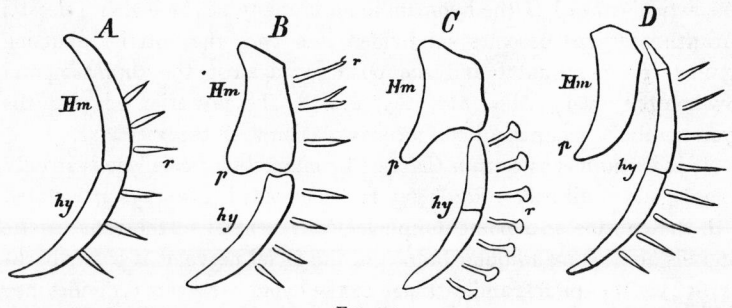

FIG. 445.

Diagram showing modification of hyoid arch in Selachians according to theory of Gegenbaur.
(After C. Gegenbaur, from A. Sedgwick, *Zoology*, 1905.) A, Notidanus; B, pentanchal Selachian;
C, Torpedo; D, Raja. *Hm*, Hyomandibula; *hy*, hyoideum or ceratohyal; *r*, branchial rays.

quadrate passage is almost obliterated. Since the hyoid arch remains
free and takes no share in the suspension of the jaws, the result is a type
of autostylism, which, however, has probably been developed independently of that found in Dipnoi and Tetrapods, and has been called
' holostylic ' by Gregory (688).

A further important question arises as to which represents the original
attachment of the mandibular arch to the chondrocranium—the
otic or the basal process. Gegenbaur (1872) argued that the connexion of
the otic process to the postorbital process was primitive and that the palato-

---

[1] In Rajidae the hyoid arch appears much modified, and, while the
hyomandibula reaches down as usual to the jaw articulation, a rod at the
dorsal end of the ceratohyal passes up behind to the skull. Gegenbaur
believed this rod to have been extended from the ceratohyal which had
become disconnected from the hyomandibula (see Fig. 445); others that it
represents an additional post-hyomandibular arch (see footnote, p. 440). But
Krivetski has recently given good evidence that, while the larger anterior
supporting cartilage is the true hyomandibula, the posterior rod is derived
from the fused bases of branchial rays (694); a conclusion supported by
embryology (de Beer, 324).

quadrate secondarily developed a palatine region and orbital process. But Huxley's view (1876) is now generally accepted (Sewertzoff, 384 ; Luther, 695 ; Gaupp, 343 ; and others) that the articulation of the orbital process with the trabecular region of the basis cranii represents in Selachians the original point of attachment. The Selachian hyomandibula is attached at a corresponding level, morphologically dorsal to the aorta and ventral to the jugular vein and exits of the nerves.

The hyomandibula of Teleostomes articulates dorsally with the lateral surface of the auditory capsule, the broad facet for its reception being usually shared by the postfrontal (sphenotic) and supratemporal (pterotic). In *Polypterus* it is formed by the opisthotic and supratemporal. The articular head of the hyomandibula in many of the higher Teleostei (Acanthopterygii) becomes subdivided into two, the anterior abutting against the postfrontal and the posterior against the supratemporal (Swinnerton, 389 ; Allis, 667, 669, 671). The posterior edge of the hyomandibula acquires a knob for articulation with the opercular.

It is by no means certain that the hyomandibular cartilage is strictly homologous in all fishes, Fig. 446. In Selachians it is always articulated with the capsule at a point morphologically ventral to the vena capitis lateralis and hyomandibular branch of the facial nerve as it passes backwards over the spiracle and cartilage to the hyoid bar where it divides into mandibular and hyoid branches. On the contrary, in all Teleostomes the hyomandibular cartilage is articulated at a point morphologically dorsal to the vena capitis lateralis or its derivatives, and the hyomandibular nerve to reach the bar passes medially and ventrally to the cartilage and then outwardly behind it, or through it as in the Holostei (Allis, 667, 669).[1] It is clear that an important difference exists in the relations of these structures, and various theories have been set forth to explain it (Schmalhausen, 699, 700 ; de Beer, 421; Edgeworth, 678-9 ; Allis, 671). Either the hyomandibula is not strictly homologous in the two cases, or there has been some radical shifting of the parts concerned.

A further difficulty is presented by *Polypterus*, in which alone the hyomandibular nerve divides near its exit so that the mandibular branch

---

[1] In some Teleosts, such as the Siluroids (Pollard, 697 ; Kindred, 537-8), the hyomandibular cartilage at an early stage is continuous with the quadrate. Pollard concluded that the Teleostean hyomandibula corresponds to the Selachian otic process, and the Selachian hyomandibula to the Teleostean stylohyal. This conclusion is not consistent with the morphological position of these elements described above ; that the temporary connexion of hyomandibula and palatoquadrate is secondary is shown by the structure of the more primitive Teleosts and lower Teleostomes (Norman, 551 ; Berrill, 672).

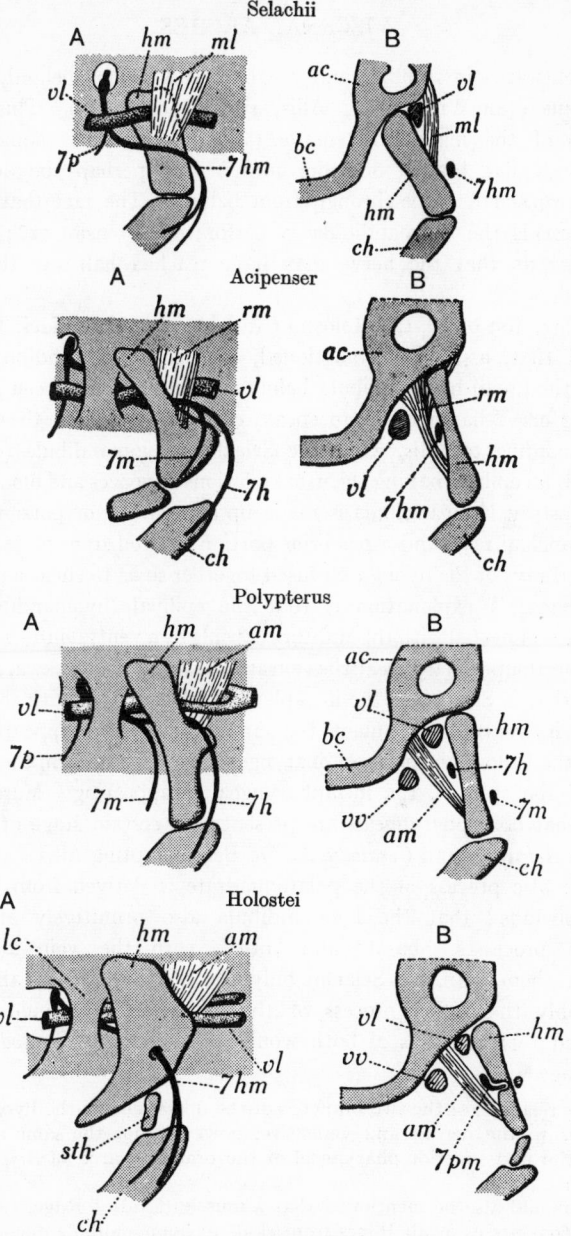

FIG. 446.

Diagrams illustrating relation of *hyomandibula* to skull, nerves, veins, and muscle in *Pisces*.
A, Left-side view ; B, transverse section. *ac*, Cut surface of auditory capsule, and *bc*, of basis cranii ;
*am*, m. adductor hyomandibulae ; *ch*, ceratohyal ; *hm*, hyomandibular cartilage ; *ml*, m. levator
hyomandibulae ; *rm*, m. retractor hyomandibulae ; *sth*, stylohyal ; *vl*, vena capitis lateralis, and
*vv*, its medio-ventral branch ; *7h*, hyoid, *7hm*, hyomandibular, *7m*, mandibular, *7p*, palatine
branches of facial nerve ; *7pm*, hyomandibular nerve piercing cartilage. *am*, *ml*, and *rm* appear to
be, at all events, partially homologous muscles.

passes outwards in front of, and the hyoidean branch behind, the hyo-mandibula (van Wijhe, 654 ; Allis, 410 ; Budgett, 10). This unusual position of the mandibular nerve (if it is the strict homologue of the mandibular branch of other forms) may perhaps be due to its having worked its way through from behind. The fact that in some Palaeoniscids the hyomandibula is perforated (Stensiö, 218 ; Watson, 646) suggests that the nerve may have reached half-way through in these fish.

Taking, first of all, the Holostei (Amioidei, Lepidosteoidei, Teleostei), we find that, as already mentioned, the main hyomandibular nerve pierces the broad hyomandibula before dividing. It has been suggested that the nerve has here, so to speak, eaten its way into the cartilage. But, according to Allis, while the Selachian hyomandibula (except in skates) is an epihyal having the usual relations to nerves and blood-vessels, the Holostean hyomandibula is made up of an anterior portion derived from branchial rays, and a posterior portion derived from more posterior branchial rays of the hyoid arch fused together so as to enclose the nerve. Schmalhausen's explanation is that the epihyal (hyomandibula) was originally connected with the auditory capsule by a ventral infrapharyngeal and a dorsal suprapharyngeal, the vein and nerve passing backward between them ; that in Selachians the infrapharyngeal has fused with the epihyal forming its ventral attachment, the suprapharyngeal disappearing ; and that in the Holostean the suprapharyngeal has fused to form the articular head of the epihyal, the infrapharyngeal disappearing. Moreover, he claims that both pharyngeals are present at a certain stage of development in *Acipenser* and *Ceratodus*.[1] De Beer, adopting Allis's suggestion that the otic process of the palatoquadrate is derived from branchial rays, concluded that the hyomandibula also primitively articulated by two processes, ' basal ' and ' otic ', with the vein and nerve between them. In the Selachii only the ' basal ' and in the Teleostomi only the ' otic ' process of the hyomandibula would then be preserved ; while traces of both would be present in *Ceratodus* at an early stage.[2]

[1] The relations of the two branches of the dorsal end of the hyoid arch in *Ceratodus* to the nerves and veins are, however, not the same as that of the inferior and superior pharyngeal of the branchial arch of *Acipenser* (see Fig. 447).

[2] It should also be mentioned that a muscle ($C_2$hd of Ruge, 1897 ; Allis, Luther, 695) passes in all Pisces from skull to hyomandibula dorsally to the vena cap. lateralis and ventrally to the hyomandibular branch of the facial. In Selachians it lies on the outer dorso-lateral face of the hyomandibula, while in all Teleostomes it is inserted more or less on its inner or ventro-median surface, Fig. 446.

Edgeworth, who has shown that the hyomandibula of Teleostomes is in early stages a cartilaginous rod situated entirely in front of the hyomandibular nerve (except in *Polypterus*) and that later it may surround the nerve by backward growth, maintains that this hyomandibula is homologous throughout the fishes, but offers no explanation of the different relation the articulation bears to vein and nerve in Selachii and Teleostomi.

On the whole, for the usually accepted view that the hyomandibula is homologous in all these fishes, there is good evidence not only from

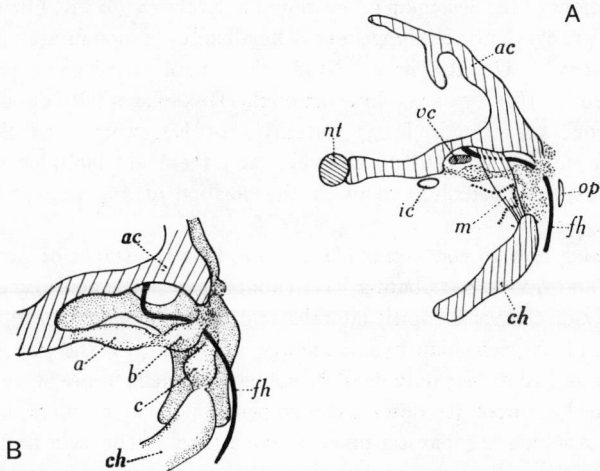

FIG. 447.

*Ceratodus Forsteri*, embryo 18·5 mm. long. A, Reconstructed thick transverse section seen from behind. *ch*, Ceratohyal; *fh*, hyomandibular branch of facial nerve; *m*, muscle; *op*, opercular. Spiracular pouch shown in dotted line at *m*. B, Diagrammatic reconstruction of cartilages *a*, *b*, *c*, derived from dorsal end of hyoid arch (cp. Fig. 446).

embryology but also from palaeontology; for it appears to have been well developed in Crossopterygii (Osteolepidoti) (Traquair, **619**; Bryant, **465**; Watson, **644, 647**)[1] and early Chondrostei. That the articular head dorsal to vein and nerve in Teleostomes is an 'otic process' is doubtful; but it is not impossible that an articulation, originally ventral in Selachians, may have moved up to a new position by passing over the bridge forming the outer wall of the jugular canal (p. 376) into which the vein and nerve have sunk in Teleostomes (Stensiö, **218**).[2] Thus we could account for a

[1] The hyomandibula is perforated in Rhizodopsis (Watson and Day, **647**).

[2] The condition in *Polypterus* might perhaps be explained on the supposition that the mandibular nerve passed in front through the wall of the jugular canal before the migration of the hyomandibular.

change from a more primitive ventral articulation in the Selachian to the more specialised condition with dorsal articulation in the Teleostome, a change perhaps related to the reduction of the otic process of the quadrate region. The inclusion of the hyomandibular nerve might still be due either to backward growth of the hyomandibula, or to its fusion with branchial rays.

Nothing is yet known about the condition of the hyomandibula in early Dipnoi, in which it was probably small and unossified; but it appears to persist in *Ceratodus* partly as a small ventral cartilage having the relations of the Selachian hyomandibula (Krawetz, 362; K. Fürbringer, 682; Allis, 671; infrapharyngeal of Schmalhausen, otoquadrate of Edgeworth, 678). On the other hand, the small cartilage apparently described by Huxley as the hyomandibula (Huxley, 535; Ridewood, 698; Sewertzoff, 592; Goodrich, 35; interhyal of Edgeworth and Schmalhausen, 700) lies laterally to the vein, and there are lateral cartilages related to the operculum more in the position of an ' otic process ',[1] Figs. 315, 447.

Turning now to the Tetrapoda, we find that the stapes of Amphibia (Anura and Apoda, see Chapter VIII.) abuts against the auditory capsule ventrally to the vena capitis lateralis and hyomandibular nerve, in the position of the Selachian hyomandibula, Fig. 449. Further, in modern Reptilia and Aves, not only does the stapes (columella auris) lie ventrally to these, but often its outer extra-stapedial portion acquires a dorsal process reaching the parotic process above them. The vein and nerve then pass through a gap comparable to the cranio-quadrate passage. In Mammalia also the extra-stapedial region abuts against the crista parotica enclosing the vein and nerve in a similar passage (Goodrich, Schmalhausen). These facts support the view that the hyomandibula of fishes is represented by the columella or stapes, and perhaps also by that dorsal region of the hyoid arch, just mentioned, which becomes attached to the crista parotica or quadrate in Tetrapods (Chapter VIII.). If further

---

[1] Edgeworth (678-9) has shown that a strand of tissue extends at an early stage from the auditory capsule to the ceratohyal in a position resembling that of the Selachian hyomandibula. Later its proximal end is chondrified as the ' otoquadrate ', attached to the auditory capsule at its inner end and the otic process of the quadrate at its outer end. The middle part of the strand forms the 'interhyal' cartilage, while the outermost part of the strand forms the hyosuspensorial ligament binding the ceratohyal to the quadrate. It is possible that individuals vary, for in the specimen here figured, Fig. 447, there are three cartilages, and the middle piece has a dorsal connexion with the crista parotica behind the hyomandibular nerve.

research bears this out, it may yet be shown that a double connexion of the hyomandibular cartilage enclosing the nerve and vein is an ancient and primitive character.

That the palatobasal articulation with the trabecular region is a very primitive feature is shown not only by its occurrence in Dipnoi and Tetrapods, but also in many of the more primitive Teleostomes (p. 273). In these last, where the palatoquadrate becomes ossified, the articulation

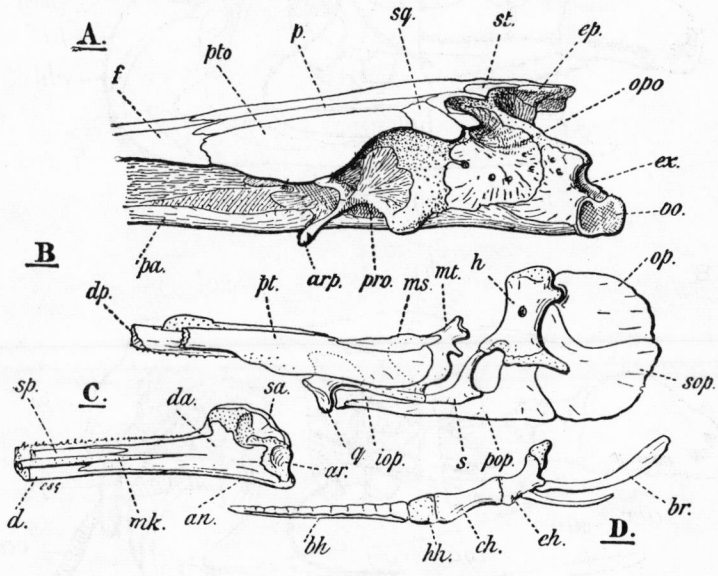

FIG. 448.

*Lepidosteus osseus*, L.  A, Oblique view of the skull from behind ; B, inner view of the right opercular bones and upper jaw broken short in front ; C, inner view of the hind end of the lower jaw ; D, lower portion of hyoid arch, belonging to B. *an*, Angular ; *ar*, articular ; *arp*, articular process for metapterygoid : *bh*, basihyal ; *bo*, basioccipital condyle ; *br*, branchiostegal ; *ch*, cerato-hyal ; *d*, dentary ; *da*, prearticular ; *dp*, palatine ; *eh*, epihyal ; *ep*, epiotic ; *ex*, lateral wing of basioccipital (fused neural arches) ; *f*, frontal ; *h*, hyomandibular ; *hh*, hypohyal ; *iop*, inter-opercular ; *mk*, Meckel's cartilage ; *ms*, endopterygoid ; *mt*, metapterygoid ; *op*, opercular ; *opo*, exoccipital (probably including opisthotic) ; *p*, parietal ; *pa*, parasphenoid ; *pop*, preopercular ; *pro*, pro-otic ; *pt*, ectopterygoid ; *pto*, postfrontal (supratemporal ?) ; *q*, quadrate ; *s*, symplectic ; *sa*, supra-angular ; *sop*, subopercular ; *sp*, splenial ? ; *sq*, tabular ? ; *st*, postparietal.  (From Goodrich, *Vert. Craniata*, 1909.)

occurs between the metapterygoid and the basitrabecular process of the basisphenoid (sometimes combined with the transverse basipterygoid process of the parasphenoid (p. 423)).  It is clearly developed in *Lepi-dosteus* (Parker, **2**), but lost in the other modern Holostei and also in modern Chondrostei, where it is represented by a ligament.  The basal process is probably represented by the ventral process of the metapterygoid in *Amia* and Teleostei (Swinnerton, **389** ; Allis, **402, 404**), often well developed and directed towards the basis cranii.[1]  That the more dorsal

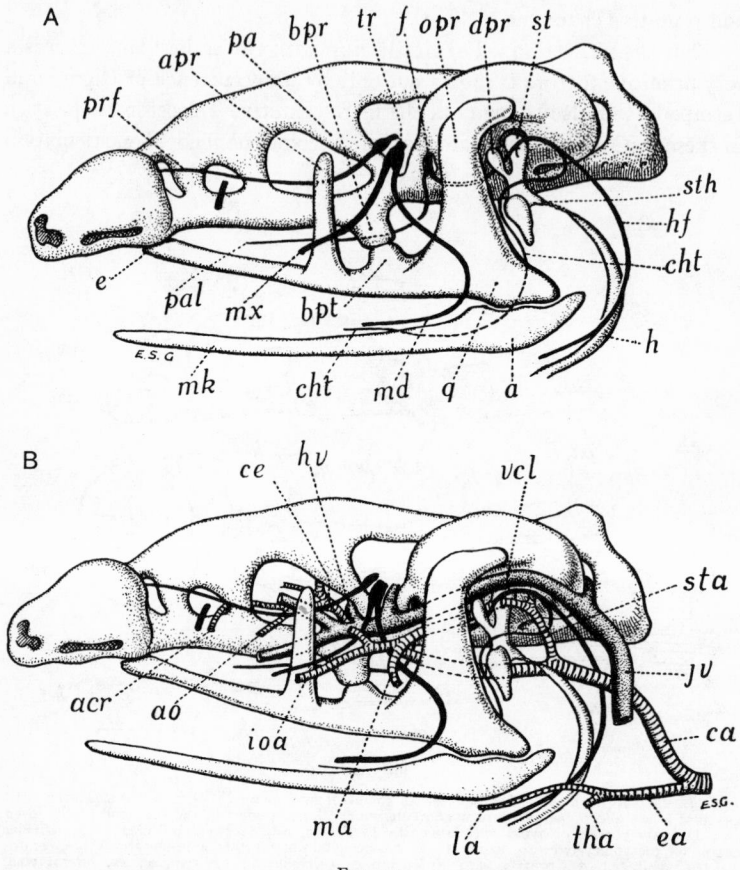

FIG. 449.

Chondrocranium, mandibular, and hyoid arches.  Diagram of primitive Tetrapod.  A, Cartilage and nerves ; B, with blood-vessels in addition.  Cartilage dotted, nerves black, arteries cross-lined, veins darkly shaded.  *a*, Articular region ; *acr*, ophthalmic ; *ao*, supraorbital ; *apr*, ascending process ; *bpr*, basitrabecular process ; *bpt*, basal process ; *ca*, internal carotid ; *ce*, cerebral ; *cht*, chorda tympani ; *dpr*, dorsal process ; *e*, ethmoid articulation of palatoquadrate with antorbital process ; *ea*, external carotid ; *f*, main branch of facial ; *h*, hyoid cornu ; *hf*, hyomandibular branch ; *hv*, hypophysial ; *ioa*, infraorbital ; *jv*, jugular ; *la*, lingual ; *ma*, mandibular ; *md*, mandibular branch ; *mk*, Meckel's cartilage ; *mx*, maxillary branch ; *opr*, otic process ; *pa*, pila antotica ; *pal*, palatine branch ; *prf*, profundus ; *q*, quadrate ; *st*, stapes (columella auris) ; *sta*, stapedial ; *sth*, stylohyal process ; *tha*, thyroid artery ; *tr*, trigeminal ; *vcl*, vena capitis lateralis.

process of the metapterygoid of Teleostomes ('metapterygoid process') represents the reduced otic process is not so well established.  Yet this

[1] The basitrabecular process is correspondingly reduced.  It forms the floor of the anterior opening of the myodome.

is probably the correct interpretation of its homology, since there is some evidence that it met the postorbital process in Palaeoniscids (Stensiö, 218), and the space included between the two processes of the metapterygoid (ventral basal and dorsal 'metapterygoid') bears the right relation to blood-vessels and nerves (Allis, 404, 678), and seems to represent the antero-ventral region of the cranio-quadrate passage, Fig. 436. If a functional otic connexion existed in primitive Teleostomes, as well as in primitive Chondrichthyes and Dipnoi, it must be a very ancient character derived from the common ancestor of all Gnathostomes.

But in later and more specialised Teleostomes the otic process is always reduced, and they evolve a special form of hyostyly (called methyostyly by Gregory, 688). It is typically developed in the Holostean series, in which the flattened hyomandibula and symplectic bones become firmly attached to the metapterygoid and quadrate, and together with the preoperculum and interoperculum form a rigid support for the jaws, Figs. 286, 303,

The hyostyly of the Chondrostei has evolved on rather different lines. For in them the hyomandibula is freer and retains a more cylindrical and elongated shape, Fig. 434. *Polypterus* resembles them in this, Fig. 435.

## THE PALATOQUADRATE IN TETRAPODA

**General Structure.**—Of great importance for the proper understanding of the morphology of the skull of Tetrapods is the history of the palatoquadrate and the dermal bones associated with it (see further: palate, p. 317). We have seen above (p. 410) that the Osteichthyes have probably been derived from early forms in which the palatoquadrate was connected at three points with the chondrocranium: (1) In front its palatine process articulated with the antorbital region; (2) behind and dorsally the otic process joined the auditory capsule above the cranio-quadrate passage; and (3) ventrally the basal process formed with the basitrabecular process a palatobasal or 'basipterygoid' articulation [1] below the cranioquadrate passage, Fig. 449. An additional connexion was probably formed with the side wall of the brain-case in

---

[1] The palatobasal articulation may be defined as that between the palatoquadrate and the trabecula. The term 'basipterygoid articulation', often applied to it, may be restricted to the later underlying and supporting connexion between the lateral wing of the parasphenoid and the pterygoid bone. The former original articulation is more or less superseded by the later one in some Tetrapoda.

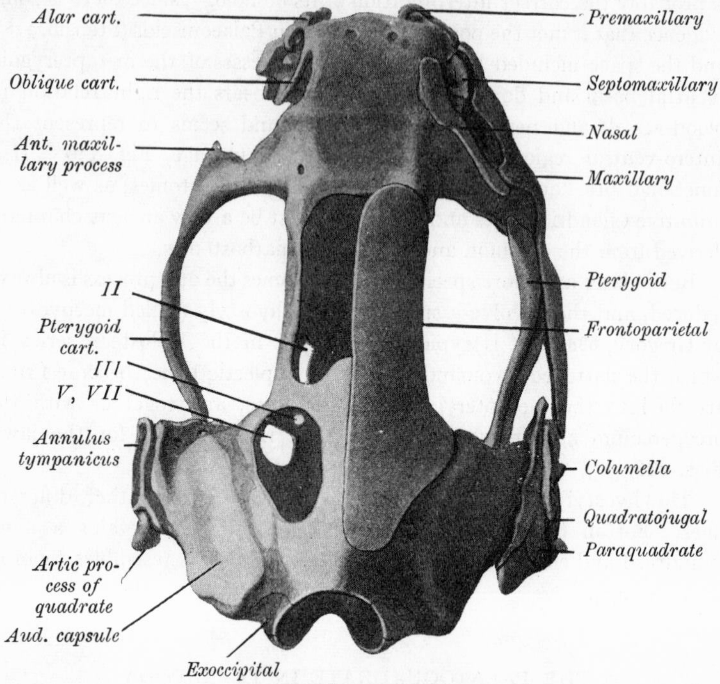

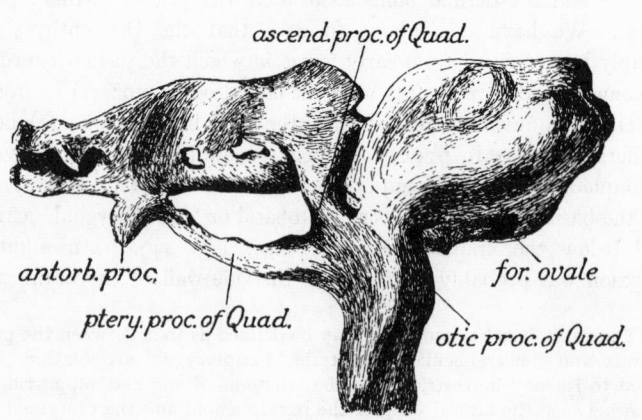

Alar cart. ——————————————— Premaxillary

Oblique cart. ——————————————— Septomaxillary

————— Nasal

Ant. maxil-
lary process ——————— Maxillary

II ——————— Pterygoid

Pterygoid
cart. ——————— Frontoparietal

III
V, VII ———

Annulus
tympanicus ———

————— Columella

————— Quadratojugal
————— Paraquadrate

Artic pro-
cess of
quadrate
Aud. capsule

Exoccipital

FIG. 450.

Skull of a young *Rana temporaria*, 2 cm. in length, just after metamorphosis, from the dorsal side. The investing bones are removed on the left side (× abt. 11).   (After Gaupp, from a model by Fr. Ziegler.)   Investing bones, *yellow*.   (From Wiedersheim, *Comp. Anatomy*.)

ascend. proc. of Quad.

antorb. proc.                                    for. ovale

ptery. proc. of Quad.                    otic proc. of Quad.

FIG. 451.

Left-side view of model of skull of *Hynobius* larva 20 mm. long (from F. H. Edgeworth, *J. of Anat.*, 1923).

the orbital region by the ascending process. Moreover, dermal palatine, ectopterygoid, and pterygoid (endopterygoid) bones strengthen the palatal surface of the palatoquadrate. The primitive Tetrapoda have a palatoquadrate complex built on the same plan; but the processus ascendens is typically better developed and may become

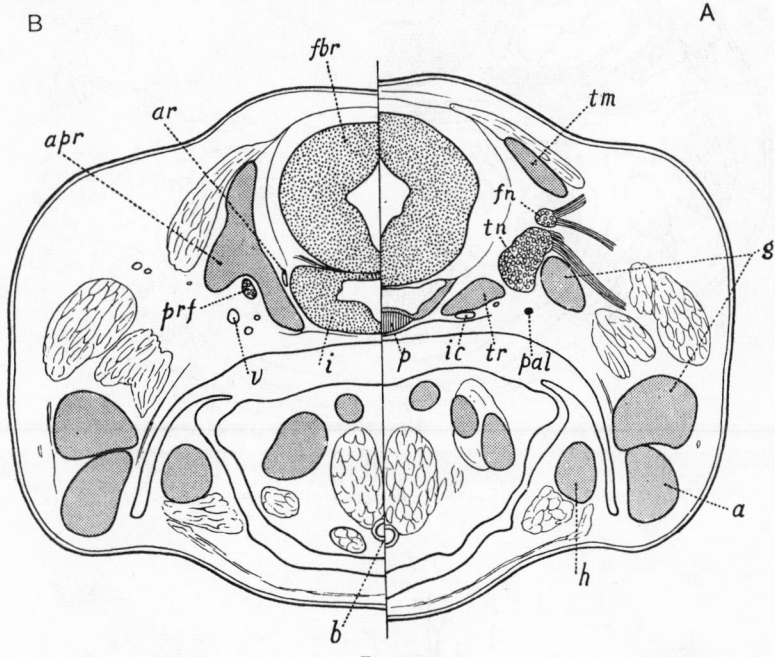

FIG. 452.

*Salamandra maculosa*, young larva. Transverse sections of head : A, More anterior, and D, more posterior ; A, posterior region of orbit ; B, through ascending process, *apr*. Cartilage grey. *a*, Articular region ; *a.c*, auditory capsule ; *an*, auditory nerve ; *ar*, artery ; *b*, basibranchial ; *bp*, basal plate ; *br*, ceratobranchial ; *brn*, brain ; *fbr*, fore-brain ; *fn*, facial ganglion and nerve ; *q*, quadrate ; *h*, hyoid arch ; *i*, infundibulum ; *ic*, internal carotid ; *m*, hind-brain ; *ms*, muscle ; *n*, dorsal lateral-line branch of facial ; *p*, pituitary body ; *pal*, palatine nerve ; *pc*, floor of facial canal ; *prf*, profundus nerve ; *s*, squamosal ; *sta*, stapedial (orbital) artery ; *tm*, taenia marginalis ; *tn*, trigeminal ganglion ; *tr*, trabecula ; *v*, vena capitis lateralis.

ossified. While the prevomer, palatine, ectopterygoid, and pterygoid firmly attached to the premaxillary and maxillary usually form a rigid bony palate, the anterior region of the palatoquadrate bar here tends to become reduced. It persists complete in some adult modern Amphibia, such as the Anura and *Ranodon* among Urodela, and, as Edgeworth has recently shown (676), is present in the young of *Crypto-branchus*, *Menopoma*, and *Hynobius*, and even in the larval Apodan *Ichthyophis*, Figs. 450-1, 506. But in the majority of adult Urodela

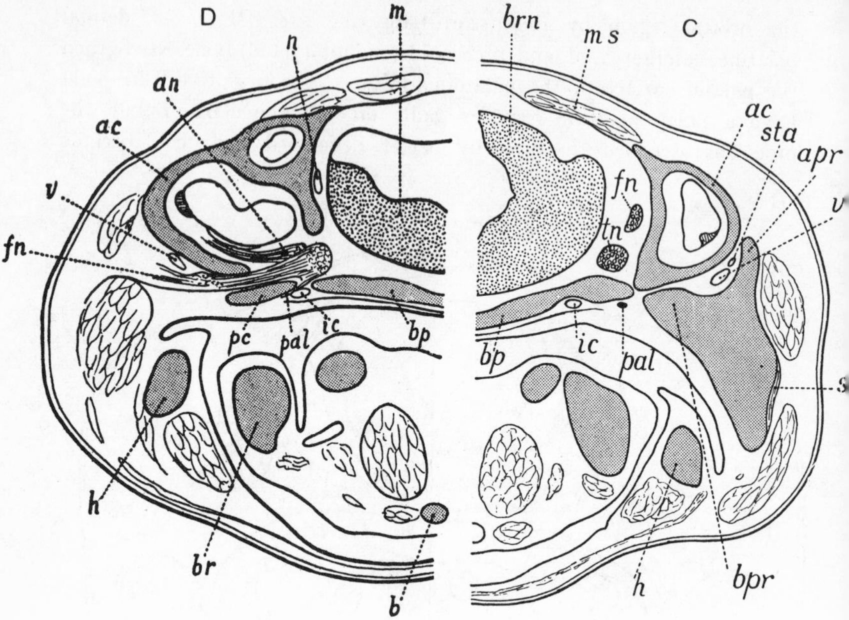

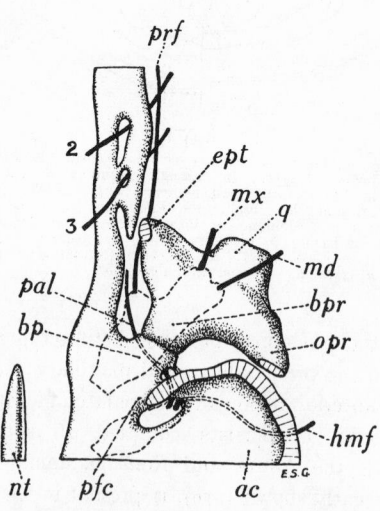

FIG. 453.

*Salamandra maculosa*, transverse sections of head of same larva as in Fig. 452; C, through basal process; D, more posterior through auditory capsule and facial foramen. Lettering as in Fig. 452.

FIG. 454.

*Necturus maculatus.* Reconstruction of right orbito-temporal region of young larva, dorsal view. Broken lines indicate position of large Gasserian and geniculate ganglia which have been removed. 2, Optic, and 3, oculomotor nerve. *ac*, Auditory capsule; *bp*, basitrabecular process; *bpr*, basal process; *ept*, ascending process; *pal*, palatine nerve; *hmf*, hyomandibular branch of facial; *md*, mandibular, and *mx*, maxillary branches of trigeminal; *nt*, tip of notochord; *opr*, otic process; *pfc*, prefacial commissure; *prf*, profundus; *q*, quadrate cartilage.

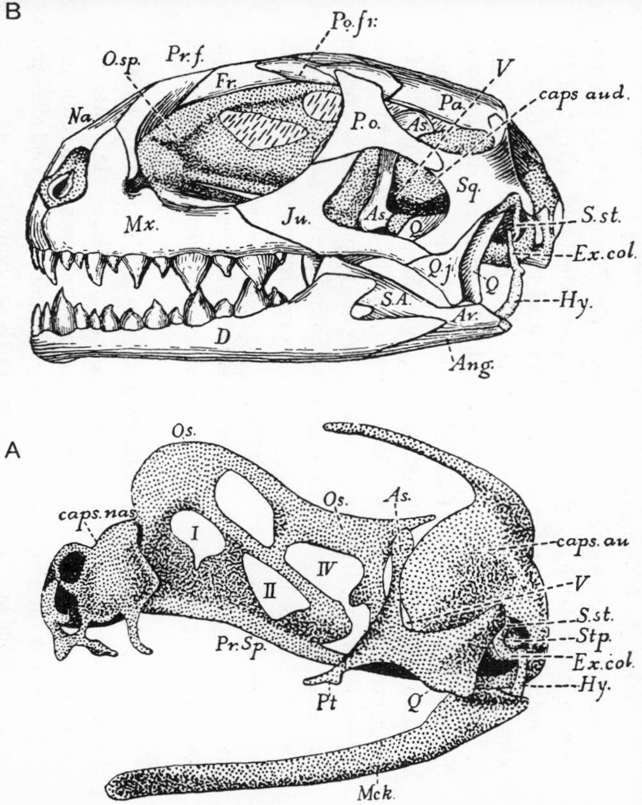

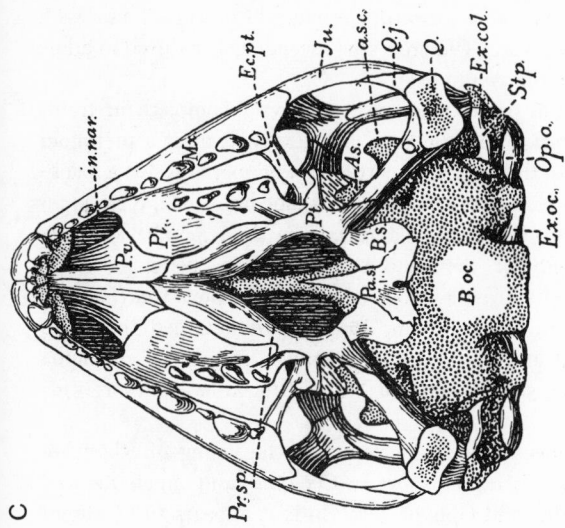

FIG. 455.

*Sphenodon punctatus* (after Howes and Swinnerton, *Tr. Zool. Soc.*, from W. K. Gregory, *J. Morph.*, 1913). A. Developing chondrocranium, etc.; B, developing skull, left-side view, and C, ventral view. *Ang*, Angular; *Ar*, articular; *As*, processus ascendens of palatoquadrate cartilages in A, ossified as alisphenoid or epipterygoid in B; *B.oc*, basioccipital; *B.s*, basisphenoid; *caps. au*, auditory capsule; *caps. nas*, nasal capsule; *D*, dentary; *Ec.pt*, ectopterygoid; *Ex.col*, extra-stapedial; *Fr*, frontal; *Hy*, hyoid cornu; *Ju*, jugal; *Mck*, Meckel's cartilage; *Mx*, maxillary; *Na*, nasal; *Op.o*, opisthotic; *Os*, orbital cartilage; *O.sp*, orbito-sphenoid; *P4*, parietal; *Pl*, palatine; *Pa.s*, parasphenoid; *Po.f*, postfrontal; *P.o*, postorbital; *Pr.f*, prefrontal; *Pr.sp*, trabecular region of interorbital septum; *Pt*, pterygoid; pterygoid process in A; *Q*, quadrate; *Q.j*, quadratojugal; *S.A*, supra-angular; *S.q*, squamosal; *S.st*, extra-stapedial; *Stp*, stapedial. Between *IV* and ascending process is seen the pila antotica in A.

the palatopterygoid region fails to reach the antorbital cartilage and is represented merely by a short forwardly produced 'pterygoid process', more reduced still in Apoda. The processus ascendens is reduced in adult Urodela and disappears in Anura.

In the Amniota the palatoquadrate is always incomplete in front, being represented anteriorly to the basal process by at most a pterygoid process, some isolated fragments of cartilage, and perhaps by a backwardly projecting process of the antorbital cartilage in *Lacerta*, Figs. 445-6 (Gaupp, **506**). Further, in Lacertilia and Ophidia the region between the basal process and body of the quadrate is reduced, being generally present only as a transient cartilaginous or procartilaginous rod (*Lacerta*) in the young (Gaupp, **506**; Broom, **460**). It is retained, however, in Rhynchocephalia, and at least in young stages in Chelonia (Parker, **574**; Kunkel, **540**; Fuchs, **503**) and Crocodilia (Parker, **570**; Shiino, **597**).

A processus ascendens is well developed in the young of Rhynchocephalia and Lacertilia, is rather short in Chelonia, and much reduced or vestigial in Crocodilia and Ophidia. In Birds it appears to be absent (Filatoff's process is probably a processus basalis (1906)), only the quadrate region of the palatoquadrate remaining in the adult. Its representative in the Mammalia is discussed elsewhere (Chapter VIII.).

This processus ascendens is an important element of the head skeleton marking the outer limit of the cavum epiptericum, and separating the profundus nerve from the maxillary branch of the trigeminal (p. 271). It was doubtless present in the young of all primitive Amniotes (Gaupp, **343**; Versluys, **625**). In the majority of Reptiles it ossifies as a distinct bone, the epipterygoid (so-called columella cranii of older authors), and as such has been described in Cotylosauria, Fig. 460, *Seymouria*, Phytosauria, Dinosauria, Ichthyosauria, Sauropterygia, Pelycosauria, and other Theromorpha, Fig. 413. Among living forms the epipterygoid is found in Rhynchocephalia, Figs. 354, 455 (Howes and Swinnerton, **528**; Schauinsland, **583**), Lacertilia, Fig. 364 (Parker, **564**; Gaupp, **506**; Rice, **376**), and Chelonia, where it is very small (Parker, **574**; Kunkel, **540**; Filatoff, **337**; Fuchs, **503**); but is lost in Ophidia and Crocodilia. The epipterygoid is represented in the Mammalia by the alisphenoid bone (see p. 436).

A second endochondral ossification appears as the quadrate bone in the posterior region of the palatoquadrate cartilage. It bears the articulation for the lower jaw, and extends upwards towards the cranium; it is present in the well-ossified, more primitive Stegocephalia and modern Amphibia (except Anura), and in all the Amniota.

The quadrate and epipterygoid, together with the dermal pterygoid, form a rigid palatoquadrate complex arch extending over the roof of the

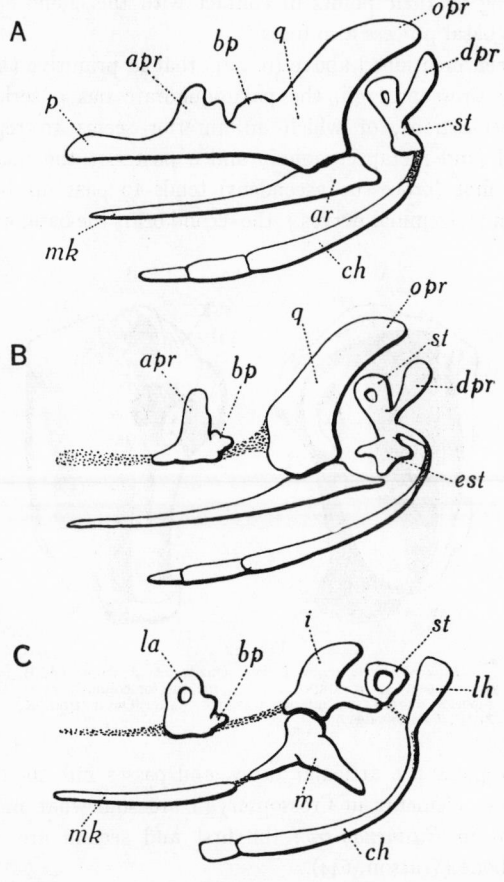

FIG. 456.

Diagrams illustrating fate of cartilaginous mandibular and hyoid arches in : A, primitive tetrapod ; B, modern reptile ; C, mammal.   *apr*, Ascending process (epipterygoid pr.) ;  *ar*, articular region ; *bp*, basal process ;  *ch*, ceratohyal ;  *dpr*, dorsal process (supra-stapedial pr.) ;  *est*, extra-stapedial ; *i*, incus (quadrate) ;  *la*, lamina ascendens (ascending pr.) ;  *lh*, laterohyal ;  *m*, malleus (articular) ; *mk*, mandibular (Meckel's cartilage) ;  *opr*, otic process ;  *p*, palatine region ;  *q*, quadrate region ; *st*, stapes.   Those regions which disappear in course of development are indicated in dots.

buccal cavity, Figs. 324, 455 ; connected in front with the prevomer and palatine, at the side with the ectopterygoid, and behind with the dermal temporal roofing (p. 317).   It may be supposed that primitively this rigid arch was somewhat movably attached (by the otic process, and basal process) to the cranium. But, as already explained (p. 411), in the Amphibia it tends to become immovable, the basipterygoid articulation being obliterated and the otic, palatine process, and even the ascending process fusing at their points of contact with the chondrocranium (in Urodela the basal process also fuses).

It has been mentioned above (p. 401) that in primitive Osteichthyes, such as the Crossopterygii, the palatoquadrate has a series of endo-chondral ossifications, of which an anterior seems to represent the epipterygoid (and metapterygoid ?) and a posterior the quadrate, Fig. 429a. The first (processus ascendens) tends to pass up between the profundus and trigeminal nerves ; the second bears the basal articulation ;

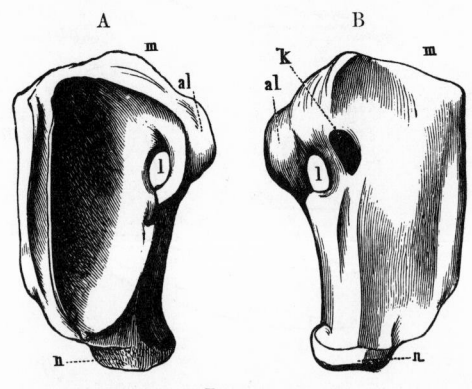

Fig. 457.

*Mosasaurus camperi*, v. Meyer. Quadrate. A, Outer, and B, inner aspect, ¼. *k*, Stapedial pit; *l*, meatus for columella ?; *m*, superior margin ; *n*, inferior margin. (After Owen, from K. Zittel, *Palaeontology*.)

the third supports the articular below and passes into the otic process above. These elements in Crossopterygii are somewhat inconstant in number, and in *Eusthenopteron* the first and second are represented by a single bone (Watson, 644).

Both the epipterygoid and quadrate bones of Tetrapods have, no doubt, been derived from those of their fish-like ancestors ; but whether the early Tetrapod also possessed a middle metapterygoid element is very doubtful. There appears to be no trace of such a separate bone in Amphibia. But in Reptilia, where this region of the palatoquadrate may persist as a little cartilage between the base of the epipterygoid and basitrabecular process (meniscus pterygoideus of Howes and Swinnerton in *Sphenodon*, and of Gaupp in *Lacerta*), it may possibly be represented by a little bone found in a similar position in certain fossil forms (*Seymouria* (*Conodectes*)), Watson, **643-4**; Broom, **455**; *Ichthyosaurus* (?), Sollas, **602**), Figs. 263, 279, 378.

From the researches of Watson, **644**, Sushkin, **678**, and others on the Stegocephalia, it appears that in these primitive Amphibia the epipterygoid was often a large and important bone in the outer wall of the cavum epiptericum, Figs. 458, 459, 460. It may sometimes extend into the basal process itself. Moreover, in some forms (*Capitosaurus*, Sushkin) it extended backwards and upwards behind a notch for the trigeminal nerve to acquire an articulation with the pro-otic region of the auditory capsule (otic process ?).

On the other hand, in Amphibia the otic process of the quadrate,

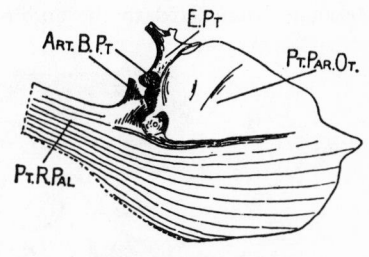

FIG. 458.

*Palaeogyrinus decorus*; inner aspect of right pterygoid and epipterygoid, *E.Pt.*, parotic wing, *Pt.Par.Ot*, and palatine ramus, *Pt.R.Pal*, of pterygoid; *Art.B*, basipterygoid articular surface; *Pt*, basal articular surface of epipterygoid. (From D. M. S. Watson, *Tr. Roy. Soc.*, 1926.)

which bone develops at the distal end of the cartilage, does not reach the capsule as it does in the Amniota. Nevertheless, Sushkin's contention

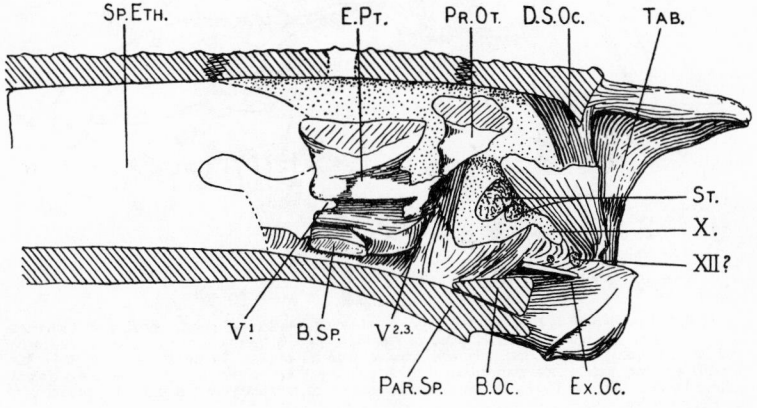

FIG. 459.

Inner view of right half of brain-case of *Capitosaurus* sp. (from D. M. S. Watson, *Phil. Trans.*, 1920). *B.Oc*, Basioccipital; *B.Sp*, basisphenoid; *D.S.Oc*, post-parietal (dermal supra-occipital); *E.Pt*, epipterygoid; *Ex.Oc*, exoccipital; *Par.Sp*, parasphenoid; *Pr.Ot*, pro-otic; *Sp.Eth*, sphenethmoid; *St*, stapes ? ; *Tab*, tabular.

that the 'process' of the Reptilia is radically different from the more ancient 'pro-otic process' of the Amphibia seems scarcely justified, since they are both ossifications in an original otic process of the primitive

cartilaginous palatoquadrate. They indicate, however, a divergence
between the two groups.

**Monimostylism, Streptostylism, and Kinetism.**—Quite independently
the palatoquadrate complex has become modified in the Amniota in
divergent directions (Versluys, **625**). On the one hand, the quadrate may
become firmly fixed to the auditory region in the adult (monimostylic

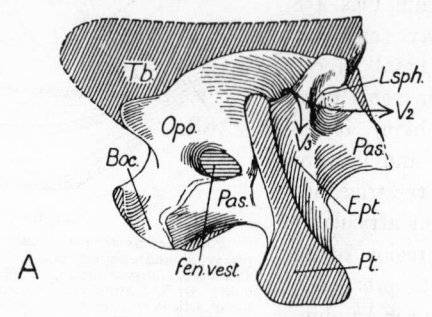

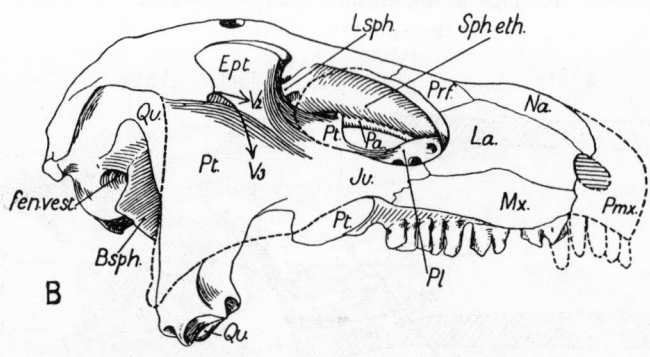

FIG. 460.

A, Left-side view of brain-case of *Eryops* sp., showing relations of epipterygoid, *Ept*, to pleurosphenoid (laterosphenoid), *Lsph*; B, skull of *Diadectes molaris* (from Gregory and Noble, *J. Morph.
and Physiol.*, 1924). *Bsph*, Basisphenoid; *fen.vest*, fenestra ovalis; *Ju*, jugal; *La*, lacrimal; *Mx*,
maxillary; *Na*, nasal; *Pa*, parasphenoid; *Pl*, palatine; *Pt*, pterygoid; *Qu*, quadrate; *Spheth*,
sphenethmoid. Arrows $V_2$ $V_3$ indicate inferred course of maxillary and mandibular branches of
trigeminal nerve.

skull, Stannius, 1856); on the other, it may become freely movable
(streptostylic skull, Stannius, 1856). The fully monimostylic condition
is established in the Chelonia and Crocodilia, among modern Reptilia,
by the sutural connexion of the otic process of the bony quadrate with
the pro-otic and opisthotic reinforced by the sutural connexion of the
pterygoid below accompanied by the obliteration of the basipterygoid

articulation and the fixation of the palatoquadrate complex to the base of the cranium, Figs. 416, 419.   The typical streptostylic condition is seen in the Lacertilia, where the bony quadrate is isolated from the epipterygoid and only connected somewhat loosely to the pterygoid below and the parotic process above by ligament, Figs. 462-3.   In the Ophidia the quadrate is still freer, and supported away from the skull by the squamosal.   Another variety of streptostylism occurs in the Archosaurian branch, where the quadrate tends to become exposed (p. 341) and the epipterygoid to be reduced.   This type culminates in the Aves, where the quadrate is again freely movable.   The third type

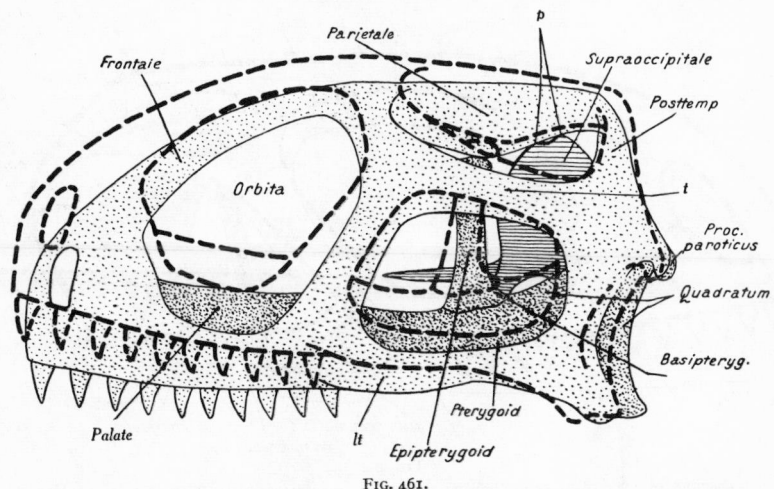

FIG. 461.

Diagram of Rhynchocephalian skull showing motion of 'maxillary segment' (dotted) on 'occipital segment' (hatched) as example of kinetism (from Versluys, *Vergl. Anat.*, 1927). *p*, Posterior hinge; *lt*, lower, and *t*, upper temporal arch.

of streptostylism develops in the Theromorpha and Mammalia, where the quadrate also becomes isolated from the epipterygoid region, and finally as the incus becomes quite freed from the skull, Figs. 456, 497 (Chapter VIII.).

Related to streptostylism is what Versluys has called the 'kinetism' of the skull (624-5, 627).   This consists in a certain degree of looseness and consequent power of motion between the dermal roofing bones and portions of the underlying chondrocranium.   For instance, although in *Sphenodon* the quadrate is firmly attached, the palatoquadrate complex is rigidly connected to the dermal roofing, and the basipterygoid articulation is less perfect in the adult than in the embryo (Schauinsland, 583; Howes and Swinnerton, 528); yet when the pterygoid muscles contract the roofing and complex together form a rigid whole slightly movable on the posterior brain-case, joined to it only by cartilage and ligament,[1] Fig. 461.

It is probable that the primitive early Reptiles had slightly movable quadrates. In Lacertilia the kinetism may be very pronounced. Here, as in *Sphenodon*, the interorbital septum is weakly developed and partly membranous while the posterior brain-case is only loosely joined to the parietals (metakinetic). Further, in such forms as *Tupinambis* and *Uromastix*, a bending of the roof becomes possible in front of the orbit (mesokinetic), Figs. 462-3. In Ophidia, also, the preorbital region of the

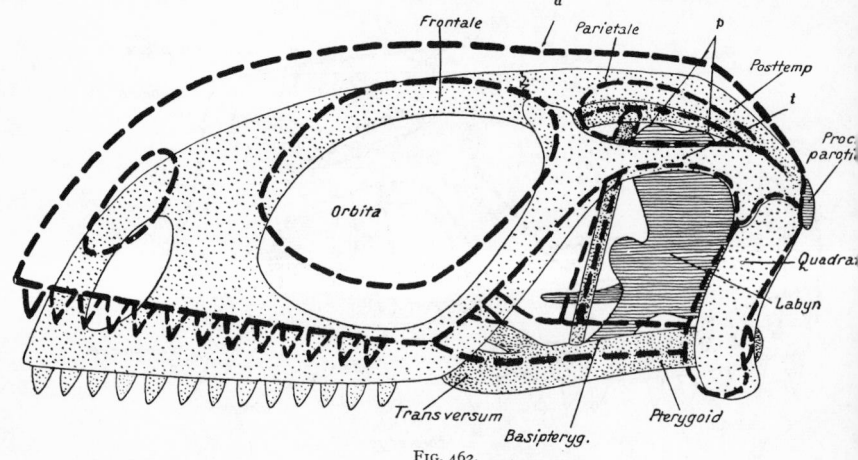

FIG. 462.

Diagram of Lacertilian skull showing motion of 'maxillary segment' (dotted) on 'occipital segment' (hatched), as example of kinetism (from Versluys, *Vergl. Anat.*, 1927). *a*, Anterior, and *p*, posterior movable hinges; *t*, upper temporal arch; *posttemp*, post-temporal arch.

skull can be lifted by the thrusting forward of the pterygoids. The Dinosaurian skull develops both metakinetic and mesokinetic specialisations, Fig. 464. Finally, in Aves, where the free quadrate is only loosely held by the delicate quadratojugal arch, metakinetism is pronounced. The pterygoid muscles are usually well developed as well as a m. orbito-quadratus (Gadow, 1891). Parrots have a markedly mesokinetic joint allowing the upper beak to be raised (Versluys, **625**). The skull is rigid from the occipital region to the preorbital, the interruption of the

---

[1] These muscles are the m. protractor pterygoidei, m. pterygosphenoidalis posterior, and m. pterygoparietalis extending from pterygoid to pro-otic and basisphenoid in fully kinetic skulls (Lacertilia). They are reduced or absent in the adults with akinetic skulls (Versluys, **769**; Edgeworth, **718**; Cords, 1904; Bradley, **426a**).

preorbital and postorbital bars frees the maxillo-quadratojugal bar, and the front region is lifted when the quadrate is brought forward. In the

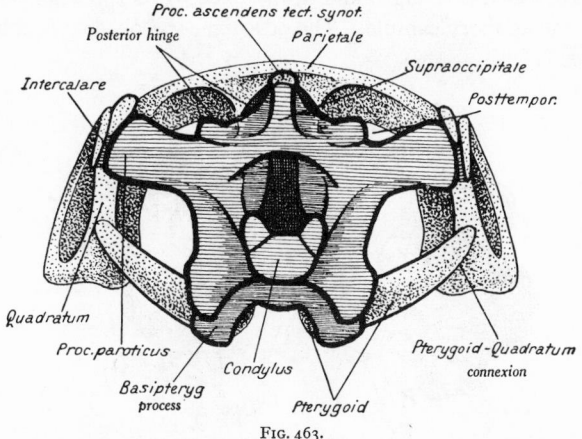

Fig. 463.

Posterior view of skull of Lacertilian showing 'occipital sigment' (hatched) movably attached to 'maxillary segment' (dotted) (from Versluys, *Vergl. Anat.*, 1927).

higher birds the basipterygoid articulation tends to disappear, the palato-quadrate complex sliding on the basisphenoid rostrum.

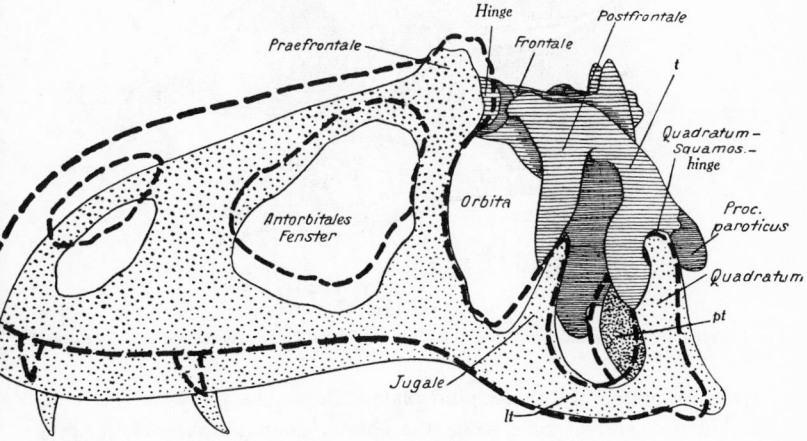

Fig. 464.

Diagram of kinetic skull of a carnivorous Dinosaur, *Creosaurus* (from Versluys, *Vergl. Anat.*, 1927). *pt*, Process of quadrate joining pterygoid. 'Occipital segment' (hatched) in this skull includes post-frontal and squamosal regions; cf. Fig. 357.

A special akinetic type of skull is developed in Theromorpha, and leads to the Mammalian structure. Here the dorsal roofing bones remain rigidly connected to the chondrocranium, and the parietals as well as the frontals take a large share in the covering of the brain; likewise the squamosal, which is enlarged and firmly fixed by its spreading squamous plate to the auditory capsule. The post-temporal opening is obliterated

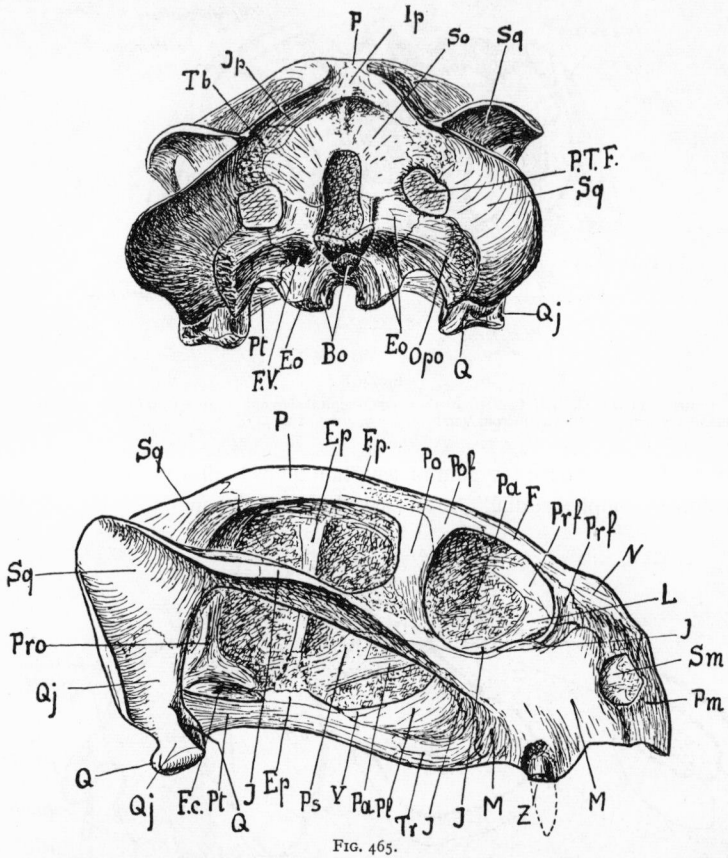

FIG. 465.

Posterior and right lateral aspect of skull of *Dicynodon* (from F. von Huene, *Palaeontol. Zeitschr.*, 1922). Lettering as in Fig. 394.

in the formation of the occipital plate. Below the pterygoid becomes fixed to the cranial base, while the epipterygoid (alisphenoid, p. 437) itself contributes largely to the lateral cranial wall (p. 262). Nevertheless, the mammalian skull is not monimostylic, for the palatoquadrate complex is interrupted, and the quadrate becomes free (p. 433).

It has been pointed out above (p. 271) that the cartilaginous lamina ascendens of the ala orbitalis of mammals, which often is separately chondrified, in all probability corresponds to the processus ascendens of lower Tetrapods, and that both originally lay in the outer wall of the cavum epiptericum outside the brain-case (p. 271). In the mammalian skull this cartilage lamina becomes ossified as the true alisphenoid, which spreads and contributes to the side wall to the cranium a new element not homologous with the various bones in fishes, birds, and reptiles to which the name alisphenoid has been applied (p. 392). The processus ascendens becomes ossified as the epipterygoid in reptiles, Figs. 455, 460, 465, and in Theriodontia this bone may be considerably expanded and develop a posterior tympanic process (Watson, 642). In Cynodontia it has a vertical plate suturally connected with the parietal and forming the lateral wall of the brain-case, while its

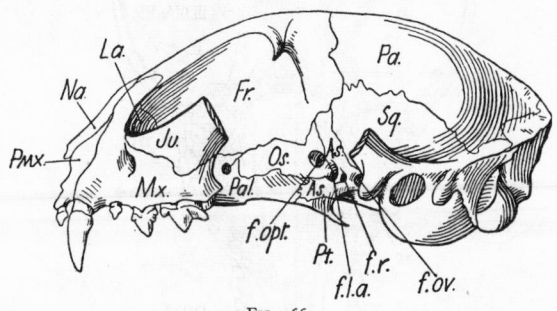

FIG. 466.

Left-side view of skull of cat, with jugal arch partly removed to show alisphenoid, *As*, and crowding together of exits for branches of fifth cranial nerve (from Gregory and Noble, *J. Morph. and Physiol.*, 1924). *f.l.a*, Foramen lacerum anterius (orbital fissure) for 3rd, 4th, 6th, and profundus nerves; *f.ov*, foramen ovale for mandibular branch; *f.r*, foramen rotundum for maxillary branch.

long posterior process reaches the tympanic region and quadrate, recalling the structure of the alisphenoid in Marsupials, Figs 394-6, 413, 467-9. At the same time the pterygoid loses its reptilian posterior limb, and takes up a position below the basitrabecular region much as the ventral pterygoid does in Mammalia (p. 370). There is little doubt that Broom's contention that the mammalian alisphenoid is derived from the epipterygoid of lower Tetrapods is correct (Broom, 327a and b, 451).

**Summary.**—Summarising some of the more important points with regard to the mandibular and hyoid skeletal arches in Gnathostomes, it may be pointed out that there is no convincing evidence that they were ever subdivided into the four paired pieces typical of the branchial arches, though traces of pharyngeal and hypo-arcual elements have been described in some fishes. The exact homology of the dorsal elements (palatoquadrate and hyomandibula) with the epibranchials is uncertain. The hyomandibular cartilage can be traced throughout the whole piscine series; but varies much in size, in function, and in its attachments (amphistylic, hyostylic, and autostylic types). In Selachians, Dipnoi, and Tetrapods it retains its primitive dorsal attachment ventral to the vena capitis lateralis and hyomandibular nerve, and it becomes converted in Tetra-

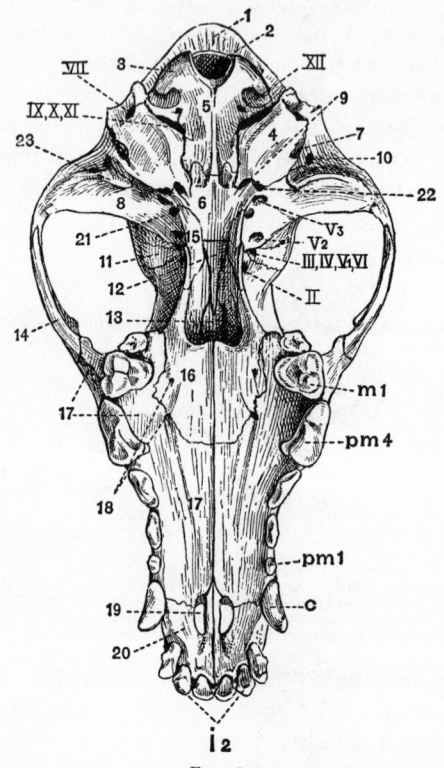

Fig. 467.

Ventral view of cranium of *Canis familiaris* (from S. H. Reynolds, *Vertebrate Skeleton*, 1913). 1, Supraoccipital ; 2, foramen magnum ; 3, occipital condyle ; 4, tympanic bulla ; 5, basioccipital ; 6, basisphenoid ; 7, external auditory meatus ; 8, glenoid fossa ; 9, foramen lacerum medium and anterior opening of carotid canal ; 10, postglenoid foramen ; 11, alisphenoid ; 12, presphenoid ; 13, vomer ; 14, jugal ; 15, pterygoid ; 16, palatal process of palatine ; 17, maxilla (palatal portion) ; 18, posterior palatine foramina ; 19, anterior palatine foramen ; 20, premaxilla ; 21, alisphenoid canal ; 22, Eustachian foramen ; 23, postglenoid process of squamosal ; *II*, optic foramen ; *III, IV, V₁, VI*, foramen lacerum anterius ; *V₂*, foramen rotundum ; *V₃*, foramen ovale ; *VII*, stylomastoid foramen ; *IX, X, XI*, foramen lacerum posterius ; *XII*, condylar foramen ; *i* 2, second incisor ; *c*, canine ; *pm* 1, *pm* 4, first and fourth premolars ; *m* 1, first molar.

pods into the columella auris (see Chapter VIII.). But in the Teleostomi its articulation with the auditory capsule shifts, possibly over the jugal canal, to a more dorsal position above the vein and nerve ; and, further, the nerve passes through the hyomandibula in Holostei.

The palatoquadrate bar extends primitively from the ethmoid to the otic region. It is usually articulated or fused in front to the antorbital process and connected further back with the chondrocranium at two points : a ventral basal process meets the trabecular region (basitrabecular process), and a dorsal otic process arching over a cranio-quadrate passage (for the vena capitis lateralis and hyomandibular nerve) meets the auditory capsule (post-orbital process, crista parotica, paroccipital process). The basal articulation is probably represented in Selachians by the orbital (ethmo-palatine) articulation, and the otic process is generally lost in these fishes. The Dipnoi alone among living fishes preserve both the basal and otic connexions. It is probable that both were present in the common ancestor of the Osteichthyes. The basal articulation occurs in Crossopterygii, early Chondrostei, and Actinopterygii; it persists in *Lepidosteus,* but is lost in other modern Teleostomes. The otic connexion no longer remains in any of the Teleostomes (Crossopterygii ?), though traces of an otic process are found in some of the more primitive forms.

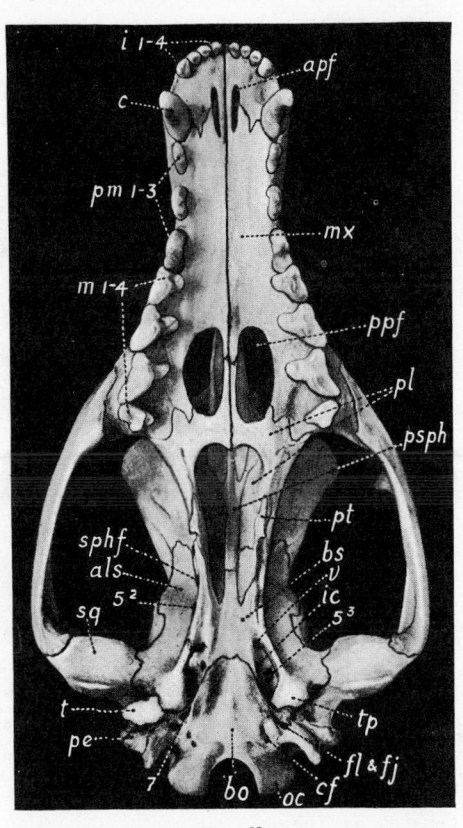

Fig. 468.

Ventral view of skull of *Thylacinus cynocephalus*. *als*, Alisphenoid; *apf*, anterior palatine foramen; *c*, canine; *cf*, condylar foramen; *fl* and *fj*, foramen lacerum posterius; *i* 1-4, incisors; *ic*, internal carotid foramen; *m* 1-4, molars; *mx*, maxillary; *oc*, exoccipital condyle; *pm* 1-3, premolars; *ppf*, posterior palatine foramen; *psph*, presphenoid region; *tp*, tympanic process of alisphenoid. See Fig. 469 for other letters and details of posterior region.

In primitive Tetrapods the palatoquadrate is complete with antorbital, basal, and otic articulations. It is further provided with a dorsal processus ascendens in the outer wall of the cavum epiptericum (p. 267), between the profundus and trigeminal nerves. This ascending process is probably a primitive structure since it is well developed in Dipnoi, and traces of it occur in the earliest Teleostomes (Crossopterygii).

The palatoquadrate cartilage may become ossified in its anterior (autopalatine), middle (metapterygoid), and posterior (quadrate) regions in Teleostomes ; but in the early Crossopterygii it is more or less completely ossified throughout. In Tetrapods the cartilage is retained complete only in some Amphibia ; and in Amniota it always breaks down, the palatine region and generally also the pterygoid regions disappearing.

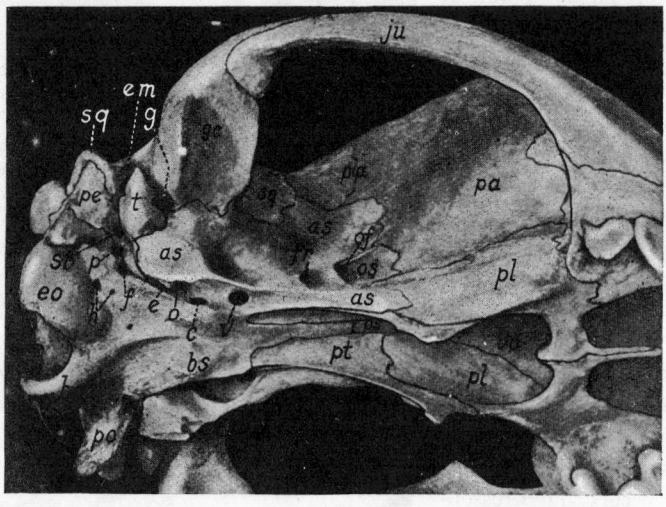

FIG. 469.

Oblique ventral view of skull of *Thylacinus cynocephalus*. *as*, Alisphenoid ; *bo*, basioccipital ; *bs*, basisphenoid ; *c*, internal carotid foramen ; *e*, Eustachian canal ; *em*, external auditory meatus ; *eo*, exoccipital condyle ; *f*, foramen caroticum posterius ; *fr*, foramen rotundum ; *g*, postglenoid foramen ; *gc*, glenoid cavity ; *h*, hypoglossal foramina ; *ju*, jugal ; *o*, for. caroticum anterius ; *of*, foramen ovale ; *os*, orbitosphenoid ; *p*, foramen lacerum posterius ; *pa*, parietal ; *pe*, periotic ; *pl*, palatine ; *ps*, presphenoid ; *pt*, pterygoid ; *sq*, squamosal ; *st*, stylomastoid foramen ; *t*, tympanic ; *v*, venous foramen ; *vo*, vomer.

Thus are left the processus ascendens and basal process articulating with the basitrabecular process, and the quadrate cartilage with the crista parotica. The former ossifies as the epipterygoid bone (alisphenoid of Mammal), and the latter as the quadrate bone (incus of Mammal).

## THE HYOBRANCHIAL APPARATUS

Excepting for its dorsal hyomandibular element the hyoid arch is generally in Gnathostomes closely associated with the branchial arches.[1] Hence the whole system is called the hyobranchial skeleton.

[1] The structure of the hyoid arch in Batoidei (p. 415, footnote 3) and the presence of a slender rod of cartilage between the hyoid and first branchial arch in Dipnoi led Dohrn (333) and others to adopt van Wijhe's conclusion,

It has been mentioned above that the branchial arches of Selachii consist of paired pharyngobranchials, epibranchials, ceratobranchials, and hypobranchials, and of median basibranchials or copulae. But this typical structure, almost fully carried out in such primitive forms as the Notidani, is never quite complete in the posterior arches, generally much modified by fusion or reduction, Figs. 424, 426-7.

The segmentation of the arches is perhaps secondary ; it is probably related to the development of special branchial muscles and allows the walls of the pharynx to be expanded and contracted for breathing and eating purposes.

The last two pharyngobranchials are generally fused, and usually only a ceratobranchial remains in addition in the last arch. The copulae are most variable. Usually situated between the successive pairs of hypobranchials, their true morphological relations and phylogenetic origin remain obscure. Gegenbaur finally concluded that each basibranchial belongs to and is derived from the arch in front of it. Only in *Heterodontus* has a copula been described between the 1st and 2nd branchial arches. The copulae tend to disappear or fuse up from before backwards, that between the 4th and 5th arch (or 6th and 7th arch in Heptanchus) remaining as a large plate for attachment of the ventral muscles and for the protection of the pericardium. This ' cardio-branchial ' is possibly of compound origin, formed of two or more posterior basibranchials. The branchial arches of the Holocephali closely resemble those of sharks.

It is characteristic of the branchial arches of the Elasmobranchii that they are bent in a $\leq$-shaped curve, the pharyngobranchial and the hypobranchial pointing backward. On the other hand, the arches of the Teleostomi, although $>$-shaped, are in one plane, the pharyngo- and hypobranchials pointing forward. Those of *Ceratodus* are intermediate, only the hypobranchial pointing backward (Allis, 1925).

The usual four paired lateral and median ventral elements are typically present in the Teleostome branchial arch, and generally ossified ; but are subject to considerable modification and reduction, especially in the posterior arches, Figs. 436, 599. The 5th arch, usually of one piece, frequently becomes conspicuously toothed forming the ' os pharyngeus inferior ' ; while the pharyngobranchials of the last three arches similarly form a toothed ' os pharyngeus superior '. Often these become

---

based on embryology, that the hyoid region includes two arches (p. 223). But the abnormal structure of the hyoid skeleton of skates is better explained otherwise (p. 415), and the rod in Dipnoi appears to be formed by the fusion of the base of branchial rays (K. Fürbringer, **682**).

powerful masticating plates armed with large teeth. In addition to the usual pharyngobranchial (inferior pharyngobranchial) a small superior

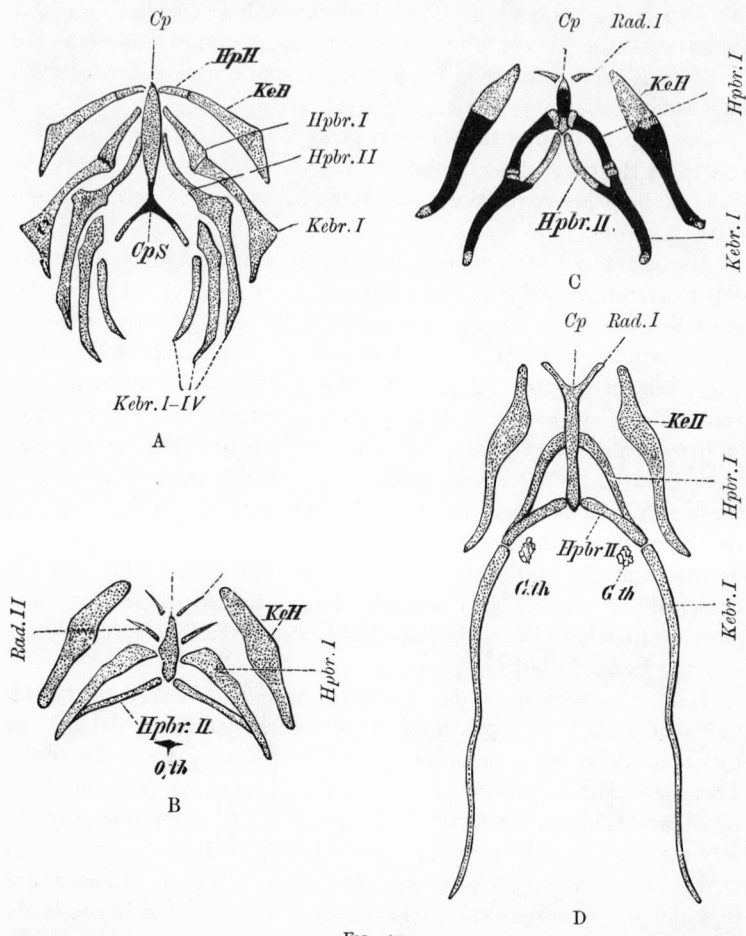

FIG. 470.

Hyobranchial apparatus of Urodeles. A, Axolotl (*Siredon* stage of *Amblystoma*); B, *Salamandra maculosa*; C, *Triton cristatus*; D, *Spelerpes fuscus. Cp, Cps, O.th,* basihyobranchial or copula; *G.th,* thyroid gland; *Hpbr. I* and *II,* first and second hypobranchial; *HpH, Rad. I,* hypohyal; *Kebr. I-IV,* first to fourth ceratobranchial; *KeH,* ceratohyal ('anterior cornu' of hyoid in Caducibranchs —the 'posterior cornu' being made up of *Hpbr. I* and *II* and *Kebr. I*). *Rad. II* arises in *Salamandra* secondarily during metamorphosis. (From Wiedersheim, *Comp. Anatomy.*)

pharyngobranchial may be present on some of the anterior arches, perhaps segmented off from the epibranchials, in *Acipenser*, Fig. 434, and some other Teleostomes (van Wijhe, **654**; Allis, **667-71**; de Beer, **421a**). The copulae are well developed and usually along the base of all the arches. *Amia* has three separate median elements, apparently representing the five basi-branchials, while Teleosts have in addition a basihyal.  A median urohyal, attached in front below the hypohyals and passing back between the sternohyoid muscles, is peculiar to the Teleostei.  It is generally considered

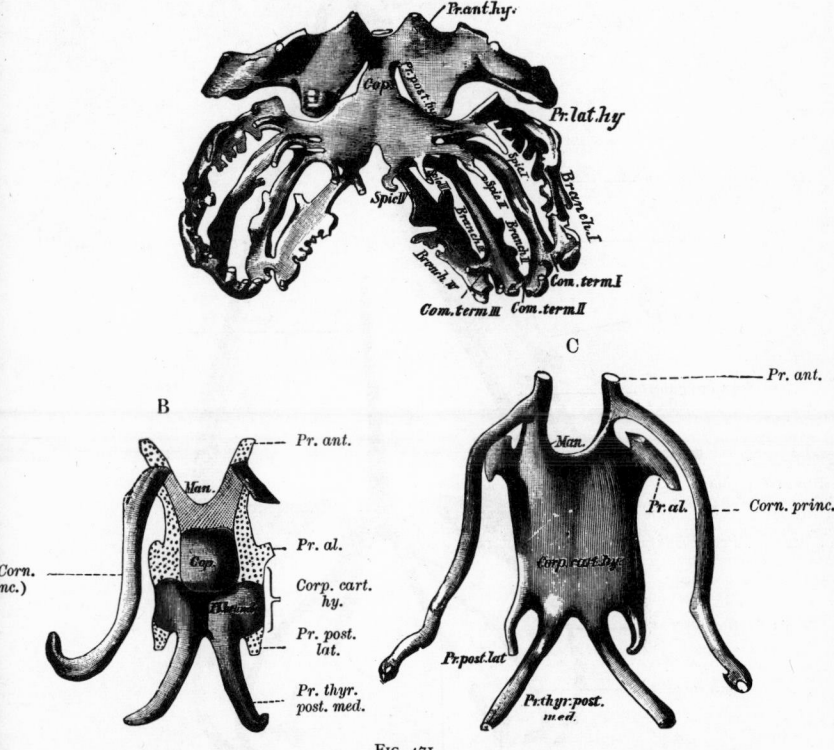

FIG. 471.

A, Hyobranchial skeleton of a larval *Rana temporaria*, 29 mm. in length, from the dorsal side ; B, the same of a larva, 15 mm. in length, at the end of metamorphosis, after disappearance of the tail ; C, hyoid cartilage of a young frog, 2 cm. in length, from the ventral side. (All these figures are from wax models after Gaupp.) A and B (in part), *Branch I-IV*, branchial arches ; *Com. term. I-III*, terminal commissures of same ; *Cop*, basal plate (copula) ; *Hy*, hyoid ; *Pr.ant.hy, Pr.lat.hy, Pr.post.hy*, anterior, lateral, and posterior processes of the hyoid ; *Spic. I-IV*, cartilaginous processes. B (in part) and C, *Corp.cart.hy*, body of hyoid cartilage ; *Corn. princ.*, anterior cornu ; *Man*, ' manu-brium ' ; *Pr.al*, alary process ; *Pr.ant*, anterior process ; *Pr.post.lat*, postero-lateral process ; *Pr.thyr.post.med*, thyroid or postero-medial process (posterior cornu). (From Wiedersheim, *Comp. Anatomy*.)

to be an ossification of the median ligament, Fig. 285.  Similar but paired bones occur in *Polypterus*, possibly enlarged branchial rays.

The hyobranchial skeleton of Amphibia is still concerned with respiration, bearing gills in the larva and also in the adult of those Urodela which have become readapted to aquatic life.  In these the

apparatus preserves many fish-like characters (Dugés, 1834 ; Wiedersheim, 651 ; Parker, 562, 573 ; Drüner, 675 ; Gaupp, 683). The Urodelan
larva may have as many as four paired ceratobranchials, two hypo-

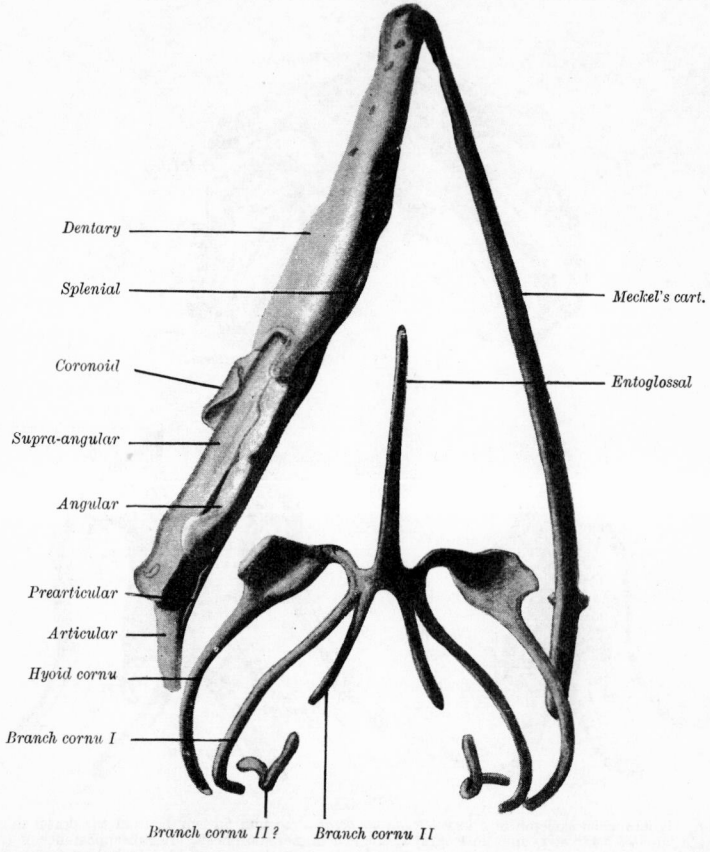

FIG. 472.

Hyobranchial skeleton and lower jaw of *Lacerta* (after Gaupp-Ziegler model, from Wiedersheim, *Comp. Anatomy*).

branchials, and behind the basihyal a copula with a posterior stilus
probably representing several basibranchials.

In adult terrestrial Amphibia the hyobranchial apparatus becomes
altered and adapted to support a projecting muscular tongue as well as to
serve for the attachment of muscles for lowering and raising the floor of the
buccal cavity in respiration (Chapter XI.). While the adult *Salamandra*
has a copula with two short ' radii ' in front, and two arches combining

to a single dorsal cornua behind, the perennibranchiate *Necturus* preserves three branchial arches, Fig. 470.

The Anuran larva possesses a cartilaginous basket-work consisting of
the ceratohyal and four branchial arches continuous with each other
dorsally and ventrally and with a median copula.  At metamorphosis
the basibranchial and hypobranchial regions become converted into an
expanded ' corpus ' or ' body ' with four paired processes, most of the
arches having disappeared.  The first process is prolonged into the slender
hyoid cornu attached dorsally to the skull.  The last process is large and

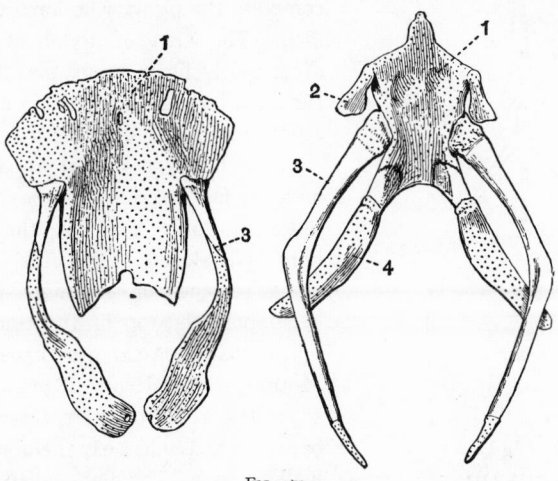

FIG. 473.

Hyoids of *Caiman latirostris* (to the left) and of *Chelone midas* (to the right) (from S. H. Reynolds,
*Vertebrate Skeleton*, 1913).   Cartilaginous portions dotted.   1, Basilingual plate or body of the hyoid ;
2, hyoid arch ;  3, first branchial arch (anterior cornu) ;  4, second branchial arch (posterior cornu).

usually ossified (processus thyreoideus), Figs. 471, 506.   The Apoda
(*Ichthyophis*) have slender remnants of four branchial arches in the adult.

The hyobranchial apparatus of the Amniota serves no longer for
breathing purposes, but chiefly for the support of the tongue, into the
base of which projects in Reptiles and Birds a processus entoglossus or
lingualis from the copula or corpus.   All the median elements combine
to form this corpus, from which usually extend three tapering arches or
cornua—a hyoid and two branchial in the more primitive forms, Fig.
472.   The whole apparatus is reduced to slender remnants in Ophidia.

Chelonians have the hyoid cornua reduced to short ventral processes,
and they are further reduced in Crocodiles and Birds.   In these also the
second branchial cornua are lost, Figs. 473, 473*a*.

The Mammalian hyobranchial apparatus has been specialised along lines different from those adopted in the Reptiles and Birds. It consists typically of a broad body or corpus, two long anterior hyoid cornua, and two short posterior cornua. The latter represent the first branchial arches. The hyoid cornu fuses at its dorsal extremity with the crista parotica (Chapter VIII.), and becomes usually subdivided into several pieces sometimes named hypohyal, ceratohyal, stylohyal, and tympanohyal (Reichert, 1837; Flower, 1870). The small tympanohyal or laterohyal joined to the crista helps to enclose the hyomandibular branch of the facial nerve in a long facial canal and complete the primary stylomastoid foramen. The next or stylohyal element, often partly ligamentous, may fuse with the fixed laterohyal and so, in man, form a prominent styloid process.

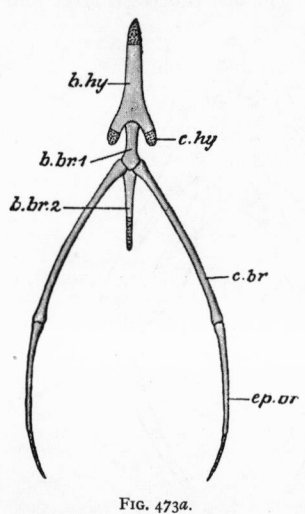

FIG. 473a.

*Columba livia.* Hyoid apparatus. The cartilaginous parts are dotted. *b.br.* 1, Basibranchials; *b.hy,* basihyal; *c.br,* ceratobranchial; *c.hy,* hyoid cornu; *ep.br,* epibranchial. (From Parker and Haswell, *Zoology.*)

But the hyobranchial apparatus we have so far described in the Tetrapods represents only part of the original branchial skeleton, for the posterior arches become more and more specialised to support the top of the trachea and are gradually converted into the skeleton of the larynx (Henle, 1839; Reichert, 1837; His, 1880; Göppert, 686-7; Gegenbaur, 170; Wilder, 947; Dubois, 1886; Kallius, 691). The mammalian glottis is protected in front by an epiglottis strengthened by a cartilage provided in lower forms with lateral wings which are represented in man by separate cuneiform cartilages. The trachea is surrounded by cartilaginous rings, the main bronchial tubes being stiffened by similar, usually incomplete cartilages. The larynx itself in Placentals is provided with a large crescentic thyroid cartilage, small paired arytenoids, and a circular cricoid, Fig. 482. It has been held by Gegenbaur and others that the thyroid is derived from the 2nd and 3rd, the epiglottis cartilage from the 4th, the cricoid, arytenoid, and perhaps the tracheal rings from the 5th branchial arch. The evidence, however, from comparative anatomy and embryology with regard to the two last arches is still somewhat incomplete.

The Amphibian larynx is strengthened by paired arytenoids, which are sometimes in Anura greatly developed and ossified to form a 'resonance box'. These appear to represent the 5th branchial arch (7th

visceral arch). They, together with laryngotracheal cartilages extending
down the trachea, are developed in Urodela from a single pair of rudiments
(Wilder, 947), but in Anura chondrify separately (Märtens, 1898). A
distinct cricoid appears in Reptilia in addition to the arytenoids, but no
true thyroid cartilage.

The Monotremata possess a much more primitive laryngeal skeleton
than the Ditremata, for in them the thyroid is represented by two distinct
arches, Fig. 474. The double origin of the Ditrematous thyroid is clear

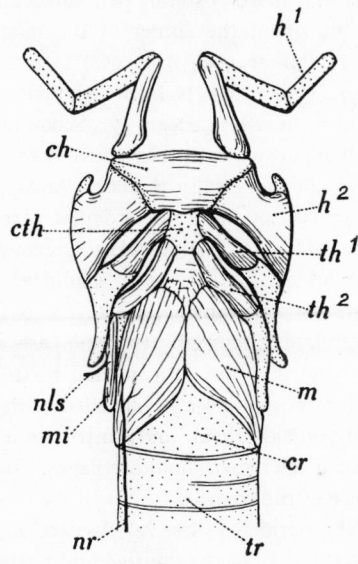

FIG. 474.

*Echidna aculeata* ; ventral view of larynx, trachea, etc. (after E. Göppert, 1901). *ch*, Basihyal
(+1st basibranchial ?) copula ; *cr*, cricoid, mostly hidden by muscles ; *cth*, thyroid copula (2nd and
3rd basibranchial) ; *h¹*, hyoid arch ; *h²*, 1st branchial arch (posterior cornu of hyoid) ; *m, mi*, muscles ;
*nls*, superior laryngeal nerve ; *nr*, recurrent nerve ; *th¹, th²*, 4th and 5th branchial arches (=thyroid
cartilage of higher mammals).

in development, and even in the adult Marsupial may be betrayed by a
foramen on either side. That the cricoid is also a modified arch is still
apparent in the embryo of Marsupials (Esdaile, 722); it seems to
represent the 4th. But the origin of the epiglottis from an arch is more
than doubtful (Kallius, 691).

Thus can be traced throughout the Gnathostomes the gradual modification of the branchial arches from their primitive branchial function to
such diverse uses as the support of the tongue and the enclosure of the
larynx ; and the evidence is derived not only from the structure and
development of the skeleton, but also from the vascular arches, the

musculature, and the distribution of the originally branchial branches of the vagus nerve.

### THE LABIAL CARTILAGES

Certain small cartilages of doubtful significance are found in the lips or marginal folds of the mouth in Elasmobranchs and some Teleostomes. They are known as labial cartilages, and in the former group consist usually of an anterior pair of simple rods or plates outside the palato-quadrate cartilage and a more posterior pair consisting of an upper and a lower segment bent round the corner of the mouth, Figs. 424, 427, 440 (Gegenbaur, 166; Parker, 569; Allis, 668).

Similar, but more elaborately fashioned, labials occur in the Holocephali, Fig. 428 (Hubrecht, 1877; Dean, 17; Schauinsland, 583). Labial cartilages, perhaps homologous with them, have been described in various Teleostomes, but are not universally present. An upper labial occurs in *Polypterus*, Fig. 296; two or more upper labial cartilages are found in various Teleosts (Stannius in Characinidae, Sagemehl, 378; Siluridae, Pollard, 696; Salmonidae, Parker, 560; Gadidae, Brooks; Gasterosteidae, Swinnerton, 389; Serranidae, Kesteven, 692, etc.), and sometimes a pair of lower labials as well. In some cases the anterior upper labials seem to fuse and give rise to a median rostral cartilage (Berrill, 672), but usually they become closely connected with the premaxillaries and maxillaries lying outside them, and contribute a smooth surface to their articulations with the mesethmoid cartilages. In the Siluridae they may support the base of the barbels.

While Pollard (696) considered these various cartilages to be the remains of the skeletal supports of a set of primitive oral cirrhi such as are found still in *Amphioxus* and Myxinoids, Figs. 518, 520, others, like Sewertzoff (701), believe them to represent vestiges of the visceral arches of two segments in front of the mandibular. For the former view there is a good deal to be said, though the evidence in favour of it is by no means decisive. Against the theory maintained by Sewertzoff it may be urged that there is no good evidence of the existence at any time of gill-pouches, arches, etc., anterior to the mandibular, that the labials are too superficial to be of visceral nature, and that the supposed vestiges of gill-pouches corresponding to them apparently occur anteriorly to the pharynx (endodermal gut). Possibly the labial cartilages are merely secondary in Gnathostomes and of no great morphological importance.

# CHAPTER VIII

## MIDDLE EAR AND EAR OSSICLES

## THE MIDDLE EAR OF TETRAPODS, AND HISTORY OF THE MAMMALIAN EAR-BONES

FEW problems in morphology have aroused more interest than that of
the origin of the ear-bones. It is a familiar fact that the Mammalia
differ from all the lower Gnathostomes in having a lower jaw composed of
a single dermal bone, the dentary, articulating with another dermal bone,
the squamosal, fixed to the skull ; also in having a chain of three ossicles
(stapes, incus, and malleus) serving to convey vibrations from the
tympanic membrane to the labyrinth lodged in the auditory capsule.
These two characteristics are intimately related, and the explanation of
the second carries with it that of the first.

In all Gnathostomes, excepting the Mammalia, the articulation for
the jaws lies between the quadrate region of the palatoquadrate above
and the articular region of Meckel's cartilage below. In all above the
Chondrichthyes, the former is usually represented by a bone, the quadrate,
and the latter by another separate bone, the articular. The remainder
of the two cartilaginous bars may be more or less reduced, leaving
some cartilage at the joint. Moreover, in Tetrapods, a tympanic membrane (see, further, pp. 460, 477) is typically present behind the quadrate
region, closing the tympanic cavity which opens internally into the
pharynx by the Eustachian tube. The membrane is composed of an

outer layer of epidermis, continuous with the general surface, a thin sheet of connective tissue, and an inner layer of endodermal epithelium continuous with that lining the tympanic cavity, the tube, and the pharynx. This epithelium, closely applied to the auditory capsule, also covers the membrana tympanica secundaria closing the fenestra ovalis (see p. 254 and Figs. 475, 481).

Concerning the homology of the auditory ossicles many different views have been held into which it is not necessary now to go in detail (see Gaupp, 731). Suffice it to say that Peters, 1868, and Albrecht, 1883 (whose main contention has been supported by Cope, 711 ; Gadow, 730 ; Dollo, 713 ; Baur, 704 ; and more recently by Drüner, 716, and Fuchs, 728), held that these ossicles were derived from the Reptilian columella auris, and that the quadrate and articular are still represented in the articulation of the lower jaw by the cartilage covering the facet of the squamosal and the condyle of the dentary, and the meniscus between them. Among the many difficulties to be met by this theory, we may now mention the fact pointed out by Gaupp that there is no meniscus and practically no cartilage in the jaw articulation of the Monotreme.

Huxley (739) held that the stapes was derived from the reptilian columella, the incus from the supra-stapedial part of the hyoid, and the malleus from the quadrate, while the articular he supposed to be represented in the condyle of the dentary. Such a view could only be put forward when the development of these parts was little understood.

The theory now generally adopted is that based on the researches of Carus (1818), Meckel (1820), and Reichert (1837), and supported by the results obtained by a vast number of workers since, among whom may be mentioned Gaupp, who has recently given a comprehensive account of the evidence (732).[1] According to the modern version of Reichert's theory, the mammalian stapes derived from the reptilian columella auris, the incus from the quadrate, and the malleus from the articular, while the dentary has acquired a new articulation with the squamosal.

A complete and satisfactory theory should account not only for the fate of the quadrate and articular, and the change in the articulation of the lower jaw, but also : (1) for the position of the ossicles with regard to the tympanic cavity ; (2) for their developmental history ; (3) for their relation to the facial nerve and chorda tympani, (4) to the blood-vessels, and (5) to the muscles attached to them ; (6) for the nerve supply of these muscles ; and (7) for the origin of the tympanic bone. In fact, evidence should be sought from the structure and development of skeleton,

[1] Gaupp has reviewed the literature up to 1899 (731-2), and van der Klaauw from 1899 to 1923 (748a).

gill-pouches, muscles, nerves, and blood-vessels, if the account of the
middle-ear region is to be completely elucidated.

It will be well to begin with a description of the middle ear of Reptiles,
studied by Peters (1869), Parker (564), Gaupp (506), and others, but more
particularly by Versluys in the Lacertilia (769, 770).  The typical columella
auris extends from the fenestra ovalis of the auditory capsule to the
tympanic membrane, Figs. 475-9.  It consists, in the Lacertilia, of a
proximal or stapedial region (stapes), and a distal extra-stapedial region

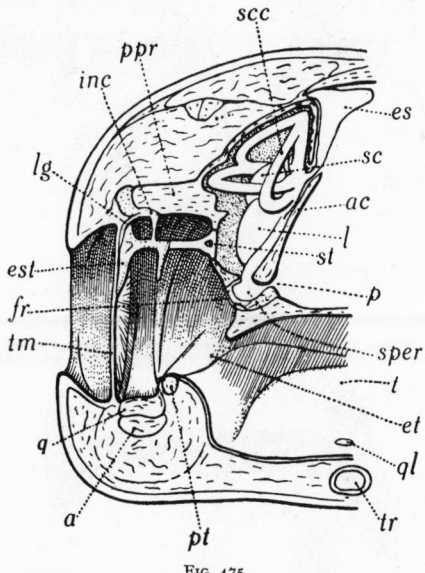

FIG. 475.

Left half of head of *Lacertilian* cut transversely through tympanic cavity and seen from behind
(from figures of J. Versluys).  *a*, Articular ;  *ac*, inner wall of auditory capsule ;  *es*, endolymphatic
sac ;  *est*, extra-stapedial cartilage ;  *et*, Eustachian tube ;  *fr*, fenestra rotunda ;  *q*, quadrate ;  *inc*,
intercalary, end of dorsal process ;  *l*, lagena ;  *p*, ductus perilymphaticus ;  *ppr*, paroccipital process
of opisthotic ;  *pt*, pterygoid ;  *gl*, glottis ;  *sc*, sacculus ;  *scc*, semicircular canal ;  *sper*, saccus perilymphaticus ;  *st*, stapes ;  *t*, tongue ;  *tm*, tympanic membrane ;  *tr*, trachea.

(extra-stapes), generally called the extra-columella.  The stapedial region
is made up of a bony rod with a cartilaginous foot-plate embedded in the
membrane closing the fenestra ovalis.  The cartilaginous extra-stapedial
region has its expanded outermost part embedded in the tympanic
membrane ; it also bears a processus internus (quadrate process) passing
downwards and forwards in the roof of the tympanic cavity, and a more
important processus dorsalis (supra-stapedial of Parker, and pr. paroticus
of Gaupp).  This latter dwindles to a ligament in the adult, except for
its upper end, which remains as a nodule (intercalary of Versluys) lodged
between the quadrate and paroccipital process (crista parotica) of the audi-

tory capsule. A strong ligament passes from the dorsal process to the outer side of the extra-stapedial. Within the Order Lacertilia the columella varies but little ; but it should be noted that the internal process is lost in the Geckonidae, Uroplatidae, and Amphisbaenidae, that in these and

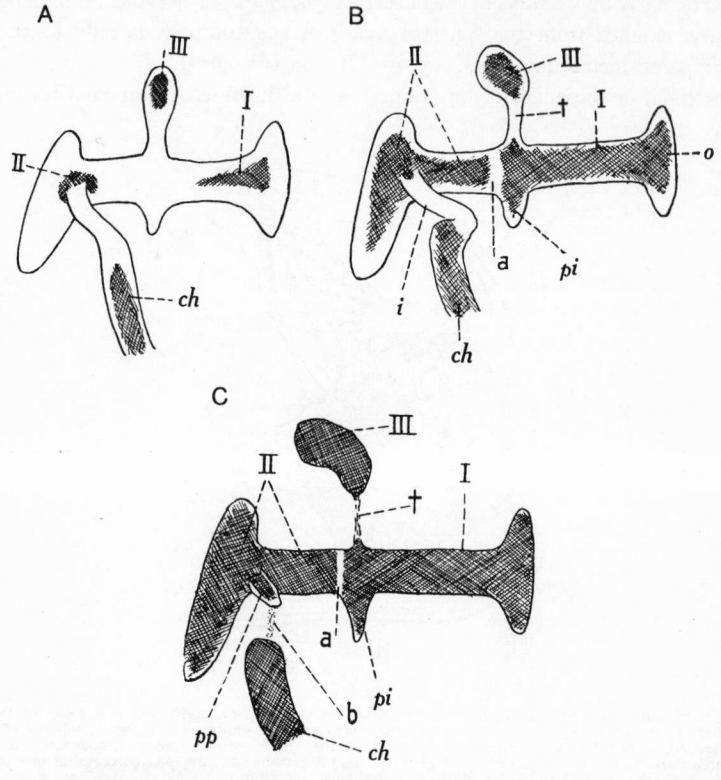

FIG. 476.

Diagrams of development of left columella auris in a *Lacertilian* ; posterior view (from J. Versluys, *Zool. Jahrb.*, 1903). A, Earliest, and C, latest stage. Blastema outlined, cartilage shaded. *I*, Otostapedial ; *II*, hyostapedial ; *III*, pars dorsalis of dorsal process (intercalary) ; *a*, temporary limit between *I* and *II* ; *ch*, cornu hyale ; *i*, pars interhyalis ; *o*, foot of otostapes fitting in fenestra ovalis ; *pi*, processus internus ; *pp*, processus posterior ; †, ligamentous vestige of base of proc. dorsalis.

a few others the ligamentous base of the dorsal process disappears, and that the base of the stapedial may be pierced by the facial (stapedial) artery in some Geckonids (Versluys, 770).

The columella is developed from the dorsal end of the hyoid arch, which is bent so as to abut against the auditory capsule at the fenestra ovalis. Its exact origin has given rise to much discussion, since many have held that the capsule contributes to its formation. In the blastematous, and even in the procartilaginous stage, the columella forms a continuous rudiment from the basal plate to the extra-stapes, and the latter is itself continuous with the top of the hyoid arch. As shown by Versluys in *Lacerta*, cartilage then appears in the proximal region of the stapes, in the dorsal process, in the extra-stapedial, and in the more ventral cornu of the hyoid arch. The proximal cartilage spreads outwards, forms the internal process, and becomes connected with the dorsal process; this whole region is known as the otostapes (Hoffmann, 737). The outer extra-stapedial element forms the processus inferior inserted in the tympanum, a small interhyal process, and grows inwards to meet the otostapes, from which it is distinguished as the hyostapes (Hoffmann, 737). The procartilaginous connexion of the hyoid cornu with the interhyal process dwindles to a mere ligament. In later stages the hyostapes fuses with the otostapes, the proximal region of the latter ossifies as a slender rod (stapes), and a new joint may be

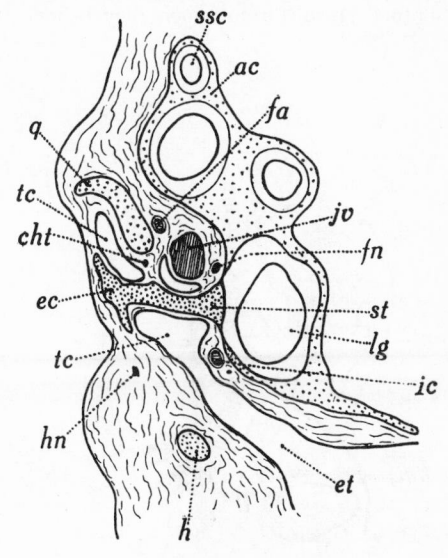

Fig. 477.

Transverse section through left auditory region of head of embryo *Lacerta*. *ac*, Auditory region; *cht*, chorda tympani; *ec*, extra-stapedial region; *et*, Eustachian tube; *fa*, stapedial (facial) artery; *fn*, hyomandibular nerve; *h*, hyoid; *jv*, jugular vein (v. capitis lateralis); *lg*, lagena; *q*, quadrate; *ssc*, semicircular canal; *st*, stapedial region of columella in fenestra ovalis; *tc*, tympanic cavity.

formed between its outer end and the cartilaginous adult extra-stapedial, Figs. 475-9.

This account of the development of the columella in *Lacerta* has been corroborated by observations on its origin in other Sauropsida since Reichert (1837) first described it in the bird, and Rathke (1839) in the snake. (Parker, Hoffmann, Gaupp, Versluys, Goodrich, 734, Rice, 376, in Lacertilia; Howes and Swinnerton, 528, Schauinsland, 583, Wyeth, 773, in *Sphenodon*; Parker, 570, Shiino, 597, in Crocodilia; Fuchs, 503, Kunkel, 540, Smith, 766, Bender, 706, Noack, 754, in Chelonia; Parker, 563, Möller, 753, Peyer, 759, Okajima, 755, Brock, 326, in

Ophidia ; Parker, 557, 568, 572, Sushkin, 608, G. W. Smith, 765, Sonies, 385, Goodrich, 734, in Aves.)

Although there is no doubt that the distal portion of the columella of Reptiles and Birds is derived from the hyoid arch ontogenetically as well as phylogenetically, it is not so certain that the whole of the proximal region is of the same origin. Several authors hold that the otostapes, or at all events its proximal base, is developed in continuity with the auditory capsule from which they believe it to be derived (Hoffmann,

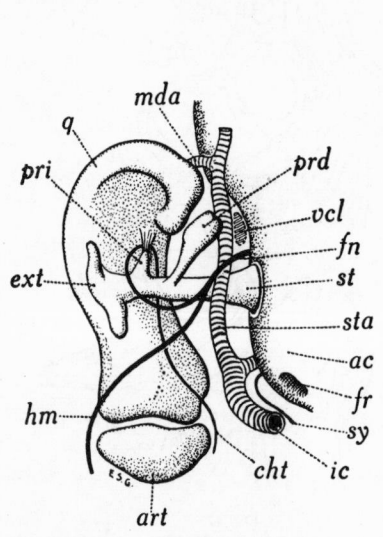

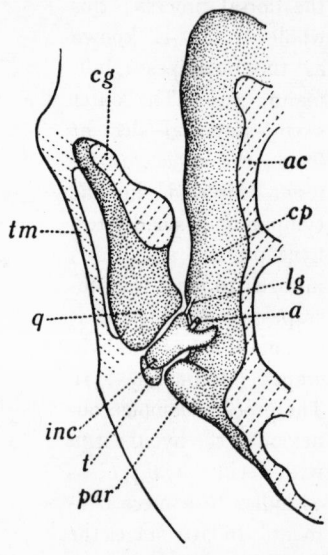

FIG. 478.

*Lacerta* embryo ; diagrammatic reconstruction of posterior view of auditory region showing columella auris, etc. *ac*, Auditory capsule ; *cht*, chorda tympani ; *ext*, extra-stapedial ; *fn*, hyomandibular branch of facial nerve ; *fr*, fenestra rotunda ; *hm*, hyoid nerve ; *ic*, internal carotid ; *mda*, mandibular artery ; *prd*, dorsal process ; *pri*, internal process ; *q*, quadrate ; *st*, stapedial region of columella fitting into fenestra ovalis ; *sta*, stapedial artery ; *sy*, sympathetic cord ; *vcl*, vena capitis lateralis in cranio-quadrate passage.

FIG. 479.

*Lacerta* embryo ; ventral view of articulation of quadrate to auditory capsule, showing intercalary cartilage wedged in between them. *a*, Artery ; *ac*, auditory capsule ; *cg*, cut surface of quadrate ; *cp*, crista parotica ; *inc*, extremity of dorsal process of columella (intercalare of Versluys) ; *lg*, ligament ; *par*, paroccipital process ; *q*, otic process of quadrate ; *t*, ventral end of supratemporal bone ; *tm*, tympanic membrane. Cartilage stippled.

Fuchs, in Lacertilia ; Möller, Okajima, in Chelonia ; and others). This view, however, seems to be conclusively disproved by careful observations on the very earliest appearance of the blastema of the columella in several forms (Versluys, 770, in Lacertilia ; Wyeth, 773, in *Sphenodon* ; G. W. Smith, 765, in *Gallus*), where it has been shown to arise separately. At most the capsular wall contributes to the formation of the cartilaginous base in some cases.

The structure of the columella is essentially the same throughout the

Reptilia; but usually the extra-stapedial (extra-columellar) region is less elaborately developed than in the Lacertilia, and the dorsal process is not separated off. Its various processes are not clearly formed in either Chelonians or Snakes; and in the latter the extra-stapedial region is not developed, and the distal end of the stapes becomes connected to the quadrate by a ligament or cartilaginous process probably representing the dorsal process.

The condition in *Sphenodon* is interesting (Huxley, **739**; Peters, 1874; Gadow, **730**; Versluys, **769**; Howes and Swinnerton, **528**; Kingsley, **745**; Osawa, **756**; Wyeth, **773**). Here the top of the hyoid cornu is continuous in the adult with the extra-stapedial; and this continuity is not secondary, as some supposed (Peters, Baur, Gadow, Osawa), but due to the retention of the original continuity visible in the procartilaginous stage in *Sphenodon* as in other

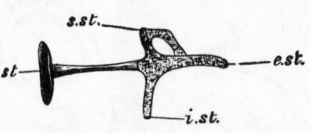

FIG. 480.

*Columba livia.* The columella auris (magnified). The cartilaginous parts are dotted. *e.st,* Extra-stapedial; *i.st,* infra-stapedial; *s.st,* supra-stapedial; *st,* stapes. (From Parker's *Zootomy.*)

Reptilia (Schauinsland, **583**; Wyeth, **773**). The dorsal process is joined to the extra-stapes by two limbs enclosing a foramen; in development the outer gives rise to the intercalary knob, while the inner grows down from it (Wyeth). Which of the two represents the base of the dorsal process in *Lacerta* is uncertain; probably the inner limb.

When the hyoid cornu becomes detached from the ' interhyal ' or infra-stapedial process of the columella, it may remain free (some Lacertilia, Ophidia, Chelonia), or it may become secondarily attached to the skull, generally by means of the intercalary (Geckonida).

In general structure and in development the columella auris of the Crocodilia resembles that of the Lacertilia (Parker, **579**; Shiino, **597**; Goldby, **733**). At first the extra-stapes is continuous by its infra-stapedial process with the ' ceratohyal ' or cornu of the hyoid; but later this middle region of the arch separates from the ventral portion and acquires a temporary connexion with the hind end of Meckel's cartilage. This remarkable fusion of parts of the hyoid and mandibular arches is soon dissolved, the connexion with Meckel's being lost in the adult. It seems to be secondary and of no great significance, Fig. 483 A.

In the embryo Chelonian the blastema of the extra-stapes may attempt, so to speak, to join the articular, but continuity is not established (Smith, **766**; Shaner, **596**).

The columella auris of Birds bears some resemblance to that of

*Sphenodon* on the one hand, and of *Crocodilus* on the other, Fig. 480. For the extra-stapedial region, though it may branch into separate processes (as in *Gallus*), is often pierced by a foramen, and carries in addition to the dorsal process (supra-stapedial) a long infra-stapedial process which may remain in continuity with the 'stylohyal' region of the hyoid

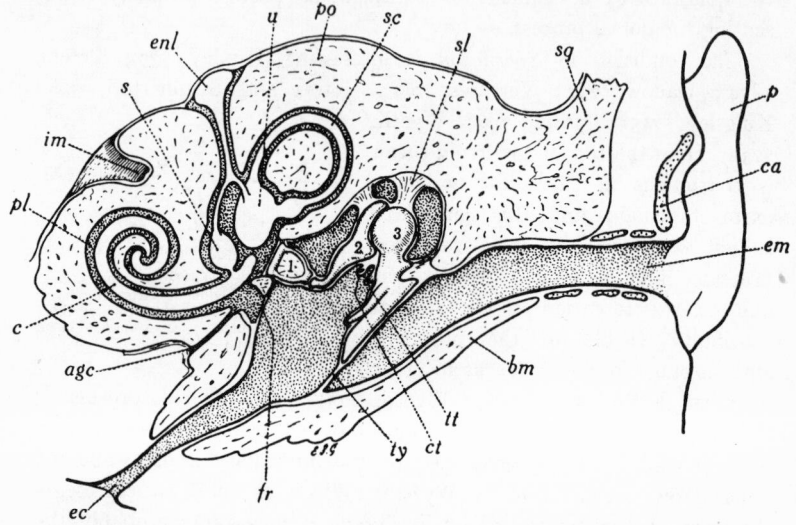

Fig. 481.

Diagram of *auditory organ* of *mammal*, seen in section. *agc*, Aquaeductus cochleae ; *bm*, bony meatus ; *c*, ductus cochlearis ; *ca*, cartilage ; *ct*, chorda tympani ; *em*, external meatus ; *enl*, saccus endolymphaticus ; *fr*, fenestra rotunda ; *im*, foramen for auditory nerve ; *p*, external pinna ; *pl*, perilymphatic cavity ; *po*, periotic ; *s*, sacculus ; *sc*, semicircular canal ; *sl*, suspensory ligament ; *sq*, squamosal ; *tt*, attachment of tensor tympani ; *ty*, tympanic membrane ; *u*, utriculus ; 1, stapes ; 2, incus ; 3, malleus.

arch. From the extra-stapes stretches forward Platner's ligament to the quadrate.

The early fossil Reptiles had a columella stretching from the fenestra ovalis to the quadrate, Figs. 334, 381. There is evidence of a dorsal process ; but the presence of an extra-stapes on the tympanum is doubtful since only the proximal region is ossified. The Cotylosauria have a stout bony stapes, perforated for the stapedial artery, and articulated to a distinct facet on the quadrate. In Ophiacodontidae and related forms a dorsal process reaches the paroccipital crest ; but in the more advanced Theromorphs the stapes approaches the mammalian type (p. 474). On the other hand, the stapes of the Seymouriamorpha is widely separated from the bony quadrate and resembles that of the Stegocephalia (Sushkin, **768**).

Turning now to the Mammalia, we find that three ear ossicles occur throughout the class (p. 449). The malleus has a processus anterior (processus Folii, or gracilis ; see p. 476) projecting forwards, and a manubrium fixed to the tympanic membrane ; by its head it is attached to the next ossicle, the incus, whose processus longus articulates with the outer end of the stapes (Frey, **724**). The latter, a pierced stirrup-shaped bone, has a basal plate fitting into the fenestra ovalis,[1] Figs. 481, 497-8.

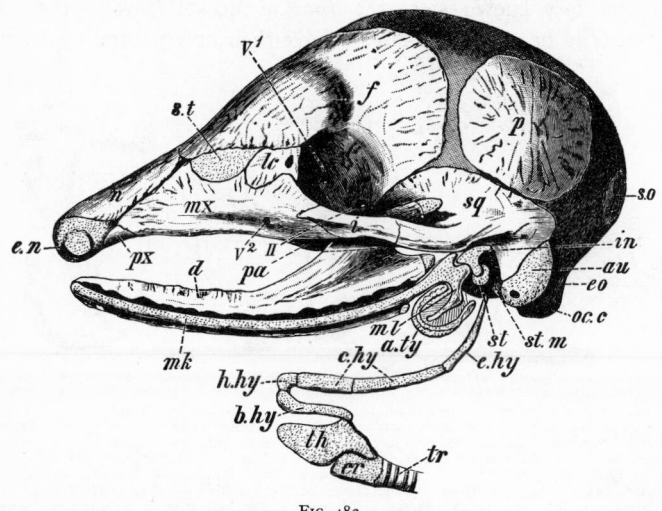

FIG. 482.

Skull of embryo of armadillo (*Tatusia hybrida*). (Modified from a drawing by W. K. Parker.) *a.ty*, Tympanic annulus ; *au*, auditory capsule ; *b.hy*, basihyal ; *c.hy*, ceratohyal ; *cr*, cricoid ; *d*, dentary ; *e.hy*, epihyal ; *e.n*, external nostril ; *eo*, exoccipital ; *f*, frontal ; *h.hy*, hypohyal ; *i*, jugal ; *in*, incus ; *lc*, lacrimal ; *mk*, Meckel's cartilage ; *ml*, malleus ; *mx*, maxilla ; *n*, nasal ; *oc.c*, occipital condyle ; *p*, parietal ; *pa*, palatine ; *px*, premaxilla ; *so*, supraoccipital ; *st*, stapes ; *s.t*, ethmoturbinal ; *st.m*, stapedius muscle ; *sq*, squamosal ; *th*, thyroid ; *tr*, trachea ; *II*, optic foramen ; *V¹*, *V²*, foramina through which the first and second divisions of the trigeminal pass out from the orbit. (From Wiedersheim, *Comp. Anatomy*.)

A very large number of observers have studied the development of the ear ossicles in various mammals since Reichert, 1837 (see Gaupp for literature up to 1913 (**731-2**), and van der Klaauw from 1899 to 1924 (**748a**)). Though the earlier workers often reached very discordant conclusions, the results of the best modern research have on the whole strongly supported the theory of Reichert. It may be considered as firmly established that the incus, malleus, and cartilage of the mandible

[1] The ossicles differ considerably in bulk and shape in the various groups (Hyrtl, Doran, **714**). In many Marsupials (Dasyuridae, Phalangistidae, Peramelidae) and in the Monotremes the stapes is imperforate and columelliform, but this condition appears to be secondary since, in *Ornithorhynchus* and *Trichosurus* at all events, it surrounds the stapedial artery in the blastematous stage (Goodrich, **734**).

are developed from an originally continuous blastematous rudiment (Salensky, 762 ; Gradenigo, Baumgarten, Dreyfus ; Kingsley and Ruddick, 746 ; Broman, 708 ; Jenkinson, 740 ; Goodrich, 734), that the incus chondrifies separately and later comes close to and even articulates with the crista parotica of the auditory capsule dorsally and the malleus ventrally, and that the cartilage of the malleus remains in continuity with the rest of Meckel's cartilage until a quite late stage, a striking fact known since the time of Meckel (1820). These and other facts to be mentioned later receive their only natural explanation

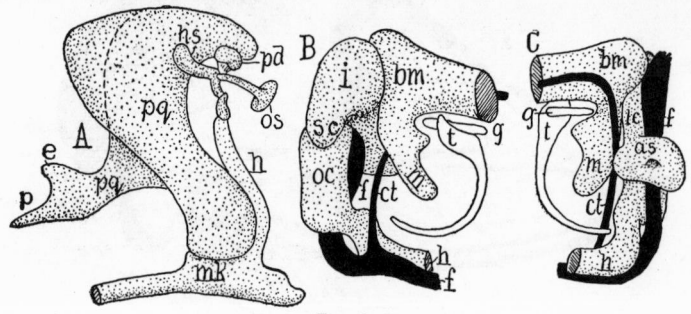

FIG. 483.

Development of auditory ossicles and related parts in A, *Crocodilus*, and B and C, *Man*. A, Outer view of palatoquadrate, *pq* ; Meckel's cartilage, *mk* ; and columella of late embryo. *e*, Processus ascendens ; *h*, hyoid ; *hs*, hyostapes ; *p*, pterygoid process ; *pd*, dorsal process ; *os*, otostapes. B, Lateral, and C, medial view of human embryo, 16 mm. long. *as*, Stapes ; *bm*, body of malleus ; *ct*, chorda tympani ; *f*, facial nerve ; *g*, prearticular (gonial) ; *i*, incus ; *lc*, long crus of incus ; *m*, manubrium mallei ; *mk*, Meckelian cartilage ; *oc*, auditory capsule ; *sc*, short crus of incus ; tympanic bone. (A after Parker, '83 ; B and C after Bromann, '99 ; from J. S. Kingsley, *Vertebrate Skeleton*, 1925.)

on the supposition that the incus and malleus represent the quadrate and articular, Figs. 482, 487-9, 494, 496-7.

On the other hand, it has been conclusively shown that the stapes develops from the hyoid arch, the earliest rudiment of which forms a continuous blastema separate from that of the mandibular arch (Kingsley, 745 ; Broman, 708 ; Jenkinson, 740 ; Goodrich, 734). The top end of the rudiment is bent at an angle so that its innermost extremity is continuous with the tissue closing the fenestra ovalis, Figs. 483-4. Here develops the stapes, as a ring round the stapedial artery, and it chondrifies separately from the ear capsule. The more distal (interhyal of some authors) ' hyostapedial ligament' remains for a time uniting the stapes to the dorsal end of the 'laterohyal' ('tympanohyal') region of the hyoid cornu, but disappears later. Meanwhile, the laterohyal and more ventral region of the cornu form a continuous cartilage which fuses with the paroccipital process of the auditory capsule. Later the dorsal region of the cornu below the laterohyal degenerates into a ligament, leaving, however, in man a considerable portion to form the styloid process (p. 446).

Comparing the mammal with the reptile, the laterohyal region in the former is seen to correspond to the dorsal process of the extra-stapedial region of the Reptilian columella, Figs. 495-6. The mammalian stapes would, then, represent the proximal region of the columella without its extra-stapedial bar and insertion in the tympanum. However, two little

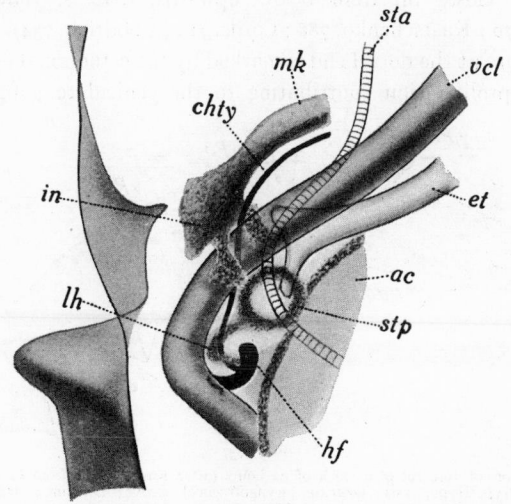

FIG. 484.

Dorsal view of reconstructed thick transverse section of left auditory region of embryo mouse, *Mus musculus*, showing ear ossicles in blastematous stage : *stp*, stapes continuous with blastema of hyoid arch ; *in*, incus and malleus continuous with each other and remainder of mandibular arch. *ac*, Auditory capsule ; *chty*, chorda tympani ; *et*, Eustachian tube ; *lh*, laterohyal ; *mk*, Meckel's cartilage ; *sta*, stapedial artery ; *vcl*, vena capitis lateralis. (E. S. Goodrich, *Quart. Jour. Micr. Sci.*, 1915.)

cartilages have been found which may represent remnants of parts of the extra-stapedial region, as suggested by van Kampen (1915) and van der Klaauw (748). The first is minute and situated in the tendon of the stapedial muscle. Discovered by the Dutch anatomist Paauw in 1645, it has since been described in man and a large number of Placentals and Marsupials (Parker, Hyrtl, Rauber), and originates from the outer end of the stapes (v. d. Klaauw, 748). The second cartilage is of doubtful origin ; it was first described by Spence in the cat (1890), and lies above the chorda tympani, between the stapes and the hyoid cornu. It has since been found in various other Mammalia (v. Kampen, 741 ; Bondy, 707 ; v. d. Klaauw, 748).

In order to establish the theory of Reichert we must now examine

the corroborative evidence from other parts in the middle ear. That the
Eustachian tube and tympanic cavity correspond in a general way
to the first or spiracular gill-slit has long been held (Huschke, 1831); but
it is no longer supposed that the tympanic membrane represents the wall
between the outgrowing endodermal pouch and the ectodermal ingrowth
which becomes pierced in the development of an ordinary gill-slit. In
the Reptilia and Aves the spiracular slit is pierced as an elongated cleft
which soon closes up from below upwards, that is, ventro-dorsally
(Versluys, 770; Kastschenko, 788; Cords, 712; Goodrich, 734). The point
of final closure at the dorsal end is marked by the ectodermal epibranchial
placode, a proliferation contributing to the geniculate ganglion, Figs.

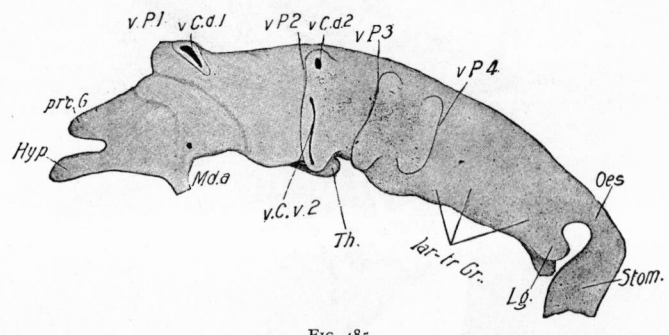

FIG. 485.

Reconstruction of fore-gut of a chick of 72 hours (after Kastschenko, from F. R. Lillie, *Develt.
Chick*, 1919). *Hyp*, Hypophysis; *lar-tr.Gr*, laryngotracheal groove; *Lg*, lung; *Md.a*, mandibular
arch; *Oes*, oesophagus; *pro.G*, preoral gut; *Stom*, stomach; *Th*, thyroid; *v.C.d*,1, 2, dorsal division
of first and second visceral clefts; *v.P.*1, 2, 3, 4, first, second, third, and fourth visceral pouches.

485-6, 495. The tympanic cavity arises from the more ventral and inner
region of the endodermal gill-pouch as a tympanic diverticulum which
expands and, becoming applied to the ectoderm, forms the tympanic
membrane.[1] In *Lacerta*, as the diverticulum enlarges it tends to surround
the columella which comes to project into the tympanic cavity from above
and behind, suspended by a fold of the lining membrane except in the
extra-columellar region, where the fold is obliterated by the junction of
an anterior with a posterior pocket. The closure of the spiracular slit,
development of the tympanic cavity from the more ventral region of the
gill-pouch, and formation of the membrane are very similar in other
Reptiles and in Birds, Figs. 485-6.

Thus the tympanic cavity and tympanum lie between the mandibular
and hyoid arches, and the columella is morphologically posterior to them.

[1] The view of some authors (for instance, Wyeth in *Sphenodon*, 773; Bender
in *Testudo*, 706) that the second gill-slit contributes to the tympanic cavity
does not seem to be well founded.

Just as in the Reptilia, so in the Mammalia the tympanic cavity and Eustachian tube are developed from the first or spiracular gill-pouch (Kastschenko, 787; Hammar, 736; Goodrich, 734). Although the cleft does

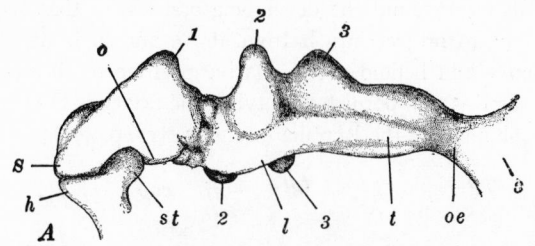

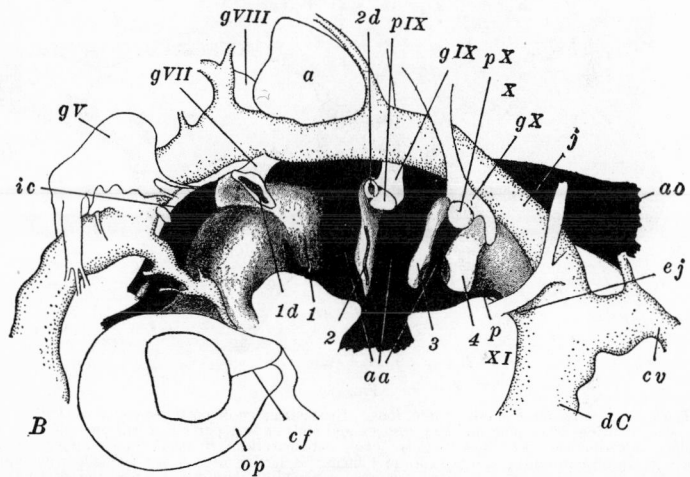

FIG. 486.

Models of pharynx and associated structures in chick (after Kastschenko, from W. E. Kellicott, *Chordate Develt.*, 1913). A, Ventro-lateral view of pharynx at beginning of third day. B, Later view of pharynx and associated nervous and vascular structures at end of third day. Nervous structures are left unshaded; arteries in solid black; veins lightly stippled; pharyngeal structures darkly stippled. *a*, Auditory sac; *aa*, aortic arches; *ao*, dorsal arches; *cf*, choroid fissure; *cv*, posterior cardinal vein; *dC*, ductus Cuvieri; *ej*, external jugular vein; *gV*, Gasserian ganglion of V. cranial nerve; *gVII*, geniculate ganglion of VII cranial nerve; *gVIII*, acustic ganglion of VIII. cranial nerve; *gIX*, ganglion petrosum of IX. cranial nerve; *gX*, ganglion nodosum of X. cranial nerve; *h*, hypophysis; *ic*, internal carotid artery; *j*, internal jugular vein; *l*, rudiment of larynx; *o*, oral evagination of fore-gut; *oe*, oesophagus; *op*, optic vesicle enclosing lens; *p*, pulmonary artery; *pIX*, placode of IX. cranial nerve; *pX*, placode of X. cranial nerve; *s*, stomach; *S*, Seessel's pocket (preoral gut); *st*, stomodaeum; *t*, rudiment of trachea; 1-4, first to fourth visceral pouches (or their ventral position, in B); *1d*, *2d*, dorsal portions of first and second visceral pouches; *IX*, glossopharyngeal nerve; *X*, vagus nerve; *XI*, hypoglossal nerve.

not appear ever to be pierced, yet the endodermal pouch comes in contact with the ectoderm in early stages between the blastematous rudiments of the mandibular and hyoid arches. The pouch soon peels off, the last contact being at that dorsal point where the ganglionic proliferation takes place. A tympanic postero-ventral diverticulum grows out, and becoming applied to a deep ectodermal invagination (external auditory meatus) forms the tympanum (see, further, p. 469). As the tympanic cavity expands it tends to surround the developing ossicles, so that the incus and malleus come to project into it from above and in front, and the stapes from above and behind. The relative position of these parts is essentially the same as that borne by the tympanic cavity to the quadrate, articular, and columella in the Reptilia (see, however, p. 477).

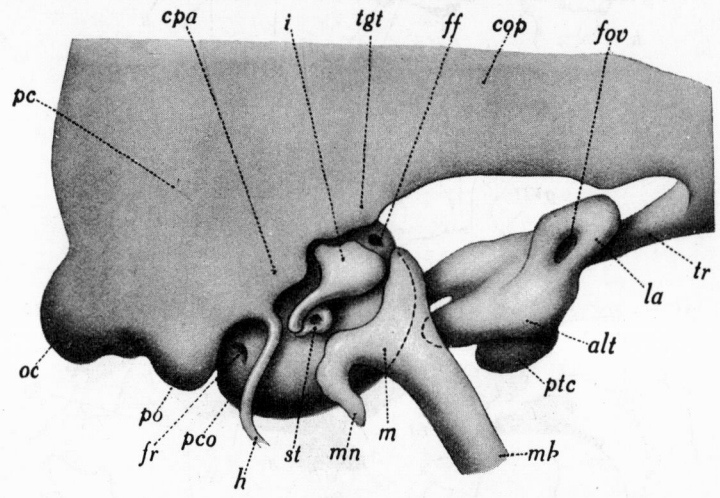

FIG. 487.

*Trichosurus vulpecula*, embryo 17 mm. long. Reconstruction of posterior region of skull; right-side view showing developing auditory ossicles and surrounding parts in cartilage. *alt*, Ala temporalis; *cop*, commissura orbito-parietalis; *cpa*, crista parotica; *ff*, facial foramen; *fov*, foramen ovale; *fr*, fenestra rotunda; *h*, hyoid cornu; *i*, incus; *la*, lamina ascendens; *m*, malleus continuous with Meckel's cartilage, *mk*; *mn*, manubrium; *oc*, occipital condyle; *pc*, pars canalicularis, and *pco*, pars cochlearis of auditory capsule; *po*, parotic process; *ptc*, pterygoid cartilage; *st*, stapes; *tgt*, tegmen tympani; *tr*, trabecula.

Of particular importance in this connexion is the position of the facial nerve and its branch the chorda tympani (Versluys, 769; Gaupp, 732; Kingsley, 745; Broman, 708; Goodrich, 734). The facial nerve in Reptilia issues from the cranial cavity by the facial foramen, and having given off the palatine branch, passes back outside the auditory capsule, runs above the columella, below the crista parotica, medial to the dorsal process and hyoid cornu, then continues down the hyoid, Figs. 477, 478, 495. On its downward course this main hyomandibular branch of the facial gives off the chorda tympani, which passes forwards lateral to the hyoid, over the tympanic cavity and columella, then downwards along the posterior surface of the quadrate to the inner side of the articular. Thence it runs forwards along Meckel's cartilage,

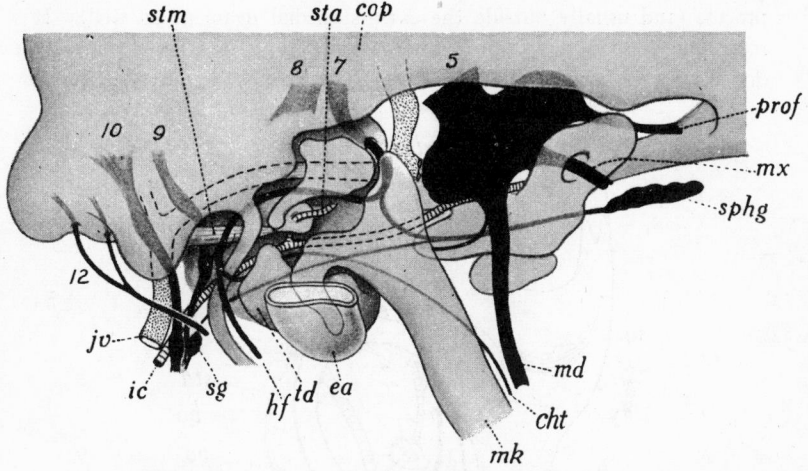

FIG. 488.

*Trichosurus vulpecula.* Same as Fig. 487, but with nerves, blood-vessels, etc., added. Nerves black ; arteries cross-lined ; veins stippled. Cartilage represented as transparent. *cop*, Commissura orbito-parietalis ; *ea*, inner part of external auditory meatus ; *md, mx*, mandibular and maxillary branches ; *prof*, profundus branch of fifth nerve ; *sg*, superior cervical sympathetic ganglion ; *td*, outer wall of tympanic diverticulum. Other letters as in Figs. 487 and 489.

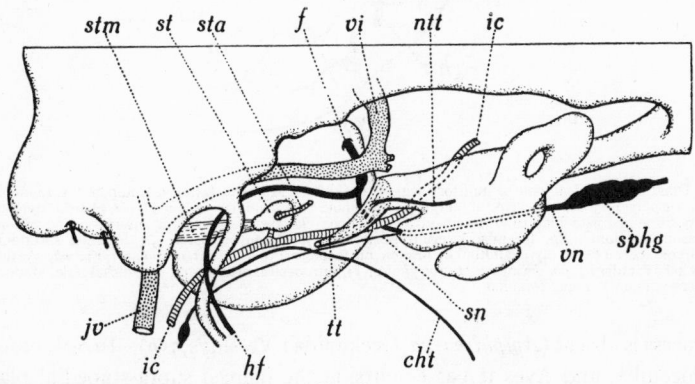

FIG. 489.

*Trichosurus vulpecula.* Same view as in Fig. 487, but with incus and malleus removed, and muscles, nerves, and blood-vessels inserted. *cht*, Chorda tympani ; *f*, facial nerve ; *hf*, hyoid branch ; *ic*, internal carotid ; *jv*, jugular vein (v. capitis lateralis) ; *ntt*, branch of trigeminal nerve ; *sphg*, sphenopalatine ganglion ; *sn*, sympathetic nerve from superior cervical ganglion ; *sta*, stapedial artery ; *stm*, stapedial muscle innervated from facial ; *tt*, m. tensor tympani ; *vi*, middle cerebral vein ; *vn*, vidian nerve formed by union of sympathetic with palatine.

anastomosing with the mandibular branch of the trigeminal nerve and supplying the lining of the mouth in the region of the lower jaw and

tongue (see p. 752).[1]   Further, it should be noticed that the chorda
tympani when crossing over the extra-stapedial passes outside the dorsal
process (and usually outside the extra-stapedial ligament as well).   It
may, however, slip forward, so to speak, and pass more directly
downwards in front of the columella in those forms in which the dorsal

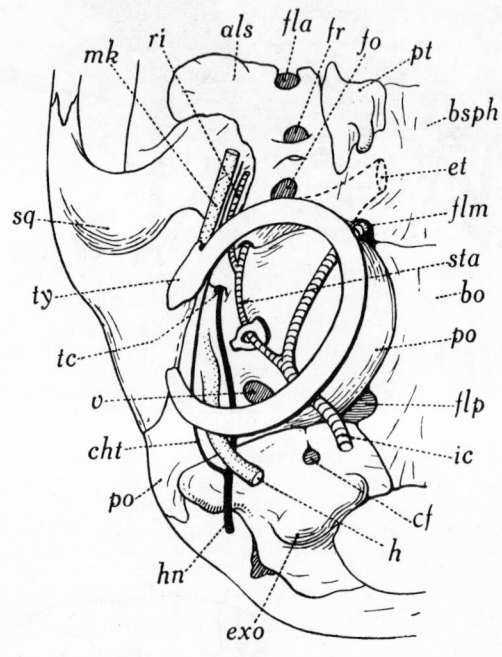

FIG. 490.

Diagram of ventral view of auditory region of skull of *Mammal* (after v. Kampen, '05, modified). *als*, Alisphenoid ; *bo*, basioccipital ; *bsph*, basisphenoid ; *cf*, condylar foramen ; *cht*, chorda tympani ; *et*, position of Eustachian tube drawn in broken line ; *fla*, foramen lacerum anterius ; *flm*, foramen lacerum medium ; *flp*, foramen lacerum posterius ; *fo*, foramen ovale ; *fr*, foramen rotundum ; *h*, hyoid cornu ; *hn*, hyomandibular branch of facial nerve ; *ic*, internal carotid ; *mk*, vestigial Meckel's cartilage ; *po*, periotic ; *pt*, pterygoid ; *ri*, infraorbital artery ; *sq*, squamosal ; *sta*, stapedial artery ; *tc*, outer facial foramen.

process is absent (*Amphisbaena*, Geckonida : Versluys, 769).   In *Sphenodon*,
Crocodilia, and Aves it passes outside the pierced supra-stapedial plate
(dorsal process).

Such is the course of the facial nerve and chorda tympani in the
middle ear of the embryo and adult of Reptiles and Birds.   Now the
chorda tympani is a postspiracular nerve, and its peculiar position in the

[1] In the adult the chorda runs inside the lower jaw, a position it reaches
usually by piercing the prearticular bone (goniale), as Gaupp has shown (732).

adult, close behind the quadrate and in front of the tympanum, needs
elucidation. The explanation is that, although in early stages the chorda
is found developing as a distinctly postspiracular branch of the hyomandibular nerve, when the slit closes the chorda gets pushed forward
and upward as the tympanic diverticulum expands behind it, Fig. 494*a*
(Versluys, 770; Goodrich, 734).

In the adult mammal the chorda tympani runs forwards over the roof
of the tympanic cavity in a fold of its lining membrane, passing between

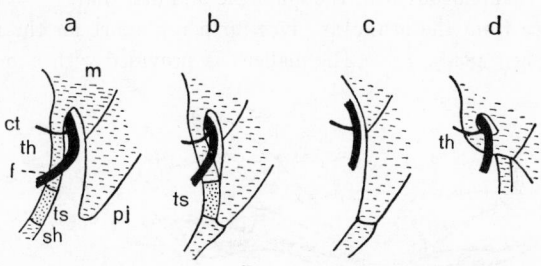

FIG. 491.

Diagrams showing fixation of hyoid to periotic, and its relation to facial nerve and chorda tympani
in various Mammalia (after P. N. van Kampen, '05, from M. Weber, *Saügetiere*, 1927). *ct*, Chorda
tympani; *f*, facial; *m*, periotic; *pj*, paroccipital process; *sh*, stylohyal; *th*, tympanohyal; *ts*,
tympano-styloid cartilage.

the crus longus incudis and the manubrium mallei, Figs. 481, 490 ; it
then turns downwards behind and below these ossicles to the lower jaw.
The general relations of the facial nerve are the same in the mammalian
embryo as in the reptilian, Figs. 484, 488-9, 496. Issuing by the facial
foramen, it gives off the palatine branch, then runs round the outer side
of the auditory capsule below the overhanging tegmen tympani and
below the crista parotica in a groove, which may be more or less
completely converted into a canal. From this it escapes behind the
stylohyal by the primitive stylomastoid foramen. On its way down the
hyoid cornu the hyomandibular nerve gives off the chorda tympani,
which passes forwards outside the cornu ; except in some Marsupials,
such as *Didelphys* (Gaupp; Toeplitz, 391), *Dasyurus* (Cords, Esdaile,
722), *Phascolarctus* (v. d. Klaauw, 748), and in *Manis* (v. Kampen, 741),
where it passes medially.[1] Similarly the hyomandibular nerve and the
chorda may in some mammals pass freely outside the hyoid cornu,
Fig. 491. Running over the tympanic cavity, the chorda tympani does
not come into close relation with the stapes, since there is no extra-
stapedial ; but it passes ‘ morphologically ’ over it and then posteriorly
to the incus to reach the inner side of the malleus, whence it continues

[1] This unusual position of the nerve seems to be secondary.

along Meckel's cartilage. In spite of many statements to the contrary, it has been conclusively shown that the chorda tympani in the mammal develops early as a postspiracular branch of the facial nerve (Froriep, 725; Broman, 708; Emmel, 719; Goodrich, 734); but in later stages it runs anteriorly to the tympanum and for the same reason throughout the Amniota. The chorda tympani, then, is postspiracular in the embryo and pretympanic in the adult.[1] Its relation to the ossicles can only satisfactorily be accounted for on the supposition that the incus and malleus are homologous with the quadrate and articular.

Evidence from the muscles gives further support for the theory of Reichert, Figs. 488-9, 492. The malleus is provided with a muscle (m.

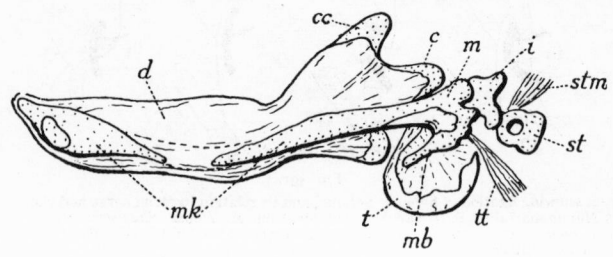

FIG. 492.

Right ramus of lower jaw of embryo *Erinaceus europaeus*, 3 inches long (after W. K. Parker, 1885). *d*, Dentary; *c*, condylar cartilage; *cc*, coronoid cartilage; *i*, incus; *m*, malleus with dermal bone (prearticular); *mb*, manubrium; *mk*, Meckel's cartilage; *st*, stapes; *stm*, stapedial muscle; *t*, tympanic; *tt*, tensor tympani muscle.

tensor tympani) attached to its medial surface and passing forwards towards the base of the skull; and to the stapes is attached a stapedial muscle passing backwards medially to the paroccipital region (Hagenbach, 1833; Parker, 561, 567; Eschweiler, 740-41; Bondy, 707). Now the former is innervated by a twig of the trigeminal nerve, and the latter by a twig from the facial nerve, which is in agreement with the view that the malleus is derived from the prespiracular mandibular arch, and the stapes from the postspiracular hyoid arch. The musculus tensor tympani is generally considered to have originated in phylogeny from the m. pterygoideus, attached to the articular region of the lower jaw in the Sauropsida, a conclusion borne out by its development in the mammal from the same rudiment as the m. pterygoideus internus (Killian,

[1] It is a remarkable fact that the chorda tympani in the chick develops as a prespiracular nerve (Goodrich, 734). In adult Gallinaceous birds it passes downwards to the lower jaw in front of the tympanic cavity (Magnien, 751; G. W. Smith, 765). An explanation of its anomalous course and exceptional development may be that it is in these birds composed of sympathetic fibres only, the postspiracular facial fibres having disappeared.

742 ; Eschweiler, 720-21 ; Edgeworth, 718). The relation of its ligament to the chorda tympani varies. Usually it reaches the malleus below the nerve ; but in Sciurus and Equus it is pierced by the nerve, and in some (including Man and the Apes) it passes above (Bondy, 707).

The mammalian stapedial muscle is probably homologous with the similar extra-stapedial muscle of crocodiles and birds (Killian, 742 ; Goodrich, 734), and possibly with the Lacertilian ' extra-columellar muscle ' of the adult Geckonida and embryonic Lacerta (Versluys, 769-70), which, however, is lateral to the hyomandibular nerve. The musculus stapedius is derived from the same source as the Sauropsidan depressor mandibulae ; but appears to be really a levator hyoidei, since it is first attached to the stylohyal and then shifts to the stapes (Edgeworth, 718).

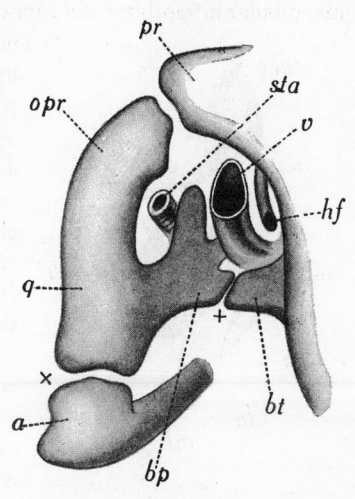

FIG. 493.

Diagram of auditory region of primitive Reptile (embryonic stage), looking from behind through cranio-quadrate passage. Lettering as in Fig. 494.

For the determination of the morphological relations of the parts of the middle ear the blood-vessels are scarcely less important than the nerves. In the reptilian and avian embryos the vena capitis lateralis (jugular vein, see p. 532) runs back from the orbit alongside the hyo-mandibular branch of the facial nerve, below the crista parotica to the neck. On its way it is medial to the quadrate, ventral to the attachment of the otic process, dorsal to the tympanic cavity and columella, and medial to the latter's dorsal process. The vena capitis lateralis of the mammalian embryo follows the same course, medial to the incus below its connexion with the auditory capsule, dorsal to the stapes and tympanic cavity, and medial to the laterohyal and cornu, Figs. 477, 489, 490, 493-6, 498.

The internal carotid, on its way to the hypophysial space, runs in all Tetrapods between the base of the skull above and the pharynx below. It gives off in the embryonic mammal a branch which passes outwards over the tympanic cavity, pierces the stapes, runs on the medial side of the incus below its connexion with the skull to the orbit, where it divides into supraorbital, infraorbital, and mandibular branches (see p. 529). This stapedial artery is developed at or near the upper end of the second or hyoidean arterial arch, and is always present in the embryo, though the region piercing the stapes may be suppressed in the adult (as in man, see p. 531). An arteria stapedialis or facialis, similar in its general distribution and origin to the a. stapedialis of mammals, occurs also in the lower Tetrapods (see p. 530). Typically it runs over the tympanic cavity, medially to the quadrate and below the otic process forwards, giving off mandibular infraorbital and supraorbital branches. It corresponds in the

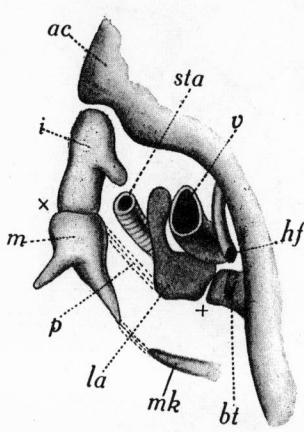

FIG. 494.

Diagram of auditory region of Mammal (embryonic stage) looking from behind through cranio-quadrate passage. *a,* Articular region of mandibular ; *ac,* auditory capsule ; *bp,* basal process ; *bt,* basitrabecular process (pr. alaris) ; *i,* incus ; *hf,* hyomandibular branch of facial nerve ; *la,* lamina ascendens; *m,* malleus ; *mk,* anterior part of Meckel's cartilage ; *opr,* otic process ; *p,* part of palato-quadrate which has disappeared ; *pr,* parotic process ; *q,* quadrate region of palato-quadrate ; *sta,* stapedial artery ; *v,* vena capitis lateralis ; +, basal (basipterygoid) articulation ; ×, original articulation of lower jaw.

middle-ear region exactly to the mammalian a. stapedialis, but varies in its relation to the base of the columella. In certain Geckonids (*Pachydactylus, Hemidactylus, Tarentola* ; Versluys, 769) and certain birds (*Procellaria, Aquila* ; Breschet, 1844 ; Doran, 714) it pierces the columella, but in certain other Geckonids (Versluys, 770) and in *Sphenodon* (Versluys, 770 ; Wyeth, 773) it runs ventrally to it, while in the majority of reptiles it passes dorsally to it. The first condition is probably primitive and the other two secondary. There can be little doubt that a stapedial artery passed through the foramen often found in the stapes of early fossil Reptilia and Amphibia (pp. 474 and 483).

**Summary.**—The chief points in the evidence with regard to the origin of the mammalian ear-bones may be summarised as follows : A comparison of the structure and development of the parts of the middle ear in Reptilia and Mammalia shows a remarkable similarity in the two groups.

From the continuous blastema of the mandibular arch, anterior to the first gill-pouch, are developed a dorsal element which becomes connected with the auditory capsule by the otic process, and a ventral Meckelian cartilage. The former becomes the quadrate in the Reptilia and the incus in the Mammalia. The posterior end of Meckel's cartilage forms the articular bone in the Reptilia and the malleus in the Mammalia, which becomes disconnected from the rest of the degenerating Meckelian cartilage. The primitive quadrato-articular joint is represented between the incus and malleus.

From the continuous blastema of the hyoid arch posterior to the first gill-pouch are developed a dorsal columella auris and a more ventral cornu hyale in the Reptilia. The columellar blastema forms later a proximal stapedial region fitting into the fenestra ovalis and a distal extra-stapedial region, which usually becomes disconnected from the hyoid cornu. From this extra-stapedial region extend a dorsal process, which connects with the paroccipital process of the skull, a quadrate

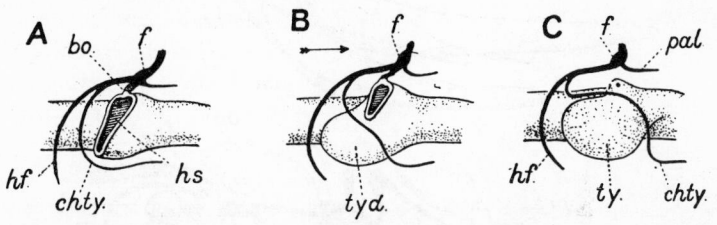

Fig. 494a.

Diagrams illustrating relation in *Amniota* of chorda tympani, *chty*, to hyoidean or spiracular slit, *hs*, and tympanic diverticulum, *tyd*, as shown in development. A, earliest, C, latest stage; right-side view. *bo*, Branchial placode; *f*, facial ganglion; *hf*, hyomandibular branch; *pal*, palatine branch. (From Goodrich, *Quart. Jour. Micr. Sci.*, 1915.)

process, and an outer part inserted in the tympanum. In the mammal the hyoid gives rise to a proximal stapes fitting into the fenestra ovalis. There is no insertion in the tympanum ; but a dorsal process for a time continuous with the hyoid cornu fuses with the crista parotica. This process (laterohyal or stylohyal) may be compared to the dorsal process of the Reptilia ; but the region between it and the stapes ('hyostapedial ligament') does not persist. The extra-stapedial region is thus less developed in the mammal ; the stapes is disconnected, and articulates now only with the incus (quadrate).[1]

[1] The acceptance of Reichert's theory does not necessarily commit us to the view that the Mammalia have been derived from forms, like the modern Reptilia, with a columella provided with a well-developed extra-stapedial region inserted in the tympanum. The position and fate of the laterohyal, the chief surviving element of the extra-stapes in the mammal, suggests that it was always posterior to the membrane. The ancestral stapes was probably stout, perforated, and attached distally to the quadrate (cp. early fossil Reptilia and Apoda). We have no clear evidence from the fossils whether or not its cartilaginous extremity spread over the tympanum, but an extra-stapedial cartilage may well have been present (Gregory, **735**). At all events the change from the reptilian to the mammalian condition was probably due to the reduced and loosened quadrate and articular being pushed in, so to speak, between the stapes and the tympanic membrane so as to form a chain of three firmly united elements connecting it to the fenestra ovalis. The retro-articular process of the reptilian articular may be compared to the manubrium mallei of the mammal.

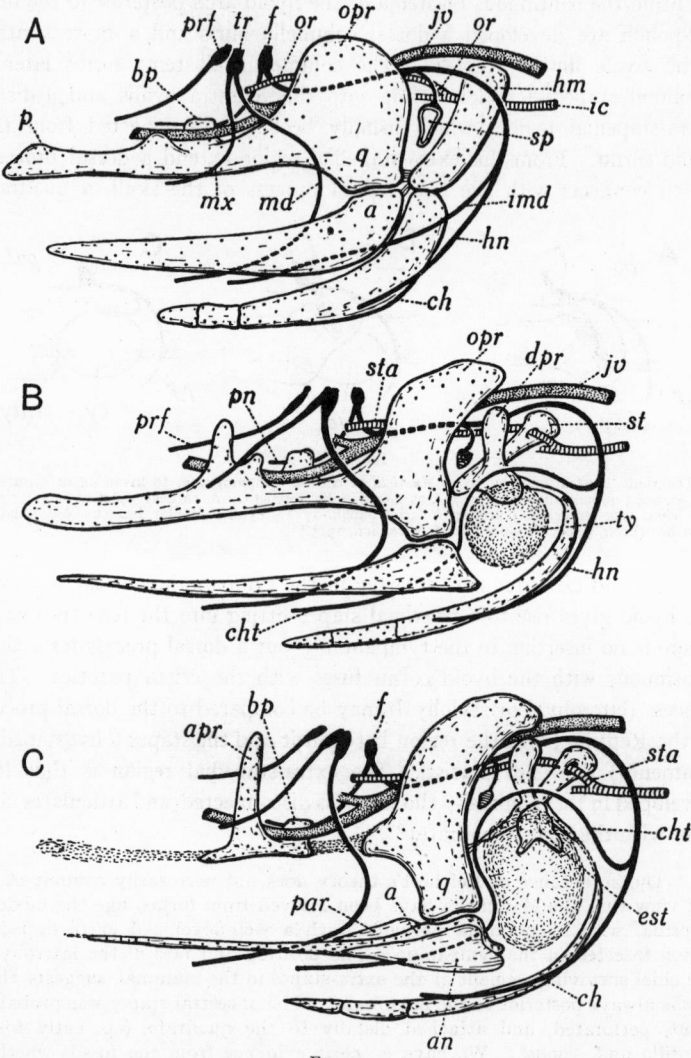

FIG. 495.

Diagrams showing relation of nerves (black), arteries (cross-lined), and veins (shaded) to *Mandibular and Hyoid* skeletal *visceral arches* (dotted) in : A, primitive autostylic Fish, B, primitive Tetrapod, and C, primitive Lacertilian. *a*, Articular region, *an*, angular bone ; *apr*, ascending process ; *bp*, basal process ; *ch*, ceratohyal ; *dpr*, dorsal process ; *f*, facial ; *hm*, hyomandibula ; *hn*, hyomandibular nerve ; *ic*, internal carotid ; *imd*, internal mandibular ; *jv*, jugular (v. capitis lateralis) ; *md*, mandibular ; *mx*, maxillary ; *opr*, otic process ; *or*, orbital = stapedial ; *p*, palatine region of palato-quadrate; *par*, prearticular bone ; *pn*, palatine ; *q*, quadrate region ; *sp*, spiracle (closed in B and C) ; *st*, stapes (base of columella) ; *sta*, stapedial ; *tr*, trigeminal ; *ty*, tympanic membrane.

The dorsal end of the hyoid cornu in Reptilia, which almost invariably becomes detached from the extra-stapedial, may become secondarily connected to the skull.[1]

The view that the stapes represents the proximal region of the columella, and that the incus and malleus represent the quadrate and articular, is further borne out by a consideration of the relation these ossicles bear to surrounding structures. In both Mammalia and Reptilia, as the spiracular or first endodermal gill-pouch separates from the ectoderm from

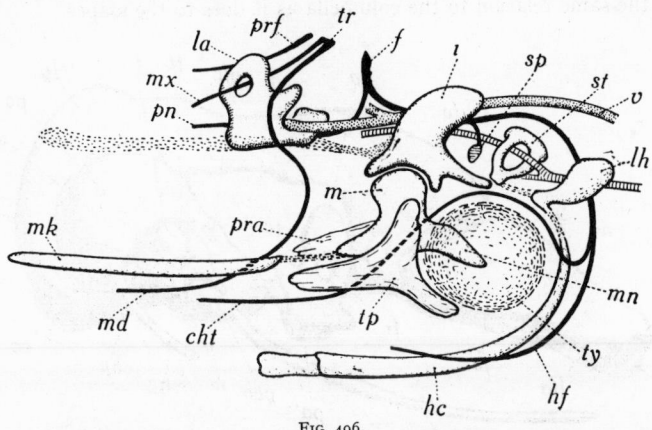

FIG. 496.

Diagram of the fate of the first two visceral arches and of their relation to nerves and blood-vessels in a *Mammal*. Left-side view. *cht*, Chorda tympani ; *f*, facial nerve ; *hc*, hyoid cornu ; *hf*, hyoid branch of facial ; *i*, incus ; *la*, lamina ascendens (epipterygoid cartilage) ; *lh*, latero-hyal, fuses with auditory capsule ; *m*, malleus ; *md*, mandibular branch ; *mk*, Meckel's cartilage ; *mn*, manubrium mallei ; *mx*, maxillary branch ; *pn*, palatine nerve ; *pra*, prearticular (processus anterior) ; *prf*, profundus nerve ; *sp*, position of closed spiracular slit and its placode ; *st*, stapes ; *tp*, tympanic (angular) ; *tr*, trigeminal nerve ; *ty*, tympanic membrane ; *v*, vena capitis lateralis. Stapedial artery, branch from internal carotid, passes through stapes ; these arteries are cross-lined.

below upwards, an ectodermal proliferation contributing to the facial ganglion marks the last point of contact (see p. 764). Whereas the proximal region of the pouch forms the Eustachian tube, a postero-ventral diverticulum of the pouch enlarges distally to form the tympanic cavity, and, becoming applied to the ectoderm, gives rise to the tympanic membrane between the mandibular and hyoid arches. This is not the original closing membrane of the spiracular slit ; but a new formation, developed in essentially the same manner and position in all Amniotes. The expanding tympanic cavity tends to surround the skeletal structures. As the cavity enlarges behind the quadrate in Reptiles the columella appears to sink into it from above and behind ; while in mammals, not

[1] The homology of the columella with the hyomandibula of fishes, of the chorda tympani, and of the stapedial artery is discussed elsewhere, see pp. 420, 464, 529, 752.

only does the stapes sink in from above and behind, but the incus and malleus from above and in front.

The relation of the facial nerve in its backward course over the columella in the Reptile is the same as that borne to the stapes in the Mammal. Of particular importance is the chorda tympani, a postspiracular but pretympanic branch of the facial which bears the same relation to the quadrate and articular as it does to the incus and malleus, and the same relation to the columella as it does to the stapes.

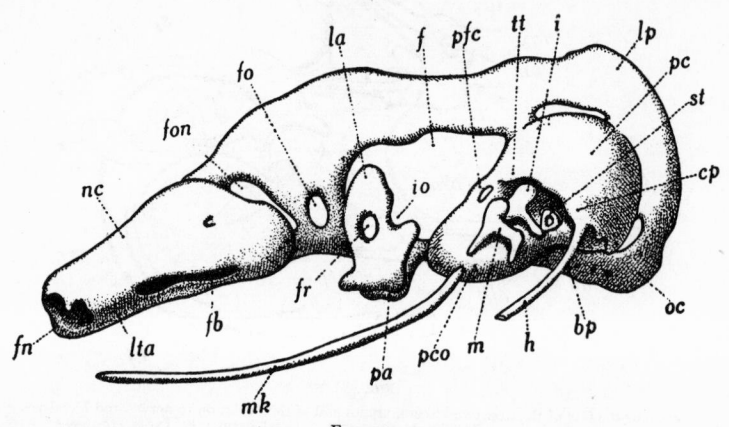

FIG. 497.

Diagram of cartilaginous skull of primitive Placental Mammal. *bp*, Fenestra rotunda; *cp*, crista parotica; *f*, fenestra pro-otica; *fb*, fenestra basalis closed behind by lamina transversa posterior; *fn*, fenestra narina; *fr*, foramen rotundum; *fo*, optic foramen; *fon*, fenestra orbitonasalis; *h*, hyoid cornu; *i*, incus; *io*, incomplete foramen ovale; *la*, lamina ascendens; *lp*, lateral plate; *lta*, lamina transversa anterior; *m*, malleus; *mk*, Meckel's cartilage; *nc*, nasal capsule; *oc*, occipital region; *pa*, basitrabecular process (pr. alaris); *pc*, canalicular region of auditory capsule, and *pco*, its cochlear region; *pfc*, prefacial commissure; *st*, stapes; *tt*, tegmen tympani.

The development and innervation (from the trigeminal) of the tensor tympani muscle, attached to the malleus, is in agreement with the view that it represents part of the pterygoid muscle attached to the articular region in the Sauropsida, and belongs to the prespiracular musculature of the mandibular arch; while the development and innervation of the stapedial muscle, attached to the mammalian stapes, is in agreement with the view that it belongs to the postspiracular musculature of the hyoid arch, and is probably homologous with a similar muscle belonging to the columella in certain Sauropsida. Probably it is a derivative of the depressor mandibulae, of which it appears to be the only remnant in the Mammal (Gaupp, 732; Edgeworth, 718; Futamura, 1907).

The course of the blood-vessels is the same in the two groups. The vena capitis lateralis, as it runs backward along the hyomandibular nerve, passes between the skull and the quadrate (that is to say, through the cranio-quadrate passage, see p. 412) ventrally to the articulation of the otic process and over the columella in the Reptile. In the Mammal it passes between the incus and the skull below the connexion of the incus to the crista parotica, and above the stapes. More striking is the fact that in the mammalian embryo the stapedial artery, derived from the root of the second aortic arch, runs forwards over the tympanic cavity,

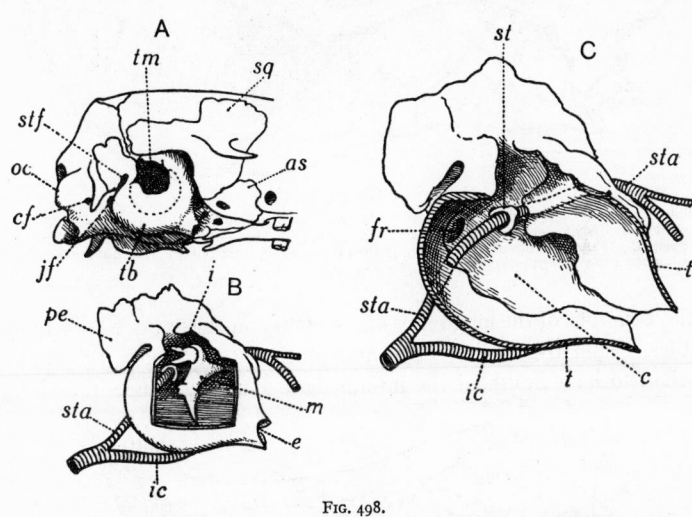

FIG. 498.

Right auditory region of skull of *Mus decumanus*, showing relation of *stapedial artery* to tympanic and auditory ossicles. A, Outer view ; B, with window cut in tympanic bulla ; C, cavity of bulla further exposed and incus and malleus removed. B and C more enlarged than A. *as*, Alisphenoid ; *c*, periotic wall ; *cf*, condylar foramen ; *fr*, fenestra rotunda ; *i*, incus ; *ic*, internal carotid ; *jf*, jugular foramen ; *m*, malleus ; *oc*, occipital condyle ; *pe*, periotic ; *sq*, squamosal ; *st*, stapes in fenestra ovalis ; *sta*, stapedial artery ; *stf*, stylomastoid foramen ; *t*, tympanic ; *tb*, tympanic bulla ; *tm*, tympanic membrane, limited by dotted line and partly concealed.

piercing the stapes, and passes forwards between incus and cranium to supply the jaws and other parts. A similar facial or stapedial artery in the Reptile pierces the stapedial region of the columella, or passes above or below it, and runs forward between quadrate and cranium to the jaws and other parts. The structure, development, and relative position of the parts are essentially the same in Birds as in Reptiles.

**New Articulation of the Lower Jaw.**—It is clear that the evidence derived from the study of the embryology and anatomy of the middle-ear region is strongly in favour of the ' Reichert theory '. But if the original articulation between the quadrate and articular is indeed represented by the joint between the incus and malleus, we are driven to the conclusion that the mammalian articulation for the lower jaw between the derma squamosal and dentary bones is a new one. How can such a radical change have taken place without interrupting the proper function of the jaws? Embryology has thrown little light on this point; but it is one

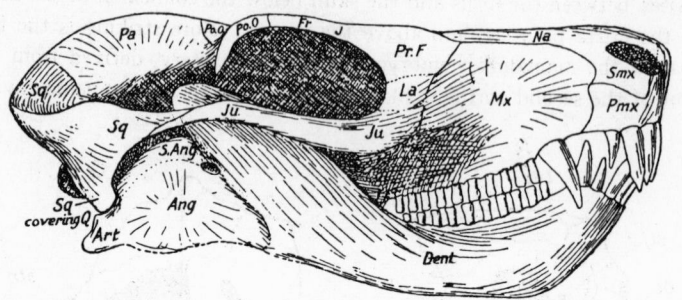

FIG. 499.

*Bauria cynops*, right-side view of skull and lower jaw restored (from R. Broom, *P.Z.S.*, 1911). *Art*, Articular; *Dent*, dentary; *Fr*, frontal; *Ju*, jugal; *L*, lacrimal; *Mx*, maxillary; *Na*, nasal; *Pa*, parietal; *Pmx*, premaxillary; *Po.O*, postorbital; *Pr.F*, prefrontal; *Qu*, quadrate; *S.Ang*, supra-angular; *Smx*, septomaxillary; *Sq*, squamosal.

of the triumphs of the long series of researches on the extinct Theromorph reptiles, begun by Owen (1845), and continued by Seeley, Broom, and Watson, to have revealed the intermediate steps by which the change

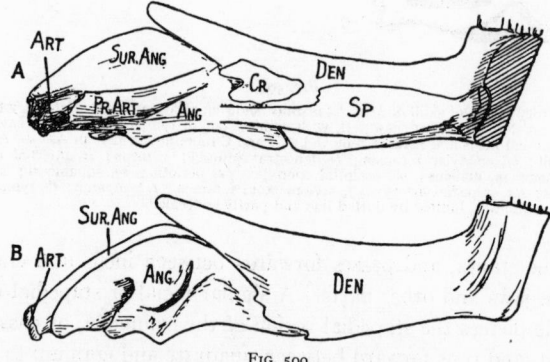

FIG. 500.

Lower jaw of *Scymnosuchus whaitsi*. A, Inner view of left ramus; B, outer view of right ramus (from D. M. S. Watson, *Ann. Mag. N.H.*, 1912). Lettering as in Fig. 377.

may have occurred from an inner quadrate to an outer squamosal articulation (Gregory, **735**).

In the more reptilian Theromorphs the stapes is found as a stout or slender rod extending from the fenestra ovalis to the quadrate to which its distal end is articulated (Dicynodontia, Broom, **709, 710**; Sollas, **602**. Pelycosauria, Case, **471**. Theriodontia, Watson, **640**), but in the higher forms the stapes may be perforated as in mammals (Thrinaxodon, Cynognathus).

In the more primitive and reptilian Theromorphs the quadrate is

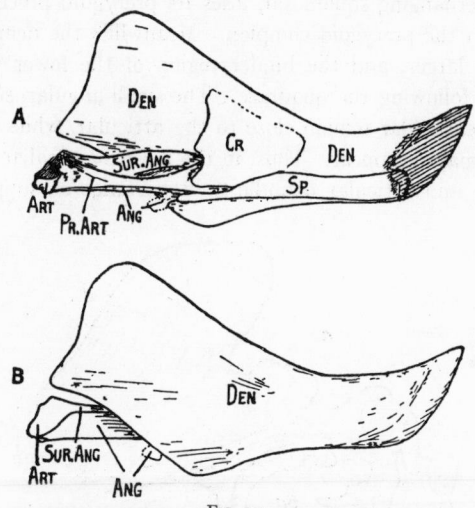

FIG. 501.

Lower jaw of *Cynognathus crateronotus.* A, Inner view of left ramus; B, outer view of right ramus. (From D. M. S. Watson, *Ann. Mag. N.H.,* 1912.) Lettering as in Fig. 377.

fixed laterally to the squamosal, by its otic process to the auditory capsule, and by an anterior process to the pterygoid; the articular is

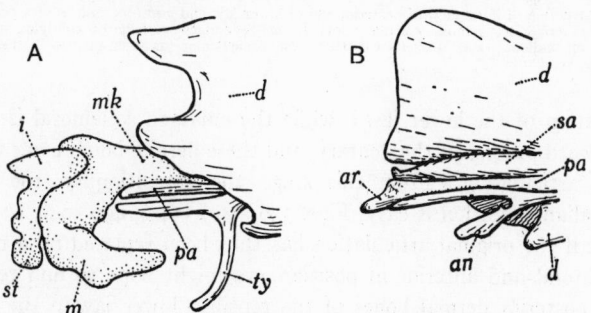

FIG. 502.

A, Outer view of posterior region of lower jaw of late embryo *Perameles,* and B, inner view of same region of *Cynodont* reptile (from R. W. Palmer, 1913). *an,* Angular; *ar,* articular; *d,* dentary; *i,* incus; *m,* malleus; *mk,* Meckel's cartilage; *pa,* prearticular in B, processus anterior mallei in A; *sa,* supra-angular; *st,* stapes.

large and of the usual type. The squamosal and quadratojugal bear much the same relation to the quadrate as in Sphenodon. Passing from the less to the more mammal-like Theriodontia, the squamosal is seen to enlarge, the quadratojugal to dwindle. The quadrate diminishes in relative size, retreats inwards together with the reduced quadratojugal below the overhanging squamosal, loses its pterygoid process, becoming loosened from the pterygoid complex. Meanwhile the dentary becomes progressively larger, and the hinder region of the lower jaw reduced, the articular following the quadrate. The small angular, supra-angular, and inner prearticular remain close to the articular, while the coronoid and splenial may disappear. Thus, in the most mammalian Cynodontia, the quadrate and articular dwindle in importance as supports for the

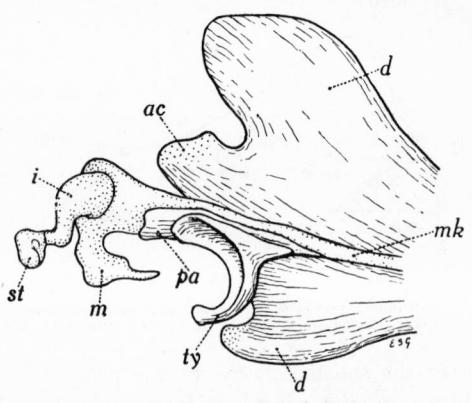

FIG. 503.

Reconstruction of inner view of posterior end of lower jaw and auditory ossicles of a pouch young of *Didelphys aurita*, left ramus. Cartilage dotted. *ac*, Secondary cartilage on condyle ; *d*, dentary ; *i*, incus ; *m*, malleus ; *mk*, Meckel's cartilage ; *pa*, prearticular (anterior process of malleus) ; *st*, stapes ; *ty*, tympanic.

articulation of the lower jaw ; while the enlarged squamosal is met by a backward process of the dentary, and these dermal bones come to share in the articulation. From this stage the transition to the typical mammalian condition is easy, Figs. 339, 340, 394-6, 499-504.

But if the original articulation has thus been replaced by a new one more lateral and anterior in position, we might hope to find remnants of the posterior dermal bones of the reptilian lower jaw in the middle-ear region of the mammal. The tympanic and processus anterior of the malleus appear to be such bones. This anterior process has long been known to develop as a separate dermal bone situated ventrally and close to Meckel's cartilage (Parker; Broman). Later it becomes ankylosed to the ossified malleus, and has been considered to represent either the angular (Parker, 567), supra-angular (v. Kampen, 741 ; Palmer,

757), or prearticular (Gaupp, **732**). Since, like the prearticular of the lower Tetrapods, the anterior process is sometimes pierced by the chorda tympani, the last seems the more probable homology.

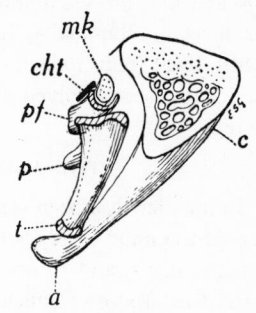

The tympanic, that dermal bone peculiar to and so characteristic of the Mammalia, which encircles and stretches the tympanum, may be derived from the reptilian angular. It arises as a crescentic bone near the malleus, with which it remains closely associated in lower Placentals and in Marsupials, and may become fused in Monotremes (Doran, **714**; Peters, 1868). In the foetal *Orycteropus* (Gadow, **730**) and Marsupial (Palmer, **757**; Toeplitz, **391**) it has a horizontal limb along Meckel's cartilage, and a ventral crescentic process, Figs. 482, 496, 502-5. The very similar angular of *Cynognathus* (Watson, **640**; Palmer) suggests that already in the Theromorph the angular was notched behind to stretch the tympanum below the level of the articular, thus leading to the mammalian condition. Already in Pelycosauria the angular is somewhat notched and extended behind in a manner suggesting that it shared in

FIG. 504.

*Didelphys aurita*, late embryo. Portion of thick transverse section reconstructed to show relations of skeletal parts near hind end of lower jaw; posterior view of right side. *a*, Angular, and *c*, condylar processes of dentary bone; *cht*, chorda tympani; *mk*, Meckel's cartilage; *p*, anterior process of tympanic; *pf*, anterior process (prearticular?) of malleus; *t*, tympanic ring of which posterior part has been cut away; a dotted line shows attachment of tympanum.

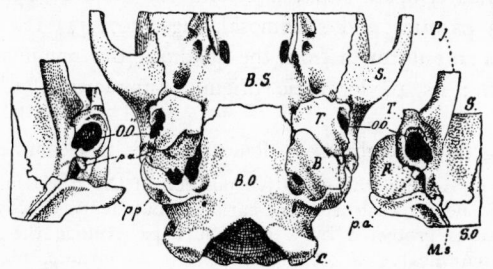

FIG. 505.

*Paradoxurus musanga*, hinder portion of young skull, ventral and lateral views (from M. Weber, 1927). *B*, Entotympanic part of bulla (removed in left figure); *B.O*, basioccipital; *B.S*, basisphenoid; *C*, occipital condyle; *M.s*, periotic; *OO*, external bony meatus; *pa*, processus postanditivus; *Pj*, processus jugalis; *pp*, processus paroccipitalis; *S*, squamosal; *S.o*, supraoccipital; *T*, tympanic.

the support of the tympanum (Watson, **640**). As Gregory has pointed out, a groove on the hinder surface of the squamosal in many Theromorphs seems to indicate the position of an external auditory meatus, and suggests that the tympanum was deeply sunk and obliquely set below this region of the skull as in mammals (Gregory, 735; Watson, 631a). For Gaupp's view that the tympanic membrane, situated dorsally to the retro-articular process and angular in modern Reptilia, and partly below this level in Mammalia, has been independently evolved in the two groups, there seems to be no justification. How the mammalian condition could have been evolved from the reptilian is clearly shown in the Theromorpha.[1]

## THE MIDDLE EAR IN AMPHIBIA

From what has been said above it will be gathered that the various parts of the middle-ear region in Reptilia and Mammalia can be shown to be homologous, and to occupy the same fundamental relative positions in the two groups. Difficulties, however, arise when the comparison is extended to the Amphibia. To begin with, the existing forms are all highly specialised, and the terrestrial Anura alone preserve a tympanum. In the Urodela and Apoda the auditory apparatus is more or less degenerate, and the Eustachian tube, tympanic cavity, and tympanum are lost, no doubt as the result of the burrowing habits of the latter and re-adaptation to aquatic life of the former. Nevertheless, the structures of the middle ear can be shown to be arranged on the same general plan, to develop in much the same way, and to occupy the same morphological position in Amphibia as in Amniota, with one notable exception, the chorda tympani.

The large tympanic membrane of the Anura is supported by a cartilaginous annulus tympani situated behind the quadrate, and attached to the crista parotica and squamosal, Figs. 507, 511-12. Developed apparently as an outgrowth from the quadrate, this annulus is peculiar to the Anura; its phylogenetic origin is unknown (Parker, 558-9; Gaupp, 504).

Extending from membrane to fenestra ovalis is a columella auris of

[1] In modern Reptilia the primitive position of the tympanum seems to be vertical and nearly flush with the surface; but in the Crocodilia it sinks somewhat, and is protected by a movable flap. Among the Lacertilia a shallow external meatus is often developed; its opening may be much narrowed. In many families the tympanum is frequently more or less completely obliterated by secondary modifications, especially among burrowing or creeping forms. This may take place by thickening, by overgrowth, or by closure of the external meatus (Versluys, 769). The Chamaeleontids and Amphisbaenids have no tympanic membrane, and the latter have lost the cavity as well. In Sphenodon there is no membrane; and all the Ophidia have lost it, together with the cavity and Eustachian tube. Yet the faculty of hearing is preserved, vibrations being communicated probably from the ground through the lower jaw. In the Class Aves a considerable external auditory meatus is present.

complex structure (Parker, 558, 559; Gaupp).   It consists of a proximal
element known as the 'operculum' (stapes of Parker), usually cartilaginous, and closing the posterior region of the fenestra but overlapping
its rim.   Articulating with the operculum and plugging the anterior
region of the fenestra is the 'plectrum' (Gaupp); from the latter's
swollen base projects a rod whose distal end is continued into an extra-
stapedial cartilage inserted into the tympanum.   The rod is usually

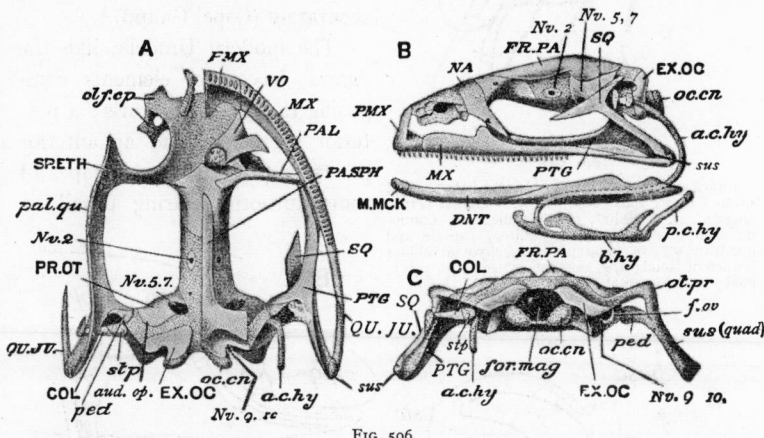

FIG. 506.

*Rana temporaria.*   The skull.   A, From beneath, with the investing bones removed on the right
side (left of figure) ;  B, from the left side, with mandible and hyoid ;  C, from behind, the investing
bones removed at *sus.*  *a.c.hy,* Anterior cornu of hyoid ;  *aud.cp,* auditory capsule ;  *b.hy,* body of hyoid ;
COL, columella ;  *DNT,* dentary ;  EX.OC, exoccipital ;  *for.mag,* foramen magnum ;  *FR.PA,* fronto-
parietal ;  M.MCK, mento-Meckelian ;  *MX,* maxilla ;  *NA,* nasal ;  *Nv. 2,* optic foramen ;  *Nv. 5, 7,*
foramen for fifth and seventh nerves ;  *Nv. 9, 10,* foramina for ninth and tenth nerves ;  *oc.cn,* occipital
condyle ;  *olf.cp,* olfactory capsule ;  *ot.pr,* otic process ;  *PAL,* palatine ;  *pal.qu,* palatoquadrate ;
*PA.SPH,* parasphenoid ;  *p.c.hy,* posterior cornu of hyoid ;  *ped,* pedicle ;  *PMX,* premaxilla ;  PR.OT,
pro-otic ;  *PTG,* pterygoid ;  *QU.JU,* quadratojugal ;  SP.ETH, sphenethmoid ;  *SQ,* paraquadrate ;
*stp,* stapes ;  *sus (quad),* suspensorium (quadrate) ;  *VO,* prevomer.   (After Howes, slightly altered.)   A
minute investing bone, the *septo-maxillary,* which is present above the maxilla, close to the nostril, is
not here represented.   (From Parker and Haswell, *Zoology.*)

ossified (meso-stapedial of Parker), and from the extra-stapedial cartilage
comes off a supra-stapedial process (dorsal process ?) which unites with
the paroccipital process and quadrate, Figs. 506-7, 512.   The operculum
is almost always present, but the plectrum may be reduced or absent, as
for instance in the adult *Bombinator* and *Phryniscus,* where the annulus
and tympanic membrane are also lost.   Many authors have studied the
development of the columella and with varying results (Reichert, 1837 ;
Parker ; Huxley, 738 ; Cope, 711 ; Villy, 771 ; Fuchs, 727 ; Gaupp,
504).   The latest and most careful researches seem to have established
that the operculum arises as an independent rudiment in the membrane
closing the fenestra ovalis (Gaupp, 343, 732 ; van Seters, 382 ; Peter, 758).[1]

[1] Nevertheless, many observers believe the operculum to be 'cut
out' of the wall of the auditory capsule.   Fusion with the edge of the

Later (during metamorphosis) the plectrum appears in the same way, as a rudiment which joins the edge of the fenestra and grows outwards in a pre-existing strand of tissue to the quadrate and beyond to the tympanum. The outermost region of the extra-stapedial chondrifies separately (Cope, Gaupp).[1]

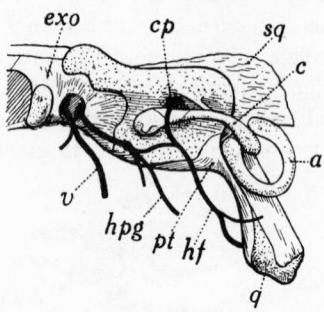

FIG. 507.

*Bufo aqua*; posterior view of right half of skull (from Parker, 1881, modified with cranial nerves added). *a*, Annulus; *c*, columella; *cp*, cranio-quadrate passage between auditory capsule and quadrate, *q*; *exo*, exoccipital; *hf*, hyomandibular branch of facial; *hpg*, glossopharyngeal; *pt*, pterygoid; *sq*, squamosal; *v*, vagus.

The modern Urodela, like the Anura, have two elements composing the columella auris : a posterior operculum and an anterior plectrum (columella and stapes of some authors) bearing usually a

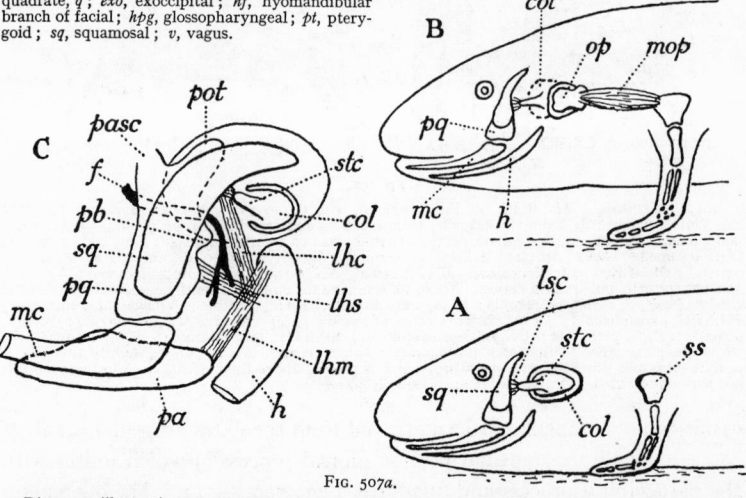

FIG. 507a.

Diagrams illustrating mechanism of communication between exterior and inner ear in Urodela. A, Aquatic larvae and aquatic adults; B, terrestrial adults; C, relation of skeleton, ligaments, and nerve in majority of Urodela (from figures of Kingsbury and Reed, *J. of Morph.*, 1909). Columella auris represented by its stylus, *stc*, its base, *col*, and separate opercular element, *op*. *f*, Hyomandibular branch of facial nerve; *h*, ceratohyal; *lhc*, ligamentum hyo-columellare; *lhm*, l. hyo-mandibulare; *lhs*, l. squamoso-columellare; *lsc*, l. squamoso-columellare; *mc*, Meckel's cartilage; *mop*, musculus opercularis; *pa*, prearticular; *pasc*, processus ascendens; *pb*, pr. basalis; *pot*, pr. oticus; *pq*, palato-quadrate; *sq*, squamosal; *ss*, suprascapula.

fenestra certainly takes place very early ; but the first rudiment of the operculum is probably independent. A separate operculum does not appear in Aglossa (van Seters, **382**).

[1] The development of the Eustachian tube and tympanic cavity of the frog is much modified owing to the very specialised structure of the head of the tadpole larva. They arise from the rudiment of the first gill-pouch as a slender

projecting 'stylus' which reaches or is connected by ligament with
the squamosal in early stages but generally with the quadrate later.
Another more ventral ligament unites the base of the columella
with the ceratohyal, Fig. 570 A. A muscle usually stretches from
the operculum to the suprascapula (m. opercularis) ; it may possibly
be homologous with the stapedial muscle of the Amniota (p. 466).
Both operculum and plectrum may be ossified. The structure and
development of this auditory apparatus has recently been very
thoroughly studied by Kingsbury and Reed (744). In the ' Amblystomid
type ' (*Amblystoma, Salamandra*), while the operculum remains free, the

plectrum tends to fuse in the
adult with the anterior edge of
the fenestra ovalis, and in Triton
it is vestigial without stylus. In
the ' Plethodont type ' the basal
plate of the plectrum fuses with
the operculum (*Necturus, Spelerpes*) and again by means of
a narrow ' isthmus ' with the
edge of the fenestra (*Desmo-
gnathus, Amphiuma*). The
muscle is often lost (*Necturus,
Cryptobranchus, Siren*, etc.),
and vibrations probably pass by
way of the lower jaw and squamosal in these aquatic forms

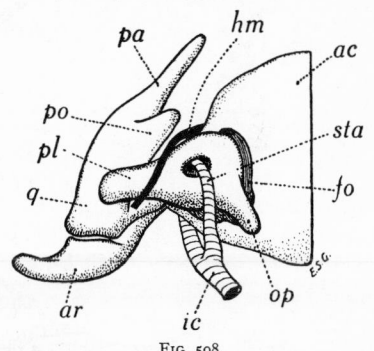

FIG. 508.

*Ichthyophis glutinosa*, embryo 3·5 cm. long. Reconstruction of auditory region, posterior view. Cartilage
shaded with dots. *ac*, Auditory capsule; *ar*, articular
region; *fo*, fenestra ovalis; *hm*, hyomandibular branch
of facial nerve; *ic*, internal carotid; *op*, operculum;
*pa*, ascending process; *pl*, plectrum (columella); *po*,
otic process; *q*, quadrate; *sta*, stapedial artery.

when the head rests on the ground. Where present the muscle possibly
communicates vibrations from the suprascapula and fore-limb in terrestrial forms, Fig. 570 A.

Clearly the auditory apparatus is specialised and degenerate in the
Urodela. That the operculum in Urodeles develops from the wall of the
auditory capsule seems to be fully established, though it appears often
to be not so much ' cut out ' of the cartilaginous wall (Huschke, 1824 ;
Reichert, Parker, Huxley) as to grow forwards from it in the membrane
closing the fenestra ovalis (Stöhr, 386 ; Kingsbury, 743 ; Reed, 760-61).
Nevertheless, since the opercular muscle is inserted on the operculum, it
is difficult to believe that this element did not originally belong to a
movable visceral arch. The plectrum, on the other hand, arises separ-

tube which only takes up its definitive position and expands to form the cavity
and membrane at metamorphosis (Villy, 771; Spemann, 767; Fox, 723).

ately in a strand stretching from the membrane of the fenestra to the squamosal and quadrate (Kingsbury and Reed, 744).[1]

The Apoda are provided with a columella consisting of a small operculum and a larger ossified plectrum, pierced by the stapedial artery in *Ichthyophis*, but not in *Hypogeophis* or *Siphonops*, Figs. 508-9, 510. Its distal end is articulated to the quadrate (Sarasin, 763; Marcus, 752; E.S.G.). According to Marcus, the rudiment of the columella of *Hypogeophis* is in the early blastematous stage continuous with the remainder of

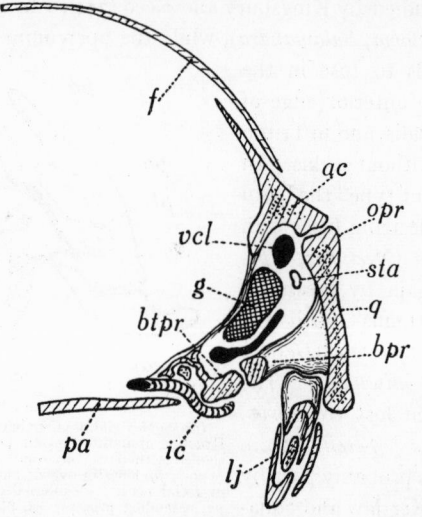

FIG. 509.

Reconstructed thick transverse section of head of *Siphonops braziliensis*, embryo 7 cm. long. *bpr*, Basal process of palatoquadrate; *btpr*, basitrabecular process; *f*, frontal; *g*, geniculate ganglion in cranio-quadrate passage; *lj*, lower jaw; *opr*, otic process of quadrate region, *q*.

the hyoid arch. This is an important observation, since it is the only case of such continuity described in an Amphibian, but confirms the opinion founded on comparative anatomy that the columella of the Amphibian represents the dorsal end of the hyoid arch and is homologous with that of the Amniota. Probably this primitive connexion has been obscured or lost in Urodela owing to the degenerate condition of the columella, and in Anura owing to the great disturbance of this region during larval development.

In attempting to work out the general homology of the Amphibian columella auris it should be remembered that, however degenerate and

---

[1] Parker (562, 573) believed the plectrum, and Witebsky (772) the whole columella, to be derived from the hyoid arch; but no proof of this origin has yet been brought forward in any Urodele or Anuran.

modified it may be in modern forms, it has probably been derived from
a columella similar to that of the primitive Reptilia. In the more primitive
Stegocephalia (Embolomeri, Rhachitomi) the stapes has an ossified
expanded proximal end fitting into the fenestra ovalis, and pierced
apparently for the stapedial artery, and a more slender distal end passing
upwards towards the tympanic notch. A process, comparable to the
dorsal supra-stapedial process of Reptiles, is attached to the parotic
process of the opisthotic and tabular bone of the cranial roof near the
tympanic notch, and there is a short extra-stapedial process, which may
have been connected by cartilage to the tympanum. But the bony
stapes is widely separated from the quadrate bone. The more specialised

Stegocephalia have a more slender and
rod-like stapes, preserving the same
general disposition (Watson, **644**; Sushkin, **768**).

In all the living Amphibia the vena
capitis lateralis passes above and the internal carotid passes below the columella
and fenestra ovalis, as in Amniota, Figs.
511-12. Moreover, the stapedial artery
(facial artery, p. 529) passes through or
above the columella on its way forwards
through the cranio-quadrate passage to
the cavum epiptericum and orbit (p. 412).
Also, as in Amniotes, the course of the
main hyomandibular branch of the facial

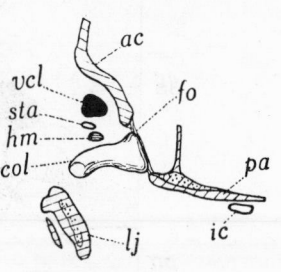

FIG. 510.

*Siphonops braziliensis*, embryo 7 cm.
long. Transverse section through left
auditory region. *ac*, Auditory capsule;
*col*, columella; *fo*, fenestra ovalis; *hm*,
hyomandibular branch of facial nerve;
*ic*, internal carotid; *lj*, lower jaw; *pa*,
parachordal plate; *sta*, stapedial artery;
*vcl*, vena capitis lateralis.

nerve is dorsal to the columella in Anura and Apoda. Only in Urodela
does a serious difficulty arise in the comparison, for here this nerve and
its branches pass either ventrally to the ' stylus ' and its ligament, Fig.
570 A, or, as in *Necturus* and *Proteus*, it divides into its jugular and
alveolar (internal mandibular, chorda tympani) branches anterior to the
' stylus ', the jugular nerve passing backwards dorsally and the alveolar
anteriorly and ventrally. The ligament, then, cannot correspond
to the true columella of the other Amphibia and Amniota, Fig.
595, but may after all represent in Urodela its dorsal process and
attachment.

The fact already referred to (p. 478), that in Anura not only the

[1] What significance is to be attached to a small cartilaginous rod recently
described by Litzelmann (**750**) behind the quadrate in the larval *Molge*, and
claimed by him to represent the hyomandibula, remains to be seen. It passes
anteriorly to both the jugular and the internal mandibular nerves, and may
possibly be a remnant of the distal region of the columella.

hyomandibular branch of the facial nerve (jugular branch) but also the internal mandibular branch (chorda tympani, p. 752) pass down behind the tympanum, while in all Amniotes the chorda tympani passes down in front of the tympanum, is a serious difficulty in comparing the two groups. It has already been explained that the chorda tympani in the Amniota

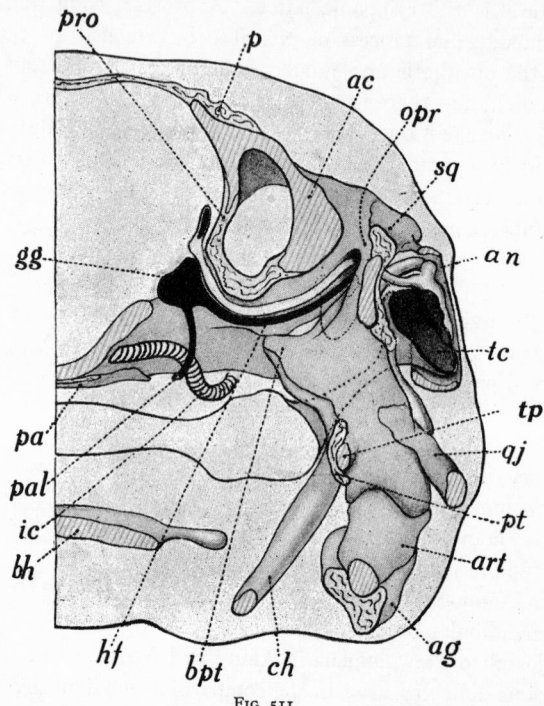

FIG. 511.

*Rana temporaria*, young; same reconstruction as in Fig. 512, but cut transversely farther forward (anterior view), and showing cranio-quadrate passage into which run hyomandibular branch of facial and accompanying v. cap. lateralis. *bpt*, Basal process; *gg*, Gasserian ganglion; *opr*, otic process; *ptp*, pterygoid process; *pa*, parasphenoid; *pal*, palatine nerve; *pro*, pro-otic; *pt*, pterygoid; *qj*, quadratojugal; *tc*, tympanic cavity exposed (Eustachian tube behind quadrate indicated by dotted line).

is post-trematic but pretympanic; in the Anura it is both post-trematic and post-tympanic, Figs. 507, 512. Gaupp (732) concluded that the tympanum is not homologous throughout the Tetrapoda and has arisen independently in the two different positions. It is unlikely, however, that two structures so similar as the tympanum of a frog and of a lizard, each situated behind the quadrate and having imbedded in it the distal end of the columella, should have been independently developed. Moreover, the presence of a tympanic notch and a columella in the Stegocephalia is clear evidence that these primitive Tetrapods, not far removed from the common ancestor of both modern Amphibia and Amniota, already possessed an auditory apparatus provided with a tympanum. Rather may we suppose that there has been in the ancestral Amniota a shifting downwards of the tympanum and forwards of the chorda tympani across the tympanum perhaps at a time when this membrane was still thick.[1]

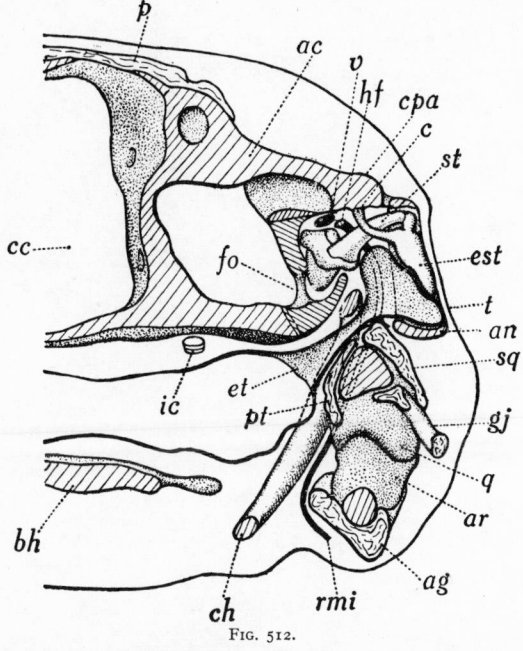

FIG. 512.

*Rana temporaria*, young. Reconstruction of thick transverse section of auditory region of left side; anterior view. *ac*, Auditory capsule; *ag*, angulosplenial; *an*, annulus; *ar*, articular cartilage; *bh*, basihyal; *c*, connexion between extra-stapedial and cranial cartilages; *cc*, cranial cavity; *ch*, ceratohyal; *cpa*, crista parotica; *est*, extra-stapedial cartilage; *et*, Eustachian tube; *fo*, fenestra ovalis;. *gj*, quadratojugal; *hf*, hyomandibular branch of facial nerve; *ic*, internal carotid; *p*, parietofrontal; *pt*, pterygoid; *q*, quadrate cartilage; *sq*, squamosal; *st*, stapes; *rmi*, ramus mandibularis internus; *t*, tympanic membrane; *v*, position of vena capitis lateralis passing through cranioquadrate passage.

Fully to account for the derivation of the Amniote from the Anuran condition, assuming the latter to be primitive, we should also have to suppose that the chorda tympani shifted dorsally over the end of the extra-stapedial cartilage, Fig. 495, or that the extra-stapedial region has been developed independently in the two groups. On the other hand, it is perhaps more probable that the Anuran condition is secondary.

[1] There can be little doubt that the Eustachian tube and tympanic cavity are homologous throughout the Tetrapoda, as evidenced by their development and innervation (Bender, **705**).

# THE TRAVELS OF WILLIAM BARTRAM

This is the first inexpensive illustrated edition of one of the most delightful books written in the 18th century. A great source work of American geography, anthropology, and natural history, it contains accurate and entertaining descriptions of the area now included in Florida, Georgia, and the Carolinas.

From 1773 to 1778, Bartram, who was a trained natural scientist, travelled through the South, noting the characteristics of almost everything he encountered. He reported on the rivers of Florida, the groves of wild oranges, the swamps, the lagoons; he made notes on the fish, tropical snakes and reptiles, the birds, both aquatic and land. Botanical specimens that he took preserved at least one valuable plant from extinction.

Descriptions of the Cherokee Indians and their march toward civilization, the festivals of the Seminoles, the customs of the Creeks — all offer the anthropologist and historian a wealth of first-hand information, much of which is not available elsewhere.

Bartram has long been recognized as a classic of both science and language. Coleridge used it as a source for "Kublai Khan" and "The Ancient Mariner," while Wordsworth, Carlyle, and Emerson all held it in high esteem.

Unabridged, with all 13 original illustrations and maps. Edited, with an introduction by Mark Van Doren. 448pp. 5⅜ x 8.

T13    Paperbound **$1.95**

# ELEMENTS OF MATHEMATICAL BIOLOGY
## by Alfred J. Lotka

Formerly published as ELEMENTS OF PHYSICAL BIOLOGY, this classic work marks the major attempt to apply modern mathematics to the problems of ontology, phylogeny, ecology, physiology, endocrinology, psychology, and other branches of biology. One of the most seminal books ever published in its field, it has had enormous influence upon the later work of such scientists as Norbert Wiener and N. Rashevsky.

Partial contents. Evolution, a system in the course of irreversible transformation. Statistical meaning of irreversibility. Evolution as redistribution. KINETICS: fundamental equations of kinetics of evolving systems. General, special cases. Analysis of the growth function. STATICS. General principles of equilibrium. Chemical equilibrium, inter-species equilibrium, circulation of the elements, the carbon dioxide cycle, the nitrogen cycle, the phosphorus cycle, moving equilibria, displacement of equilibrium, parameters of state. DYNAMICS. Energy transformers of nature, relation of the transformation to available sources, correlating apparatus, adjustors, consciousness, function, origin, energy relations of consciousness. List of publications by A. J. Lotka. 36 tables. Analytical synopsis of chapters. 72 figures. xxx + 460pp. 5⅜ x 8.     Paperbound **$2.95**

# THE ORIGIN OF LIFE
## by A. I. Oparin

This is a classic of biochemistry—the first detailed exposition of the theory that living tissue was preceded upon earth by a long and gradual evolution of nitrogen and carbon compounds. It is still one of the basic works in any science library, as is proved by repeated reference to it in later books and monography.

A historical introduction first covers theories of the origin of life from the Greeks, through the middle ages and Renaissance, to moderns. Three basic theories are examined in light of modern knowledge: that life spontaneously arises perpetually; that life has always been present in the universe as a separate basic substance; that life arose once at some distant period of the earth's past.

Techniques of modern biochemistry are then applied to the problem by Dr. Oparin, and the topic is considered afresh in the following chapters: primary forms of carbon and nitrogen compounds; origin of organic substances, primary proteins; origin of primarily colloidal systems; origin and further evolution of primary organisms.

"Easily the most scholarly authority on the question . . . it will be a landmark for discussion for a long time to come," **NEW YORK TIMES.** "Every physiologist and biochemist should call it to the attention of his students . . . chemists will want to read this volume over and over again," **AMERICAN CHEMICAL SOCIETY JOURNAL**

231-item bibliography, especially strong on Russian and Eastern European publications. 16-page introduction by the translator, S. Morgulis, University of Nebraska, considers later discoveries exemplifying Oparin's theories. Index. xxv + 270pp. 5⅜ x 8.

S213 Paperbound **$1.75**

# A SHORT HISTORY OF ANATOMY AND PHYSIOLOGY FROM THE GREEKS TO HARVEY
## (The Evolution of Anatomy)

## by Charles Singer

This corrected edition of a classic work on the history of anatomy and physiology is still the most interesting intermediate study of the subject currently available. It traces the evolution of anatomy from prescientific times through the Greek and Roman periods, the Dark Ages and the Renaissance, up to the age of Harvey and the beginning of modern scientific concepts. Primary attention is centered on individuals, movements and periods that definitely advanced anatomical knowledge.

In the first of four chronological sections, the author considers the period before 50 B.C., in Sicily, Ionia, Athens and Alexandria. He covers the work of Plato, Diocles, Aristotle, Theophrastus, Herophilus and Erasistratus, along with the Alexandrians and their experiments in anatomy and human vivisection. In Part 2, later Roman and Greek anatomical writers are discussed, with emphasis falling upon Galen's anatomical philosophy and achievements and his physiological system. Part 3 deals principally with the rise of the universities and the anatomical work of such figures as Mondino, da Vinci, Berengar, Estienne, Linacre, Sylvius and others. The final section is concerned with Vesalius as artist, humanist, naturalist; with a discussion of his *Fabrica;* and with his rivals and followers up to Harvey. A Vesalian Atlas contains nudes, skeletons and muscle tabulae from the *Epitome* and *Fabrica.*

Revision of 1925 edition entitled THE EVOLUTION OF ANATOMY. Index of names. 20 plates, 270 extremely interesting illustrations of medieval, ancient, renaissance, oriental origin. xii + 209pp. 5⅜ x 8.

T389 Paperbound $1.50

# Catalogue of Dover
## SCIENCE BOOKS

## BOOKS THAT EXPLAIN SCIENCE

**THE NATURE OF LIGHT AND COLOUR IN THE OPEN AIR, M. Minnaert.** Why is falling snow sometimes black? What causes mirages, the fata morgana, multiple suns and moons in the sky; how are shadows formed? Prof. Minnaert of U. of Utrecht answers these and similar questions in optics, light, colour, for non-specialists. Particularly valuable to nature, science students, painters, photographers. "Can best be described in one word—fascinating!" Physics Today. Translated by H. M. Kremer-Priest, K. Jay. 202 illustrations, including 42 photos. xvi + 362pp. 5⅜ x 8. T196 Paperbound **$1.95**

**THE RESTLESS UNIVERSE, Max Born.** New enlarged version of this remarkably readable account by a Nobel laureate. Moving from sub-atomic particles to universe, the author explains in very simple terms the latest theories of wave mechanics. Partial contents: air and its relatives, electrons and ions, waves and particles, electronic structure of the atom, nuclear physics. Nearly 1000 illustrations, including 7 animated sequences. 325pp. 6 x 9. T412 Paperbound **$2.00**

**MATTER AND LIGHT, THE NEW PHYSICS, L. de Broglie.** Non-technical papers by a Nobel laureate explain electromagnetic theory, relativity, matter, light, radiation, wave mechanics, quantum physics, philosophy of science. Einstein, Planck, Bohr, others explained so easily that no mathematical training is needed for all but 2 of the 21 chapters. "Easy simplicity and lucidity . . . should make this source-book of modern physcis available to a wide public," Saturday Review. Unabridged. 300pp. 5⅜ x 8. T35 Paperbound **$1.60**

**THE COMMON SENSE OF THE EXACT SCIENCES, W. K. Clifford.** Introduction by James Newman, edited by Karl Pearson. For 70 years this has been a guide to classical scientific, mathematical thought. Explains with unusual clarity basic concepts such as extension of meaning of symbols, characteristics of surface boundaries, properties of plane figures, vectors, Cartesian method of determining position, etc. Long preface by Bertrand Russell. Bibliography of Clifford. Corrected. 130 diagrams redrawn. 249pp. 5⅜ x 8. T61 Paperbound **$1.60**

**THE EVOLUTION OF SCIENTIFIC THOUGHT FROM NEWTON TO EINSTEIN, A. d'Abro.** Einstein's special, general theories of relativity, with historical implications, analyzed in non-technical terms. Excellent accounts of contributions of Newton, Riemann, Weyl, Planck, Eddington, Maxwell, Lorentz, etc., are treated in terms of space, time, equations of electromagnetics, finiteness of universe, methodology of science. "Has become a standard work," Nature. 21 diagrams. 482pp. 5⅜ x 8. T2 Paperbound **$2.00**

**BRIDGES AND THEIR BUILDERS, D. Steinman, S. R. Watson.** Engineers, historians, everyone ever fascinated by great spans will find this an endless source of information and interest. Dr. Steinman, recent recipient of Louis Levy Medal, is one of the great bridge architects, engineers of all time. His analysis of great bridges of history is both authoritative and easily followed. Greek, Roman, medieval, oriental bridges; modern works such as Brooklyn Bridge, Golden Gate Bridge, etc. described in terms of history, constructional principles, artistry, function. Most comprehensive, accurate semi-popular history of bridges in print in English. New, greatly revised, enlarged edition. 23 photographs, 26 line drawings. xvii + 401pp. 5⅜ x 8. T431 Paperbound **$1.95**

**CONCERNING THE NATURE OF THINGS, Sir William Bragg.** Christmas lectures at Royal Society by Nobel laureate, dealing with atoms, gases, liquids, and various types of crystals. No scientific background is needed to understand this remarkably clear introduction to basic processes and aspects of modern science. "More interesting than any bestseller," London Morning Post. 32pp. of photos. 57 figures. xii + 232pp. 5⅜ x 8.　　　T31 Paperbound **$1.35**

**THE RISE OF THE NEW PHYSICS, A. d'Abro.** Half million word exposition, formerly titled "The Decline of Mechanism," for readers not versed in higher mathematics. Only thorough explanation in everyday language of core of modern mathematical physical theory, treating both classical, modern views. Scientifically impeccable coverage of thought from Newtonian system through theories of Dirac, Heisenberg, Fermi's statistics. Combines history, exposition; broad but unified, detailed view, with constant comparison of classical, modern views. "A must for anyone doing serious study in the physical sciences," J. of the Franklin Inst. "Extraordinary faculty . . . to explain ideas and theories . . . in language of everyday life," Isis. Part I of set: philosophy of science, from practice of Newton, Maxwell, Poincaré, Einstein, etc. Modes of thought, experiment, causality, etc. Part II: 100 pp. on grammar, vocabulary of mathematics, discussions of functions, groups, series, Fourier series, etc. Remainder treats concrete, detailed coverage of both classical, quantum physics: analytic mechanics, Hamilton's principle, electromagnetic waves, thermodynamics, Brownian movement, special relativity, Bohr's atom, de Broglie's wave mechanics, Heisenberg's uncertainty, scores of other important topics. Covers discoveries, theories of d'Alembert, Born, Cantor, Debye, Euler, Foucault, Galois, Gauss, Hadamard, Kelvin, Kepler Laplace, Maxwell, Pauli, Rayleigh Volterra, Weyl, more than 180 others. 97 illustrations. ix + 982pp. 5⅜ x 8.
　　　T3 Vol. 1 Paperbound **$2.00**
　　　T4 Vol. II Paperbound **$2.00**

**SPINNING TOPS AND GYROSCOPIC MOTION, John Perry.** Well-known classic of science still unsurpassed for lucid, accurate, delightful exposition. How quasi-rigidity is induced in flexible, fluid bodies by rapid motions; why gyrostat falls, top rises; nature, effect of internal fluidity on rotating bodies; etc. Appendixes describe practical use of gyroscopes in ships, compasses, monorail transportation. 62 figures. 128pp. 5⅜ x 8.
　　　T416 Paperbound **$1.00**

**FOUNDATIONS OF PHYSICS, R. B. Lindsay, H. Margenau.** Excellent bridge between semi-popular and technical writings. Discussion of methods of physical description, construction of theory; valuable to physicist with elementary calculus. Gives meaning to data, tools of modern physics. Contents: symbolism, mathematical equations; space and time; foundations of mechanics; probability; physics, continua; electron theory; relativity; quantum mechanics; causality; etc. "Thorough and yet not overdetailed. Unreservedly recommended," Nature. Unabridged corrected edition. 35 illustrations. xi + 537pp. 5⅜ x 8.　　　S377 Paperbound **$2.45**

**FADS AND FALLACIES IN THE NAME OF SCIENCE, Martin Gardner.** Formerly entitled "In the Name of Science," the standard account of various cults, quack systems, delusions which have masqueraded as science: hollow earth fanatics, orgone sex energy, dianetics, Atlantis, Forteanism, flying saucers, medical fallacies like zone therapy, etc. New chapter on Bridey Murphy, psionics, other recent manifestations. A fair reasoned appraisal of eccentric theory which provides excellent innoculation. "Should be read by everyone, scientist or non-scientist alike," R. T. Birge, Prof. Emeritus of Physics, Univ. of Calif; Former Pres., Amer. Physical Soc. x + 365pp. 5⅜ x 8.　　　T394 Paperbound **$1.50**

**ON MATHEMATICS AND MATHEMATICIANS, R. E. Moritz.** A 10 year labor of love by discerning, discriminating Prof. Moritz, this collection conveys the full sense of mathematics and personalities of great mathematicians. Anecdotes, aphorisms, reminiscences, philosophies, definitions, speculations, biographical insights, etc. by great mathematicians, writers: Descartes, Mill, Locke, Kant, Coleridge, Whitehead, etc. Glimpses into lives of great mathematicians, from Archimedes to Euler, Gauss, Weierstrass. To mathematicians, a superb browsing-book. To laymen, exciting revelation of fullness of mathematics. Extensive cross index. 410pp. 5⅜ x 8.　　　T489 Paperbound **$1.95**

**GUIDE TO THE LITERATURE OF MATHEMATICS AND PHYSICS, N. G. Parke III.** Over 5000 entries under approximately 120 major subject headings, of selected most important books, monographs, periodicals, articles in English, plus important works in German, French, Italian, Spanish, Russian (many recently available works). Covers every branch of physics, math, related engineering. Includes author, title, edition, publisher, place, date, number of volumes, number of pages. 40 page introduction on basic problems of research, study provides useful information on organization, use of libraries, psychology of learning, etc. Will save you hours of time. 2nd revised edition. Indices of authors, subjects. 464pp. 5⅜ x 8.　　　S447 Paperbound **$2.49**

**THE STRANGE STORY OF THE QUANTUM, An Account for the General Reader of the Growth of Ideas Underlying Our Present Atomic Knowledge, B. Hoffmann.** Presents lucidly, expertly, with barest amount of mathematics, problems and theories which led to modern quantum physics. Begins with late 1800's when discrepancies were noticed; with illuminating analogies, examples, goes through concepts of Planck, Einstein, Pauli, Schroedinger, Dirac, Sommerfield, Feynman, etc. New postscript through 1958. "Of the books attempting an account of the history and contents of modern atomic physics which have come to my attention, this is the best," H. Margenau, Yale U., in Amer. J. of Physics. 2nd edition. 32 tables, illustrations. 275pp. 5⅜ x 8.　　　T518 Paperbound **$1.45**

2

# HISTORY OF SCIENCE
# AND PHILOSOPHY OF SCIENCE

**THE VALUE OF SCIENCE, Henri Poincaré.** Many of most mature ideas of "last scientific universalist" for both beginning, advanced workers. Nature of scientific truth, whether order is innate in universe or imposed by man, logical thought vs. intuition (relating to Weierstrass, Lie, Riemann, etc), time and space (relativity, psychological time, simultaneity), Herz's concept of force, values within disciplines of Maxwell, Carnot, Mayer, Newton, Lorentz, etc. iii + 147pp. 5⅜ x 8. S469 Paperbound **$1.35**

**PHILOSOPHY AND THE PHYSICISTS, L. S. Stebbing.** Philosophical aspects of modern science examined in terms of lively critical attack on ideas of Jeans, Eddington. Tasks of science, causality, determinism, probability, relation of world physics to that of everyday experience, philosophical significance of Planck-Bohr concept of discontinuous energy levels, inferences to be drawn from Uncertainty Principle, implications of "becoming" involved in 2nd law of thermodynamics, other problems posed by discarding of Laplacean determinism. 285pp. 5⅜ x 8. T480 Paperbound **$1.65**

**THE PRINCIPLES OF SCIENCE, A TREATISE ON LOGIC AND THE SCIENTIFIC METHOD, W. S. Jevons.** Milestone in development of symbolic logic remains stimulating contribution to investigation of inferential validity in sciences. Treats inductive, deductive logic, theory of number, probability, limits of scientific method; significantly advances Boole's logic, contains detailed introduction to nature and methods of probability in physics, astronomy, everyday affairs, etc. In introduction, Ernest Nagel of Columbia U. says, "[Jevons] continues to be of interest as an attempt to articulate the logic of scientific inquiry." liii + 786pp. 5⅜ x 8. S446 Paperbound **$2.98**

**A HISTORY OF ASTRONOMY FROM THALES TO KEPLER, J. L. E. Dreyer.** Only work in English to give complete history of cosmological views from prehistoric times to Kepler. Partial contents: Near Eastern astronomical systems, Early Greeks, Homocentric spheres of Euxodus, Epicycles, Ptolemaic system, Medieval cosmology, Copernicus, Kepler, much more. "Especially useful to teachers and students of the history of science . . . unsurpassed in its field," Isis. Formerly "A History of Planetary Systems from Thales to Kepler." Revised foreword by W. H. Stahl. xvii + 430pp. 5⅜ x 8. S79 Paperbound **$1.98**

**A CONCISE HISTORY OF MATHEMATICS, D. Struik.** Lucid study of development of ideas, techniques, from Ancient Near East, Greece, Islamic science, Middle Ages, Renaissance, modern times. Important mathematicians described in detail. Treatment not anecdotal, but analytical development of ideas. Non-technical—no math training needed. "Rich in content, thoughtful in interpretations," U.S. Quarterly Booklist. 60 illustrations including Greek, Egyptian manuscripts, portraits of 31 mathematicians. 2nd edition. xix + 299pp. 5⅜ x 8. S255 Paperbound **$1.75**

**THE PHILOSOPHICAL WRITINGS OF PEIRCE, edited by Justus Buchler.** A carefully balanced expositon of Peirce's complete system, written by Peirce himself. It covers such matters as scientific method, pure chance vs. law, symbolic logic, theory of signs, pragmatism, experiment, and other topics. "Excellent selection . . . gives more than adequate evidence of the range and greatness," Personalist. Formerly entitled "The Philosophy of Peirce." xvi + 368pp. T217 Paperbound **$1.95**

**SCIENCE AND METHOD, Henri Poincaré.** Procedure of scientific discovery, methodology, experiment, idea-germination—processes by which discoveries come into being. Most significant and interesting aspects of development, application of ideas. Chapters cover selection of facts, chance, mathematical reasoning, mathematics and logic; Whitehead, Russell, Cantor, the new mechanics, etc. 288pp. 5⅜ x 8. S222 Paperbound **$1.35**

**SCIENCE AND HYPOTHESIS, Henri Poincaré.** Creative psychology in science. How such concepts as number, magnitude, space, force, classical mechanics developed, how modern scientist uses them in his thought. Hypothesis in physics, theories of modern physics. Introduction by Sir James Larmor. "Few mathematicians have had the breadth of vision of Poincaré, and none is his superior in the gift of clear exposition," E. T. Bell. 272pp. 5⅜ x 8. S221 Paperbound **$1.35**

**ESSAYS IN EXPERIMENTAL LOGIC, John Dewey.** Stimulating series of essays by one of most influential minds in American philosophy presents some of his most mature thoughts on wide range of subjects. Partial contents: Relationship between inquiry and experience; dependence of knowledge upon thought; character logic; judgments of practice, data, and meanings; stimuli of thought, etc. viii + 444pp. 5⅜ x 8. T73 Paperbound **$1.95**

**WHAT IS SCIENCE, Norman Campbell.** Excellent introduction explains scientific method, role of mathematics, types of scientific laws. Contents: 2 aspects of science, science and nature, laws of chance, discovery of laws, explanation of laws, measurement and numerical laws, applications of science. 192pp. 5⅜ x 8. S43 Paperbound **$1.25**

**FROM EUCLID TO EDDINGTON: A STUDY OF THE CONCEPTIONS OF THE EXTERNAL WORLD, Sir Edmund Whittaker.** Foremost British scientist traces development of theories of natural philosophy from western rediscovery of Euclid to Eddington, Einstein, Dirac, etc. 5 major divisions: Space, Time and Movement; Concepts of Classical Physics; Concepts of Quantum Mechanics; Eddington Universe. Contrasts inadequacy of classical physics to understand physical world with present day attempts of relativity, non-Euclidean geometry, space curvature, etc. 212pp. 5⅜ x 8. T491 Paperbound **$1.35**

**THE ANALYSIS OF MATTER, Bertrand Russell.** How do our senses accord with the new physics? This volume covers such topics as logical analysis of physics, prerelativity physics, causality, scientific inference, physics and perception, special and general relativity, Weyl's theory, tensors, invariants and their physical interpretation, periodicity and qualitative series. "The most thorough treatment of the subject that has yet been published," The Nation. Introduction by L. E. Denonn. 422pp. 5⅜ x 8. T231 Paperbound **$1.95**

**LANGUAGE, TRUTH, AND LOGIC, A. Ayer.** A clear introduction to the Vienna and Cambridge schools of Logical Positivism. Specific tests to evaluate validity of ideas, etc. Contents: function of philosophy, elimination of metaphysics, nature of analysis, a priori, truth and probability, etc. 10th printing. "I should like to have written it myself," Bertrand Russell. 160pp. 5⅜ x 8. T10 Paperbound **$1.25**

**THE PSYCHOLOGY OF INVENTION IN THE MATHEMATICAL FIELD, J. Hadamard.** Where do ideas come from? What role does the unconscious play? Are ideas best developed by mathematical reasoning, word reasoning, visualization? What are the methods used by Einstein, Poincaré, Galton, Riemann? How can these techniques be applied by others? One of the world's leading mathematicians discusses these and other questions. xiii + 145pp. 5⅜ x 8. T107 Paperbound **$1.25**

**GUIDE TO PHILOSOPHY, C. E. M. Joad.** By one of the ablest expositors of all time, this is not simply a history or a typological survey, but an examination of central problems in terms of answers afforded by the greatest thinkers: Plato, Aristotle, Scholastics, Leibniz, Kant, Whitehead, Russell, and many others. Especially valuable to persons in the physical sciences; over 100 pages devoted to Jeans, Eddington, and others, the philosophy of modern physics, scientific materialism, pragmatism, etc. Classified bibliography. 592pp. 5⅜ x 8. T50 Paperbound **$2.00**

**SUBSTANCE AND FUNCTION, and EINSTEIN'S THEORY OF RELATIVITY, Ernst Cassirer.** Two books bound as one. Cassirer establishes a philosophy of the exact sciences that takes into consideration new developments in mathematics, shows historical connections. Partial contents: Aristotelian logic, Mill's analysis, Helmholtz and Kronecker, Russell and cardinal numbers, Euclidean vs. non-Euclidean geometry, Einstein's relativity. Bibliography. Index. xxi + 464pp. 5⅜ x 8. T50 Paperbound **$2.00**

**FOUNDATIONS OF GEOMETRY, Bertrand Russell.** Nobel laureate analyzes basic problems in the overlap area between mathematics and philosophy: the nature of geometrical knowledge, the nature of geometry, and the applications of geometry to space. Covers history of non-Euclidean geometry, philosophic interpretations of geometry, especially Kant, projective and metrical geometry. Most interesting as the solution offered in 1897 by a great mind to a problem still current. New introduction by Prof. Morris Kline, N.Y. University. "Admirably clear, precise, and elegantly reasoned analysis," International Math. News. xii + 201pp. 5⅜ x 8. S233 Paperbound **$1.60**

**THE NATURE OF PHYSICAL THEORY, P. W. Bridgman.** How modern physics looks to a highly unorthodox physicist—a Nobel laureate. Pointing out many absurdities of science, demonstrating inadequacies of various physical theories, weighs and analyzes contributions of Einstein, Bohr, Heisenberg, many others. A non-technical consideration of correlation of science and reality. xi + 138pp. 5⅜ x 8. S33 Paperbound **$1.25**

**EXPERIMENT AND THEORY IN PHYSICS, Max Born.** A Nobel laureate examines the nature and value of the counterclaims of experiment and theory in physics. Synthetic versus analytical scientific advances are analyzed in works of Einstein, Bohr, Heisenberg, Planck, Eddington, Milne, others, by a fellow scientist. 44pp. 5⅜ x 8. S308 Paperbound **60¢**

**A SHORT HISTORY OF ANATOMY AND PHYSIOLOGY FROM THE GREEKS TO HARVEY, Charles Singer.** Corrected edition of "The Evolution of Anatomy." Classic traces anatomy, physiology from prescientific times through Greek, Roman periods, dark ages, Renaissance, to beginning of modern concepts. Centers on individuals, movements, that definitely advanced anatomical knowledge. Plato, Diocles, Erasistratus, Galen, da Vinci, etc. Special section on Vesalius. 20 plates. 270 extremely interesting illustrations of ancient, Medieval, enaissance, Oriental origin. xii + 209pp. 5⅜ x 8. T389 Paperbound **$1.75**

**SPACE - TIME - MATTER, Hermann Weyl.** "The standard treatise on the general theory of relativity," (Nature), by world renowned scientist. Deep, clear discussion of logical coherence of general theory, introducing all needed tools: Maxwell, analytical geometry, non-Euclidean geometry, tensor calculus, etc. Basis is classical space-time, before absorption of relativity. Contents: Euclidean space, mathematical form, metrical continuum, general theory, etc. 15 diagrams. xviii + 330pp. 5⅜ x 8. S267 Paperbound **$1.75**

4

**MATTER AND MOTION, James Clerk Maxwell.** Excellent exposition begins with simple particles, proceeds gradually to physical systems beyond complete analysis; motion, force, properties of centre of mass of material system; work, energy, gravitation, etc. Written with all Maxwell's original insights and clarity. Notes by E. Larmor. 17 diagrams. 178pp. 5⅜ x 8.                                                                    S188 Paperbound **$1.25**

**PRINCIPLES OF MECHANICS, Heinrich Hertz.** Last work by the great 19th century physicist is not only a classic, but of great interest in the logic of science. Creating a new system of mechanics based upon space, time, and mass, it returns to axiomatic analysis, understanding of the formal or structural aspects of science, taking into account logic, observation, a priori elements. Of great historical importance to Poincaré, Carnap, Einstein, Milne. A 20 page introduction by R. S. Cohen, Wesleyan University, analyzes the implications of Hertz's thought and the logic of science. 13 page introduction by Helmholtz. xlii + 274pp. 5⅜ x 8.                                                                    S316 Clothbound **$3.50**
S317 Paperbound **$1.75**

**FROM MAGIC TO SCIENCE, Charles Singer.** A great historian examines aspects of science from Roman Empire through Renaissance. Includes perhaps best discussion of early herbals, penetrating physiological interpretation of "The Visions of Hildegarde of Bingen." Also examines Arabian, Galenic influences; Pythagoras' sphere, Paracelsus; reawakening of science under Leonardo da Vinci, Vesalius; Lorica of Gildas the Briton; etc. Frequent quotations with translations from contemporary manuscripts. Unabridged, corrected edition. 158 unusual illustrations from Classical, Medieval sources. xxvii + 365pp. 5⅜ x 8.                                                                    T390 Paperbound **$2.00**

**A HISTORY OF THE CALCULUS, AND ITS CONCEPTUAL DEVELOPMENT, Carl B. Boyer.** Provides laymen, mathematicians a detailed history of the development of the calculus, from beginnings in antiquity to final elaboration as mathematical abstraction. Gives a sense of mathematics not as technique, but as habit of mind, in progression of ideas of Zeno, Plato, Pythagoras, Eudoxus, Arabic and Scholastic mathematicians, Newton, Leibniz, Taylor, Descartes, Euler, Lagrange, Cantor, Weierstrass, and others. This first comprehensive, critical history of the calculus was originally entitled "The Concepts of the Calculus." Foreword by R. Courant. 22 figures. 25 page bibliography. v + 364pp. 5⅜ x 8.
S509 Paperbound **$2.00**

**A DIDEROT PICTORIAL ENCYCLOPEDIA OF TRADES AND INDUSTRY, Manufacturing and the Technical Arts in Plates Selected from "L'Encyclopédie ou Dictionnaire Raisonné des Sciences, des Arts, et des Métiers" of Denis Diderot.** Edited with text by C. Gillispie. First modern selection of plates from high-point of 18th century French engraving. Storehouse of technological information to historian of arts and science. Over 2,000 illustrations on 485 full page plates, most of them original size, show trades, industries of fascinating era in such great detail that modern reconstructions might be made of them. Plates teem with men, women, children performing thousands of operations; show sequence, general operations, closeups, details of machinery. Illustrates such important, interesting trades, industries as sowing, harvesting, beekeeping, tobacco processing, fishing, arts of war, mining, smelting, casting iron, extracting mercury, making gunpowder, cannons, bells, shoeing horses, tanning, papermaking, printing, dying, over 45 more categories. Professor Gillispie of Princeton supplies full commentary on all plates, identifies operations, tools, processes, etc. Material is presented in lively, lucid fashion. Of great interest to all studying history of science, technology. Heavy library cloth. 920pp. 9 x 12.
T421 2 volume set **$18.50**

**DE MAGNETE, William Gilbert.** Classic work on magnetism, founded new science. Gilbert was first to use word "electricity," to recognize mass as distinct from weight, to discover effect of heat on magnetic bodies; invented an electroscope, differentiated between static electricity and magnetism, conceived of earth as magnet. This lively work, by first great experimental scientist, is not only a valuable historical landmark, but a delightfully easy to follow record of a searching, ingenious mind. Translated by P. F. Mottelay. 25 page biographical memoir. 90 figures. lix + 368pp. 5⅜ x 8.                        S470 Paperbound **$2.00**

**HISTORY OF MATHEMATICS, D. E. Smith.** Most comprehensive, non-technical history of math in English. Discusses lives and works of over a thousand major, minor figures, with footnotes giving technical information outside book's scheme, and indicating disputed matters. Vol. I: A chronological examination, from primitive concepts through Egypt, Babylonia, Greece, the Orient, Rome, the Middle Ages, The Renaissance, and to 1900. Vol. II: The development of ideas in specific fields and problems, up through elementary calculus. "Marks an epoch . . . will modify the entire teaching of the history of science," George Sarton. 2 volumes, total of 510 illustrations, 1355pp. 5⅜ x 8. Set boxed in attractive container.                                                            T429, 430 Paperbound, the set **$5.00**

**THE PHILOSOPHY OF SPACE AND TIME, H. Reichenbach.** An important landmark in development of empiricist conception of geometry, covering foundations of geometry, time theory, consequences of Einstein's relativity, including: relations between theory and observations; coordinate definitions; relations between topological and metrical properties of space; psychological problem of visual intuition of non-Euclidean structures; many more topics important to modern science and philosophy. Majority of ideas require only knowledge of intermediate math. "Still the best book in the field," Rudolf Carnap. Introduction by R. Carnap. 49 figures. xviii + 296pp. 5⅜ x 8.                            S443 Paperbound **$2.00**

**FOUNDATIONS OF SCIENCE: THE PHILOSOPHY OF THEORY AND EXPERIMENT, N. Campbell.**
A critique of the most fundamental concepts of science, particularly physics. Examines why certain propositions are accepted without question, demarcates science from philosophy, etc. Part I analyzes presuppositions of scientific thought: existence of material world, nature of laws, probability, etc; part 2 covers nature of experiment and applications of mathematics: conditions for measurement, relations between numerical laws and theories, error, etc. An appendix covers problems arising from relativity, force, motion, space, time. A classic in its field. "A real grasp of what science is," Higher Educational Journal.
xiii + 565pp. 5⅝ x 8⅜.                                                    S372 Paperbound **$2.95**

**THE STUDY OF THE HISTORY OF MATHEMATICS** and **THE STUDY OF THE HISTORY OF SCIENCE,**
**G. Sarton.** Excellent introductions, orientation, for beginning or mature worker. Describes duty of mathematical historian, incessant efforts and genius of previous generations. Explains how today's discipline differs from previous methods. 200 item bibliography with critical evaluations, best available biographies of modern mathematicians, best treatises on historical methods is especially valuable. 10 illustrations. 2 volumes bound as one.
113pp. + 75pp. 5⅜ x 8.                                                    T240 Paperbound **$1.25**

# MATHEMATICAL PUZZLES

**MATHEMATICAL PUZZLES OF SAM LOYD,** selected and edited by **Martin Gardner.** 117 choice puzzles by greatest American puzzle creator and innovator, from his famous "Cyclopedia of Puzzles." All unique style, historical flavor of originals. Based on arithmetic, algebra, probability, game theory, route tracing, topology, sliding block, operations research, geometrical dissection. Includes famous "14-15" puzzle which was national craze, "Horse of a Different Color" which sold millions of copies. 120 line drawings, diagrams. Solutions.
xx + 167pp. 5⅜ x 8.                                                       T498 Paperbound **$1.00**

**SYMBOLIC LOGIC and THE GAME OF LOGIC, Lewis Carroll.** "Symbolic Logic" is not concerned with modern symbolic logic, but is instead a collection of over 380 problems posed with charm and imagination, using the syllogism, and a fascinating diagrammatic method of drawing conclusions. In "The Game of Logic" Carroll's whimsical imagination devises a logical game played with 2 diagrams and counters (included) to manipulate hundreds of tricky syllogisms. The final section, "Hit or Miss" is a lagniappe of 101 additional puzzles in the delightful Carroll manner. Until this reprint edition, both of these books were rarities costing up to $15 each. Symbolic Logic: Index. xxxi + 199pp. The Game of Logic: 96pp.
2 vols. bound as one. 5⅜ x 8.                                             T492 Paperbound **$1.50**

**PILLOW PROBLEMS and A TANGLED TALE, Lewis Carroll.** One of the rarest of all Carroll's works, "Pillow Problems" contains 72 original math puzzles, all typically ingenious. Particularly fascinating are Carroll's answers which remain exactly as he thought them out, reflecting his actual mental process. The problems in "A Tangled Tale" are in story form, originally appearing as a monthly magazine serial. Carroll not only gives the solutions, but uses answers sent in by readers to discuss wrong approaches and misleading paths, and grades them for insight. Both of these books were rarities until this edition, "Pillow Problems" costing up to $25, and "A Tangled Tale" $15. Pillow Problems: Preface and Introduction by Lewis Carroll. xx + 109pp. A Tangled Tale: 6 illustrations. 152pp. Two vols.
bound as one. 5⅜ x 8.                                                     T493 Paperbound **$1.50**

**NEW WORD PUZZLES, G. L. Kaufman.** 100 brand new challenging puzzles on words, combinations, never before published. Most are new types invented by author, for beginners and experts both. Squares of letters follow chess moves to build words; symmetrical designs made of synonyms; rhymed crostics; double word squares; syllable puzzles where you fill in missing syllables instead of missing letter; many other types, all new. Solutions. "Excellent," Recreation. 100 puzzles. 196 figures. vi + 122pp. 5⅜ x 8.
                                                                          T344 Paperbound **$1.00**

**MATHEMATICAL EXCURSIONS, H. A. Merrill.** Fun, recreation, insights into elementary problem solving. Math expert guides you on by-paths not generally travelled in elementary math courses—divide by inspection, Russian peasant multiplication; memory systems for pi; odd, even magic squares; dyadic systems; square roots by geometry; Tcheuichev's machine; dozens more. Solutions to more difficult ones. "Brain stirring stuff . . . a classic," Genie.
50 illustrations. 145pp. 5⅜ x 8.                                          T350 Paperbound **$1.00**

**THE BOOK OF MODERN PUZZLES, G. L. Kaufman.** Over 150 puzzles, absolutely all new material based on same appeal as crosswords, deduction puzzles, but with different principles, techniques. 2-minute teasers, word labyrinths, design, pattern, logic, observation puzzles, puzzles testing ability to apply general knowledge to peculiar situations, many others.
Solutions. 116 illustrations. 192pp. 5⅜ x 8.                              T143 Paperbound **$1.00**

**MATHEMAGIC, MAGIC PUZZLES, AND GAMES WITH NUMBERS, R. V. Heath.** Over 60 puzzles, stunts, on properties of numbers. Easy techniques for multiplying large numbers mentally, identifying unknown numbers, finding date of any day in any year. Includes The Lost Digit, 3 Acrobats, Psychic Bridge, magic squares, triangles, cubes, others not easily found elsewhere. Edited by J. S. Meyer. 76 illustrations. 128pp. 5⅜ x 8.          T110 Paperbound **$1.00**

**PUZZLE QUIZ AND STUNT FUN, J. Meyer.** 238 high-priority puzzles, stunts, tricks—math puzzles like The Clever Carpenter, Atom Bomb, Please Help Alice; mysteries, deductions like The Bridge of Sighs, Secret Code; observation puzzlers like The American Flag, Playing Cards, Telephone Dial; over 200 others with magic squares, tongue twisters, puns, anagrams. Solutions. Revised, enlarged edition of "Fun-To-Do." Over 100 illustrations. 238 puzzles, stunts, tricks. 256pp. 5⅜ x 8. **T337 Paperbound $1.00**

**101 PUZZLES IN THOUGHT AND LOGIC, C. R. Wylie, Jr.** For readers who enjoy challenge, stimulation of logical puzzles without specialized math or scientific knowledge. Problems entirely new, range from relatively easy to brainteasers for hours of subtle entertainment. Detective puzzles, find the lying fisherman, how a blind man identifies color by logic, many more. Easy-to-understand introduction to logic of puzzle solving and general scientific method. 128pp. 5⅜ x 8. **T367 Paperbound $1.00**

**CRYPTANALYSIS, H. F. Gaines.** Standard elementary, intermediate text for serious students. Not just old material, but much not generally known, except to experts. Concealment, Transposition, Substitution ciphers; Vigenere, Kasiski, Playfair, multafid, dozens of other techniques. Formerly "Elementary Cryptanalysis." Appendix with sequence charts, letter frequencies in English, 5 other languages, English word frequencies. Bibliography. 167 codes. New to this edition: solutions to codes. vi + 230pp. 5⅜ x 8⅜. **T97 Paperbound $1.95**

**CRYPTOGRAPY, L. D. Smith.** Excellent elementary introduction to enciphering, deciphering secret writing. Explains transposition, substitution ciphers; codes; solutions; geometrical patterns, route transcription, columnar transposition, other methods. Mixed cipher systems; single, polyalphabetical substitutions; mechanical devices; Vigenere; etc. Enciphering Japanese; explanation of Baconian biliteral cipher; frequency tables. Over 150 problems. Bibliography. Index. 164pp. 5⅜ x 8. **T247 Paperbound $1.00**

**MATHEMATICS, MAGIC AND MYSTERY, M. Gardner.** Card tricks, metal mathematics, stage mind-reading, other "magic" explained as applications of probability, sets, number theory, etc. Creative examination of laws, applications. Scores of new tricks, insights. 115 sections on cards, dice, coins; vanishing tricks, many others. No sleight of hand—math guarantees success. "Could hardly get more entertainment . . . easy to follow," Mathematics Teacher. 115 illustrations. xii + 174pp. 5⅜ x 8. **T335 Paperbound $1.00**

**AMUSEMENTS IN MATHEMATICS, H. E. Dudeney.** Foremost British originator of math puzzles, always witty, intriguing, paradoxical in this classic. One of largest collections. More than 430 puzzles, problems, paradoxes. Mazes, games, problems on number manipulations, unicursal, other route problems, puzzles on measuring, weighing, packing, age, kinship, chessboards, joiners', crossing river, plane figure dissection, many others. Solutions. More than 450 illustrations. viii + 258pp. 5⅜ x 8. **T473 Paperbound $1.25**

**THE CANTERBURY PUZZLES H. E. Dudeney.** Chaucer's pilgrims set one another problems in story form. Also Adventures of the Puzzle Club, the Strange Escape of the King's Jester, the Monks of Riddlewell, the Squire's Christmas Puzzle Party, others. All puzzles are original, based on dissecting plane figures, arithmetic, algebra, elementary calculus, other branches of mathematics, and purely logical ingenuity. "The limit of ingenuity and intricacy," The Observer. Over 110 puzzles, full solutions. 150 illustrations. viii + 225 pp. 5⅜ x 8. **T474 Paperbound $1.25**

**MATHEMATICAL PUZZLES FOR BEGINNERS AND ENTHUSIASTS, G. Mott-Smith.** 188 puzzles to test mental agility. Inference, interpretation, algebra, dissection of plane figures, geometry, properties of numbers, decimation, permutations, probability, all are in these delightful problems. Includes the Odic Force, How to Draw an Ellipse, Spider's Cousin, more than 180 others. Detailed solutions. Appendix with square roots, triangular numbers, primes, etc. 135 illustrations. 2nd revised edition. 248pp. 5⅜ x 8. **T198 Paperbound $1.00**

**MATHEMATICAL RECREATIONS, M. Kraitchik.** Some 250 puzzles, problems, demonstrations of recreation mathematics on relatively advanced level. Unusual historical problems from Greek, Medieval, Arabic, Hindu sources; modern problems on "mathematics without numbers," geometry, topology, arithmetic, etc. Pastimes derived from figurative, Mersenne, Fermat numbers: fairy chess; latruncles: reversi; etc. Full solutions. Excellent insights into special fields of math. "Strongly recommended to all who are interested in the lighter side of mathematics," Mathematical Gaz. 181 illustrations. 330pp. 5⅜ x 8. **T163 Paperbound $1.75**

# FICTION

**FLATLAND, E. A. Abbott.** A perennially popular science-fiction classic about life in a 2-dimensional world, and the impingement of higher dimensions. Political, satiric, humorous, moral overtones. This land where women are straight lines and the lowest and most dangerous classes are isosceles triangles with 3° vertices conveys brilliantly a feeling for many concepts of modern science. 7th edition. New introduction by Banesh Hoffmann. 128pp. 5⅜ x 8. **T1 Paperbound $1.00**

**SEVEN SCIENCE FICTION NOVELS OF H. G. WELLS.** Complete texts, unabridged, of seven of Wells' greatest novels: The War of the Worlds, The Invisible Man, The Island of Dr. Moreau, The Food of the Gods, First Men in the Moon, In the Days of the Comet, The Time Machine. Still considered by many experts to be the best science-fiction ever written, they will offer amusements and instruction to the scientific minded reader. "The great master," Sky and Telescope. 1051pp. 5⅜ x 8. T264 Clothbound **$3.95**

**28 SCIENCE FICTION STORIES OF H. G. WELLS.** Unabridged! This enormous omnibus contains 2 full length novels—Men Like Gods, Star Begotten—plus 26 short stories of space, time, invention, biology, etc. The Crystal Egg, The Country of the Blind, Empire of the Ants, The Man Who Could Work Miracles, Aepyornis Island, A Story of the Days to Come, and 20 others "A master . . . not surpassed by . . . writers of today," The English Journal. 915pp. 5⅜ x 8. T265 Clothbound **$3.95**

**FIVE ADVENTURE NOVELS OF H. RIDER HAGGARD.** All the mystery and adventure of darkest Africa captured accurately by a man who lived among Zulus for years, who knew African ethnology, folkways as did few of his contemporaries. They have been regarded as examples of the very best high adventure by such critics as Orwell, Andrew Lang, Kipling. Contents: She, King Solomon's Mines, Allan Quatermain, Allan's Wife, Maiwa's Revenge. "Could spin a yarn sc full of suspense and color that you couldn't put the story down," Sat. Review. 821pp. 5⅜ x 8. T108 Clothbound **$3.95**

# CHESS AND CHECKERS

**LEARN CHESS FROM THE MASTERS, Fred Reinfeld.** Easiest, most instructive way to improve your game—play 10 games against such masters as Marshall, Znosko-Borovsky, Bronstein, Najdorf, etc., with each move graded by easy system. Includes ratings for alternate moves possible. Games selected for interest, clarity, easily isolated principles. Covers Ruy Lopez, Dutch Defense, Vienna Game openings; subtle, intricate middle game variations; all-important end game. Full annotations. Formerly "Chess by Yourself." 91 diagrams. viii + 144pp. 5⅜ x 8. T362 Paperbound **$1.00**

**REINFELD ON THE END GAME IN CHESS, Fred Reinfeld.** Analyzes 62 end games by Alekhine, Flohr, Tarrasch, Morphy, Capablanca, Rubinstein, Lasker, Reshevsky, other masters. Only 1st rate book with extensive coverage of error—tell exactly what is wrong with each move you might have made. Centers around transitions from middle play to end play. King and pawn, minor pieces, queen endings; blockage, weak, passed pawns, etc. "Excellent . . . a boon," Chess Life. Formerly "Practical End Play." 62 figures. vi + 177pp. 5⅜ x 8. T417 Paperbound **$1.25**

**HYPERMODERN CHESS as developed in the games of its greatest exponent, ARON NIMZOVICH,** edited by Fred Reinfeld. An intensely original player, analyst, Nimzovich's approaches startled, often angered the chess world. This volume, designed for the average player, shows how his iconoclastic methods won him victories over Alekhine, Lasker, Marshall, Rubinstein, Spielmann, others, and infused new life into the game. Use his methods to startle opponents, invigorate play. "Annotations and introductions to each game . . . are excellent," Times (London). 180 diagrams. viii + 220pp. 5⅜ x 8. T448 Paperbound **$1.35**

**THE ADVENTURE OF CHESS, Edward Lasker.** Lively reader, by one of America's finest chess masters, including: history of chess, from ancient Indian 4-handed game of Chaturanga to great players of today; such delights and oddities as Maelzel's chess-playing automaton that beat Napoleon 3 times; etc. One of most valuable features is author's personal recollections of men he has played against—Nimzovich, Emanuel Lasker, Capablanca, Alekhine, etc. Discussion of chess-playing machines (newly revised). 5 page chess primer. 11 illustrations. 53 diagrams. 296pp. 5⅜ x 8. S510 Paperbound **$1.45**

**THE ART OF CHESS, James Mason.** Unabridged reprinting of latest revised edition of most famous general study ever written. Mason, early 20th century master, teaches beginning, intermediate player over 90 openings; middle game, end game, to see more moves ahead, to plan purposefully, attack, sacrifice, defend, exchange, govern general strategy. "Classic . . . one of the clearest and best developed studies," Publishers Weekly. Also included, a complete supplement by F. Reinfeld, "How Do You Play Chess?", invaluable to beginners for its lively question-and-answer method. 448 diagrams. 1947 Reinfeld-Bernstein text. Bibliography. xvi + 340pp. 5⅜ x 8. T463 Paperbound **$1.85**

**MORPHY'S GAMES OF CHESS, edited by P. W. Sergeant.** Put boldness into your game by flowing brilliant, forceful moves of the greatest chess player of all time. 300 of Morphy's best games, carefully annotated to reveal principles. 54 classics against masters like Anderssen, Harrwitz, Bird, Paulsen, and others. 52 games at odds; 54 blindfold games; plus over 100 others. Follow his interpretation of Dutch Defense, Evans Gambit, Giuoco Piano, Ruy Lopez, many more. Unabridged reissue of latest revised edition. New introduction by F. Reinfeld. Annotations, introduction by Sergeant. 235 diagrams. x + 352pp. 5⅜ x 8. T386 Paperbound **$1.75**

# DOVER SCIENCE BOOKS

**WIN AT CHECKERS, M. Hopper.** (Formerly "Checkers.") Former World's Unrestricted Checker Champion discusses principles of game, expert's shots, traps, problems for beginner, standard openings, locating best move, end game, opening "blitzkrieg" moves to draw when behind, etc. Over 100 detailed questions, answers anticipate problems. Appendix. 75 problems with solutions, diagrams. 79 figures. xi + 107pp. 5⅜ x 8.     T363 Paperbound **$1.00**

**HOW TO FORCE CHECKMATE, Fred Reinfeld.** If you have trouble finishing off your opponent, here is a collection of lightning strokes and combinations from actual tournament play. Starts with 1-move checkmates, works up to 3-move mates. Develops ability to lock ahead, gain new insights into combinations, complex or deceptive positions; ways to estimate weaknesses, strengths of you and your opponent. "A good deal of amusement and instruction," Times, (London). 300 diagrams. Solutions to all positions. Formerly "Challenge to Chess Players." 111pp. 5⅜ x 8.     T417 Paperbound **$1.25**

**A TREASURY OF CHESS LORE, edited by Fred Reinfeld.** Delightful collection of anecdotes, short stories, aphorisms by, about masters; poems, accounts of games, tournaments, photographs; hundreds of humorous, pithy, satirical, wise, historical episodes, comments, word portraits. Fascinating "must" for chess players; revealing and perhaps seductive to those who wonder what their friends see in game. 49 photographs (14 full page plates). 12 diagrams. xi + 306pp. 5⅜ x 8.     T458 Paperbound **$1.75**

**WIN AT CHESS, Fred Reinfeld.** 300 practical chess situations, to sharpen your eye, test skill against masters. Start with simple examples, progress at own pace to complexities. This selected series of crucial moments in chess will stimulate imagination, develop stronger, more versatile game. Simple grading system enables you to judge progress. "Extensive use of diagrams is a great attraction," Chess. 300 diagrams. Notes, solutions to every situation. Formerly "Chess Quiz." vi + 120pp. 5⅜ x 8.     T433 Paperbound **$1.00**

# MATHEMATICS:
# ELEMENTARY TO INTERMEDIATE

**HOW TO CALCULATE QUICKLY, H. Sticker.** Tried and true method to help mathematics of everyday life. Awakens "number sense"—ability to see relationships between numbers as whole quantities. A serious course of over 9000 problems and their solutions through techniques not taught in schools: left-to-right multiplications, new fast division, etc. 10 minutes a day will double or triple calculation speed. Excellent for scientist at home in higher math, but dissatisfied with speed and accuracy in lower math. 256pp. 5 x 7¼.
Paperbound **$1.00**

**FAMOUS PROBLEMS OF ELEMENTARY GEOMETRY, Felix Klein.** Expanded version of 1894 Easter lectures at Göttingen. 3 problems of classical geometry: squaring the circle, trisecting angle, doubling cube, considered with full modern implications: transcendental numbers, pi, etc. "A modern classic . . . no knowledge of higher mathematics is required," Scientia. Notes by R. Archibald. 16 figures. xi + 92pp. 5⅜ x 8.     T298 Paperbound **$1.00**

**HIGHER MATHEMATICS FOR STUDENTS OF CHEMISTRY AND PHYSICS, J. W. Mellor.** Practical, not abstract, building problems out of familiar laboratory material. Covers differential calculus, coordinate, analytical geometry, functions, integral calculus, infinite series, numerical equations, differential equations, Fourier's theorem probability, theory of errors, calculus of variations, determinants. "If the reader is not familiar with this book, it will repay him to examine it," Chem. and Engineering News. 800 problems. 189 figures. xxi + 641pp. 5⅜ x 8.     S193 Paperbound **$2.25**

**TRIGONOMETRY REFRESHER FOR TECHNICAL MEN, A. A. Klaf.** 913 detailed questions, answers cover most important aspects of plane, spherical trigonometry—particularly useful in clearing up difficulties in special areas. Part I: plane trig, angles, quadrants, functions, graphical representation, interpolation, equations, logs, solution of triangle, use of slide rule, etc. Next 188 pages discuss applications to navigation, surveying, elasticity, architecture, other special fields. Part 3: spherical trig, applications to terrestrial, astronomical problems. Methods of time-saving, simplification of principal angles, make book most useful. 913 questions answered. 1738 problems, answers to odd numbers. 494 figures. 24 pages of formulas, functions. x + 629pp. 5⅜ x 8.     T371 Paperbound **$2.00**

**CALCULUS REFRESHER FOR TECHNICAL MEN, A. A. Klaf.** 756 questions examine most important aspects of integral, differential calculus. Part I: simple differential calculus, constants, variables, functions, increments, logs, curves, etc. Part 2: fundamental ideas of integrations, inspection, substitution, areas, volumes, mean value, double, triple integration, etc. Practical aspects stressed. 50 pages illustrate applications to specific problems of civil, nautical engineering, electricity, stress, strain, elasticity, similar fields. 756 questions answered. 566 problems, mostly answered. 36pp. of useful constants, formulas. v + 431pp. 5⅜ x 8.     T370 Paperbound **$2.00**

**MONOGRAPHS ON TOPICS OF MODERN MATHEMATICS, edited by J. W. A. Young.** Advanced mathematics for persons who have forgotten, or not gone beyond, high school algebra. 9 monographs on foundation of geometry, modern pure geometry, non-Euclidean geometry, fundamental propositions of algebra, algebraic equations, functions, calculus, theory of numbers, etc. Each monograph gives proofs of important results, and descriptions of leading methods, to provide wide coverage. "Of high merit," Scientific American. New introduction by Prof. M. Kline, N.Y. Univ. 100 diagrams. xvi + 416pp. 6⅛ x 9¼.
S289 Paperbound **$2.00**

**MATHEMATICS IN ACTION, O. G. Sutton.** Excellent middle level application of mathematics to study of universe, demonstrates how math is applied to ballistics, theory of computing machines, waves, wave-like phenomena, theory of fluid flow, meteorological problems, statistics, flight, similar phenomena. No knowledge of advanced math required. Differential equations, Fourier series, group concepts, Eigenfunctions, Planck's constant, airfoil theory, and similar topics explained so clearly in everyday language that almost anyone can derive benefit from reading this even if much of high-school math is forgotten. 2nd edition. 88 figures. viii + 236pp. 5⅜ x 8.
T450 Clothbound **$3.50**

**ELEMENTARY MATHEMATICS FROM AN ADVANCED STANDPOINT, Felix Klein.** Classic text, an outgrowth of Klein's famous integration and survey course at Göttingen. Using one field to interpret, adjust another, it covers basic topics in each area, with extensive analysis. Especially valuable in areas of modern mathematics. "A great mathematician, inspiring teacher, . . . deep insight," Bul., Amer. Math Soc.

**Vol. I. ARITHMETIC, ALGEBRA, ANALYSIS.** Introduces concept of function immediately, enlivens discussion with graphical, geometric methods. Partial contents: natural numbers, special properties, complex numbers. Real equations with real unknowns, complex quantities. Logarithmic, exponential functions, infinitesimal calculus. Transcendence of e and pi, theory of assemblages. Index. 125 figures. ix + 274pp. 5⅜ x 8.
S151 Paperbound **$1.75**

**Vol. II. GEOMETRY.** Comprehensive view, accompanies space perception inherent in geometry with analytic formulas which facilitate precise formulation. Partial contents: Simplest geometric manifold; line segments, Grassman determinant principles, classication of configurations of space. Geometric transformations: affine, projective, higher point transformations, theory of the imaginary. Systematic discussion of geometry and its foundations. 141 illustrations. ix + 214pp. 5⅜ x 8.
S151 Paperbound **$1.75**

**A TREATISE ON PLANE AND ADVANCED TRIGONOMETRY, E. W. Hobson.** Extraordinarily wide coverage, going beyond usual college level, one of few works covering advanced trig in full detail. By a great expositor with unerring anticipation of potentially difficult points. Includes circular functions; expansion of functions of multiple angle; trig tables; relations between sides, angles of triangles; complex numbers; etc. Many problems fully solved. "The best work on the subject," Nature. Formerly entitled "A Treatise on Plane Trigonometry." 689 examples. 66 figures. xvi + 383pp. 5⅜ x 8.
S353 Paperbound **$1.95**

**NON-EUCLIDEAN GEOMETRY, Roberto Bonola.** The standard coverage of non-Euclidean geometry. Examines from both a historical and mathematical point of view geometries which have arisen from a study of Euclid's 5th postulate on parallel lines. Also included are complete texts, translated, of Bolyai's "Theory of Absolute Space," Lobachevsky's "Theory of Parallels." 180 diagrams. 431pp. 5⅜ x 8.
S27 Paperbound **$1.95**

**GEOMETRY OF FOUR DIMENSIONS, H. P. Manning.** Unique in English as a clear, concise introduction. Treatment is synthetic, mostly Euclidean, though in hyperplanes and hyperspheres at infinity, non-Euclidean geometry is used. Historical introduction. Foundations of 4-dimensional geometry. Perpendicularity, simple angles. Angles of planes, higher order. Symmetry, order, motion; hyperpyramids, hypercones, hyperspheres; figures with parallel elements; volume, hypervolume in space; regular polyhedroids. Glossary. 78 figures. ix + 348pp. 5⅜ x 8.
S182 Paperbound **$1.95**

# MATHEMATICS: INTERMEDIATE TO ADVANCED

## GEOMETRY (EUCLIDEAN AND NON-EUCLIDEAN)

**THE GEOMETRY OF RENÉ DESCARTES.** With this book, Descartes founded analytical geometry. Original French text, with Descartes's own diagrams, and excellent Smith-Latham translation. Contains: Problems the Construction of Which Requires only Straight Lines and Circles; On the Nature of Curved Lines; On the Construction of Solid or Supersolid Problems. Diagrams. 258pp. 5⅜ x 8.
S68 Paperbound **$1.50**

# DOVER SCIENCE BOOKS

**THE WORKS OF ARCHIMEDES, edited by T. L. Heath.** All the known works of the great Greek mathematician, including the recently discovered Method of Archimedes. Contains: On Sphere and Cylinder, Measurement of a Circle, Spirals, Conoids, Spheroids, etc. Definitive edition of greatest mathematical intellect of ancient world. 186 page study by Heath discusses Archimedes and history of Greek mathematics. 563pp. 5⅜ x 8.    S9 Paperbound **$2.00**

**COLLECTED WORKS OF BERNARD RIEMANN.** Important sourcebook, first to contain complete text of 1892 "Werke" and the 1902 supplement, unabridged. 31 monographs, 3 complete lecture courses, 15 miscellaneous papers which have been of enormous importance in relativity, topology, theory of complex variables, other areas of mathematics. Edited by R. Dedekind, H. Weber, M. Noether, W. Wirtinger. German text; English introduction by Hans Lewy. 690pp. 5⅜ x 8.    S226 Paperbound **$2.85**

**THE THIRTEEN BOOKS OF EUCLID'S ELEMENTS, edited by Sir Thomas Heath.** Definitive edition of one of very greatest classics of Western world. Complete translation of Heiberg text, plus spurious Book XIV. 150 page introduction on Greek, Medieval mathematics, Euclid, texts, commentators, etc. Elaborate critical apparatus parallels text, analyzing each definition, postulate, proposition, covering textual matters, refutations, supports, extrapolations, etc. This is the full Euclid. Unabridged reproduction of Cambridge U. 2nd edition. 3 volumes. 995 figures. 1426pp. 5⅜ x 8.    S88, 89, 90, 3 volume set, paperbound **$6.00**

**AN INTRODUCTION TO GEOMETRY OF N DIMENSIONS, D. M. Y. Sommerville.** Presupposes no previous knowledge of field. Only book in English devoted exclusively to higher dimensional geometry. Discusses fundamental ideas of incidence, parallelism, perpendicularity, angles between linear space, enumerative geometry, analytical geometry from projective and metric views, polytopes, elementary ideas in analysis situs, content of hyperspacial figures. 60 diagrams. 196pp. 5⅜ x 8.    S494 Paperbound **$1.50**

**ELEMENTS OF NON-EUCLIDEAN GEOMETRY, D. M. Y. Sommerville.** Unique in proceeding step-by-step. Requires only good knowledge of high-school geometry and algebra, to grasp elementary hyperbolic, elliptic, analytic non-Euclidean Geometries; space curvature and its implications; radical axes; homopethic centres and systems of circles; parataxy and parallelism; Gauss' proof of defect area theorem; much more, with exceptional clarity. 126 problems at chapter ends. 133 figures. xvi + 274pp. 5⅜ x 8.    S460 Paperbound **$1.50**

**THE FOUNDATIONS OF EUCLIDEAN GEOMETRY, H. G. Forder.** First connected, rigorous account in light of modern analysis, establishing propositions without recourse to empiricism, without multiplying hypotheses. Based on tools of 19th and 20th century mathematicians, who made it possible to remedy gaps and complexities, recognize problems not earlier discerned. Begins with important relationship of number systems in geometrical figures. Considers classes, relations, linear order, natural numbers, axioms for magnitudes, groups, quasi-fields, fields, non-Archimedian systems, the axiom system (at length), particular axioms (two chapters on the Parallel Axioms), constructions, congruence, similarity, etc. Lists: axioms employed, constructions, symbols in frequent use. 295pp. 5⅜ x 8.    S481 Paperbound **$2.00**

# CALCULUS, FUNCTION THEORY (REAL AND COMPLEX), FOURIER THEORY

**FIVE VOLUME "THEORY OF FUNCTIONS" SET BY KONRAD KNOPP.** Provides complete, readily followed account of theory of functions. Proofs given concisely, yet without sacrifice of completeness or rigor. These volumes used as texts by such universities as M.I.T., Chicago, N.Y. City College, many others. "Excellent introduction . . . remarkably readable, concise, clear, rigorous," J. of the American Statistical Association.

**ELEMENTS OF THE THEORY OF FUNCTIONS, Konrad Knopp.** Provides background for further volumes in this set, or texts on similar level. Partial contents: Foundations, system of complex numbers and Gaussian plane of numbers, Riemann sphere of numbers, mapping by linear functions, normal forms, the logarithm, cyclometric functions, binomial series. "Not only for the young student, but also for the student who knows all about what is in it," Mathematical Journal. 140pp. 5⅜ x 8.    S154 Paperbound **$1.35**

**THEORY OF FUNCTIONS, PART I, Konrad Knopp.** With volume II, provides coverage of basic concepts and theorems. Partial contents: numbers and points, functions of a complex variable, integral of a continuous function, Cauchy's intergral theorem, Cauchy's integral formulae, series with variable terms, expansion and analytic function in a power series, analytic continuation and complete definition of analytic functions, Laurent expansion, types of singularities. vii + 146pp. 5⅜ x 8.    S156 Paperbound **$1.35**

**THEORY OF FUNCTIONS, PART II, Konrad Knopp.** Application and further development of general theory, special topics. Single valued functions, entire, Weierstrass. Meromorphic functions: Mittag-Leffler. Periodic functions. Multiple valued functions. Riemann surfaces. Algebraic functions. Analytical configurations, Riemann surface. x + 150pp. 5⅜ x 8.    S157 Paperbound **$1.35**

11

**PROBLEM BOOK IN THE THEORY OF FUNCTIONS, VOLUME I, Konrad Knopp.** Problems in elementary theory, for use with Knopp's "Theory of Functions," or any other text. Arranged according to increasing difficulty. Fundamental concepts, sequences of numbers and infinite series, complex variable, integral theorems, development in series, conformal mapping. Answers. viii + 126pp. 5⅜ x 8.                                    S 158 **Paperbound $1.35**

**PROBLEM BOOK IN THE THEORY OF FUNCTIONS, VOLUME II, Konrad Knopp.** Advanced theory of functions, to be used with Knopp's "Theory of Functions," or comparable text. Singularities, entire and meromorphic functions, periodic, analytic, continuation, multiple-valued functions, Riemann surfaces, conformal mapping. Includes section of elementary problems. "The difficult task of selecting . . . problems just within the reach of the beginner is here masterfully accomplished," AM. MATH. SOC. Answers. 138pp. 5⅜ x 8.
S159 Paperbound **$1.35**

**ADVANCED CALCULUS, E. B. Wilson.** Still recognized as one of most comprehensive, useful texts. Immense amount of well-represented, fundamental material, including chapters on vector functions, ordinary differential equations, special functions, calculus of variations, etc., which are excellent introductions to these areas. Requires only one year of calculus. Over 1300 exercises cover both pure math and applications to engineering and physical problems. Ideal reference, refresher. 54 page introductory review. ix + 566pp. 5⅜ x 8.
S504 Paperbound **$2.45**

**LECTURES ON THE THEORY OF ELLIPTIC FUNCTIONS, H. Hancock.** Reissue of only book in English with so extensive a coverage, especially of Abel, Jacobi, Legendre, Weierstrass, Hermite, Liouville, and Riemann. Unusual fullness of treatment, plus applications as well as theory in discussing universe of elliptic integrals, originating in works of Abel and Jacobi. Use is made of Riemann to provide most general theory. 40-page table of formulas. 76 figures. xxiii + 498pp. 5⅜ x 8.                                    S483 Paperbound **$2.55**

**THEORY OF FUNCTIONALS AND OF INTEGRAL AND INTEGRO-DIFFERENTIAL EQUATIONS, Vito Volterra.** Unabridged republication of only English translation. General theory of functions depending on continuous set of values of another function. Based on author's concept of transition from finite number of variables to a continually infinite number. Includes much material on calculus of variations. Begins with fundamentals, examines generalization of analytic functions, functional derivative equations, applications, other directions of theory, etc. New introduction by G. C. Evans. Biography, criticism of Volterra's work by E. Whittaker. xxxx + 226pp. 5⅜ x 8.                                    S502 Paperbound **$1.75**

**AN INTRODUCTION TO FOURIER METHODS AND THE LAPLACE TRANSFORMATION, Philip Franklin.** Concentrates on essentials, gives broad view, suitable for most applications. Requires only knowledge of calculus. Covers complex qualities with methods of computing elementary functions for complex values of argument and finding approximations by charts; Fourier series; harmonic anaylsis; much more. Methods are related to physical problems of heat flow, vibrations, electrical transmission, electromagnetic radiation, etc. 828 problems, answers. Formerly entitled "Fourier Methods." x + 289pp. 5⅜ x 8.
S452 Paperbound **$1.75**

**THE ANALYTICAL THEORY OF HEAT, Joseph Fourier.** This book, which revolutionized mathematical physics, has been used by generations of mathematicians and physicists interested in heat or application of Fourier integral. Covers cause and reflection of rays of heat, radiant heating, heating of closed spaces, use of trigonometric series in theory of heat, Fourier integral, etc. Translated by Alexander Freeman. 20 figures. xxii + 466pp. 5⅜ x 8.
S93 Paperbound **$2.00**

**ELLIPTIC INTEGRALS, H. Hancock.** Invaluable in work involving differential equations with cubics, quatrics under root sign, where elementary calculus methods are inadequate. Practical solutions to problems in mathematics, engineering, physics; differential equations requiring integration of Lamé's, Briot's, or Bouquet's equations; determination of arc of ellipse, hyperbola, lemiscate; solutions of problems in elastics; motion of a projectile under resistance varying as the cube of the velocity; pendulums; more. Exposition in accordance with Legendre-Jacobi theory. Rigorous discussion of Legendre transformations. 20 figures. 5 place table. 104pp. 5⅜ x 8.                                    S484 Paperbound **$1.25**

**THE TAYLOR SERIES, AN INTRODUCTION TO THE THEORY OF FUNCTIONS OF A COMPLEX VARIABLE, P. Dienes.** Uses Taylor series to approach theory of functions, using ordinary calculus only, except in last 2 chapters. Starts with introduction to real variable and complex algebra, derives properties of infinite series, complex differentiation, integration, etc. Covers biuniform mapping, overconvergence and gap theorems, Taylor series on its circle of convergence, etc. Unabridged corrected reissue of first edition. 186 examples, many fully worked out. 67 figures. xii + 555pp. 5⅜ x 8.                                    S391 Paperbound **$2.75**

**LINEAR INTEGRAL EQUATIONS, W. V. Lovitt.** Systematic survey of general theory, with some application to differential equations, calculus of variations, problems of math, physics. Includes: integral equation of 2nd kind by successive substitutions; Fredholm's equation as ratio of 2 integral series in lambda, applications of the Fredholm theory, Hilbert-Schmidt theory of symmetric kernels, application, etc. Neumann, Dirichlet, vibratory problems. ix + 253pp. 5⅜ x 8.                                    S175 Clothbound **$3.50**
S176 Paperbound **$1.60**

**DICTIONARY OF CONFORMAL REPRESENTATIONS, H. Kober.** Developed by British Admiralty to solve Laplace's equation in 2 dimensions. Scores of geometrical forms and transformations for electrical engineers, Joukowski aerofoil for aerodynamics, Schwartz-Christoffel transformations for hydro-dynamics, transcendental functions. Contents classified according to analytical functions describing transformations with corresponding regions. Glossary. Topological index. 447 diagrams. 6⅛ x 9¼. ·S160 Paperbound **$2.00**

**ELEMENTS OF THE THEORY OF REAL FUNCTIONS, J. E. Littlewood.** Based on lectures at Trinity College, Cambridge, this book has proved extremely successful in introducing graduate students to modern theory of functions. Offers full and concise coverage of classes and cardinal numbers, well ordered series, other types of series, and elements of the theory of sets of points. 3rd revised edition. vii + 71pp. 5⅜ x 8. S171 Clothbound **$2.85**
S172 Paperbound **$1.25**

**INFINITE SEQUENCES AND SERIES, Konrad Knopp.** 1st publication in any language. Excellent introduction to 2 topics of modern mathematics, designed to give student background to penetrate further alone. Sequences and sets, real and complex numbers, etc. Functions of a real and complex variable. Sequences and series. Infinite series. Convergent power series. Expansion of elementary functions. Numerical evaluation of series. v + 186pp. 5⅜ x 8. S152 Clothbound **$3.50**
S153 Paperbound **$1.75**

**THE THEORY AND FUNCTIONS OF A REAL VARIABLE AND THE THEORY OF FOURIER'S SERIES, E. W .Hobson.** One of the best introductions to set theory and various aspects of functions and Fourier's series. Requires only a good background in calculus. Exhaustive coverage of: metric and descriptive properties of sets of points; transfinite numbers and order types; functions of a real variable; the Riemann and Lebesgue integrals; sequences and series of numbers; power-series; functions representable by series sequences of continuous functions; trigonometrical series; representation of functions by Fourier's series; and much more. "The best possible guide," Nature. Vol. I: 88 detailed examples, 10 figures. Index. xv + 736pp. Vol. II: 117 detailed examples, 13 figures. x + 780pp. 6⅛ x 9¼.
Vol. I: S387 Paperbound **$3.00**
Vol. II: S388 Paperbound **$3.00**

**ALMOST PERIODIC FUNCTIONS, A. S. Besicovitch.** Unique and important summary by a well known mathematician covers in detail the two stages of development in Bohr's theory of almost periodic functions: (1) as a generalization of pure periodicity, with results and proofs; (2) the work done by Stepanof, Wiener, Weyl, and Bohr in generalizing the theory. xi + 180pp. 5⅜ x 8. S18 Paperbound **$1.75**

**INTRODUCTION TO THE THEORY OF FOURIER'S SERIES AND INTEGRALS, H. S. Carslaw.** 3rd revised edition, an outgrowth of author's courses at Cambridge. Historical introduction, rational, irrational functions, infinite sequences and series, functions of a single variable, definite integral, Fourier series, and similar topics. Appendices discuss practical harmonic analysis, periodogram analysis, Lebesgue's theory. 84 examples. xiii + 368pp. 5⅜ x 8. S48 Paperbound **$2.00**

# SYMBOLIC LOGIC

**THE ELEMENTS OF MATHEMATICAL LOGIC, Paul Rosenbloom.** First publication in any language. For mathematically mature readers with no training in symbolic logic. Development of lectures given at Lund Univ., Sweden, 1948. Partial contents: Logic of classes, fundamental theorems, Boolean algebra, logic of propositions, of propositional functions, expressive languages, combinatory logics, development of math within an object language, paradoxes, theorems of Post, Goedel, Church, and similar topics. iv + 214pp. 5⅜ x 8. S227 Paperbound **$1.45**

**INTRODUCTION TO SYMBOLIC LOGIC AND ITS APPLICATION, R. Carnap.** Clear, comprehensive, rigorous, by perhaps greatest living master. Symbolic languages analyzed, one constructed. Applications to math (axiom systems for set theory, real, natural numbers), topology (Dedekind, Cantor continuity explanations), physics (general analysis of determination, causality, space-time topology), biology (axiom system for basic concepts). "A masterpiece," Zentralblatt für Mathematik und Ihre Grenzgebiete. Over 300 exercises. 5 figures. xvi + 241pp. 5⅜ x 8. S453 Paperbound **$1.85**

**AN INTRODUCTION TO SYMBOLIC LOGIC, Susanne K. Langer.** Probably clearest book for the philosopher, scientist, layman—no special knowledge of math required. Starts with simplest symbols, goes on to give remarkable grasp of Boole-Schroeder, Russell-Whitehead systems, clearly, quickly. Partial Contents: Forms, Generalization, Classes, Deductive System of Classes, Algebra of Logic, Assumptions of Principia Mathematica, Logistics, Proofs of Theorems, etc. "Clearest . . . simplest introduction . . . the intelligent non-mathematician should have no difficulty," MATHEMATICS GAZETTE. Revised, expanded 2nd edition. Truth-value tables. 368pp. 5⅜ 8. S164 Paperbound **$1.75**

**TRIGONOMETRICAL SERIES, Antoni Zygmund.** On modern advanced level. Contains carefully organized analyses of trigonometric, orthogonal, Fourier systems of functions, with clear adequate descriptions of summability of Fourier series, proximation theory, conjugate series, convergence, divergence of Fourier series. Especially valuable for Russian, Eastern European coverage. 329pp. 5⅜ x 8. S290 Paperbound **$1.50**

**THE LAWS OF THOUGHT, George Boole.** This book founded symbolic logic some 100 years ago. It is the 1st significant attempt to apply logic to all aspects of human endeavour. Partial contents: derivation of laws, signs and laws, interpretations, eliminations, conditions of a perfect method, analysis, Aristotelian logic, probability, and similar topics. xvii + 424pp. 5⅜ x 8. S28 Paperbound **$2.00**

**SYMBOLIC LOGIC, C. I. Lewis, C. H. Langford.** 2nd revised edition of probably most cited book in symbolic logic. Wide coverage of entire field; one of fullest treatments of paradoxes; plus much material not available elsewhere. Basic to volume is distinction between logic of extensions and intensions. Considerable emphasis on converse substitution, while matrix system presents supposition of variety of non-Aristotelian logics. Especially valuable sections on strict limitations, existence theorems. Partial contents: Boole-Schroeder algebra; truth value systems, the matrix method; implication and deductibility; general theory of propositions; etc. "Most valuable," Times, London. 506pp. 5⅜ x 8. S170 Paperbound **$2.00**

# GROUP THEORY AND LINEAR ALGEBRA, SETS, ETC.

**LECTURES ON THE ICOSAHEDRON AND THE SOLUTION OF EQUATIONS OF THE FIFTH DEGREE, Felix Klein.** Solution of quintics in terms of rotations of regular icosahedron around its axes of symmetry. A classic, indispensable source for those interested in higher algebra, geometry, crystallography. Considerable explanatory material included. 230 footnotes, mostly bibliography. "Classical monograph . . . detailed, readable book," Math. Gazette. 2nd edition. xvi + 289pp. 5⅜ x 8. S314 Paperbound **$1.85**

**INTRODUCTION TO THE THEORY OF GROUPS OF FINITE ORDER, R. Carmichael.** Examines fundamental theorems and their applications. Beginning with sets, systems, permutations, etc., progresses in easy stages through important types of groups: Abelian, prime power, permutation, etc. Except 1 chapter where matrices are desirable, no higher math is needed. 783 exercises, problems. xvi + 447pp. 5⅜ x 8. S299 Clothbound **$3.95** S300 Paperbound **$2.00**

**THEORY OF GROUPS OF FINITE ORDER, W. Burnside.** First published some 40 years ago, still one of clearest introductions. Partial contents: permutations, groups independent of representation, composition series of a group, isomorphism of a group with itself, Abelian groups, prime power groups, permutation groups, invariants of groups of linear substitution, graphical representation, etc. "Clear and detailed discussion . . . numerous problems which are instructive," Design News. xxiv + 512pp. 5⅜ x 8. S38 Paperbound **$2.45**

**COMPUTATIONAL METHODS OF LINEAR ALGEBRA, V. N. Faddeeva,** translated by C. D. Benster. 1st English translation of unique, valuable work, only one in English presenting systematic exposition of most important methods of linear algebra—classical, contemporary. Details of deriving numerical solutions of problems in mathematical physics. Theory and practice. Includes survey of necessary background, most important methods of solution, for exact, iterative groups. One of most valuable features is 23 tables, triple checked for accuracy, unavailable elsewhere. Translator's note. x + 252pp. 5⅜ x 8. S424 Paperbound **$1.95**

**THE CONTINUUM AND OTHER TYPES OF SERIAL ORDER, E. V. Huntington.** This famous book gives a systematic elementary account of the modern theory of the continuum as a type of serial order. Based on the Cantor-Dedekind ordinal theory, which requires no technical knowledge of higher mathematics, it offers an easily followed analysis of ordered classes, discrete and dense series, continuous series, Cantor's transfinite numbers. "Admirable introduction to the rigorous theory of the continuum . . . reading easy," Science Progress. 2nd edition. viii + 82pp. 5⅜ x 8. S129 Clothbound **$2.75** S130 Paperbound **$1.00**

**THEORY OF SETS, E. Kamke.** Clearest, amplest introduction in English, well suited for independent study. Subdivisions of main theory, such as theory of sets of points, are discussed, but emphasis is on general theory. Partial contents: rudiments of set theory, arbitrary sets, their cardinal numbers, ordered sets, their order types, well-ordered sets, their cardinal numbers. vii + 144pp. 5⅜ x 8. S141 Paperbound **$1.35**

**CONTRIBUTIONS TO THE FOUNDING OF THE THEORY OF TRANSFINITE NUMBERS, Georg Cantor.** These papers founded a new branch of mathematics. The famous articles of 1895-7 are translated, with an 82-page introduction by P. E. B. Jourdain dealing with Cantor, the background of his discoveries, their results, future possibilities. ix + 211pp. 5⅜ x 8. S45 Paperbound **$1.25**

# DOVER SCIENCE BOOKS

## NUMERICAL AND GRAPHICAL METHODS, TABLES

**JACOBIAN ELLIPTIC FUNCTION TABLES, L. M. Milne-Thomson.** Easy-to-follow, practical, not only useful numerical tables, but complete elementary sketch of application of elliptic functions. Covers description of principle properties; complete elliptic integrals; Fourier series, expansions; periods, zeros, poles, residues, formulas for special values of argument; cubic, quartic polynomials; pendulum problem; etc. Tables, graphs form body of book: Graph, 5 figure table of elliptic function sn (u m); cn (u m); dn (u m). 8 figure table of complete elliptic integrals K, K′, E, E′, nome q. 7 figure table of Jacobian zeta-function Z(u). 3 figures. xi + 123pp. 5⅜ x 8. S194 Paperbound **$1.35**

**TABLES OF FUNCTIONS WITH FORMULAE AND CURVES, E. Jahnke, F. Emde.** Most comprehensive 1-volume English text collection of tables, formulae, curves of transcendent functions. 4th corrected edition, new 76-page section giving tables, formulae for elementary functions not in other English editions. Partial contents: sine, cosine, logarithmic integral; error integral; elliptic integrals; theta functions; Legendre, Bessel, Riemann, Mathieu, hypergeometric functions; etc. "Out-of-the-way functions for which we know no other source." Scientific Computing Service, Ltd. 212 figures. 400pp. 5⅝ x 8⅜. S133 Paperbound **$2.00**

**MATHEMATICAL TABLES, H. B. Dwight.** Covers in one volume almost every function of importance in applied mathematics, engineering, physical sciences. Three extremely fine tables of the three trig functions, inverses, to 1000th of radian; natural, common logs; squares, cubes; hyperbolic functions, inverses; $(a^2 + b^2)$ exp: ½a; complete elliptical integrals of 1st, 2nd kind; sine, cosine integrals; exponential integrals; Ei(x) and Ei(−x); binomial coefficients; factorials to 250; surface zonal harmonics, first derivatives; Bernoulli, Euler numbers, their logs to base of 10; Gamma function; normal probability integral; over 60pp. Bessel functions; Riemann zeta function. Each table with formulae generally used, sources of more extensive tables, interpolation data, etc. Over half have columns of differences, to facilitate interpolation. viii + 231pp. 5⅜ x 8. S445 Paperbound **$1.75**

**PRACTICAL ANALYSIS, GRAPHICAL AND NUMERICAL METHODS, F. A. Willers.** Immensely practical hand-book for engineers. How to interpolate, use various methods of numerical differentiation and integration, determine roots of a single algebraic equation, system of linear equations, use empirical formulas, integrate differential equations, etc. Hundreds of shortcuts for arriving at numerical solutions. Special section on American calculating machines, by T. W. Simpson. Translation by R. T. Beyer. 132 illustrations. 422pp. 5⅜ x 8.
S273 Paperbound **$2.00**

**NUMERICAL SOLUTIONS OF DIFFERENTIAL EQUATIONS, H. Levy, E. A. Baggott.** Comprehensive collection of methods for solving ordinary differential equations of first and higher order. 2 requirements: practical, easy to grasp; more rapid than school methods. Partial contents: graphical integration of differential equations, graphical methods for detailed solution. Numerical solution. Simultaneous equations and equations of 2nd and higher orders. "Should be in the hands of all in research and applied mathematics, teaching," Nature. 21 figures. viii + 238pp. 5⅜ x 8. S168 Paperbound **$1.75**

**NUMERICAL INTEGRATION OF DIFFERENTIAL EQUATIONS, Bennet, Milne, Bateman.** Unabridged republication of original prepared for National Research Council. New methods of integration by 3 leading mathematicians: "The Interpolational Polynomial," "Successive Approximation," A. A. Bennett, "Step-by-step Methods of Integration," W. W. Milne. "Methods for Partial Differential Equations," H. Bateman. Methods for partial differential equations, solution of differential equations to non-integral values of a parameter will interest mathematicians, physicists. 288 footnotes, mostly bibliographical. 235 item classified bibliography. 108pp. 5⅜ x 8. S305 Paperbound **$1.35**

## Write for free catalogs!

*Indicate your field of interest. Dover publishes books on physics, earth sciences, mathematics, engineering, chemistry, astronomy, anthropology, biology, psychology, philosophy, religion, history, literature, mathematical recreations, languages, crafts, art, graphic arts, etc.*

*Write to Dept. catr*
*Dover Publications, Inc.*
Science A　　　　　　　*180 Varick St., N. Y. 14, N. Y.*